Teacher Edition

Macmillan McGraw-Hill

Math Connects

1

Table of Contents

Volume 2

Authors

Altieri • Balka • Day • Gonsalves • Grace • Krulik

Malloy • Molix-Bailey • Moseley • Mowry • Myren

Price • Reynosa • Santa Cruz • Silbey • Vielhaber

Macmillan/McGraw-Hill

Contents

Start Smart

1 **Problem Solving**: Goldenrods **2**

2 Number and Operations: Zoo Animals. **3**

3 Algebra: Watermelon **5**

4 Measurement: Longleaf Pines **7**

5 Geometry: Sand Castles **9**

6 Data Analysis: Illinois Forest **11**

Contents

Chapter 1 Describe and Compare Numbers

Are You Ready for Chapter 1? 14

Family Letter 15

1 Extend a Pattern . . . . . Algebra 17

2 Create a Pattern . . . . . Algebra 19

3 Problem-Solving Strategy

Look for a Pattern . . . . . Algebra 21

4 Numbers to 10 23

5 Numbers 11 to 15 27

6 Numbers 16 to 20 29

Mid-Chapter Check/Spiral Review 31

7 Problem-Solving Investigation

Choose a Strategy . . . . . Algebra 33

8 Compare Numbers . . . . . Algebra 35

Extra Practice 37

Game Time The Bigger the Better 38

9 Order Numbers . . . . . Algebra 39

Problem Solving in Science 41

Chapter Review/Test 43

Test Practice 45

= Hands-On Activity

Focal Points and Connections
See page iv for key.

G1-FP2 *Number and Operations*

H.O.T. Problems
Higher Order Thinking 36

Problem Solving 18, 28, 30, 40

WRITING IN MATH 20

Contents

Chapter 2 Develop Addition Concepts

Are You Ready for Chapter 2? 48
Family Letter 49
1 Addition Stories 51
2 Modeling Addition 53
3 Addition Sentences .... Algebra 55
Extra Practice 57
Game Time Snack Time 58
4 Adding Zero .... Algebra 59
5 Problem-Solving Strategy
Write a Number Sentence .... Algebra 61
Mid-Chapter Check/Spiral Review 63
6 Ways to Make 4, 5, and 6 65
7 Ways to Make 7, 8, and 9 67
8 Ways to Make 10, 11, and 12 69
9 Problem-Solving Investigation
Choose a Strategy 73
10 Vertical Addition 75
Problem Solving in Health 77
Chapter Review/Test 79
Test Practice 81

Focal Points and Connections
See page iv for key.

G1-FP1 *Number and Operations* and *Algebra*

H.O.T. Problems
Higher Order Thinking 54, 60, 66, 76

Problem Solving 52, 68

Writing in Math 56

Contents

Chapter 3 Develop Subtraction Concepts

Are You Ready for Chapter 3? 84
Family Letter 85
1 Subtraction Stories 87
2 Modeling Subtraction 89
3 Subtraction Sentences . . . . . Algebra 91
Extra Practice 93
Game Time Subtracting to Swim 94
4 Subtract Zero and All . . . . . Algebra 95
5 Problem-Solving Strategy
Draw a Picture 97
Mid-Chapter Check/Spiral Review 99
6 Subtract from 4, 5, and 6 101
7 Subtract from 7, 8, and 9 103
8 Problem-Solving Investigation
Choose a Strategy 105
9 Subtract from 10, 11, and 12 107
10 Vertical Subtraction 111
Problem Solving in Social Studies 113
Chapter Review/Test 115
Test Practice 117

= Hands-On Activity

Tech Link = Technology Link

Focal Points and Connections
See page iv for key.

G1-FP1 *Number and Operations* and *Algebra*

H.O.T. Problems
Higher Order Thinking 92, 102, 104

Problem Solving 88, 96, 112

Writing in Math 90

Contents

Chapter 4 Organize and Use Data

Are You Ready for Chapter 4? 120

Family Letter 121

1 Sort and Classify 123

2 Picture Graphs 125

3 Problem-Solving Strategy

Make a Table 127

4 Tally Charts 129

Mid-Chapter Check/Spiral Review 131

5 Read a Bar Graph 133

Extra Practice 135

Game Time Animal Race 136

6 Make a Bar Graph 137

7 Problem-Solving Investigation

Choose a Strategy .... Algebra 141

8 Certain or Impossible 143

Problem Solving in Science 145

Chapter Review/Test 147

Test Practice 149

Focal Points and Connections
See page iv for key.

G1-FP5C *Measurement* and *Data Analysis*

H.O.T. Problems
Higher Order Thinking 140, 144

Problem Solving 124, 126

WRITING IN MATH 130

Contents

CHAPTER 5 Develop Addition Strategies

Are You Ready for Chapter 5? 152
Family Letter 153
1 Add in Any Order .... Algebra 155
2 Count On 1, 2, or 3 157
Extra Practice 159
Game Time All Mixed Up 160
3 Problem-Solving Strategy
Act It Out 161
4 Add 1, 2, or 3 163
5 Use a Number Line to Add 165
Mid-Chapter Check/Spiral Review 167
6 Doubles 169
7 Doubles Plus 1 171
8 Problem-Solving Investigation
Choose a Strategy 173
Problem Solving in Social Studies 175
Chapter Review/Test 177
Test Practice 179

= Hands-On Activity

Focal Points and Connections
See page iv for key.

G1-FP2 *Number and Operations*
G1-FP6C *Algebra*

H.O.T. Problems
Higher Order Thinking 156, 170

Problem Solving 166, 172

Writing in Math 158

Contents

Chapter 6 Develop Subtraction Strategies

Are You Ready for Chapter 6? 182

Family Letter 183

1 Count Back 1, 2, or 3 185

2 Problem-Solving Strategy

Write a Number Sentence . . . . . Algebra 187

3 Use a Number Line to Subtract 189

Mid-Chapter Check/Spiral Review 191

4 Problem-Solving Investigation

Choose a Strategy 193

5 Use Doubles to Subtract 195

6 Relate Addition to Subtraction . . . . . Algebra 197

7 Fact Families . . . . . Algebra 199

Extra Practice 201

Game Time Related or Not? 202

Problem Solving in Science 203

Chapter Review/Test 205

Test Practice 207

Focal Points and Connections
See page iv for key.

G1-FP2 *Number and Operations*
G1-FP6C *Algebra*

H.O.T. Problems
Higher Order Thinking 200

Problem Solving 186, 198

Writing in Math 196

Contents

Chapter 7 Measure Time

Are You Ready for Chapter 7? 210

Family Letter 211

1 Ordering Events 213

2 Time to the Hour 215

3 Time to the Half Hour 217

4 Problem-Solving Strategy

Make a Table 219

Mid-Chapter Check/Spiral Review 221

5 Telling Time to the Hour and Half Hour 223

6 Relate Time to Events 227

Extra Practice 229

Game Time Switch It! 230

7 Problem-Solving Investigation

Choose a Strategy 231

Problem Solving in Music 233

Chapter Review/Test 235

Test Practice 237

= Hands-On Activity

Focal Points and Connections
See page iv for key.

G1-FP5C *Measurement* and *Data Analysis*

H.O.T. Problems
Higher Order Thinking 226

Problem Solving 214, 216

Writing in Math 218

Contents

Chapter 8 Recognize Number Patterns

Are You Ready for Chapter 8? 240

Family Letter 241

1 Counting to 20 243

2 Counting by Tens 245

3 Problem-Solving Strategy

Look for a Pattern 247

4 Hundred Chart 249

Mid-Chapter Check/Spiral Review 253

5 Estimating With Groups of Tens 255

6 Problem-Solving Investigation

Choose a Strategy 257

7 Skip Counting by 2s, 5s, and 10s . . . . . Algebra 259

8 Skip Counting on a Hundred Chart . . . . . Algebra 261

9 Even and Odd 263

Extra Practice 265

Game Time Slide Through the Digits 266

Problem Solving in Social Studies 267

Chapter Review/Test 269

Test Practice 271

Focal Points and Connections
See page iv for key.

G1-FP2 *Number and Operations*

H.O.T. Problems
Higher Order Thinking 244, 260

Problem Solving 246, 256, 264

WRITING IN MATH 252

CHAPTER 9

Compare Measurements

Are You Ready for Chapter 9? 274

Family Letter 275

1 Compare and Order Lengths 277

2 Nonstandard Units of Length 279

3 Problem-Solving Strategy

Guess and Check 281

Extra Practice 283

Game Time Busy Beavers 284

4 Compare and Order Weights 285

Mid-Chapter Check/Spiral Review 289

5 Compare and Order Capacities 291

6 Compare and Order Temperatures 295

7 Problem-Solving Investigation

Choose a Strategy 299

8 Compare Areas 301

9 Order Areas 305

Problem Solving in Science 307

Chapter Review/Test 309

Test Practice 311

= Hands-On Activity

Tech Link = Technology Link

Focal Points and Connections
See page iv for key.

G1-FP2 *Number and Operations*
G1-FP5C *Measurement* and *Data Analysis*

H.O.T. Problems
Higher Order Thinking 304

Problem Solving 280, 294, 298, 306

WRITING IN MATH 278

Contents

Chapter 10 Solve Addition and Subtraction Problems

Are You Ready for Chapter 10? 314
Family Letter 315
1 Doubles 317
2 Doubles Plus 1 319
Extra Practice 321
Game Time Circle Up 322
3 Make a 10 to Add . . . . Algebra 323
4 Problem-Solving Strategy
Draw a Picture . . . . Algebra 325
Mid-Chapter Check/Spiral Review 327
5 Use Doubles to Subtract 329
6 Relate Addition and Subtraction . . . . Algebra 331
7 Problem-Solving Investigation
Choose a Strategy . . . . Algebra 333
8 Fact Families . . . . Algebra 335
9 Ways to Model Numbers 339
Problem Solving in Social Studies 341
Chapter Review/Test 343
Test Practice 345

Focal Points and Connections
See page iv for key.

G1-FP2 *Number and Operations*
G1-FP6C *Algebra*

H.O.T. Problems
Higher Order Thinking 320, 324, 332

Problem Solving 318, 330

WRITING IN MATH 338

Contents

Chapter 11 Identify Coins

Are You Ready for Chapter 11? 348

Family Letter 349

1 Pennies and Nickels 351

2 Pennies and Dimes 353

3 Pennies, Nickels, and Dimes 355

4 Counting Money 357

5 Problem-Solving Strategy

Act It Out 359

Mid-Chapter Check/Spiral Review 361

6 Equal Amounts 363

7 Quarters 365

8 Problem-Solving Investigation

Choose a Strategy 369

9 Money Amounts 371

Extra Practice 373

Game Time Who Has More? 374

Problem Solving in Social Studies 375

Chapter Review/Test 377

Test Practice 379

= Hands-On Activity

Tech Link = Technology Link

Focal Points and Connections
See page iv for key.

G1-FP4C *Number and Operations* and *Algebra*

H.O.T. Problems
Higher Order Thinking 354

Problem Solving 352, 356, 358, 372

WRITING IN MATH 364

Contents

CHAPTER 12 Identify Geometric Figures

Are You Ready for Chapter 12? 382

Family Letter 383

1 Three-Dimensional Figures 385

2 Faces and Corners 387

3 Problem-Solving Strategy

Look for a Pattern 389

4 Two- and Three-Dimensional Figures 391

Extra Practice 393

Game Time Corners 394

5 Two-Dimensional Figures 395

Mid-Chapter Check/Spiral Review 397

6 Problem-Solving Investigation

Choose a Strategy 399

7 Position 401

8 Make New Figures 405

9 Give and Follow Directions 407

Problem Solving in Art 409

Chapter Review/Test 411

Test Practice 413

Focal Points and Connections
See page iv for key.

G1-FP3 *Geometry*

H.O.T. Problems
Higher Order Thinking 396, 406

Problem Solving 388, 392, 404

WRITING IN MATH 386

Contents

Chapter 13 Understand Place Value

Are You Ready for Chapter 13? 416

Family Letter 417

1 Tens 419

2 Tens and Ones 423

Extra Practice 425

Game Time Lizzie the Lizard 426

3 Problem-Solving Strategy
Guess and Check .... Algebra 427

4 Numbers to 50 429

5 Numbers to 100 433

Mid-Chapter Check/Spiral Review 437

6 Estimate Numbers 439

7 Problem-Solving Investigation
Choose a Strategy 441

8 Compare Numbers to 100 .... Algebra 443

9 Order Numbers to 100 .... Algebra 445

Problem Solving in Science 447

Chapter Review/Test 449

Test Practice 451

= Hands-On Activity

Tech Link = Technology Link

Focal Points and Connections
See page iv for key.

G1-FP2 *Number and Operations*

H.O.T. Problems
Higher Order Thinking 422

Problem Solving 436, 440, 444, 446

Writing in Math 424

Contents

Chapter 14 Describe Fractional Parts

Are You Ready for Chapter 14? 454

Family Letter 455

1 Equal Parts 457

2 Problem-Solving Strategy
Draw a Picture 459

3 One Half 461

4 One Third and One Fourth 463

Extra Practice 465

Game Time The Equalizer 466

Mid-Chapter Check/Spiral Review 467

5 Non-Unit Fractions 469

6 Fractions of a Set 471

7 Problem-Solving Investigation
Choose a Strategy 473

Problem Solving in Science 475

Chapter Review/Test 477

Test Practice 479

Focal Points and Connections
See page iv for key.

G1-FP3 *Geometry*

H.O.T. Problems
Higher Order Thinking 464

Problem Solving 458, 462

WRITING IN MATH 470

Contents

Chapter 15 Solve Two-Digit Addition and Subtraction Problems

Are You Ready for Chapter 15? 482

Family Letter. 483

1 Add and Subtract Tens 485

2 Add with Two-Digit Numbers. 487

3 Problem-Solving Strategy

Guess and Check . . . . Algebra 489

4 Add Two-Digit Numbers. 491

Extra Practice 493

Game Time Adding Colors 494

5 Estimate Sums 495

Mid-Chapter Check/Spiral Review. 497

6 Subtract with Two-Digit Numbers 499

7 Subtract Two-Digit Numbers 501

8 Problem-Solving Investigation

Choose a Strategy. 503

9 Estimate Differences 505

Problem Solving in Social Studies 507

Chapter Review/Test 509

Test Practice 511

= Hands-On Activity

Focal Points and Connections
See page iv for key.

G1-FP4C *Number and Operations* and *Algebra*

H.O.T. Problems
Higher Order Thinking 488

Problem Solving 492, 496, 500, 502

WRITING IN MATH 506

Contents

Looking Ahead

1 Missing Addends LA3

2 Count on Tens and Ones LA5

3 Hundreds, Tens, Ones LA7

4 Place Value to 1,000 . . . . LA9

5 Measure to the Nearest Inch LA11

6 Measure to the Nearest Centimeter LA13

H.O.T. Problems
Higher Order Thinking LA10

Problem Solving LA4, LA6, LA12, LA14

WRITING IN MATH LA8

Problem-Solving Projects

1 I Spy Patterns! P3

2 Fruit Kabob Factory P7

3 Let's Go to the Zoo! P11

4 Toys From the Past and Present P15

Contents

Student Handbook

Concept and Skills Bank **CS1**

Reference

Preparing for Standardized Tests **TP1**

English-Spanish Glossary **G1**

Facts Practice **FP1**

Photo Credits

WorkMat 1: Ten-Frame

WorkMat 2: Ten-Frames

WorkMat 3: Part-Part-Whole

WorkMat 4: Number Lines

WorkMat 5: Number Lines

WorkMat 6: Grid

WorkMat 7: Tens and Ones Chart

WorkMat 8: Hundreds, Tens, and Ones Chart

Contents

CHAPTER 9

Chapter Overview

Chapter-at-a-Glance

In Chapter 9, the emphasis is on students exploring measurement through direct comparison and nonstandard units.

Lesson		Math Objective	State/Local Standards
9-1	**Compare and Order Lengths** (pp. 277–278)	Compare and order the lengths of two or more objects using direct comparison.	
9-2	**Nonstandard Units of Length** (pp. 279–280)	Measure length using nonstandard units.	
9-3	**Problem-Solving Strategy: Guess and Check** (pp. 281–282)	Use the *guess and check* strategy to solve problems.	
9-4	**Compare and Order Weights** (pp. 285–288)	Compare and order the weights of two or more objects.	
9-5	**Compare and Order Capacities** (pp. 291–294)	Compare and order the capacities of two or more objects.	
9-6	**Compare and Order Temperatures** (pp. 295–298)	Compare and order two or more objects according to relative temperatures.	
9-7	**Problem-Solving Investigation: Choose a Strategy** (pp. 299–300)	Choose the best strategy to solve a problem.	
9-8	**Compare Areas** (pp. 301–304)	Compare the areas of two or more shapes.	
9-9	**Order Areas** (pp. 305–306)	Order the areas of two or more shapes.	

Compare Measurements

BIG Idea Understanding how to correctly measure an object often shows students how to properly space objects and teaches that the longer the measuring unit, the fewer units needed to measure.

- Measuring using nonstandard units frequently involves estimating.
- Measuring involves adding together units to find the total length, weight/mass, capacity, or area.

Algebra Readiness In Lesson 9-1, students prepare for Algebra by ordering objects from shortest to longest. In Lesson 9-2, students are introduced to the abstract Algebra concept of a *unit.*

Measurement Readiness In Lessons 9-1, 9-2, 9-4, 9-5, 9-6, 9-8, and 9-9, students prepare for Measurement by exploring the length, weight/mass, capacity, temperature, and area of objects.

Focal Points and Connections

G1-FP2 *Number and Operations:* **Developing an understanding of whole number relationships, including grouping in tens and ones**

Children compare and order whole numbers (at least to 100) to develop an understanding of and solve problems involving the relative sizes of these numbers. They think of whole numbers between 10 and 100 in terms of groups of tens and ones (especially recognizing the numbers 11 to 19 as 1 group of ten and particular numbers of ones). They understand the sequential order of the counting numbers and their relative magnitudes and represent numbers on a number line.

G1-FP5C *Measurement* **and** *Data Analysis:* Children strengthen their sense of number by solving problems involving measurements and data. Measuring by laying multiple copies of a unit end to end and then counting the units by using groups of tens and ones supports children's understanding of number lines and number relationships. Representing measurements and discrete data in picture and bar graphs involves counting and comparisons that provide another meaningful connection to number relationships.

Skills Trace
Vertical Alignment

Kindergarten

In kindergarten, students learned to:
- Explore the length, height, weight, and capacity of objects.
- Order objects by length (shorter/longer).

First Grade

During this chapter, students learn to:
- Measure lengths, areas and capacities, using nonstandard units such as paper clips.
- Use direct comparison to compare and order objects according to length, weight, temperature, capacity, and area.
- Use strategies and skills to solve problems.

After this chapter, students learn to:
- Identify, describe, and classify geometric figures. (Chapter 12)

Second Grade

In second grade, students learn to:
- Estimate measurements.

Backmapping and Vertical Alignment
McGraw-Hill's *Math Connects* program was conceived and developed with the final results in mind: student success in Algebra 1 and beyond. The authors, using the **NCTM Focal Points and Focal Connections** as their guide, developed this brand-new series by backmapping from Algebra 1 concepts, and vertically aligning the topics so that they build upon prior skills and concepts and serve as a foundation for future topics.

Math Vocabulary

The following math vocabulary words for Chapter 9 are listed in the glossary of the ***Student Edition***. You can find interactive definitions in 13 languages in the ***eGlossary*** at macmillanmh.com.

covers less/least

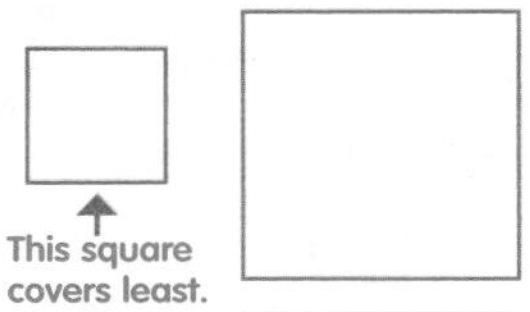

covers more/most

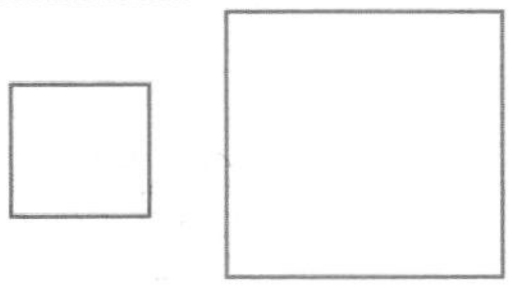

heavy/heavier/heaviest weighs more (weighs the most); example: an orange is heavier than a paper clip (p. 285)

holds less/least (p. 291)

holds more/most (p. 291)

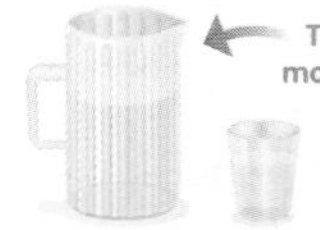

length how long or far something is (p. 277)

light/lighter/lightest weighs less; the baby is lighter than the man; the balloon is lighter than the baby (p. 285)

long/longer/longest a way to compare the lengths of two (or more) objects (p. 277)

measure to find the length, height, or weight using standard or nonstandard units (p. 279)

short/shorter/shortest to compare length or height of two (or more) objects (p. 277)

unit an object used to measure (p. 279)

weight a measurement that tells how heavy or light an object is (p. 285)

Visual Vocabulary Cards Use Visual Vocabulary Cards to introduce and reinforce the vocabulary in this chapter. (The Define/Example/Ask routine is printed on the back of each card.)

Chapter 9 Chapter Planner

Suggested Pacing		
Instruction	Review and Assessment	TOTAL
9 days	2 days	**11 days**

Diagnostic Assessment
Are You Ready? (p. 274)

	Lesson 9-1 (Pacing: 1 day)	Lesson 9-2 (Pacing: 1 day)	Lesson 9-3 (Pacing: 1 day)
Lesson/ Objective	**Compare and Order Lengths** (pp. 277–278) **Objective:** Compare and order the lengths of two or more objects using direct comparison.	**Nonstandard Units of Length** (pp. 279–280) **Objective:** Measure length using nonstandard units.	Problem-Solving Strategy **Guess and Check** (pp. 281–282) **Objective:** Use the *guess and check* strategy to solve problems.
State/Local Standards			
Math Vocabulary	**length** **short/shorter/shortest** **long/longer/longest**	**measure** **unit**	
Lesson Resources	**Materials** unsharpened pencils, crayons, markers, straightedge **Other Resources** CRM Leveled Worksheets (pp. 6–10) Daily Reteach • 5-Minute Check Problem of the Day	**Materials** crayons, large paper clips, pencils **Manipulatives** connecting cubes, pattern blocks **Other Resources** CRM Leveled Worksheets (pp. 11–15) Daily Reteach • 5-Minute Check Problem of the Day	**Manipulatives** connecting cubes **Other Resources** CRM Leveled Worksheets (pp. 16–20) Daily Reteach • 5-Minute Check Problem of the Day *A Wet Week*
Technology Math Online		Math Adventures Concepts in Motion	
Reaching All Learners	Below Level, p. 277B BL English Learners, p. 277B ELL Early Finishers, p. 277B OL AL	Below Level, p. 279B BL English Learners, p. 279B ELL Early Finishers, p. 279B OL AL	Gifted and Talented, p. 281B AL English Learners, p. 281B ELL Early Finishers, p. 281B OL AL
Alternate Lessons	*Math Their Way,* p. 120 *IMPACT Mathematics:* Unit G	*Math Their Way,* p. 135	

Extra Practice (p. 283)
Game Time: Busy Beavers (p. 284)

KEY

BL Below/Approaching Level · OL On Level · AL Above/Beyond Level · ELL English Learners
SE Student Edition · TE Teacher Edition · CRM Chapter 3 Resource Masters · CD-Rom
Transparency · Flip Chart · Real-World Problem Solving Library

	Lesson 9-4 (Pacing: 1 day)	Lesson 9-5 (Pacing: 1 day)	Lesson 9-6 (Pacing: 1 day)
Lesson/ Objective	**Compare and Order Weights** (pp. 285–288) **Objective:** Compare and order the weights of two or more objects.	**Compare and Order Capacities** (pp. 291–294) **Objective:** Compare and order the capacities of two or more objects.	**Compare and Order Temperatures** (pp. 295–298) **Objective:** Compare and order two or more objects according to relative temperatures.
State/Local Standards			
Math Vocabulary	**weight** **heavy/heavier/heaviest** **light/lighter/lightest**	**holds more/most** **holds less/least**	**hot** **cold**
Lesson Resources	**Materials** classroom items to weigh (stapler, paper clip, crayons, box of crayons, etc.) **Manipulatives** pan balance **Other Resources** CRM Leveled Worksheets (pp. 21–25) Daily Reteach • 5-Minute Check Problem of the Day	**Materials** various containers such as a measuring cup, a jar, milk carton, ice cream carton, drinking glass, and bottle; rice, sand or water **Other Resources** CRM Leveled Worksheets (pp. 26–30) Daily Reteach • 5-Minute Check Problem of the Day	**Materials** real objects of varying temperatures such as a heating pad, a hot-water bottle, room-temperature water, a cold can of soda, and an ice cube **Other Resources** CRM Leveled Worksheets (pp. 31–35) Daily Reteach • 5-Minute Check Problem of the Day
Technology Math Online			
Reaching All Learners	Gifted and Talented, p. 285B AL English Learners, p. 285B ELL Early Finishers, p. 285B OL AL	Gifted and Talented, p. 291B AL English Learners, p. 291B ELL Early Finishers, p. 291B OL AL	Gifted and Talented, p. 295B AL English Learners, p. 295B ELL Early Finishers, p. 295B OL AL
Alternate Lessons	*Math Their Way,* p. 132 *IMPACT Mathematics:* Unit G	*Math Their Way,* p. 131 *IMPACT Mathematics:* Unit G	

Formative Assessment
- Mid-Chapter Check (p. 289)
- Spiral Review (p. 290)

CHAPTER 9

Chapter Planner

	Lesson 9-7 (Pacing: 1 day)	Lesson 9-8 (Pacing: 1 day)	Lesson 9-9 (Pacing: 1 day)
Lesson/ Objective	Problem-Solving Investigation **Choose a Strategy** (pp. 299–300) **Objective:** Choose the best strategy to solve a problem.	**Compare Areas** (pp. 301–304) **Objective:** Compare the areas of two or more shapes.	**Order Areas** (pp. 305–306) **Objective:** Order the areas of two or more shapes.
State/Local Standards			
Math Vocabulary		**cover more/most** **cover less/least**	
Lesson Resources	**Other Resources** CRM Leveled Worksheets (pp. 36–40) Daily Reteach • 5-Minute Check Problem of the Day *A Wet Week*	**Materials** crayons, map of United States, construction paper **Manipulatives** connecting cubes, color tiles or pattern blocks **Other Resources** CRM Leveled Worksheets (pp. 41–45) Daily Reteach • 5-Minute Check Problem of the Day	**Materials** rectangles of varying sizes cut from wax paper, marker, grid on overhead transparency **Manipulatives** color tiles or pattern blocks **Other Resources** CRM Leveled Worksheets (pp. 46–50) Daily Reteach • 5-Minute Check Problem of the Day
Technology Math Online			
Reaching All Learners	Gifted and Talented, p. 299B AL English Learners, p. 299B ELL Early Finishers, p. 299B OL AL	Below Level, p. 301B BL English Learners, p. 301B ELL Early Finishers, p. 301B OL AL	Below Level, p. 305B BL English Learners, p. 305B ELL Early Finishers, p. 305B OL AL
Alternate Lesson			

Problem Solving in Science (p. 307)

Summative Assessment
- Chapter Review/Test (p. 309)
- Test Practice (p. 311)

Assessment Options

Diagnostic Assessment

- SE *Option 1:* Are You Ready? (p. 274)
- *Option 2:* Online Quiz macmillanmh.com
- CRM *Option 3:* Diagnostic Test (p. 52)
- CRM *Option 4:* Chapter Pretest (p. 53)

Formative Assessment

- TE Alternate Teaching Strategies (every lesson)
- SE Talk About It (every lesson)
- SE Writing in Math (every lesson)
- SE Check (every lesson)
- TE Line Up (every lesson)
- SE Mid-Chapter Check (p. 289)
- CRM Mid-Chapter Test (p. 54)

Summative Assessment

- SE Chapter Review/Test (p. 309)
- SE Test Practice (p. 311)
- CRM Vocabulary Test (p. 55)
- CRM Leveled Chapter Tests (pp. 62–71)
- CRM Cumulative Test Practice (pp. 72–73)
- CRM Listening Assessment (pp. 58–59)
- CRM Oral Assessment (pp. 56–57)
- Exam*View*® Assessment Suite
- Advance Tracker

Professional Development

Targeted professional development has been articulated throughout **McGraw-Hill's *Math Connects*** program. The **McGraw-Hill Professional Development Video Library** provides short videos that support the **NCTM Focal Points and Focal Connections**. For more information, visit macmillanmh.com.

Model Lessons

Instructional Strategies

Assessment Tips

Students will learn about direct comparison and nonstandard measurement by using different objects to measure length, weight, and capacity.

- During this chapter, students can be placed in pairs or small groups to do the measuring activities
- Create a chart listing the objects you want the students to measure, including both direct comparison and nonstandard measurement.
- As groups of students complete the various measurement activities, check them off on the chart.
- Ask students clarifying questions during these measurement activities to get them to elaborate and extend their thinking.

Teacher Notes

CHAPTER 9

Learning Stations

Cross-Curricular Links

Reading

pair | KINESTHETIC, SOCIAL

How Tall?

- With a partner, read *Ten Beads Tall.*
- Get 2 strings and thread 10 beads onto each string. Tie the string off on both ends.
- Measure the length of objects in your classroom. On a sheet of paper, record 5 objects that are 10 beads tall or long.

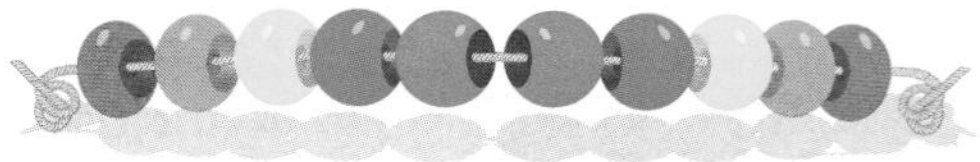

Teacher Note: Large, wooden beads would work best. If those are unavailable, use the largest beads possible.

Materials:

- *Ten Beads Tall* by Pam Adams
- string or yarn cut into 2 foot pieces
- large beads

Art

individual | VISUAL/ SPATIAL

Paint Bursts

- Make a paint burst. Get as much paint on a paint brush as you can. Bump the brush down on your paper and then pick the brush back up.
- Paint a picture using paint bursts. Use different sizes of paint brushes and different colors.
- What did you notice about the size of the brush and the size of the paint bursts? Which brushes could hold more paint and make bigger bursts?

Materials:

- tempera paint
- construction paper
- different-sized paint brushes
- cups of water

Language Arts

individual | LINGUISTIC, LOGICAL

The Write Strip

- Choose 5 strips of paper. Make sure they are all different sizes.
- Choose the smallest piece of paper. Place stickers on the paper until it is filled up.
- Choose the next smallest piece of paper and fill it with stickers.
- Fill up each piece of paper.
- Write what you notice about how many stickers each strip holds.
- What is the unit you are using to measure?

Teacher Note: Cut the pieces of paper ahead of time. Cut all sizes, from small squares to long strips.

Materials:

- writing paper cut into small strips

Science

pair | LOGICAL

Nature Numbers

- Make a chart like the one at this station.
- Choose one object and place it on one side of the balance.
- Place paper clips on the other side until the sides are balanced. Write how many paper clips that object weighs.
- Weigh each of the other objects. Circle the object that weighs the most. Draw a square around the object that weighs the least.

Teacher Note: Have an example recording chart for students to copy. It should have a table with columns for the name of the object and the weight in paper clips.

Materials:
- pan balance
- items from outside, such as small rocks, sticks, bag of dirt, or shells
- paper clips
- recording chart sample

Social Studies

individual | INTRAPERSONAL

Daytime Timeline

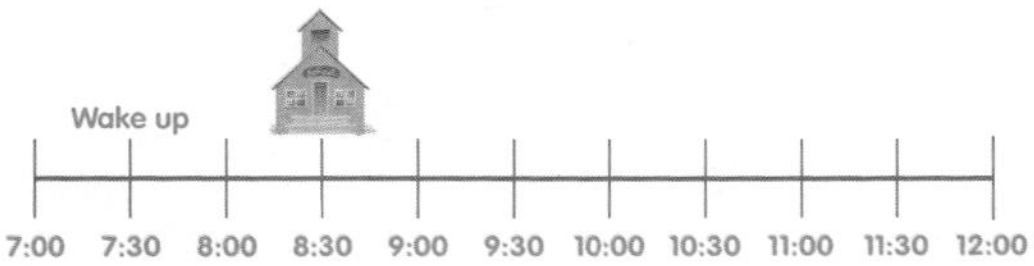

- Create a timeline of your day.
- Your timeline should go from 7:00 in the morning to 8:00 in the evening.
- Write or draw activities you do every day on your timeline near the time you do the activity.
- Look at the different space between your different activities. Are they different lengths apart?

Teacher Note: Have a timeline example hanging up for students to model from.

Materials:
- paper
- pencil

Calendar Time

Length of a School Month

- Have students sit in front of the classroom calendar. Review with students how to make tally marks. Have a volunteer make tally marks on the chalkboard as the class counts all the days in one month. Label the tally marks *Total Days in 1 Month*.
- **What days of the week do we come to school?** Monday, Tuesday, Wednesday, Thursday, and Friday
- Have a volunteer make tally marks on the chalkboard as the class counts the school days in one month. Point to the days as the class counts. Do not count weekend days. Label these tally marks *School Days*.
- **Why are the two numbers different?** There is no school on the weekends. **Do we go to school the same number of days every month? Why or why not?** No; some months have a different number of days, or they have holidays.

Introduce the Chapter

Real World: Simon Says

Have students stand and play the game Simon Says. When a student does not follow directions correctly, the student sits until a new game starts. Use commands that suggest length, weight, and capacity. For example:

- **Simon says, "Stretch up tall."**
- **Simon says, "Sit down low."**
- **Simon says, "Hold air in your cheeks."**
- **Simon says, "Cup your hands."**

Have students turn to p. 273.

- **Have you ever seen a meerkat?**
- **Which one is tallest?**

Key Vocabulary

Introduce the key vocabulary in the chapter using the routine below.

Define: **Shorter** is a word used to compare the length or height of two or more objects.
Example: The length of my pencil is shorter than the length of my desk.
Ask: What are some other things in the classroom that can be compared using *shorter?*

CHAPTER 9

Compare Measurements

Key Vocabulary
length
measure
unit
weight

Explore
Put an X on the tallest.
Circle the shortest.
Check students' answers.

Chapter 9 two hundred seventy-three 273

FOLDABLES Study Organizer — Dinah Zike's Foldables

Guide students to create a 3-Tab Foldable for comparing measurements.

1. Fold a sheet of poster board like a hot dog.

2. With the poster horizontal, and the fold of the hot dog up, fold the right side toward the center, trying to cover on half of the poster.

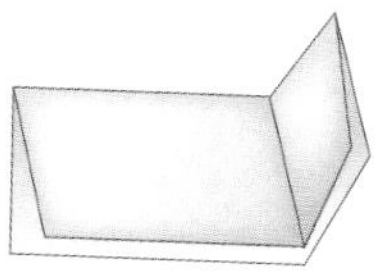

3. Fold the left side over the right side to make a book with three folds.

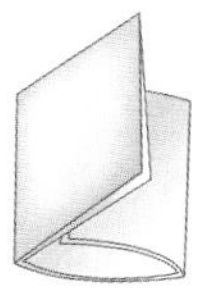

4. Open the folded book. Place your hands between the two thicknesses of the poster and cut up the two valleys on one side only. This will form three tabs. Label the tabs *Length*, *Weight*, and *Capacity*.

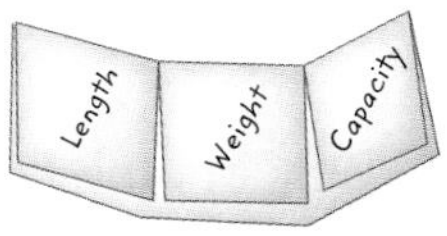

When to Use It *Lessons 9-2, 9-4, and 9-5. (Additional instructions for using the Foldable with these lessons are found on pp. 289 and 309.)*

Name ____________________

Math Online
Take the Chapter Readiness Quiz at macmillanmh.com.

Are You Ready for Chapter 9?

Circle the longer one.

1. 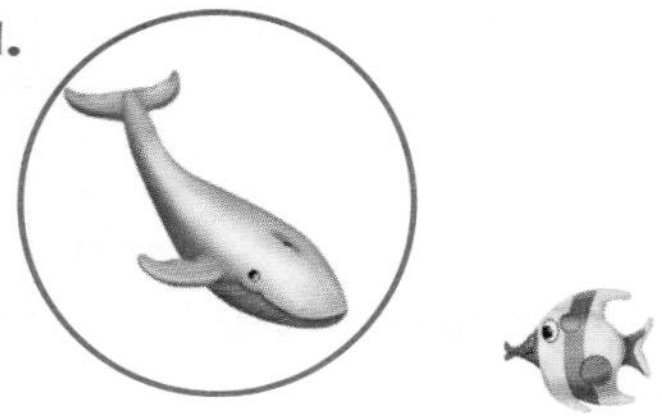

2. 

Underline the object that is heavier.

3. 

4. 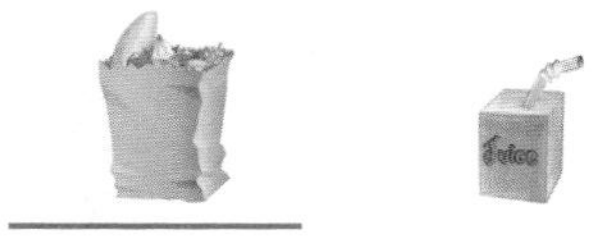

Put an **X** on the container that holds less.

5. 

6. 

Look at the string.

7. 

Find something that is longer. ________

Find something that is shorter. ________

Check students' answers.

This page checks skills needed for Chapter 9.

Diagnostic Assessment

Check for students' prerequisite skills before beginning the chapter.

- **Option 1:** ***Are You Ready for Chapter 9?***
  SE Student Edition, p. 274
- **Option 2:** ***Online Assessment***
  Math Online macmillanmh.com
- **Option 3:** ***Diagnostic Test***
  CRM Chapter 9 Resource Masters, p. 52

RTI (Response to Intervention)

Apply the Results Based on the results of the diagnostic assessment on p. 274, use the chart below to address individual needs before and during the chapter.

TIER 3 Intensive Intervention

If students miss five or more of the exercises:

Then use Chapter 7 of *Math Triumphs*, an intensive math intervention program from McGraw-Hill.

TIER 2 Strategic Intervention below/approaching grade level	TIER 1 On-Level	Above/Beyond Level
If students miss three or four in: **Exercises 1–7**	**If** students miss two in: **Exercises 1–7**	**If** students miss one or less in: **Exercises 1–7**
Then choose a resource:	**Then** choose a resource:	**Then** choose a resource:
Strategic Intervention Guide (p. 108) TE Smart Start 4: Longleaf Pines Math Online Concepts in Motion	TE Learning Stations (pp. 273G–273H) TE Chapter Project (p. 275) CRM Game: *What Are Your Measurements?* My Math Zone Chapter 8 Math Online Fact Dash	TE Learning Stations (pp. 273G–273H) TE Chapter Project (p. 275) Real-World Problem Solving: *A Wet Week* My Math Zone Chapters 8 and 9 Math Online Games

MATH at HOME

Before you begin Chapter 9:

- Read the Math at Home letter found on p. 275, with the class and have each student sign it.
- Send home copies of the Math at Home letter with each student.
- Use the Spanish letter on p. 276 for students with Spanish-speaking parents or guardians.

WRITING IN MATH

Starting the Chapter

Ask each student to list:

- Five things that are longer than the student's pencil.
- Five things that are heavier than the student's pencil.
- Five things that can hold more than what the student can hold in his or her hands.
- Five things that are hotter than a juice box.

Read-Aloud Anthology

For an optional reading activity to introduce this chapter's math concepts, see the Read-Aloud Anthology on p. TR33.

MATH at HOME

Dear Family,

Today my class started Chapter 9, **Compare Measurements**. In this chapter, I will learn about length, weight, capacity, temperature, and area. Here is an activity we can do and a list of books we can read together.

Love, ______________________

Activity

Tape pages of newsprint together to make a long strip. On the strip trace the outline of your hand with fingers spread and use different objects, such as books or shoes, to measure the length of the outline. Repeat and trace your child's hand. Compare the measurements.

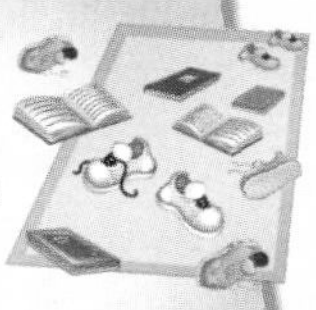

Key Vocabulary

measure to find the length, height, or weight using standard or nonstandard units

Math Online Click on the eGlossary link at macmillanmh.com to find out more about these words. There are 13 languages.

Books to Read

Who Sank the Boat?
by Pamela Allen
Putnam Juvenile, 1996.

A Pig is Big
by Douglas Florian
Greenwillow Books, 2000.

Biggest, Strongest, Fastest
by Steve Jenkins
Houghton Mifflin Company, 1997.

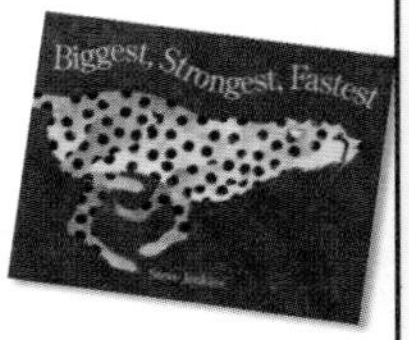

two hundred seventy-five 275

Chapter 9 Project

Length Seek and Find

Solve: Find the longest object in the classroom.

- Give small teams time over the week to measure the length of objects using connecting cubes.
- Have them record their findings. Challenge them to find the longest object in the classroom.
- Compare the teams' results to see which one found the longest item in the classroom.

CRM *Refer to Chapter 9 Resource Masters p. 60 for a rubric to assess students' progress on this project*

MATEMÁTICAS en CASA

Estimada familia:

Hoy mi clase comenzó el Capítulo 9, **Compara medidas**. En este capítulo, aprenderé sobre la longitud, el peso y el volumen. A continuación, hay una actividad que podemos hacer y una lista de libros que podemos leer juntos.

Cariños, ______________________

Actividad

Unan varias páginas de periódico con cinta adhesiva para hacer una tira larga. Dibujen el contorno de su hijo(a) sobre el papel y usen diferentes objetos, como libros o zapatos, para medir la longitud del contorno. Repitan el ejercicio y dibujen sus siluetas. Comparen las medidas.

Vocabulario clave

medir calcular la longitud, el peso o el volumen en base a comparaciones

Math Online Visiten el enlace eGlossary en macmillanmh.com para averiguar más sobre estas palabras, las cuales se muestran en 13 idiomas.

Libros recomendados

¿Hay algo más grande que una ballena azul?
de Robert E. Wells
Editorial Juventud, 2000.

Carrie está a la altura
de Linda Williams Aber
The Kane Press, 2005.

Dime que tan lejos esta de aqui (los estupendos whiz kids)
de Shirley Willis
Franklin Watts, 2000.

Chapter 9 Literature List

Lesson	Book Title
9-1	**The Long and Short of It** Cheryl Nathan and Lisa McCourt
9-2	**How Big Is a Foot?** Rolf Myller
9-3	**Inch by Inch** Leo Lionni
9-4	**Just a Little Bit** Ann Tompert
9-5	**The Mitten** Jan Brett
9-6	**Math for All Seasons** Greg Tang
9-8	**Bigger, Better, BEST!** Stuart J. Murphy
9-9	**Bigger, Better, BEST!** Stuart J. Murphy
Any	**A Pig is Big** Douglas Florian
Any	**Who Sank the Boat?** Pamela Allen
Any	**Biggest, Strongest, Fastest** Steve Jenkins

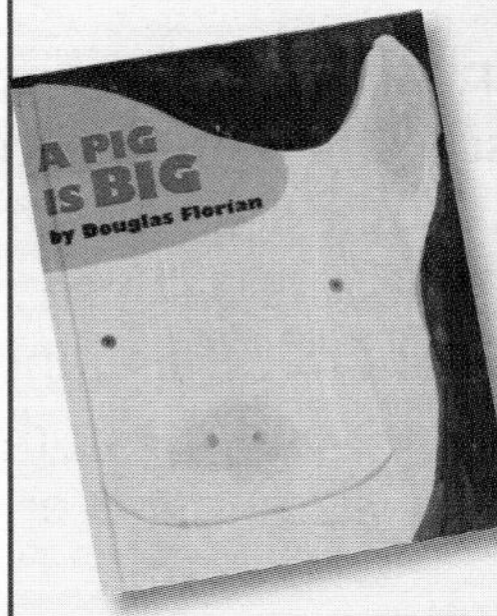

ELL National ESL Standards Alignment for Chapter 9

Lesson, Page	ESL Standard	Modality	Level
9-1, p 277B	Goal 2, Standard 1, d	Logical, Social	Intermediate
9-2, p 279B	Goal 2, Standard 3, i	Visual/Spatial	Intermediate
9-3, p 281B	Goal 2, Standard 2, f	Linguistic, Logical	Advanced
9-4, p 285B	Goal 2, Standard 2, j	Logical, Visual/Spatial	Intermediate
9-5, p 291B	Goal 2, Standard 2, f	Kinesthetic, Intrapersonal	Intermediate
9-6, p 295B	Goal 1, Standard 3, e	Kinesthetic, Linguistic	Intermediate
9-7, p 299B	Goal 2, Standard 2, f	Linguistic, Intrapersonal	Advanced
9-8, p 301B	Goal 2, Standard 1, f	Logical, Kinesthetic	Intermediate
9-9, p 305B	Goal 1, Standard 3, b	Logical, Kinesthetic	Intermediate

The National ESL Standards can be found in the Teacher Reference Handbook.

LESSON 9-1

Compare and Order Lengths

Lesson Planner

Objective

Compare and order the lengths of two or more objects using direct comparison.

Vocabulary

length, **long/longer/longest**, **short/shorter/shortest**

Resources

Materials: unsharpened pencils, crayons, markers, straightedge

Literature Connection: *The Long and Short of It* by Cheryl Nathan and Lisa McCourt

Alternate Lessons: Use "Body Measurements" on page 120 of *Math Their Way* to provide practice exploring length.
Use *IMPACT Mathematics:* Unit G to provide practice with comparing and ordering length.

Teacher Technology
TeacherWorks

Focus on Math Background

In this lesson, students will explore length as a measurable attribute. This lesson will help first graders understand length as a property that describes the distance between two points. Students will use vocabulary such as longer than, shorter than, and the same length as in order to describe and make direct comparisons between the relative size of two or more objects.

Daily Routine

Use these suggestions before beginning the lesson on p. 277.

5-Minute Check

(Reviews Lesson 8-9)

Write even or odd.

1. 44 even
2. 23 odd
3. 32 even
4. 90 even

Problem of the Day

Jamie counts:

35, ___, 25, 20, ___, ___, 5, 0.

Fill in the missing numbers. 30, 15, 10

LINE UP Have students line up in two lines, one with boys and one with girls.

- **Which line is longer?** Sample answer: the line with girls.
- **By how many students?** 3 students

Building Math Vocabulary

Write the terms **shorter** and **longer** on the board. Discuss the terms and be sure to explain the difference between *shorter/**shortest*** and *longer/**longest**.*

- Draw three lines of different **length** on the board.
- **Which line is shortest?** Label it. **Which is longest?** Label it.
- Select students to come up and draw lines that are longer or shorter than your line.

Differentiated Instruction

Small Group Options

Option 1 VISUAL/SPATIAL

Below Level BL

Materials: variety of classroom items, connecting cubes

- Have each student in the group connect ten cubes together to make a measuring stick.
- Using the measuring sticks, have students measure items in the classroom such as a pencil, scissors, bottle of glue, ruler, a sheet of paper, and a shoe.
- Have students record whether the items are longer or shorter than their measuring stick of cubes.
- If two students measure the same item but get different answers, lead a discussion on how to properly measure an item by lining up one end of the item with one end of the measuring tool.

Option 2 LOGICAL, SOCIAL

English Language Learners ELL

Core Vocabulary: who's, length, side by side
Common Use Verb: compare

See Math This strategy allows students to practice comparing relative lengths.

- Demonstrate that length is how long something is.
- Ask two students to come to the front and stand with their feet side by side.
- Ask: **"Who's** foot is longer?" Use a stretching hand motion to indicate *longer*.
- Repeat with legs (sitting down) or arms as time permits.
- Extend strategy by allowing students to order themselves from shortest to longest for any given body part.

Independent Work Options

Option 1 LOGICAL

Early Finishers OL AL

Materials: straightedge (ruler), paper, crayons, connecting cubes

- Divide students into pairs. Have each student draw 8 dots on a sheet of paper and label them from A to H.
- Have students trade papers and connect the dots in order using a straightedge.
- Have students use connecting cubes to measure each line.

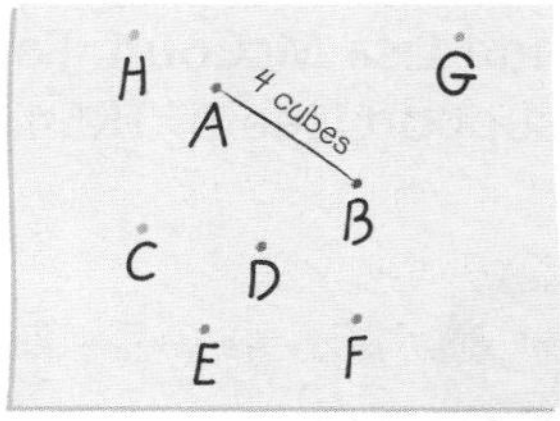

Option 2

Student Technology

Math Online macmillanmh.com

Option 3

Learning Station: Reading (p. 273G)

Direct students to the Reading Learning Station for more opportunities to explore and extend the lesson concept.

Option 4

Problem-Solving Practice

Reinforce problem-solving skills and strategies with the Problem-Solving
Practice worksheet.

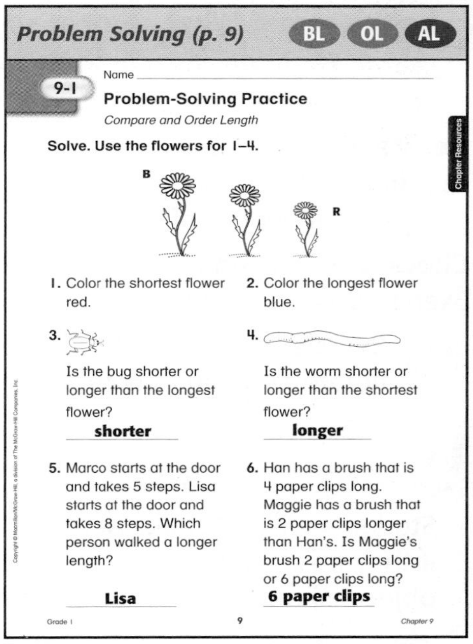

Problem Solving (p. 9) BL OL AL

Name ______

9-1 **Problem-Solving Practice**
Compare and Order Length

Solve. Use the flowers for 1–4.

B R

1. Color the shortest flower red.
2. Color the longest flower blue.
3. Is the bug shorter or longer than the longest flower? **shorter**
4. Is the worm shorter or longer than the shortest flower? **longer**
5. Marco starts at the door and takes 5 steps. Lisa starts at the door and takes 8 steps. Which person walked a longer length? **Lisa**
6. Han has a brush that is 4 paper clips long. Maggie has a brush that is 2 paper clips longer than Han's. Is Maggie's brush 2 paper clips long or 6 paper clips long? **6 paper clips**

Grade 1 9 Chapter 9

1 Introduce

Activity Choice 1 • Hands-On

Show students a crayon and a marker.

- **Which is longer? Which is shorter?**
- Add a pencil. Invite a student to order the objects according to **length**.
- **Who can find something that is as long as ____? Who can find something as short as ____?**

Activity Choice 2 • Literature

Introduce the lesson with *The Long and Short of It* by Cheryl Nathan and Lisa McCourt. For additional support, see p. TR54.

2 Teach

Give each student a new, unsharpened pencil and a two-column chart. On one side, have them write *longer* and on the other *shorter*.

- Allow students five minutes to find items in the classroom that are longer and shorter than the unsharpened pencil. Have them draw or record the items on their paper.
- **What did you find that was longer than the pencil?** Sample answers: a desk, a book, the board.
- **What did you find that was shorter than the pencil?** Sample answers: a crayon, an eraser, a piece of chalk.
- **If you sharpened the pencil, would the results be the same? Why?** Sample answer: No; the results would be different because the pencil would be shorter.

Get Ready Use the section at the top of p. 277 to reinforce the lesson concept. Help students compare the length of objects.

Check Observe students as you work through Exercises 1–4 as a class.

Exercise 4 Assess student comprehension before assigning practice exercises.

! COMMON ERROR!

Students will not make accurate measurements if they misalign the objects. To compare length, objects should be aligned front or rear.

Name ______________________

Hands-On Activity

Compare and Order Lengths

Get Ready

Main Idea

I will compare and order the length of objects.

Vocabulary

length

short / shorter / shortest

long / longer / longest

You can compare the length of objects.

Check 1.–3. Answers will vary depending on objects measured.

Find the objects in your classroom. Compare. Circle the object.

1. Which is shorter?

2. Which is longer?

3. Order the lengths from shortest to longest. Write 1, 2, or 3.

____ ____ ____

4. **Talk About It** What else could you use to compare lengths?
Sample answer: erasers, pieces of paper, pencils

Reteach (p. 6) BL

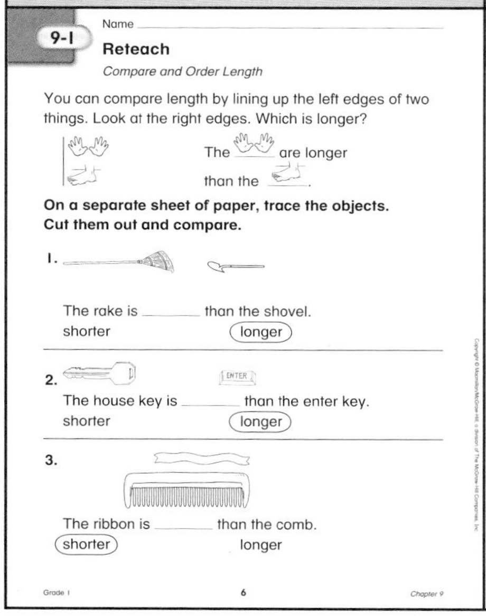
9-1 Name ______

Reteach

Compare and Order Length

You can compare length by lining up the left edges of two things. Look at the right edges. Which is longer?

The ____ are longer than the ____.

On a separate sheet of paper, trace the objects. Cut them out and compare.

1. The rake is ______ than the shovel.
shorter (longer)

2. The house key is ______ than the enter key.
shorter (longer)

3. The ribbon is ______ than the comb.
(shorter) longer

Grade 1 6 Chapter 9

Skills Practice (p. 7) OL

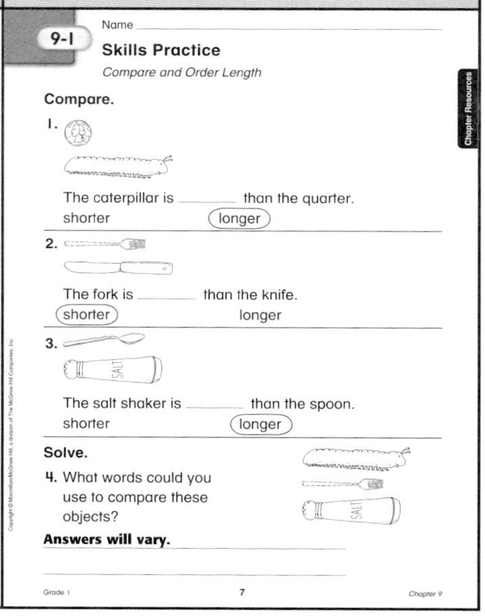
9-1 Name ______

Skills Practice

Compare and Order Length

Compare.

1. The caterpillar is ______ than the quarter.
shorter (longer)

2. The fork is ______ than the knife.
(shorter) longer

3. The salt shaker is ______ than the spoon.
shorter (longer)

Solve.

4. What words could you use to compare these objects?

Answers will vary.

Grade 1 7 Chapter 9

Chapter Resources

Practice 5.–8. Answers will vary depending on objects measured.

Find the objects in your classroom. Compare. Circle the object.

5. Which is shorter?

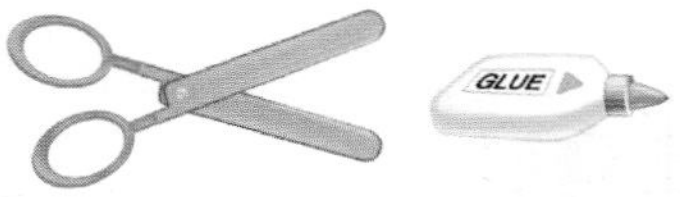

6. Which is longer?

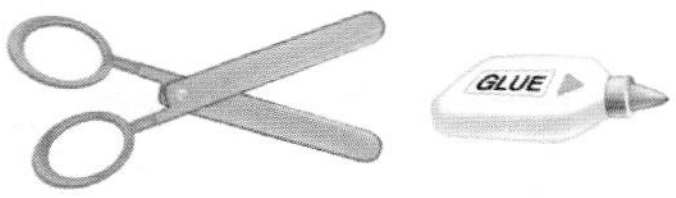

7. Order the lengths from longest to shortest. Write 1, 2, or 3.

____ ____ ____

8. Order the lengths from shortest to longest. Write 1, 2, or 3.

____ ____ ____

9. **WRITING IN MATH** How would Exercise 8 change if you ordered the lengths from longest to shortest?

Sample answer: I would write 1 under the longest object. I would write 3 under the shortest object.

Math at Home Activity: Find two objects in the kitchen and have your child describe them by comparing their lengths.

Enrich (p. 10) AL

9-1 Name

Enrich

Ordering Supplies

Look at the pictures below. Take out the same school supplies.

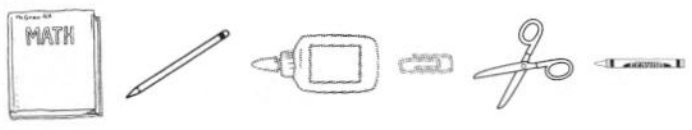

1. Choose 3 objects. Put them in order by length. Draw a picture.

Answers will vary.

2. What item was the longest? The shortest? Write a sentence telling about the order.

Answers will vary.

Grade 1 10 Chapter 9

Homework Practice (p. 8) OL

9-1 Name

Homework Practice

Compare and Order Length

Compare.

1. 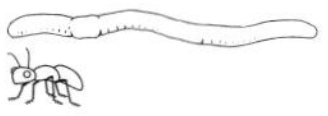

The ant is ____ than the worm.
(shorter) longer

2. 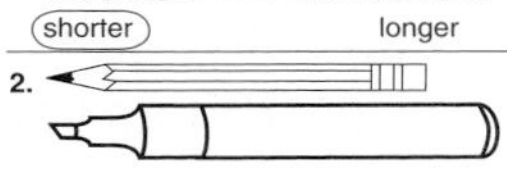

The marker is ____ than the pencil.
shorter (longer)

3. 

The bracelet is ____ than the hair pin.
shorter (longer)

Solve.

4. What words could you use to compare these objects?

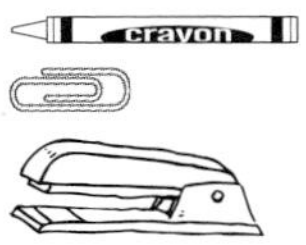

Answers will vary.

Grade 1 8 Chapter 9

BL Alternate Teaching Strategy

If students have trouble directly comparing the lengths of objects . . .

Then use one of the following reteach options.

1 CRM **Daily Reteach Worksheet** (p. 6)

2 **Use a Reference** Have students set one of each pair of objects on a blank paper. Students can draw a line from end to end of the object using a straightedge and then compare the other object to this reference line.

3 Practice

Differentiate practice, using these leveled assignments for Exercises 5–9.

Level	Assignment
BL Below/ Approaching Level	Line up each set of objects along one end for students.
OL On Level	Complete exercises independently.
AL Above/Beyond Level	Measure each picture with a ruler and write the lengths in inches.

4 Assess

Formative Assessment

- **How can you tell which is longer: a marker or crayon?** Sample answer: Line them up and see which is longer.

WRITING IN MATH Have students write a few sentences comparing the length of their feet with the feet of a friend, sibling, or parent.

Quick Check **Are students continuing to struggle with comparing the lengths of objects?**

If Yes → Small Group Options (p. 277B)
Strategic Intervention Guide (p. 108)

If No → Independent Work Options (p. 277B)
CRM Skills Practice Worksheet (p. 7)
CRM Enrich Worksheet (p. 10)

LESSON 9-2

Nonstandard Units of Length

Lesson Planner

Objective

Measure length using nonstandard units.

Vocabulary

measure, unit

Resources

Materials: crayons, large paper clips, pencils

Manipulatives: connecting cubes, pattern blocks

Literature Connection: *How Big Is a Foot?* by Rolf Myller

Alternate Lesson: Use "Measuring Strings" on page 135 of *Math Their Way* to provide practice with nonstandard units of measurement.

Teacher Technology

TeacherWorks • Concepts in Motion

Focus on Math Background

This lesson introduces students to non-standard units used to measure length. Students will repeat connecting cubes and other non-standard materials along a distance starting from a base line to an end point on an assortment of different sized objects. When a first grader understands the importance of iterating the same unit along an object and leaving no gaps in between, the student will develop an appreciation for standardized units, such as inches and feet.

Daily Routine

Use these suggestions before beginning the lesson on p. 279.

5-Minute Check

(Reviews Lesson 9-1)

Write which item is longer.

1. your teacher's shoe	paper clip	shoe
2. pencil	desk	desk
3. sheet of paper	folder	folder

Write which item is shorter.

4. pencil eraser	crayon	pencil eraser
5. ruler	marker	marker

Problem of the Day

Jan's favorite movie is on television tonight at 7:00. It lasts for 2 hours. Her bedtime is 8:30. Can Jan watch the whole movie? If not, how much will she miss? no; a half hour

LINE UP Have the students make paper clip chains between 1 and 10 paper clips long. Then tell students to line up by shortest to longest chain.

Building Math Vocabulary

Write the terms **measure** and **unit** on the board. Explain that you measure to find how long something is and that the unit is what you use to measure with.

- Explain that you can use everyday objects or parts of your body to measure. **What are some other things you could use to measure?** Sample answers: paces, fingers, hands, books
- Have a student measure a classroom item using each nonstandard unit suggested. Record the results on the board.

Differentiated Instruction

Small Group Options

Option 1 LOGICAL

Gifted and Talented AL

Materials: paper clips, connecting cubes

- Divide students into two groups, and give each group the same three objects to measure.
- Have one group use paper clips to measure. The other group will use cubes.
- Ask each group to record their measurements.
- Then have students share the measurements with the other group. Ask students to explain why their measurements differ.

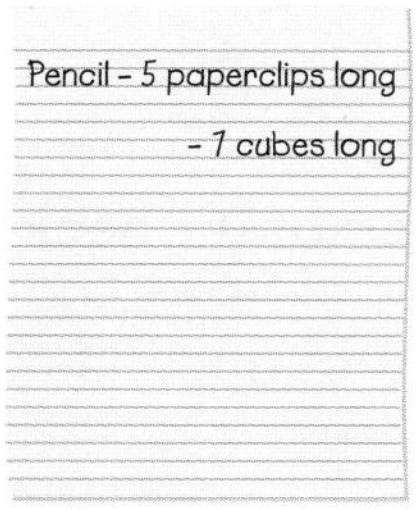

Option 2 LINGUISTIC, LOGICAL

English Language Learners ELL

Materials: 3-column chart paper, connecting cubes
Core Vocabulary: items, think about, examine
Common Use Verb: find

Write Math This strategy allows groups to work cooperatively and use multiple modalities to judge length, the best answer and to vocalize their reasoning.

- Divide the class into small groups.
- Post a 3-column chart that has "Less than 1 cube," "Less than 6 cubes," "Less than 18 cubes" written in the columns.
- Have each group find a classroom item to fit into each column.
- As a group, they must decide which item best fits the column description and draw it on the poster.
- Discuss results as a class.

Independent Work Options

Option 1 LINGUISTIC

Early Finishers OL AL

Materials: paper, pencil, connecting cubes or two-colored counters

- Ask students to work in a small group to write a number story.
- Have groups exchange number stories and discuss what strategy they are going to use to solve the problem.
- Ask students to share the number story they solved and the strategy they used to solve it.

Option 2

Student Technology

Math Online macmillanmh.com

Option 3

Learning Station: Language Arts (p. 273G)

Direct students to the Language Arts Learning Station for more opportunities to explore and extend the lesson concept.

1 Introduce

Activity Choice 1 • Review

Write on the board and read aloud the following:

Sixteen sparrows are in a tree. Eight sparrows fly down to the birdbath. How many sparrows are still in the tree?

- **What do we know?** There were 16 sparrows in the tree. Eight flew to the birdbath.
- **What do we want to find?** the number of sparrows still in the tree
- **What strategy would you use to solve this problem?** Sample answers: write a number sentence; draw a picture
- **How many sparrows are still in the tree?** 8 sparrows

Activity Choice 2 • Literature

Introduce the lesson with *Inch by Inch* by Leo Lionni. For additional support, see p. TR54.

2 Teach

Have students read the problem on page 281. Guide them through the problem-solving steps.

Understand Using the questions, review what students know and what they need to find.

Plan Have them discuss their strategy.

Solve Guide students to guess how long the carrot is using connecting cubes.

- **Is the carrot 2 cubes long?** No, that is too short.
- **Is the carrot 7 cubes long?** No, that is too long.
- **Is the carrot 5 cubes long?** Yes.

Check Have students line up the connecting cubes beneath the carrot to check their answer.

COMMON ERROR!

Students may not understand the *guess and check* strategy. Explain to students how finding what is wrong about the first guess will help them find a more accurate second guess.

Name ______________________

Problem-Solving Strategy
Guess and Check

Main Idea
I will guess and check to solve a problem.

How many cubes long is the carrot?

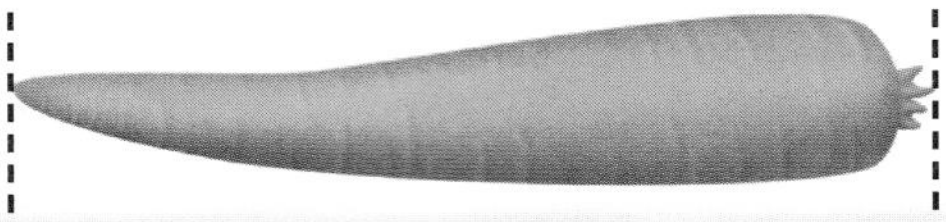

Understand
What do I need to find?
Circle the question.

Plan
How will I solve the problem?

Solve
Guess and Check
Try 2 cubes. That is too short.
Try 7 cubes. That is too long.
Try 5 cubes. That is right!
__5__ cubes

Check
Look back.
Is my answer reasonable?
Check students' explanations.

Reteach (pp. 16–17) BL

9-3 Name ______
Reteach (1)
Problem-Solving Strategy: Guess and Check

Ruben needs to find a picture of a school bus for his art class. The picture can't be longer than 4 cubes. Look at Ruben's picture. How long is it?

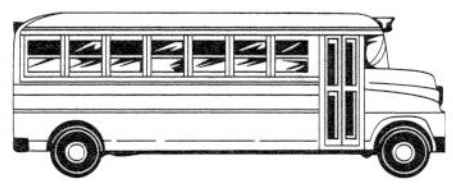

Step 1 Understand	What do I know? Ruben needs a picture of a school bus. It has to be shorter than 4 cubes. What do I need to find out? **How long the picture is.**
Step 2 Plan	How will I solve the problem? **I can guess and check with** ____.
Step 3 Solve	Guess and Check **Answers will vary.** The bus is about ____ cubes long.
Step 4 Check	Look back. Was my guess close to the answer? **Answers will vary.**

Grade 1 16 Chapter 9

Skills Practice (p. 18) OL

9-3 Name ______
Skills Practice
Problem-Solving Strategy: Guess and Check

About how many ____ long is each item? Guess. Then measure.

1.
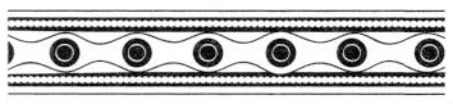
Guess: about ____ paper clips **Answers will vary.**
Measure: about ____ paper clips

2.
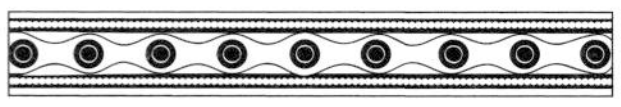
Guess: about ____ paper clips **Answers will vary.**
Measure: about ____ paper clips

3.
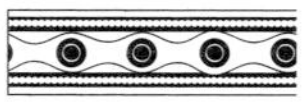
Guess: about ____ paper clips **Answers will vary.**
Measure: about ____ paper clips

Grade 1 18 Chapter 9

Try It

Remember
Understand
Plan
Solve
Check

About how many [cube] long is each object?
Guess. Then measure.

1. 

Guess: about 7 cubes

Measure: about 7 cubes

2. 

Guess: about 3 cubes

Measure: about 3 cubes

3. 

Guess: about 6 cubes

Measure: about 6 cubes

4. 

Guess: about 2 cubes

Measure: about 2 cubes

Math at Home Activity: Ask your child to guess how many paper clips long his or her shoe is. Then, check it using actual paper clips.

Enrich (p. 20) AL	*Homework Practice (p. 19)* OL

9-3 Name ______
Enrich
How Many Books?

Think about your math book. Stand it up and see how tall it is. Then estimate and draw a line from each object on the left to its possible height on the right.

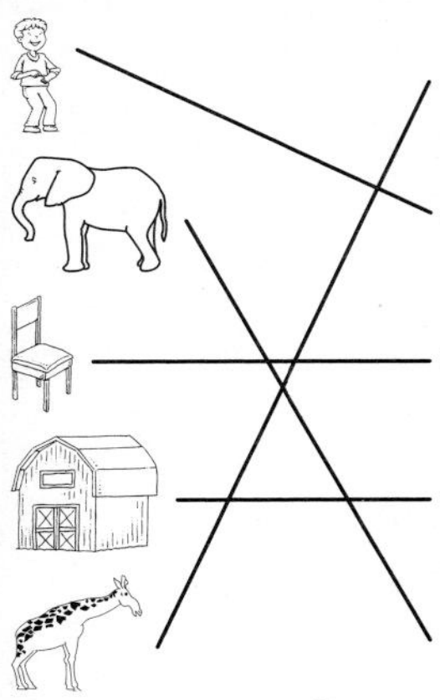

Grade 1 20 Chapter 9

9-3 Name ______
Homework Practice
Problem-Solving Strategy: Guess and Check

About how many [cube] long is each item?
Guess. Then measure to see if you were close.

1. 
Guess: about ____ cubes
Measure: about ____ cubes
Answers will vary.

2. 
Guess: about ____ cubes
Measure: about ____ cubes
Answers will vary.

3. 
Guess: about ____ cubes
Measure: about ____ cubes
Answers will vary.

Grade 1 19 Chapter 9

Try It Observe students as you work through Exercises 1–4 as a class.

BL Alternate Teaching Strategy

If students have trouble measuring . . .

Then use one of the following reteach options.

1 CRM **Daily Reteach Worksheet** (pp. 16–17)

2 **Connecting Cubes** Remind students to line up the first cube with the end of the object they are measuring. They should also be sure the cubes are lined up in a straight line.

3 Practice

Differentiate practice, using these leveled assignments for Exercises 1–4.

Level	Assignment
BL Below/ Approaching Level	Help students use their cubes correctly.
OL On Level	Complete exercises independently.
AL Above/Beyond Level	Complete exercises without the cubes.

4 Assess

Formative Assessment

How are these problems different?

- *Jamil measured 3 things. The book measured 10 cubes. It was the shortest. Which was longest?*
- *Jamil measured 3 things. The book measured 10 cubes. The chair seat measured 15, and the folder measured 13. Which was longest?* Sample answer: The second problem has more facts in it.

WRITING IN MATH Have students write a word problem that they could use guess and check to solve.

Quick Check **Are students continuing to struggle with using a problem-solving strategy to solve?**

If Yes → Strategic Intervention Guide (p. 108)
If No → Independent Work Options (p. 281B)
CRM Skills Practice Worksheet (p. 18)
CRM Enrich Worksheet (p. 20)

Extra Practice

Review Lessons 9-1 to 9-3

Objective: Review and assess mastery of previous lessons' skills and concepts.

- Review with students how to line units up end to end with no space in between when measuring.
- Students may not understand how to complete the chart. Draw the first row on the board, and measure a pair of scissors together. Circle the unit used in the second column, enter the measurement in the third column.
- Students may be more comfortable working in pairs. Permit them to work with a partner if desired.
- If students finish early, have them measure the objects using the other unit and then compare the two results.

Practice with Technology

Math Online Have students visit macmillanmh.com for additional practice with online activities, games, and quizzes.

Name 1–6. See students' answers.

	Find the object.	Circle the unit.	Measure the object.
1.	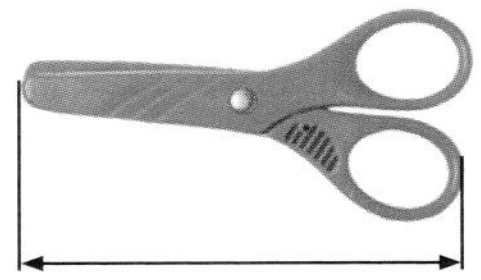	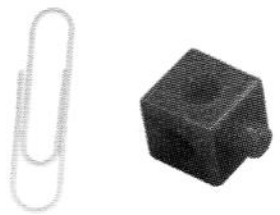	about ____
2.	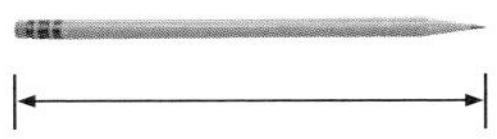	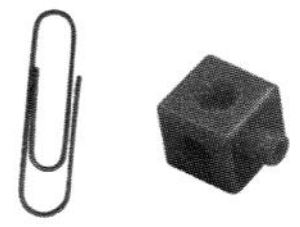	about ____
3.	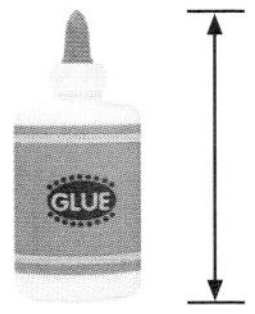	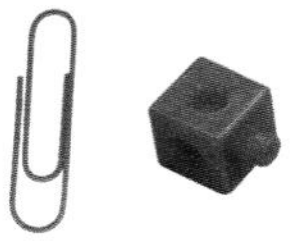	about ____
4.	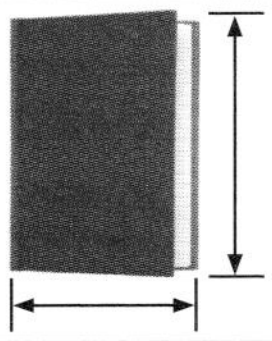	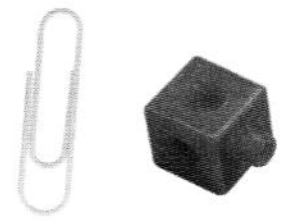	about ____ about ____
5.	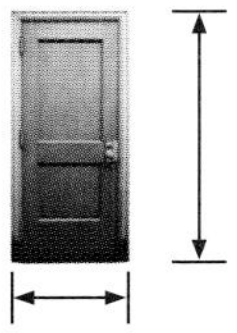	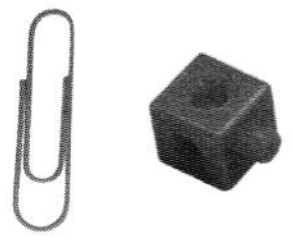	about ____ about ____
6.	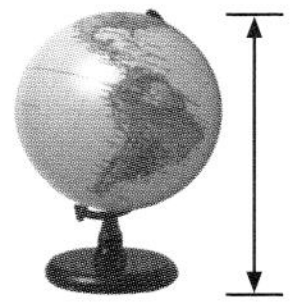	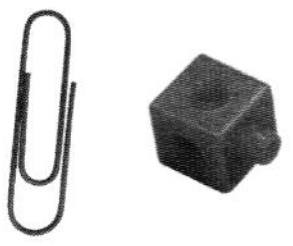	about ____

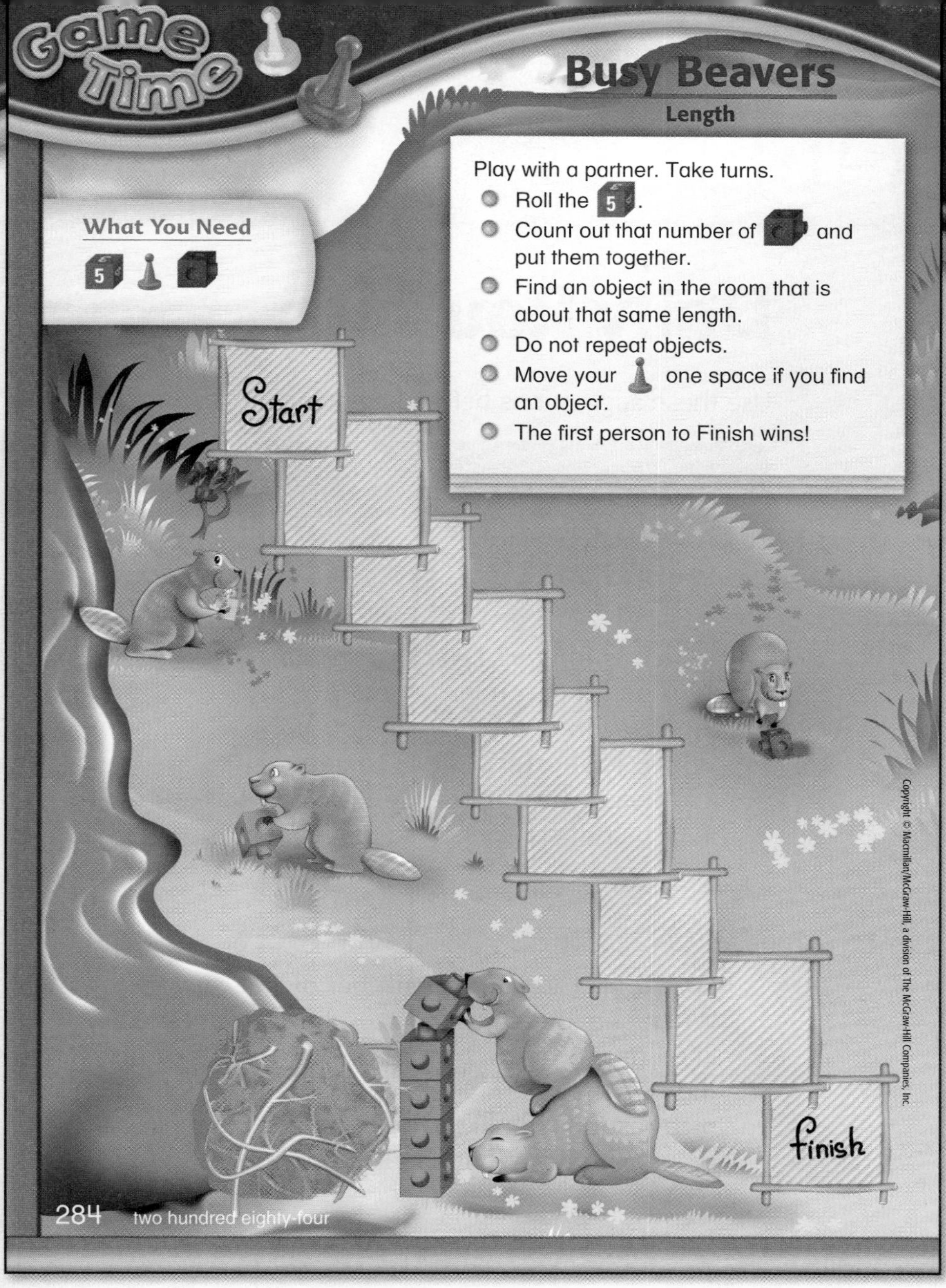

Busy Beavers

Math Concept: Measure Length Using Nonstandard Units

Materials: game pieces

Manipulatives: connecting cubes, red number cube

Introduce the game on page 284 to your students to play as a class, in small groups, or at a learning workstation to review concepts introduced in this chapter.

Instructions

- Assign each player a game piece. Decide which player will go first.
- The player will roll the number cube, count out that many connecting cubes, and put them together.
- The player must then find an object in the classroom that is about the same length. Players may not repeat objects.
- If a player finds an object of that length, he or she advances the game piece one space.
- Alternate turns between players repeating the above steps.
- The first player to reach *Finish* wins.

Extend the Game

Use the sum of two number cubes to determine the number of connecting cubes. This challenges students to find larger objects while practicing basic addition facts.

Differentiated Practice

Use these leveling suggestions to differentiate the game for all learners.

Level	Assignment
BL Below/Approaching Level	Allow students to play in teams of two so they have help when searching for and measuring objects.
OL On Level	Have students play the game with the rules as written.
AL Above/Beyond Level	Have students use a ruler instead of connecting cubes. Students must search for an object with a length equal to the number of inches rolled.

LESSON 9-4

Compare and Order Weights

Lesson Planner

Objective

Compare and order the weights of two or more objects.

Vocabulary

weight, heavy/heavier/heaviest, light/lighter/lightest

Resources

Materials: classroom items to weigh (stapler, paper clips, crayons, box of crayons, etc.)

Manipulatives: pan balance

Literature Connection: "Just a Little Bit" by Ann Tompert

Alternate Lessons: Use "Weighing and Comparing" on page 132 of *Math Their Way* to provide practice exploring weight.
Use *IMPACT Mathematics:* Unit G to provide practice comparing and ordering weights.

Teacher Technology
TeacherWorks

Focus on Math Background

In this lesson, students will explore the property of weight as a measurable attribute. Unlike length, weight is less concrete because students cannot measure it or make direct comparisons by simply looking at two objects. When directly comparing the two objects, students have to feel how heavy or how light the items are.

For the world of science, the differentiation of weight and mass is necessary. An object's mass on Earth is the same anywhere else in the universe, but an object's weight changes if the pull of gravity changes. For example, the mass of a bowling ball is the same on Earth as it would be on the Moon. However, the same bowling ball would have different weights on Earth versus the Moon.

For the purpose of common life, weight and mass can be treated as the same. Students will explore the property of weight/mass as a measurable attribute in this lesson. To compare and order objects' weights/masses, students will be asked to hold various objects in each hand. Students will also be encouraged to use a pan balance and nonstandard units to compare the weights/masses of objects.

Daily Routine

Use these suggestions before beginning the lesson on p. 285.

5-Minute Check

(Reviews Lesson 9-3)

Which is longer? Check to see.

1. A pencil or a ruler? ruler

2. A crayon or a paper clip? crayon

Which is shorter? Check to see.

1. A waste basket or a desk? waste basket

2. A pair of scissors or an eraser? eraser

Problem of the Day

Lucy took 12 pictures with her digital camera. When she looked at them on her computer, Lucy liked only 8 of the pictures. How many pictures did Lucy not like? 4 pictures If she took 5 more pictures that she liked, how many pictures in all would she have that she liked? 13 pictures

LINE UP After students line up for recess, lunch, or dismissal, ask one student to pick up a classroom object and show it to the class. Ask each student to name another object and tell whether it is lighter or heavier than the first.

Building Math Vocabulary

Write **weight** on the board. Explain that **heavier** and **lighter** are words used to compare weights.

- Have students fold a sheet of paper in half.
- On one side, have them draw or write examples of things that are light. On the other side, have them draw or write examples of things that are heavy.
- Ask students to give examples to write on the chalkboard. Challenge students to name something heavier or lighter than the example given before them.

Differentiated Instruction

Small Group Options

Option 1 KINESTHETIC, LOGICAL

Gifted and Talented AL

Materials: cup measure; pint, quart, half-gallon, and gallon containers; rice, beans, or small beads; funnel

- Divide students into pairs. Have pairs use the cup measure and count out how many cups of rice, beans, or beads fill a pint, a quart, a half-gallon, and a gallon. Have them record the results.
- After pairs record all their results, have them compare and discuss their results with others.
- To extend the activity, have pairs find how many pints make a quart, half-gallon, and gallon and record these results.
- Pairs could also find how many quarts are in a half-gallon and a gallon and how many half-gallons are in a gallon.

Option 2 KINESTHETIC, INTRAPERSONAL

English Language Learners ELL

Materials: connecting cubes, box
Core Vocabulary: tower, same, different
Common Use Verb: build

See Math This strategy teaches capacity through manipulatives.

- Explain capacity by flipping a full box of linked cubes over so that they stand as a solid in the same shape as the box.
- Give identical sets of cubes to each group to build a tower. Students must use all cubes.
- Compare their towers to the original box. Discuss why the towers look different but have the same capacity.

Use this worksheet to provide additional support for English Language Learners.

English Language Learners (p. 127) ELL

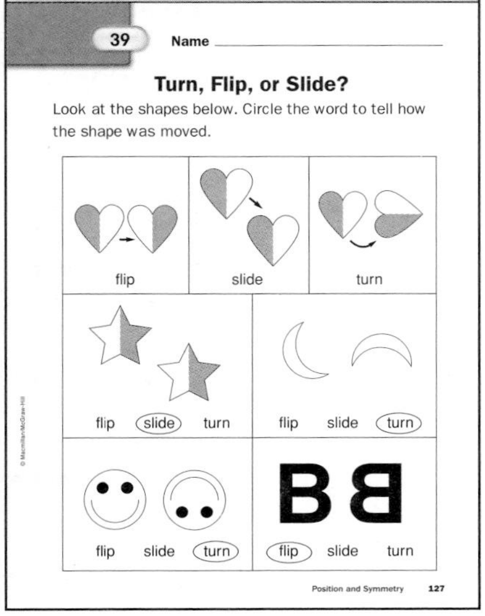

39 Name

Turn, Flip, or Slide?

Look at the shapes below. Circle the word to tell how the shape was moved.

flip	slide	turn
flip (slide) turn	flip slide (turn)	
flip slide (turn)	(flip) slide turn	

Position and Symmetry 127

Independent Work Options

Option 1 KINESTHETIC, LOGICAL

Early Finishers OL AL

Materials: variety of containers, cup measure, rice, beans or small beads, funnel

Label the containers with letters. Prepare charts with three columns labeled *container, estimate*, and *tally.*

- Have students select a container and estimate how many cups of rice, beans, or small beads will fill the container.
- Have students count aloud as they fill the container and record the results with tally marks.
- Students should estimate and fill three to five containers.

Option 2

Student Technology

Math Online macmillanmh.com

Option 3

Learning Station: Art (p. 273G)

Direct students to the Art Learning Station for more opportunities to explore and extend the lesson concept.

Option 4

Problem-Solving Practice

Reinforce problem-solving skills and strategies with the Problem-Solving Practice worksheet.

Problem Solving (p. 29) BL OL AL

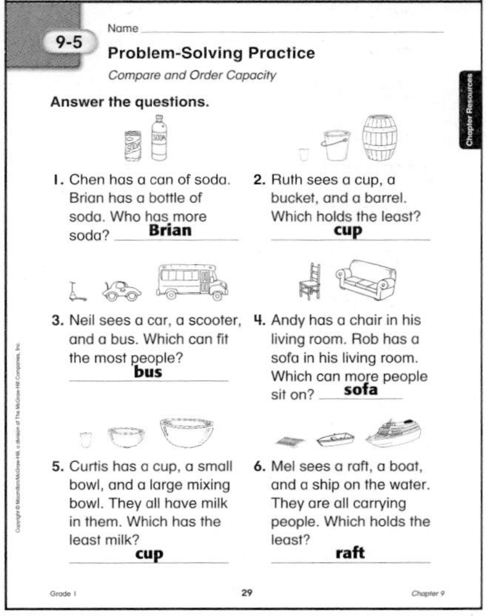

9-5 Name

Problem-Solving Practice

Compare and Order Capacity

Answer the questions.

1. Chen has a can of soda. Brian has a bottle of soda. Who has more soda? **Brian**
2. Ruth sees a cup, a bucket, and a barrel. Which holds the least? **cup**
3. Neil sees a car, a scooter, and a bus. Which can fit the most people? **bus**
4. Andy has a chair in his living room. Rob has a sofa in his living room. Which can more people sit on? **sofa**
5. Curtis has a cup, a small bowl, and a large mixing bowl. They all have milk in them. Which has the least milk? **cup**
6. Mel sees a raft, a boat, and a ship on the water. They are all carrying people. Which holds the least? **raft**

Grade 1 29 Chapter 9

9-5

1 Introduce

Activity Choice 1 • Hands-On

Display for the class a measuring cup, a jar, a milk carton, and an ice-cream container.

- **Look at these containers. Which do you think holds most? Why?** Sample answer: ice cream container; it looks the largest. **Which do you think holds least? Why?** Sample answer: milk carton; it looks the smallest
- Use the measuring cup to fill each container with water one by one. Test the containers and place them in order from what holds the most to holds the least.
- **Can you find a container in the classroom that could hold more?** Sample answers: trash can; flower pot.

Activity Choice 2 • Literature

Introduce the lesson with *The Mitten* by Jan Brett. For additional support, see p. TR54.

Name ______________________

Compare and Order Capacities

Get Ready

Main Idea

I will compare and order the capacity of objects.

Vocabulary

holds more/most

holds less/least

Containers can hold different amounts.

The glass **holds less** than the pitcher. The pitcher **holds more** than the glass. **Capacity** tells how much something holds.

Check

Circle the object in each pair that holds less.

1.

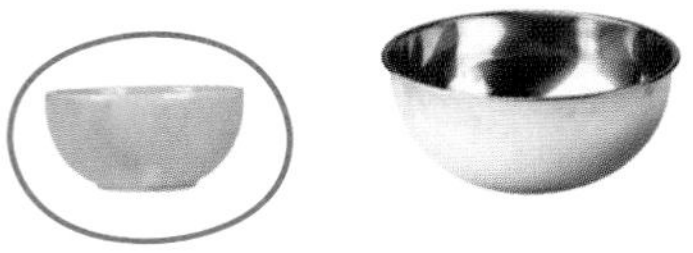

2.

Circle the object in each pair that holds more.

3.

4.

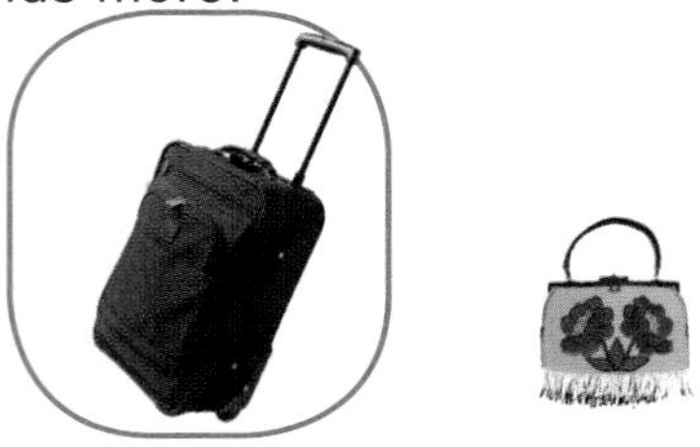

Reteach (p. 26) BL

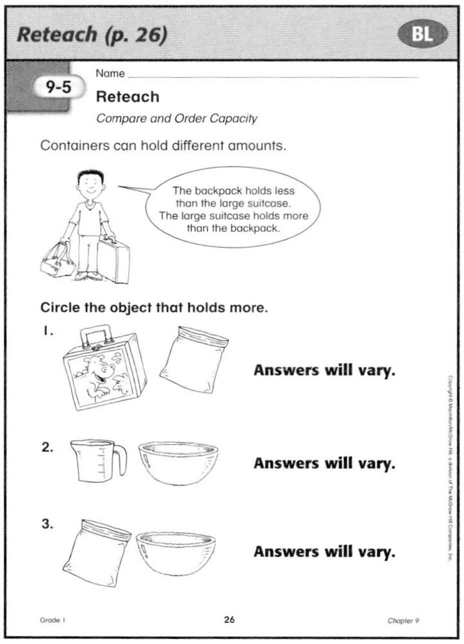

Name ______

9-5 **Reteach**

Compare and Order Capacity

Containers can hold different amounts.

Circle the object that holds more.

1. **Answers will vary.**

2. **Answers will vary.**

3. **Answers will vary.**

Grade 1 26 Chapter 9

Circle the object that holds the least.

5.

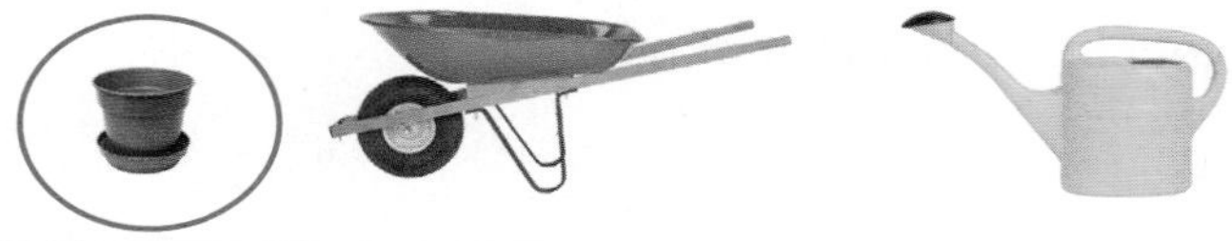

6.

Order the objects by capacity.
Write 1 for holds the least, 2, and 3 for holds the most.

7.

1 3 2

8.

1 2 3

9. **Talk About It** If you had 2 containers, how could you find out which container holds more? Sample answer: By pouring water or rice into the one I think is smaller and then pouring that into the larger container. If the container I think is larger isn't filled, then it is the larger container.

GO on

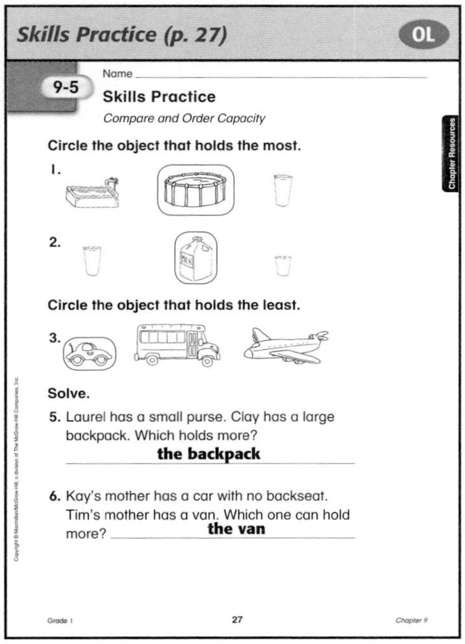

Skills Practice (p. 27) OL

9-5 Name ______

Skills Practice

Compare and Order Capacity

Circle the object that holds the most.

1.

2.

Circle the object that holds the least.

3.

Solve.

5. Laurel has a small purse. Clay has a large backpack. Which holds more? **the backpack**

6. Kay's mother has a car with no backseat. Tim's mother has a van. Which one can hold more? **the van**

Grade 1 27 Chapter 9

2 Teach

Show students various containers such as a drinking glass, a baby bottle, and a pitcher.

- Ask students to guess which container holds the most and which holds the least.
- **We will fill the containers with water to check our work.** Fill the smallest container with water. Then pour the water into the medium-sized container. **Which container holds more? Explain.** Answers will vary depending on containers used.
- Follow the same procedure with the largest container.
- Have students order the containers from holds the most to holds the least.

Get Ready Use the section at the top of page 292 to reinforce the lesson concept.

Check Observe students as you work through Exercises 1–9 as a class.

Exercise 9 Assess student comprehension before assigning practice exercises.

COMMON ERROR!

When exploring volume with containers, students may fill the large container first and try to pour it into the small containers. Make sure they start with the smallest.

BL Alternate Teaching Strategy

If students have trouble telling which container holds the most or the least . . .

Then use one of the following reteach options.

1. CRM **Daily Reteach Worksheet** (p. 26)
2. **Making Connections** Give students three containers that vary in size. Encourage students to use rice, sand, or water to experiment with the capacity of each container. Then have students order the containers from holds the most to holds the least. Remind students that they can test the capacity of objects while playing in the sandbox.

3 Practice

Differentiate practice, using these leveled assignments for Exercises 10–22.

Level	Assignment
BL Below/ Approaching Level	Have students place a finger on the largest object before deciding which object holds more or holds less.
OL On Level	Complete exercises independently.
AL Above/Beyond Level	Label each image in every problem with *holds least* or *holds most.*

Name ______________________

Practice

Circle the object in each pair that holds less.

10.

11.
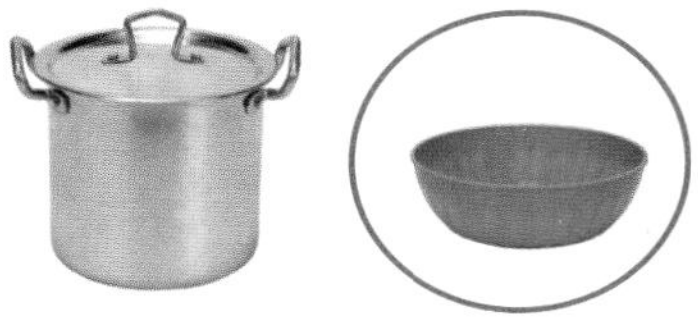

12.
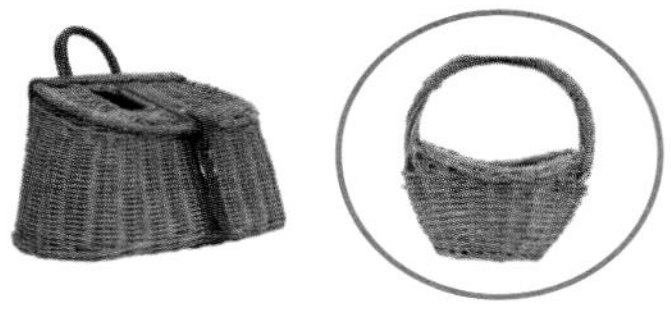

13.

Circle the object in each pair that holds more.

14.
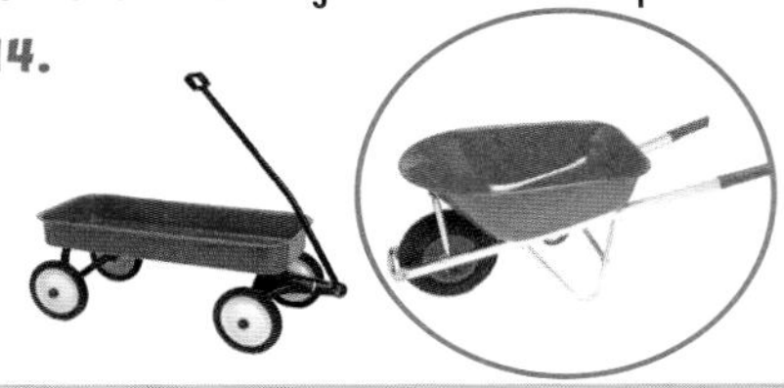

15.
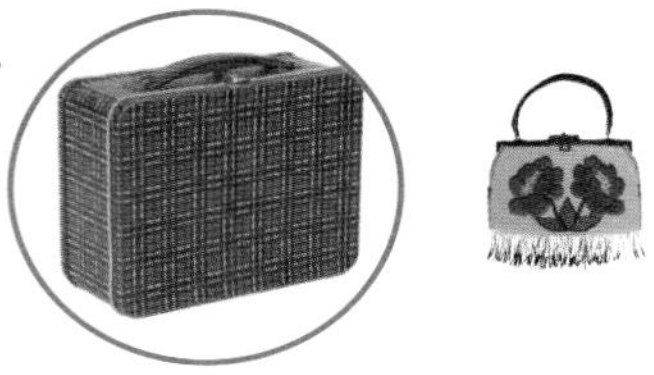

16.

17.
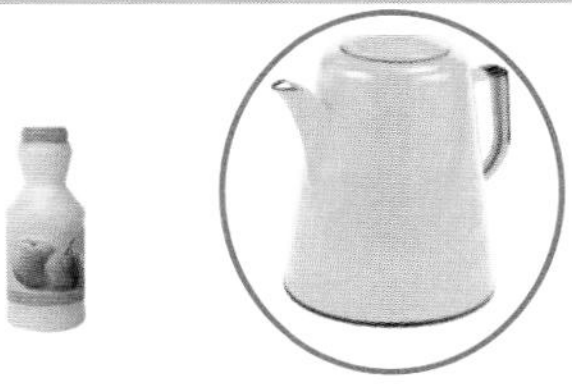

Circle the object that holds the least.

18.

Enrich (p. 30) AL

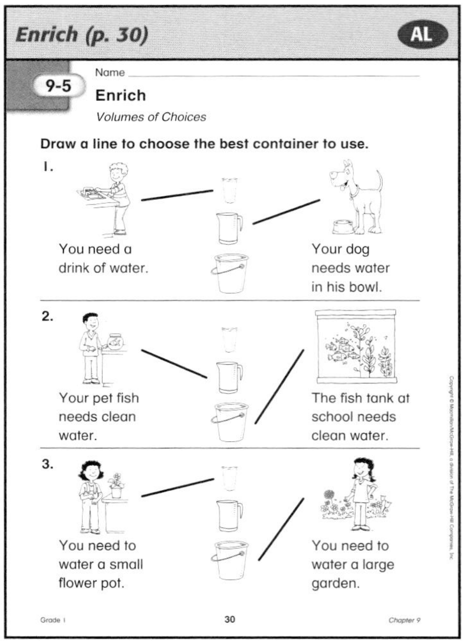
9-5
Name ______
Enrich
Volumes of Choices

Draw a line to choose the best container to use.

1. You need a drink of water. — Your dog needs water in his bowl.
2. Your pet fish needs clean water. — The fish tank at school needs clean water.
3. You need to water a small flower pot. — You need to water a large garden.

Grade 1 30 Chapter 9

Circle the object that holds the most.

19.

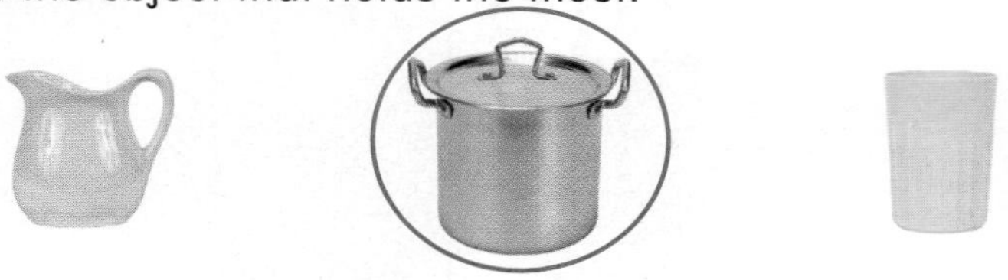

Order the objects by capacity.
Write 1 for holds the least, 2, and 3 for holds the most.

20.

3 2 1

21.

3 1 2

Problem Solving

22. **Visual Thinking** How many cubes in each?
Use cubes to help.

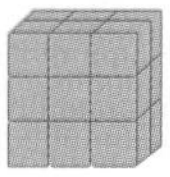 18 cubes 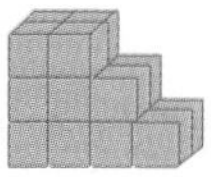 18 cubes

Math at Home Activity: Give your child two containers that can hold liquid. Ask your child which container holds more. Test to see if your child is right.

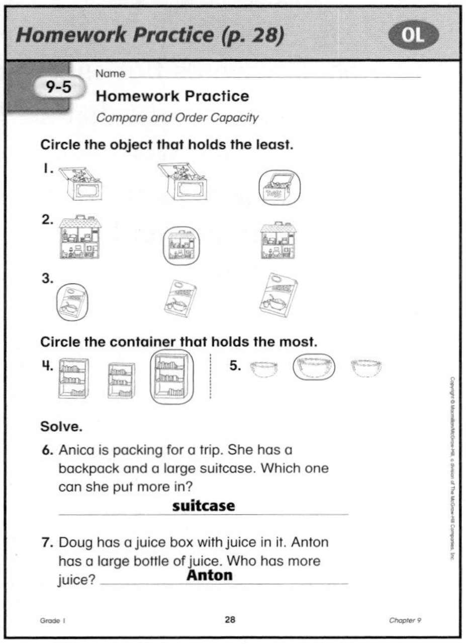

Homework Practice (p. 28) OL

9-5 Name ______

Homework Practice

Compare and Order Capacity

Circle the object that holds the least.

1.

2.

3.

Circle the container that holds the most.

4. 5.

Solve.

6. Anica is packing for a trip. She has a backpack and a large suitcase. Which one can she put more in? **suitcase**

7. Doug has a juice box with juice in it. Anton has a large bottle of juice. Who has more juice? **Anton**

Grade 1 28 Chapter 9

4 Assess

Formative Assessment

- **If you wanted to fill a kids pool with water, what kind of container would you use to carry water to it? Why?** Sample answer: a big bucket because it holds a lot of water.

WRITING IN MATH Have students explain why a gardener cannot put the same amount of dirt in every flower pot.

Quick Check **Are students continuing to struggle with exploring capacities?**

If Yes → Strategic Intervention Guide (p. 110)

If No → Independent Work Options (p. 293B)

CRM Skills Practice Worksheet (p. 27)

CRM Enrich Worksheet (p. 30)

9-6 Compare and Order Temperatures

Lesson Planner

Objective
Compare and order two or more objects according to relative temperatures.

Vocabulary
hot/hotter/hottest, cold/colder/coldest

Resources
Materials: real objects of varying temperatures such as a heating pad, a hot-water bottle, room-temperature water, a cold can of soda, and an ice cube
Literature Connection: *Math For All Seasons* by Greg Tang
Teacher Technology
TeacherWorks

Daily Routine

Use these suggestions before beginning the lesson on p. 295.

5-Minute Check
(Reviews Lesson 9-5)

Draw three containers. Show the containers in order from the one that holds the most to the one that holds the least.

Problem of the Day
Sam picked five yellow flowers and two red flowers from the garden on Tuesday. He picked six more red flowers from the garden on Friday. How many flowers did Sam pick in all? 13 flowers

LINE UP As you prepare for recess, lunch, or dismissal, toss a bean bag to one student and say "hot." The student names something that is hot and lines up. Then the student continues the game by calling either "hot" or "cold" and tossing the bean bag to a classmate. Continue until everyone is in line.

Building Math Vocabulary
Write the vocabulary words **hot** and **cold** on the board.

- Have students name objects that are hot. List them on the board under the word *hot.*
- Have students name objects that are cold. List them on the board under the word *cold.*
- Compare the two lists.

Differentiated Instruction

Small Group Options

Option 1 Gifted and Talented AL

LOGICAL

Materials: multiple copies of the weather pages from the newspaper, paper, pencil.

- Have students work in pairs.
- Students need to study the weather page of a newspaper. Have students write down the first three days' temperatures listed on the weather page. After they write the temperatures down, they need to put them in order from hottest to coldest.
- Have students then choose three different States from the weather page and the reported temperature from that state's capital. Then have the students order the state's temperatures from hottest to coldest.

C09-01A-105759.ai

Option 2 English Language Learners ELL

KINESTHETIC, LINGUISTIC

Materials: 3 bottles of water: 1 hot, 1 room temperature, and 1 cold, each with a drop of different food color

Do Math This strategy gives students experience comparing and ordering temperatures.

- Pour a bowl of each type of water for each group.
- Allow students to feel each, and decide on an order.
- Label each bottle with hot, warm, or cold. Have students repeat temperature vocabulary.
- Have students explain their order.
- Order the original bottles from coldest to hottest. Discuss the different strategies used.

Use this worksheet to provide additional support for English Language Learners.

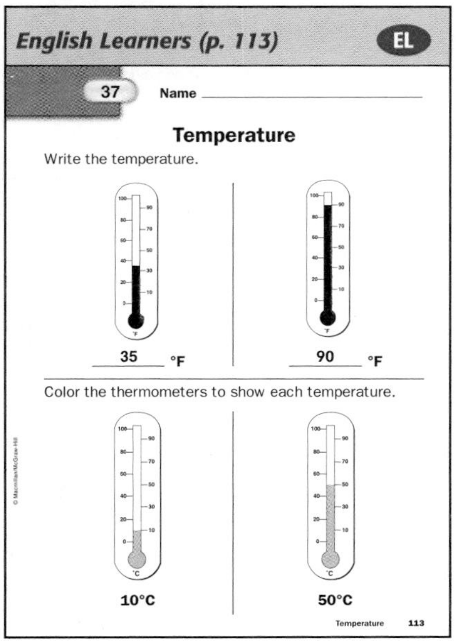

English Learners (p. 113) EL

37 Name ______

Temperature

Write the temperature.

35 °F

90 °F

Color the thermometers to show each temperature.

10°C

50°C

Temperature 113

Independent Work Options

Option 1 Early Finishers OL AL

VISUAL/SPATIAL

Materials: blank paper, markers

- Have students work in pairs.
- Each student uses three pieces of paper to draw three separate pictures showing objects that are hot, hotter, and hottest.
- The students switch papers and compare and order their partners' drawings by numbering them 1, 2, and 3.
- Repeat with pictures of objects that show cold, colder, and coldest.

Option 2 Student Technology

Math Online macmillanmh.com

Option 3 Learning Station: Language Arts (p. 273G)

Direct students to the Language Arts Learning Station for more opportunities to explore the lesson concept.

Option 4 Problem-Solving Practice

Reinforce problem-solving skills and strategies with the Problem-Solving Practice worksheet.

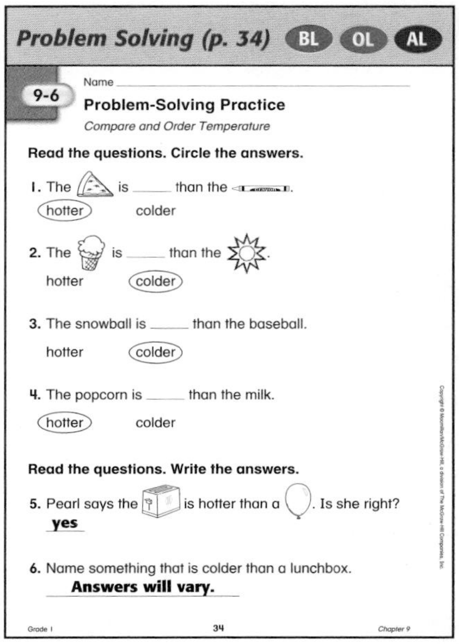

Problem Solving (p. 34) BL OL AL

Name ______

9-6 **Problem-Solving Practice**

Compare and Order Temperature

Read the questions. Circle the answers.

1. The ___ is ___ than the ___.
(hotter) colder

2. The ___ is ___ than the ___.
hotter (colder)

3. The snowball is ___ than the baseball.
hotter (colder)

4. The popcorn is ___ than the milk.
(hotter) colder

Read the questions. Write the answers.

5. Pearl says the ___ is hotter than a ___. Is she right?
yes

6. Name something that is colder than a lunchbox.
Answers will vary.

Grade 1 34 Chapter 9

1 Introduce

Activity Choice 1 • Hands-On

Display several objects of different temperatures, such as a heating pad on medium setting, a filled hot-water bottle, a cup of water at room temperature, a cold can of soda, and an ice cube.

- Have students file past the objects and touch each one. Then hold up the items, two at a time. **Which is hotter? Which is colder?**

Activity Choice 2 • Literature

Introduce the lesson with *Math for All Seasons* by Greg Tang. For additional support, see p. TR55.

Name ____________________

Compare and Order Temperatures

Get Ready

Main Idea

I will compare and order objects by their temperature.

Vocabulary

hot/hotter/hottest

cold/colder/coldest

You can tell if objects are hot or cold.

This object is **hot**.

This object is **cold**.

You can order objects by how hot they are.

hot

hotter

hottest

You can order objects by how cold they are.

cold

colder

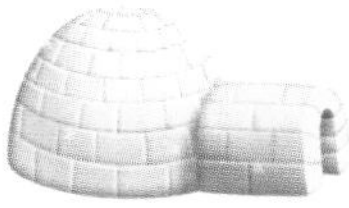

coldest

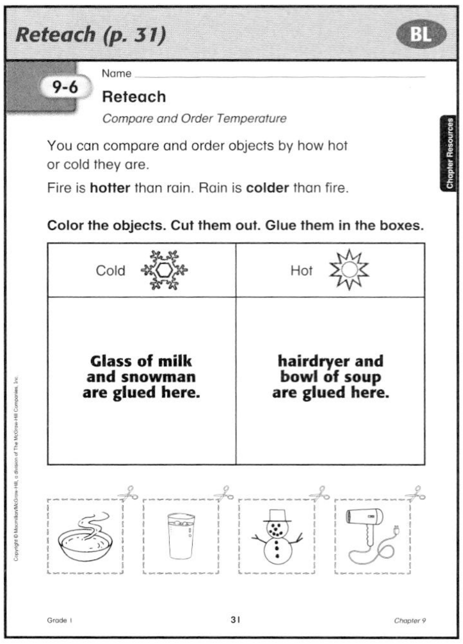

Reteach (p. 31) BL

9-6 Name ______

Reteach

Compare and Order Temperature

You can compare and order objects by how hot or cold they are.

Fire is **hotter** than rain. Rain is **colder** than fire.

Color the objects. Cut them out. Glue them in the boxes.

Cold	Hot
Glass of milk and snowman are glued here.	**hairdryer and bowl of soup are glued here.**

Grade 1 31 Chapter 9

These tires have been recycled for a playground!

C

The first graders at Gladmere Elementary collected juice boxes to recycle.

Monday Collection

Class	Juice Boxes Collected
Mrs. Wilson's Class	12
Ms. York's Class	8

How many juice boxes did the classes collect in all?

20 boxes

FOLD DOWN

D

Create the Book

Guide students to create their book.

- Have them fold the page in half.
- Ask them to write their name on page A.
- Explain that page A is the front cover and page D is the back cover. If necessary, have them practice flipping through the book in order.
- Guide them in reading the information and word problems on each of the pages.

Use the Student Pages

Have students work individually or in pairs to solve the word problem on page D.

Page D If students have trouble reading the chart, ask them to look at the top row and name the two things the chart is about. If students have trouble solving the word problem, remind students of problem-solving strategies such as drawing a picture, acting it out, or writing a number sentence to solve.

WRITING IN MATH Have students use the chart on page D to write a word problem about comparing the number of cans collected.

Extend the Activity

Collect used milk cartons for the next few days. Reuse them according to a student's suggestion. Make sure students rinse out the cartons before placing them in the collection box.

Chapter Review/Test

FOLDABLES Dinah Zike's Foldables

Use this lesson suggestion to incorporate the Foldable during the chapter. Students can then use their Foldable to review for the test.

Lesson 9-5 On the front of the "Capacity" tab, glue or tape two objects that have different capacities. For example, you might glue two bottle caps of different sizes. Label the objects with the terms "holds more" and "holds less." Under the tab, define the term capacity and use direct comparison and nonstandard units to describe the measurement of capacity.

Vocabulary Review

Review chapter vocabulary using the following.

- **eGlossary** at macmillanmh.com

Vocabulary Test

CRM **Chapter 9 Resource Masters** (p. 55)

Assess student comprehension of the chapter vocabulary with the Vocabulary Test.

Math Online **Chapter Test**

Alternative summative assessment options are available online at macmillanmh.com.

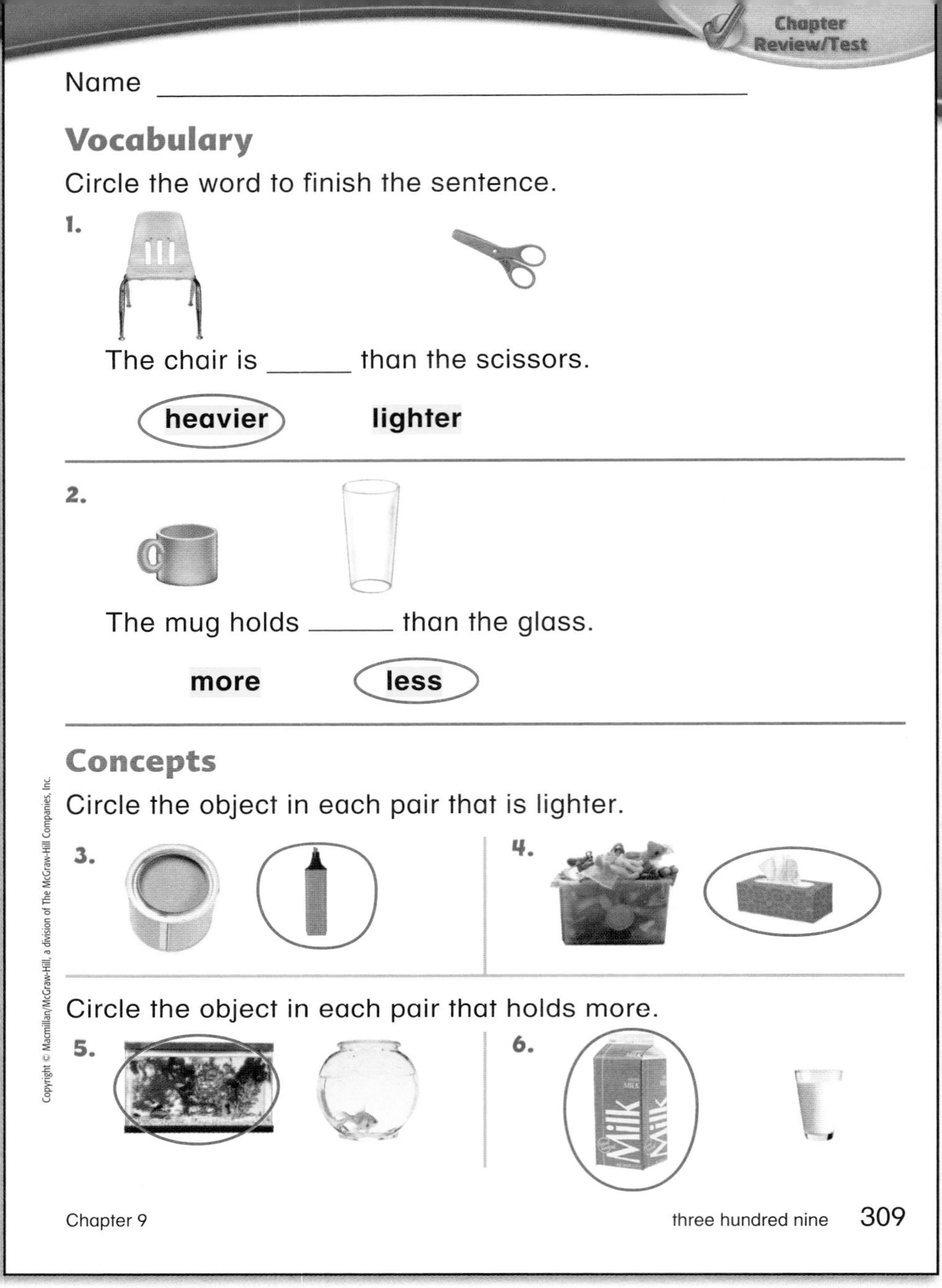

Name ____________________

Vocabulary

Circle the word to finish the sentence.

1. The chair is ______ than the scissors.

(heavier) lighter

2. The mug holds ______ than the glass.

more (less)

Concepts

Circle the object in each pair that is lighter.

3. 4.

Circle the object in each pair that holds more.

5. 6.

Chapter 9 Project

Length Seek and Find

Alone, in pairs, or in small groups, have students discuss the results of their completed chapter project with the class. Assess their work using the Chapter Project rubric found in Chapter 9 Resource Masters on page 60.

Circle the object in each pair that is hotter.

7.

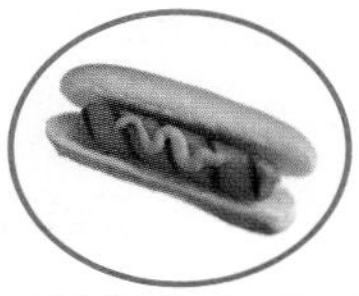

8.

Write about how many .

9.

4 cubes

10.

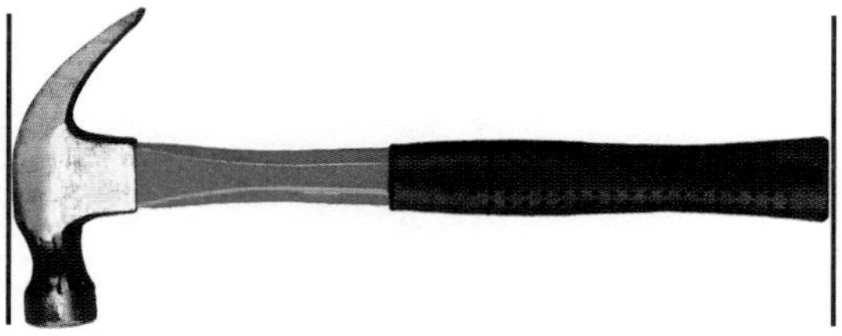

6 cubes

11.

2 cubes

12.

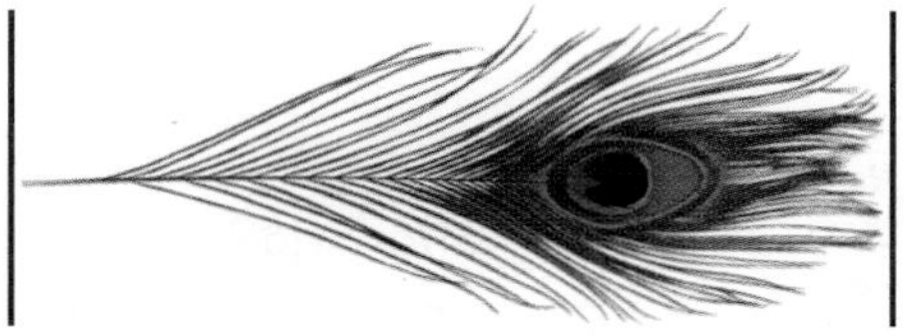

5 cubes

Problem Solving

13. A piece of blue string is 8 paper clips long. A piece of red string is 6 paper clips longer than the blue string. How long is the red string?

14 paper clips

Summative Assessment

Use these alternate leveled chapter tests to differentiate assessment for the specific needs of your students.

Leveled Chapter 9 Tests			
Form	**Type**	**Level**	**CRM Pages**
1	Multiple Choice	BL	62–63
2A	Multiple Choice	OL	64–65
2B	Multiple Choice	OL	66–67
2C	Free Response	AL	68–69
2D	Free Response	AL	70–71

BL = below/approaching grade level
OL = on grade level
AL = above/beyond grade level

ExamView Assessment Suite Customize and create multiple versions of your Chapter Test and their answer keys.

Data-Driven Decision-Making

Based on the results of the Chapter Review/Test, use the following to review concepts that continue to present students with problems.

Exercises	State/Local Standards	What's the Math?	Error Analysis	Resources for Review
1–6		Explore weight and capacity.	Mixes up words and circles incorrect word. Circles both words. Circles the incorrect image.	Strategic Intervention Guide (p. 108) CRM Chapter 9 Resource Masters (Reteach Worksheets) **Math Online** Concepts in Motion Math Adventures
7–12		Measuring length using nonstandard units.	Does not use correct number of cubes.	

Test Practice

Formative Assessment

- Use Student Edition pp. 311–312 as practice and cumulative review. The questions are written in the same style as many state tests.
- You can use these two pages to benchmark student progress, or as an alternative homework assignment.

Additional practice pages can be found in the Chapter 9 Resources Masters.

CRM Chapter 9 Resource Masters

Cumulative Test Practice

- Multiple Choice format (pp. 62–67, 72)
- Free Response format (pp. 68–71, 73)

ExamView Assessment Suite Create practice worksheets or tests that align to your state standards.

Math Online

For additional practice visit macmillanmh.com.

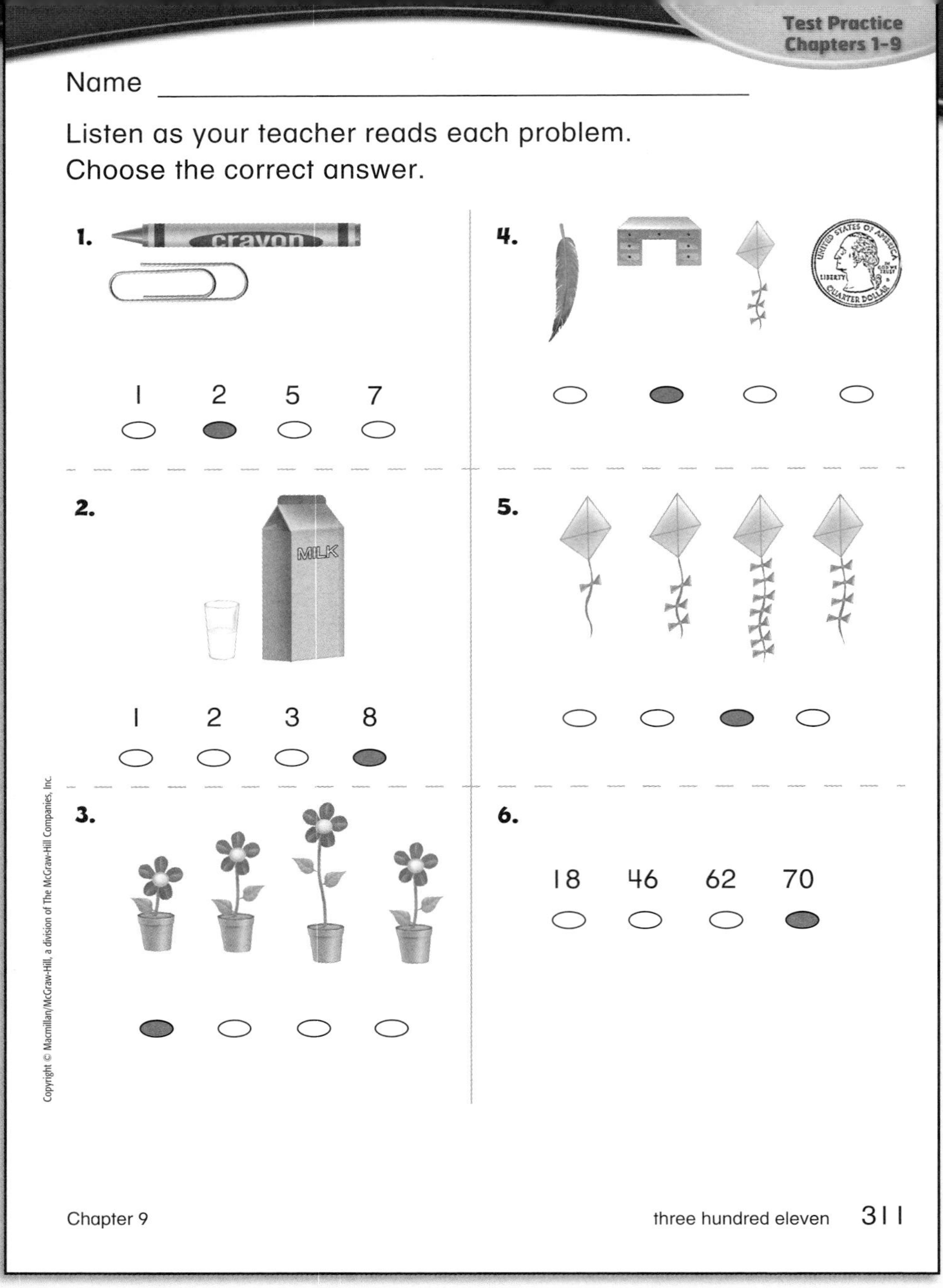

Test Practice Chapters 1-9

Name ______________________

Listen as your teacher reads each problem.
Choose the correct answer.

1. 1 2 5 7

2. 1 2 3 8

3.

4.

5.

6. 18 46 62 70

Copyright © Macmillan/McGraw-Hill, a division of The McGraw-Hill Companies, Inc.

Chapter 9 three hundred eleven 311

Test-Taking Tips

For the Teacher

- Make sure you have the students' attention before reading the test questions.
- Make sure each student understands the directions before beginning the test.

For the Student

- Make sure students check that they have filled in an oval for each test question.
- Have students write on their tests if it helps them.

7.

10.

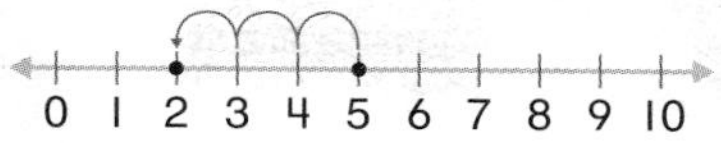

8 − 5 5 − 3

10 − 8 7 − 3

8. 4, 6, 8, ______

9 10 11 12

11. Tai saw 5 seals at the zoo. Jim saw 3 bears. How many animals did they see in all?

8 animals

9.

10:00 6:00

8:00 2:00

12. What number is 10 less than 75?

65

Test Directions for Teachers

Read the following directions to students before they begin. Then read each question followed by a pause to allow students time to work and choose an answer. The first test item can be worked as a class example.

- **Write your name at the top of the page.**
- **I am going to read each question to you. Listen carefully to the entire question before you choose an answer.**

Multiple Choice

1. Look at the crayon and paper clip. About how many paper clips long is the crayon?
2. Look at the glass and the milk carton. About how many glasses will fill the milk carton?
3. Look at flowers. Mark the flower that is the shortest.
4. Mark the object that is heavier than a book.
5. Look at the kites. Mark the kite that has the most bows.
6. What number is one more than 69?

- **Turn the page over.**

7. Mark the object that is lighter than a quarter.
8. Look at the group of numbers. What number comes next?
9. Look at the analog clock. Mark the digital clock that shows the same time.
10. Look at the number line. What fact does the number line show?

Short Response

11. Tai saw 5 seals at the zoo. Jim saw 3 bears. How many animals did they see in all?
12. What number is 10 less than 75?

CHAPTER 10

Chapter Overview

Chapter-at-a-Glance

In Chapter 10, the emphasis is on addition and subtraction strategies, including doubles facts, doubles plus 1 facts, making ten to add, and fact families.

Lesson	Math Objective	State/Local Standards
10-1 Doubles (pp. 317–318)	Use doubles facts to add.	
10-2 Doubles Plus 1 (pp. 319–320)	Use doubles plus 1 facts to add.	
10-3 Make a 10 to Add (pp. 323–324)	Use the strategy to make a 10 to find sums.	
10-4 Problem-Solving Strategy: Draw a Picture (pp. 325–326)	Use the *draw a picture* strategy to solve problems.	
10-5 Use Doubles to Subtract (pp. 329–330)	Relate doubles addition facts to subtraction facts.	
10-6 Relate Addition and Subtraction (pp. 331–332)	Identify patterns in related addition and subtraction sentences.	
10-7 Problem-Solving Investigation: Choose a Strategy (pp. 333–334)	Choose the best strategy to solve a problem.	
10-8 Fact Families (pp. 335–338)	Identify patterns in fact families.	
10-9 Ways to Model Numbers (pp. 339–340)	Use models to make a number in different ways.	

Solve Addition and Subtraction Problems

BIG Idea Previously, students learned addition and subtraction strategies to 12. In this chapter, the relationship between addition and subtraction is emphasized as students explore, analyze and learn strategies for facts through 20.

- Addition and subtraction strategies addressed in this chapter include using doubles to add and subtract and making a 10 to add.
- The work in this chapter also places a strong focus on the inverse operations of addition and subtraction. Encourage students to use a related addition fact to find the answer to a subtraction fact.

Algebra Readiness In Lessons 10-8, and 10-9, students prepare for algebra by using the Commutative Property of Addition.

Focal Points and Connections

G1-FP2 *Number and Operations:* **Developing an understanding of whole number relationships, including grouping in tens and ones**

Children compare and order whole numbers (at least to 100) to develop an understanding of and solve problems involving the relative sizes of these numbers. They think of whole numbers between 10 and 100 in terms of groups of tens and ones (especially recognizing the numbers 11 to 19 as 1 group of ten and particular numbers of ones). They understand the sequential order of the counting numbers and their relative magnitudes and represent numbers on a number line.

G1-FP6C *Algebra:* Through identifying, describing, and applying number patterns and properties in developing strategies for basic facts, children learn about other properties of numbers and operations, such as odd and even (e.g., "Even numbers of objects can be paired, with none left over"), and 0 as the identity element for addition.

Skills Trace
Vertical Alignment

Kindergarten

In kindergarten, students learned to:

- Understand simple addition and subtraction problems.
- Model addition and subtraction using concrete objects.
- Use concrete objects to show different ways to make 4, 5, 6, 7, 8, and 9.
- Understand simple subtraction problems.
- Use concrete objects to take away from 4, 5, 6, 7, 8, and 9.

First Grade

During this chapter, students learn to:

- Use doubles to add and subtract.
- Relate addition and subtraction.
- Understand fact families.
- Name numbers in different ways.

After this chapter, students learn to:

- Identify pennies, nickels, dimes, and quarters by name and value. (Chapter 11)

Second Grade

In second grade, students learn to:

- Identify and use the Commutative and Associative Properties of Addition.
- Regroup during addition and subtraction.

BackMapping and Vertical Alignment

McGraw-Hill's *Math Connects* program was conceived and developed with the final results in mind: student success in Algebra 1 and beyond. The authors, using the **NCTM Focal Points and Focal Connections** as their guide, developed this brand-new series by backmapping from Algebra 1 concepts, and vertically aligning the topics so that they build upon prior skills and concepts and serve as a foundation for future topics.

Math Vocabulary

The following math vocabulary words for Chapter 10 are listed in the glossary of the ***Student Edition.*** You can find interactive definitions in 13 languages in the ***eGlossary*** at macmillanmh.com.

doubles two addends that are the same number (p. 317)

doubles plus 1 two addends in which one number is one larger than the other (p. 319)

fact family addition and subtraction sentences that use the same numbers (p. 335)

Visual Vocabulary Cards Use Visual Vocabulary Card 18 to introduce and reinforce the vocabulary in this chapter. (The Define/Example/Ask routine is printed on the back of each card.)

CHAPTER 10 Chapter Planner

Suggested Pacing		
Instruction	Review and Assessment	TOTAL
9 days	2 days	**11 days**

Diagnostic Assessment
Are You Ready? (p. 314)

	Lesson 10-1 (Pacing: 1 day)	Lesson 10-2 (Pacing: 1 day)	Lesson 10-3 (Pacing: 1 day)
Lesson/ Objective	**Doubles** (pp. 317–318) **Objective:** Use doubles facts to add.	**Doubles Plus 1** (pp. 319–320) **Objective:** Use doubles plus 1 facts to add.	**Make a 10 to Add** (pp. 323–324) **Objective:** Use the strategy make a 10 to find sums.
State/Local Standards			
Math Vocabulary			
Lesson Resources	**Materials** dominoes overhead with domino outline **Manipulatives** two-colored counters **Other Resources** CRM Leveled Worksheets (pp. 6–10) Daily Reteach • 5-Minute Check Problem of the Day	**Materials** WorkMat 6: Grid **Manipulatives** connecting cubes **Other Resources** CRM Leveled Worksheets (pp. 11–15) Daily Reteach • 5-Minute xCheck Problem of the Day	**Materials** egg carton, WorkMat 1: Ten-Frame, overhead with ten-frame **Manipulatives** two-colored counters, connecting cubes **Other Resources** CRM Leveled Worksheets (pp. 16–28) Daily Reteach • 5-Minute Check Problem of the Day
Technology Math Online	Math Song Track 11 Math Adventures	Math Song Track 11 Math Adventures	Math Song Track 11 Math Tool Chest, Counter Level 1 Math Adventures Concepts in Motion
Reaching All Learners	Below Level, p. 317B BL English Learners, p. 317B ELL Early Finishers, p. 317B OL AL	Below Level, p. 319B BL English Learners, p. 319B ELL Early Finishers, p. 319B OL AL	Gifted and Talented, p. 323B AL English Learners, p. 323B ELL Early Finishers, p. 323B OL AL
Alternate Lessons	*IMPACT Mathematics:* Unit B	*IMPACT Mathematics:* Units B and G	*Math Their Way,* p. 314 *IMPACT Mathematics:* Units B and H

Extra Practice (p. 321)
Game Time: Circle Up! (p. 322)

KEY
BL Below/Approaching Level
OL On Level
AL Above/Beyond Level
ELL English Learners
SE Student Edition
TE Teacher Edition
CRM Chapter 3 Resource Masters
CD-Rom
Transparency
Flip Chart
Real-World Problem Solving Library

Solve Addition and Subtraction Problems

	Lesson 10-4 (Pacing: 1 day)	Lesson 10-5 (Pacing: 1 day)	Lesson 10-6 (Pacing: 1 day)
Lesson/ Objective	Problem-Solving Strategy **Draw a Picture** (pp. 325–326) **Objective:** Use the *draw a picture* strategy to solve problems.	**Use Doubles to Subtract** (pp. 329–330) **Objective:** Relate doubles addition facts to subtraction facts.	**Relate Addition and Subtraction** (pp. 331–332) **Objective:** Identify patterns in related addition and subtraction sentences.
State/Local Standards			
Math Vocabulary			
Lesson Resources	**Other Resources** CRM Leveled Worksheets (pp. 21–25) Daily Reteach • 5-Minute Check Problem of the Day *Double the Number*	**Materials** string or masking tape, dominoes **Manipulatives** two-colored counters **Other Resources** CRM Leveled Worksheets (pp. 26–30) Daily Reteach • 5-Minute Check Problem of the Day	**Materials** number-sentence strips **Manipulatives** connecting cubes **Other Resources** CRM Leveled Worksheets (pp. 31–35) Daily Reteach • 5-Minute Check Problem of the Day
Technology Math Online		Math Song Track 11 Math Adventures Concepts in Motion	Math Song Track 11 Math Adventures Concepts in Motion
Reaching All Learners	Gifted and Talented, p. 325B AL English Learners, p. 325B ELL Early Finishers, p. 325B OL AL	Gifted and Talented, p. 329B AL English Learners, p. 329B ELL Early Finishers, p. 329B OL AL	Below Level, p. 331B BL English Learners, p. 331B ELL Early Finishers, p. 331B OL AL
Alternate Lessons			*Math Their Way*, pp. 181–182 *IMPACT Mathematics*: Unit B

Formative Assessment
- Mid-Chapter Check (p. 327)
- Spiral Review (p. 328)

CHAPTER 10

Chapter Planner

	Lesson 10-7 Pacing: 1 day	Lesson 10-8 Pacing: 1 day	Lesson 10-9 Pacing: 1 day
Lesson/ Objective	Problem-Solving Investigation **Choose a Strategy** (pp. 333–334) **Objective:** Choose the best strategy to solve a problem.	**Fact Families** (Tech Link) (pp. 335–338) **Objective:** Identify patterns in fact families.	**Ways to Model Numbers** (pp. 339–340) **Objective:** Use models to make a number in different ways.
State/Local Standards			
Math Vocabulary			
Lesson Resources	**Other Resources** CRM Leveled Worksheets (pp. 36–40) Daily Reteach • 5-Minute Check Problem of the Day *Double the Number*	**Other Resources** CRM Leveled Worksheets (pp. 41–45) Daily Reteach • 5-Minute Check Problem of the Day	**Materials:** WorkMat 3: Part-Part-Whole, poster board, index cards **Manipulatives** two-colored counters **Other Resources** CRM Leveled Worksheets (pp. 46–50) Daily Reteach • 5-Minute Check Problem of the Day
Technology Math Online		Math Song Track 12 Math Tool Chest, Counter Level 1 Concepts in Motion	Math Song Track 11 Concepts in Motion
Reaching All Learners	Below Level, p. 333B BL English Learners, p. 333B ELL Early Finishers, p. 333B OL AL	Below Level, p. 335B BL English Learners, p. 335B ELL Early Finishers, p. 335B OL AL	Below Level, p. 339B BL English Learners, p. 339B ELL Early Finishers, p. 339B OL AL
Alternate Lessons		*IMPACT Mathematics*: Unit G	*IMPACT Mathematics*: Unit B

Problem Solving in Social Studies (p. 341)

Summative Assessment
- Chapter Review/Test (p. 343)
- Test Practice (p. 345)

What the Research Says . . .

Cognitively Guided Instruction (CGI)

This chapter provides students with opportunities to solve addition problems that use "join" or "part-part-whole." This type of classification, used with Cognitively Guided Instruction (CGI), helps teachers select problems for instruction and interpret how students solve these problems.

Type	Description	Example
Join	Involves a direct or implied action in which a set is increased by a certain amount.	Two children are playing in the park. Four more children join them. How many children are now playing in the park? 6 children
Part-Part-Whole	The whole is unknown; the problem gives the two parts and asks to find the size of the whole.	Four boys and six girls are roller skating. How many children are roller skating? 10 children

Teacher Notes

Assessment Options

Diagnostic Assessment

- SE *Option 1*: Are You Ready? (p. 314)
- *Option 2*: Online Quiz (macmillanmh.com)
- CRM *Option 3*: Diagnostic Test (p. 52)
- CRM *Option 4*: Chapter Pretest (p. 53)

Formative Assessment

- TE Alternate Teaching Strategies (every lesson)
- SE Talk About It (every lesson)
- SE Writing in Math (every lesson)
- SE Check (every lesson)
- TE Line Up (every lesson)
- SE Mid-Chapter Check (p. 327)
- CRM Mid-Chapter Test (p. 54)

Summative Assessment

- SE Chapter Review/Test (p. 343)
- SE Test Practice (p. 345)
- CRM Vocabulary Test (p. 55)
- CRM Leveled Chapter Tests (pp. 62–71)
- CRM Cumulative Test Practice (pp. 72–73)
- CRM Listening Assessment (pp. 58–59)
- CRM Oral Assessment (pp. 56–57)
- Exam*View*® Assessment Suite
- Advance Tracker

Professional Development

Targeted professional development has been articulated throughout **McGraw-Hill's *Math Connects*** program. The **McGraw-Hill Professional Development Video Library** provides short videos that support the **NCTM Focal Points and Focal Connections**. For more information, visit macmillanmh.com.

Model Lessons

Instructional Strategies

CHAPTER 10

Learning Stations

Cross-Curricular Links

Reading

pair | LOGICAL, VISUAL/SPATIAL

Fun with Maisy

- Read *Count with Maisy*.
- Work together to write new pages for the numbers 11, 12, and 13.
- Write the number names for 11, 12, and 13.
- Illustrate your pages.

Materials:

- *Count with Maisy* by Lucy Cousins
- pencil, crayons, markers, and construction paper

Art

individual | KINESTHETIC

Doubling Your Fun – Paper Dolls

- Fold your paper like a fan.
- Use your pencil to draw half a person on the folded edge of the paper.
- Use scissors to cut along the lines. Be sure not to cut down the folded sides.
- Unfold your paper and decorate the dolls.
- Put the dolls in two groups. Create a subtraction story you could model.

Teacher Note: Make sure students understand to cut the paper dolls at the hands and not the fold. You may want to leave a folded fan as an example.

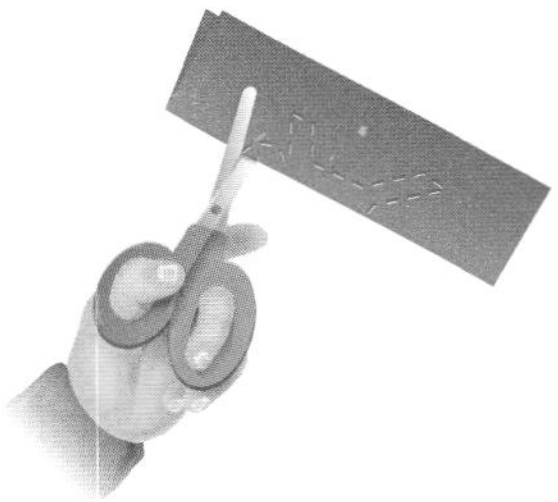

Materials:

- construction paper
- samples of folded paper
- samples of finished paper dolls
- decorating materials
- scissors

Social Studies

individual | INTRAPERSONAL

What Families Need

- Draw a map that shows 3 streets of a town.
- On one street show 3 places people live.
- On another street show 3 places that have things people need.
- On the last street show 3 places people go for fun.
- Write a number sentence that adds up all the places you drew.

Teacher Note: Provide community magazines or newspapers to give students ideas about places in their town.

Materials:

- construction paper
- markers or crayons

Solve Addition and Subtraction Problems

Science

pair | SOCIAL

Body Doubles

- Brainstorm with your partner some things people have two of.
- Draw them on your paper under **I have 2**...
- Brainstorm with your partner some things animals have four of.
- Draw them on your paper under **Animals have 4**...
- What is the doubles fact for 2?
- What is the doubles fact for 4?
- Can you think of something that has 6 legs? Can you think of something that has 8 legs?

Materials:

- construction paper folded in half, one side labeled "I have two..."; the other side labeled "Animals have 4..."
- crayons, markers

Language Arts

individual | LINGUISTIC

Math Rhymes

- Find a math word from this chapter that rhymes with each of the words below.

  gum *mad* *trouble*

- When you find all the words, write a sentence using each one.

Teacher Note: Provide the rhyming words and the math vocabulary words on index cards so students can match them up as they say them aloud.

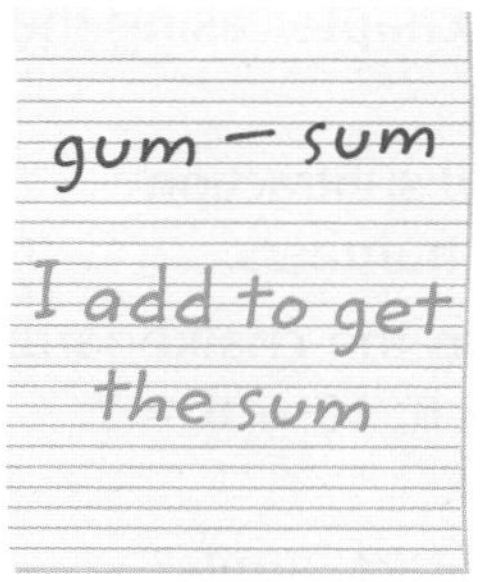

Materials:

- paper
- pencil

Calendar Time

Just the Facts

- Write the name of the current month on the calendar poster. Fill in the numbers for the days of the month.
- Write 4 + 5 = 9 on the chalkboard.
- **What day of the week is the 4th? the 5th? the 9th?**
- Have students find the numbers on the calendar and tell you which days of the week they fall on.
- Repeat with other addition and subtraction sentences.

Teacher Note: Show students that counting 5 days from the 4th puts them on the 9th.

Introduce the Chapter

Real World: Adding and Subtracting

Share with students that they are going to learn ways to add and subtract. Explain that there are many different strategies to help them solve addition and subtraction problems.

- Have five students stand. Then have five more students stand.
- **How many students are standing?** 10 students
- **How do you know?** Sample answers: counted them, used doubles to add
- **How can you show a subtraction problem using the same numbers?** Have 5 students sit.

Have students turn to p. 313.

- **How many birds do you count?** 14 birds
- **Cover up the red and green birds. Now how many do you count?** 5 birds

Review Vocabulary

Introduce the key vocabulary in the chapter using the routine below.

Define: A fact family is addition and subtraction sentences that use the same three numbers.

Example: Write these problems on the chalkboard: 6 + 7 = 13; 7 + 6 = 13; 13 − 7 = 6; 13 − 6 = 7. This is a fact family.

Ask: What numbers make up this fact family?

CHAPTER 10

Solve Addition and Subtraction Problems

Review Vocabulary
doubles
doubles plus one

Explore

There were 7 birds on the cliff. 6 more landed. How many birds are there now?

13 birds

FOLDABLES Study Organizer Dinah Zike's Foldables

Guide students to create their Layered-Look Foldables for solving addition and subtraction problems.

1. Stack two 8½ x 11 sheets of paper so that the back sheet is one inch higher than the front sheet.

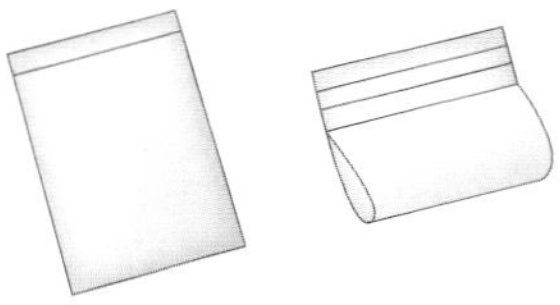

2. Bring the bottom of both sheets upward and align the edges so that all of the layers or tabs are the same distance apart.

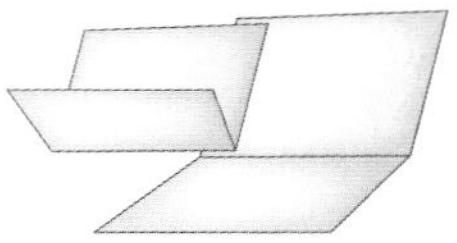

3. When all tabs are an equal distance apart, fold the papers and crease well.

4. Open the papers and glue them together along the valley or inner center fold, or staple them along the mountain.

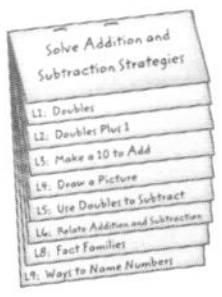

When to Use It *Lessons 10-1, 10-2, 10-3, 10-4, 10-6, 10-8, and 10-9. (Additional instructions for using the Foldable with these lessons are found on pp. 327 and 343.)*

Name ______________________

Math Online
Take the Chapter Readiness Quiz at macmillanmh.com.

Are You Ready for Chapter 10?

Add or subtract.

1. 6 + 5 = 11   2. 7 − 3 = 4   3. 2 + 3 = 5

4.	5.	6.	7.
9 + 1 = 10	8 + 4 = 12	3 − 2 = 1	6 − 3 = 3

Use doubles to add or subtract.

8. 3 + 3 = 6   9. 12 − 6 = 6

10. 4 + 4 = 8   11. 10 − 5 = 5

12. 2 + 2 = 4   13. 8 − 4 = 4

14. 5 + 5 = 10   15. 6 − 3 = 3

16. There were 8 children at the party. 3 children left. How many children are at the party now?
5 children

This page checks skills needed for Chapter 10.

Diagnostic Assessment

Check for students' prerequisite skills before beginning the chapter.

- **Option 1:** ***Are You Ready for Chapter 10?***
  SE Student Edition, p. 314
- **Option 2:** ***Online Assessment***
  Math Online macmillanmh.com
- **Option 3:** ***Diagnostic Test***
  CRM Chapter 10 Resource Masters, p. 52

RTI (Response to Intervention)

Apply the Results Based on the results of the diagnostic assessment on p. 314, use the chart below to address individual needs before beginning the chapter.

TIER 3 Intensive Intervention

If students miss eleven or more of the exercises:

Then use Chapters 1, 2, 3, and 5 of *Math Triumphs*, an intensive math intervention program from McGraw-Hill.

TIER 2 Strategic Intervention below/approaching grade level	TIER 1 On-Level	Above/Beyond Level
If students miss five to ten in: **Exercises 1–16**	**If** students miss three or four in: **Exercises 1–16**	**If** students miss two or less in: **Exercises 1–16**
Then choose a resource:	**Then** choose a resource:	**Then** choose a resource:
Strategic Intervention Guide (pp. 80–85) CRM Chapter 5 Resource Masters (Reteach Worksheets) Math Online Concepts in Motion	TE Learning Stations (pp. 313G–313H) TE Chapter Project (p. 315) CRM Game: *Subtraction Action* Math Adventures My Math Zone Chapter 9 Math Online Fact Dash	TE Learning Stations (pp. 313G–313H) TE Chapter Project (p. 315) Real-World Problem Solving: *Double the Number* Math Adventures My Math Zone Chapters 9 and 10 Math Online Games

MATH at HOME

Before you begin Chapter 10:

- Read the Math at Home letter on p. 315 with the class and have each student sign it.
- Send home copies of the Math at Home letter with each student.
- Use the Spanish letter on p. 316 for students with Spanish-speaking parents or guardians.

WRITING IN ▶ MATH

Starting the Chapter
Ask students to write about ways they use addition and subtraction outside of school, such as at home or at the store. Have them illustrate one of the ways they use addition or subtraction outside of school.

Read-Aloud Anthology
For an optional reading activity to introduce this chapter's math concepts, see the Read-Aloud Anthology on p. TR34.

MATH at HOME

Dear Family,

Today my class started Chapter 10, **Solve Addition and Subtraction Problems**. In this chapter, I will learn to use strategies for addition and subtraction with numbers up to 20. Here is an activity we can do and a list of books we can read together.

Love, ______________

Activity

Take turns flipping through the pages of the phone book. Say "RRRRRING" to stop the flipping. Close your eyes and point to a number. Add the first two digits of the number together. Repeat using three numbers. Ask your child which two numbers they decided to add together first and why.

Review Vocabulary

doubles two addends that are the same number

6 + 6 = **12** 9 + 9 = **18**

doubles plus one

7 + 8 = **15** Think 7 + 7 = 14

Math Online Click on the eGlossary link at macmillanmh.com to find out more about these words. There are 13 languages.

Books to Read

Twenty is Too Many
by Katie Duke
Dutton Juvenile, 2000.

Counting Wildflowers
by Bruce McMillan
HarperTrophy, 1995.

The Warlord's Beads
by Virginia Walton Pilegard
Pelican Publishing Company, 2001.

Chapter 10 Project

Addition Strategy Cards

- Students make a set of addition strategy cards they can use to solve problems. Each card will include the strategy and number sentences to illustrate the strategy.
- Each student or small group should make one card for the following strategies: doubles facts, doubles plus 1 facts, and fact families.
- Students should write each strategy on a separate index card and include examples of number sentences that illustrate the strategy.
- Students can also write phrases and hints on each card that direct them in how to use the strategy.
- Strategy cards can be kept in a folder, portfolio, or at a math station to help students complete math problems using various strategies.

CRM *Refer to Chapter 10 Resource Masters on p. 60 for a rubric to assess students' progress on this project.*

MATEMÁTICAS en CASA

Estimada familia:

Hoy mi clase comenzó el Capítulo 10, **Resuelve problemas de suma y de resta.** En este capítulo, aprenderé a usar estrategias para sumar y restar con números hasta el 20. A continuación, hay una actividad que podemos hacer y una lista de libros que podemos leer juntos.

Cariños, ____________________

Actividad

Túrnense en hojear las páginas de la guía telefónica. Digan "RRRRRING" para dejar de hojear. Cierren los ojos y señalen un número telefónico. Sumen los tres primeros dígitos del número. Pregúntenle a su hijo(a) qué par de números decidieron sumar primero y por qué.

Repaso de vocabulario

dobles operaciones donde los dos sumandos son iguales.

$6 + 6 = 12$ $9 + 9 = 18$

dobles más uno

$7 + 8 = 15$ Piensa $7 + 7 = 14$

Math Online Visiten el enlace eGlossary en macmillanmh.com para averiguar más sobre estas palabras, las cuales se muestran en 13 idiomas.

Libros recomendados

¿Cuantos osos hay?
de Cooper Edens
Antheneum Books, 1994.

Las semillas magicas
de Mitsumasa Anno
Fondo de cultura
Economica USA, 2005.

ELL National ESL Standards Alignment for Chapter 10

Lesson, Page	ESL Standard	Modality	Level
10-1, p 317B	Goal 2, Standard 3, k	Visual/Spatial, Linguistic	Intermediate
10-2, p 319B	Goal 2, Standard 3, h	Kinesthetic	Intermediate
10-3, p 323B	Goal 1, Standard 3, f	Visual/Spatial	Intermediate
10-4, p 325B	Goal 1, Standard 3, e	Intrapersonal, Social	Advanced
10-5, p 329B	Goal 2, Standard 2, f	Visual/Spatial	Intermediate
10-6, p 331B	Goal 2, Standard 2, a	Visual/Spatial	Intermediate
10-7, p 333B	Goal 2, Standard 1, h	Linguistic	Advanced
10-8, p 335B	Goal 1, Standard 3, k	Visual/Spatial	Beginning
10-9, p 339B	Goal 2, Standard 2, c	Visual/Spatial	Intermediate

The National ESL Standards can be found in the Teacher Reference Handbook.

Chapter 10 Literature List

Lesson	Book Title
10-1	**Counting Is for the Birds** Frank Mazzola, Jr.
10-2	**Plant Fruits and Seeds** David M. Schwartz
10-3	**MATH-terpieces** Greg Tang
10-4	**Oh My Gosh, Mrs. McNosh!** Sarah Weeks
10-5	**Double the Ducks** Stuart J. Murphy
10-6	**Domino Addition** Lynette Long, Ph.D.
10-8	**One Moose, Twenty Mice** Clare Beaton
10-9	**12 Ways to Get to 11** Eve Merriam
Any	**Twenty is Too Many** Katie Duke
Any	**Counting Wildflowers** Bruce McMillan
Any	**The Warlord's Beads** Virginia Walton Pilegard

LESSON 10-1

Doubles

Lesson Planner

Objective

Use doubles facts to add.

Review Vocabulary

doubles

Resources

Materials: dominoes, overhead with domino outline

Manipulatives: two-colored counters

Literature Connection: *Counting Is for the Birds* by Frank Mazzola, Jr.

Alternate lesson: Use *IMPACT Mathematics*: Unit B to provide practice with doubles facts.

Teacher Technology

TeacherWorks • Math Songs Track 11 Lesson Plan

Focus on Math Background

In this lesson, students will focus on recalling doubles facts to 20. Doubles, such as 3 + 3, are typically the first family of addition facts that students master due to the predictable doubling pattern that unfolds when calculating the sum of two like addends. Students will draw upon their facility with doubles to master other closely related addition facts, including near doubles—*"2 + 2 is 4 and one more is 5."*

Daily Routine

Use these suggestions before beginning the lesson on p. 317.

5-Minute Check

(Reviews Lesson 9-9)

1. Does your hand or your desk cover more area? hand
2. Does a piece of paper or chalkboard cover more area? chalkboard
3. Name an object that covers more area than your hand. Answers will vary.

Problem of the Day

Clayton has 4 red marbles and 7 blue marbles. How many marbles does he have in all? 11 marbles

LINE UP Pick one student to line up. Have one more join him or her.

- **How many students are in line?** 2 students **What doubles fact is this?** 1 + 1 = 2
- Have two more students join the line. **What doubles fact is this?** 2 + 2 = 4
- Continue doubling until no more doubles can be made.

Review Math Vocabulary

- Ask three students to come to the front of the class. Then have three more join them.
- Write 3 + 3 on the board. Remind students that the numbers in an addition fact are called addends. **What is the sum of these addends?** 6
- **When two addends are the same, the fact is called a double. Say this double.** 3 + 3 = 6

Differentiated Instruction

Small Group Options

Option 1 Below Level BL

SOCIAL, KINESTHETIC

This activity will work best with groups of eight or more students.

- Divide students into two equal groups. If there are an odd number of students, pick one to help you write on the board.
- **What addition sentence models these groups?** See students' work. Write the double on the chalkboard.
- **What subtraction sentence can you write using these same three numbers?** See students' work. Write the fact on the board.
- Repeat the procedure for the next lower double. Continue until all doubles have been covered.

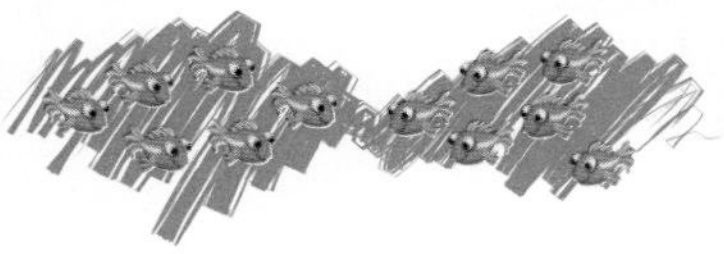

Option 2 English Language Learners ELL

VISUAL/SPATIAL, LINGUISTIC

Materials: set of dominoes, overhead dominoes
Core Vocabulary: matching cards, double
Common Use Verbs: to take turns, touch

Talk Math This lesson interactively engages students in recognizing doubles and practicing vocabulary.

- Each player takes 5 dominoes from pile. One domino from the pile is put face up in the middle of playing surface.
- Players take turns using patterns to match one side of their domino with another player's domino.
- When students recognize a matching pattern, they say: **"Double 4s."** Place dominoes so matching ends touch.

Use this worksheet to provide additional support for English Language Learners.

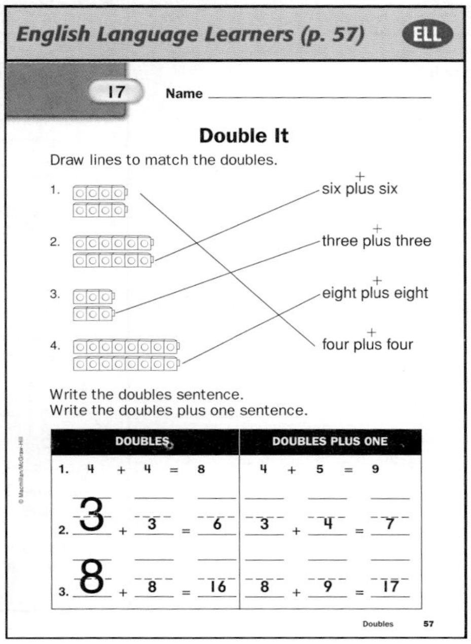

English Language Learners (p. 57) ELL

17 Name ______

Double It

Draw lines to match the doubles.

1. six plus six
2. three plus three
3. eight plus eight
4. four plus four

Write the doubles sentence.
Write the doubles plus one sentence.

DOUBLES					DOUBLES PLUS ONE				
1. 4	+	4	=	8	4	+	5	=	9
2. 3	+	3	=	6	3	+	4	=	7
3. 8	+	8	=	16	8	+	9	=	17

© Macmillan/McGraw-Hill

Doubles 57

Independent Work Options

Option 1 Early Finishers OL AL

VISUAL/SPATIAL

Materials: pattern blocks

- Have each student choose a number from 1 to 10, take that many pattern blocks, and arrange the blocks in a pattern on a sheet of paper.
- Have students extend their pattern in pencil to make a double. Then have them develop a strategy and write a doubles fact for the pattern.
- Have students repeat with a different number of pattern blocks.

Option 2 Student Technology

Math Online macmillanmh.com

Math Songs, "The Addition Boogie" Track 11 • Math Adventures

Option 3 Learning Station: Art (p. 313G)

Direct students to the Art Learning Station for more opportunities to explore and extend the lesson concept.

Option 4 Problem-Solving Practice

Reinforce problem-solving skills and strategies with the Problem-Solving Practice worksheet.

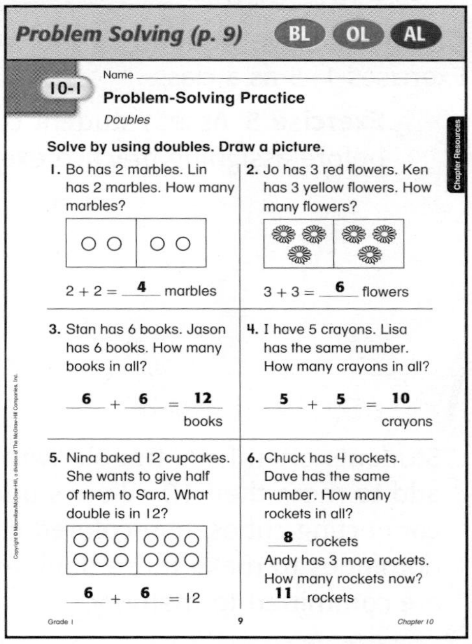

Problem Solving (p. 9) BL OL AL

10-1 Name ______

Problem-Solving Practice

Doubles

Chapter Resources

Solve by using doubles. Draw a picture.

1. Bo has 2 marbles. Lin has 2 marbles. How many marbles?
   2 + 2 = **4** marbles
2. Jo has 3 red flowers. Ken has 3 yellow flowers. How many flowers?
   3 + 3 = **6** flowers
3. Stan has 6 books. Jason has 6 books. How many books in all?
   6 + **6** = **12** books
4. I have 5 crayons. Lisa has the same number. How many crayons in all?
   5 + **5** = **10** crayons
5. Nina baked 12 cupcakes. She wants to give half of them to Sara. What double is in 12?
   6 + **6** = 12
6. Chuck has 4 rockets. Dave has the same number. How many rockets in all?
   8 rockets
   Andy has 3 more rockets. How many rockets now?
   11 rockets

Copyright © Macmillan/McGraw-Hill, a division of The McGraw-Hill Companies, Inc.

Grade 1 9 Chapter 10

10-1

1 Introduce

Activity Choice 1 • Hands-On

- Clap your hands five times as students count silently.
- **How many times did I clap?** 5 times
- Have students clap the same number of times you clapped. **How many times did you clap?** 5 times
- **How can you find the total number of times we clapped?** Add 5 + 5.
- Write 5 + 5 on the chalkboard. Explain that when you add a number to itself, the fact is called a **double**.
- **What is the sum of this double?** 10

Activity Choice 2 • Literature

Introduce the lesson with *Counting Is for the Birds* by Frank Mazzola, Jr. For additional support, see p. TR55.

2 Teach

Display a domino-shaped outline on the overhead.

- Put four two-colored counters on the left side of the domino. **How many counters?** 4 counters
- Put four counters on the right side of the domino. **How many counters in all?** 8 counters
- **Ask students to point out the pattern.** 4 + 4 = 8

Get Ready Use the section at the top of p. 317 to reinforce the lesson concept. Guide students through reviewing doubles facts.

Check Observe students as you work through Exercises 1–5 as a class.

Exercise 5 Assess student comprehension before assigning practice exercises.

COMMON ERROR!

Students often have trouble with doubles that add to more than 10. Allow students to use connecting cubes, two-colored counters, or dominoes to make these doubles until they are committed to memory.

Name ______________________

Doubles

Get Ready

Main Idea

I will use doubles facts to add.

Review Vocabulary

doubles

The addends are the same in a doubles fact.

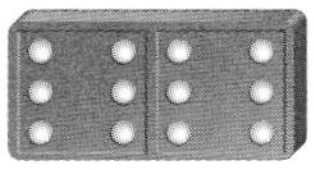
6 + 6 = **12**

8 + 8 = **16**

Check

Draw the missing dots to show a double.
Write the doubles fact.

Look at the sum to help you find the doubles fact.

1. 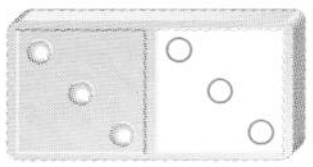
3 + 3 = 6

2. 
7 + 7 = 14

Draw dots to show the doubles.
Write the addends.

3. 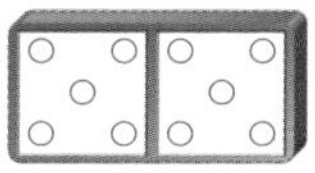
5 + 5 = 10

4. 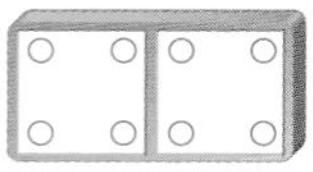
4 + 4 = 8

5. **Talk About It** Can you use doubles to make 15? Why or why not? Sample answer: No, because 15 cannot be split evenly.

Reteach (p. 6) BL

10-1 Name ______

Reteach

Doubles

The two addends in doubles are the same.

7 + 7 = 14 (addends)

  7
+ 7
 14

Find each sum. You can use ○.

1. 5 + 5 = **10** sum
2. 3 + 3 = **6** sum
3. 9 + 9 = **18** sum
4. 4 + 4 = **8** sum

Find each sum. Circle the doubles.

5. 6 + 6 = **12**
6. 4 + 2 = **6**
7. 2 + 2 = **4**
8. 5 + 2 = **7**
9. 8 + 8 = **16**
10. 1 + 1 = **2**
11. 7 + 2 = **9**
12. 7 + 7 = **14**
13. 6 + 3 = **9**

Grade 1 6 Chapter 10

Skills Practice (p. 7) OL

10-1 Name ______

Skills Practice

Doubles

Draw marbles to show the doubles.
Write the addends and the sums.

1. 4 + 4 = 8
2. **8** + **8** = **16**
3. **9** + **9** = **18**
4. **7** + **7** = **14**

Add.

5. 6 + 6 = **12**
6. 5 + 5 = **10**
7. 8 + 8 = **16**
8. 3 + 3 = **6**
9. 2 + 2 = **4**

Solve. Show your work.

10. Bill has 9 marbles. Wally has same number. How many marbles do they have in all?
9 + **9** = **18** marbles

Grade 1 7 Chapter 10

Practice

Draw the missing dots to show a double.
Write the doubles fact.

6. 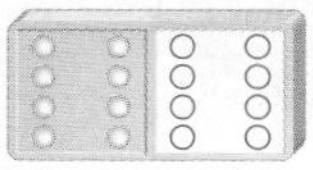

8 + 8 = 16

7. 

7 + 7 = 14

8. 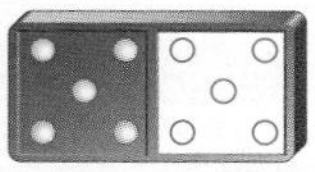

5 + 5 = 10

9. 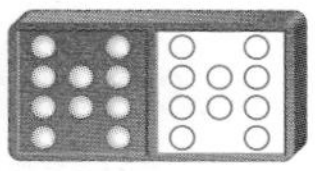

10 + 10 = 20

Draw dots to show the doubles.
Write the addends.

10. 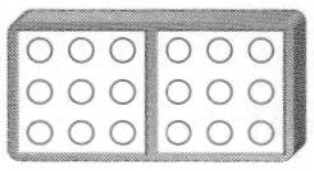

9 + 9 = 18

11. 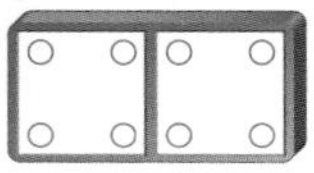

4 + 4 = 8

12. 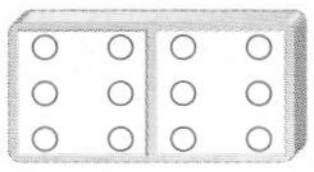

6 + 6 = 12

13. 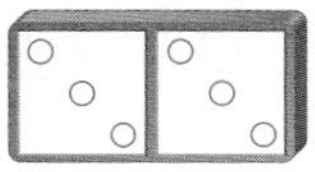

3 + 3 = 6

Problem Solving

14. **Critical Thinking** How many doubles facts can you make with your fingers? 6
Sample answer: 0 + 0; 1 + 1; 2 + 2; 3 + 3; 4 + 4; 5 + 5

Math at Home Activity: Say a number from 0-10. Have your child say a doubles fact using that number.

BL Alternate Teaching Strategy

If students do not understand the concept of doubles . . .

Then use one of the following reteach options.

1. CRM **Daily Reteach Worksheet** (p. 6)
2. **Domino Math** Give students several dominoes, divided into those that show doubles and those that do not show doubles. Help students recognize that a double domino has the same number of dots on each side.

3 Practice

Differentiate practice using these leveled assignments for Exercises 6–14.

Level	Assignment
BL Below/ Approaching Level	Allow students to use connecting cubes, two-colored counters, or double dominoes.
OL On Level	Complete the exercises independently.
AL Above/Beyond Level	Write the related subtraction fact for each double.

4 Assess

Formative Assessment

- Give students a pile of dominoes. Have them separate out the dominoes with doubles. Ask students to justify their thinking.

WRITING IN MATH Have students write about a time at their home when they encountered or used doubles.

Quick Check **Are students continuing to struggle with learning doubles?**

If Yes → Small Group Options (p. 317B)

If No → Independent Work Options (p. 317B)

CRM Skills Practice Worksheet (p. 7)

CRM Enrich Worksheet (p. 10)

Enrich (p. 10) AL

10-1 Name ____
Enrich
Rolling Doubles!

Play a game with a partner.

3 6

4	8	10
2	6	12

How to play:
- Roll the cube.
- Double the number.
- Find the sum and color it.

If you roll a number already colored, you lose your turn.
The first one to color all the boxes wins!

Grade 1 10 Chapter 10

Homework Practice (p. 8) OL

10-1 Name ____
Homework Practice
Doubles

Draw the missing dots to show the doubles.
Write the doubles fact.

1. 6 + 6 = 12
2. 8 + 8 = 16
3. 7 + 7 = 14
4. 9 + 9 = 18
5. 5 + 5 = 10
6. 3 + 3 = 6

Solve.

7. Jon has 5 coins. Nina has the same number. How many coins do they have in all? Show your work.
5 + 5 = 10 coins
8. Emma and Josh both have 7 quarters. How many quarters do they have altogether?
7 + 7 = 14 quarters

Grade 1 8 Chapter 10

LESSON 10-2

Doubles Plus 1

Lesson Planner

Objective

Use doubles plus 1 facts to add.

Review Vocabulary

doubles plus 1

Resources

Materials: WorkMat 6: Grid

Manipulatives: connecting cubes

Literature Connection: *Plant Fruits and Seeds* by David M. Schwartz

Alternate lesson: Use *IMPACT Mathematics*: Unit B and G to provide practice with doubles plus 1 facts.

Teacher Technology

TeacherWorks • Math Songs Track 11 Lesson Plan

Focus on Math Background

This lesson builds upon students' familiarity with doubles facts by introducing a closely related strategy called "doubles plus one." This is a powerful strategy that helps foster numerical reasoning and confidence when children are unable to instantly recall a less familiar number fact. For example, if a student does not remember 5 + 6, he/she could use 5 + 5 = 10 and then count on one more to get 11.

Daily Routine

Use these suggestions before beginning the lesson on p. 319.

5-Minute Check

(Reviews Lesson 10-1)

Add.

1. 5 + 5 = 10
2. 4 + 4 = 8
3. 8 + 8 = 16
4. 6 + 6 = 12
5. 1 + 1 = 2
6. 9 + 9 = 18

Problem of the Day

Stacy has 2 books in her bag. She goes to the library and gets 1 more. How many books does Stacy have? 3 books

LINE UP Have two students form a line.

- **How many students are in line?** 2 students **What is the doubles fact for 2?** 2 + 2 = 4
- Have three students join the line. **What is the doubles plus 1 fact the students made?** 2 + 3 = 5
- **How many students are now in line?** 5 students **What is the doubles fact for 5?** 5 + 5 = 10
- **How many students should get in line to make a doubles plus 1 fact?** 6 students
- Have six students join the line. **How many students are now in line?** 11 students **What is the doubles plus 1 fact the students made?** 5 + 6 = 11

Review Math Vocabulary

- **Name a doubles fact.** Sample answer: 3 + 3 = 6. Write the fact on the chalkboard. **In this fact, what are the addends?** 3; 3
- **If I add 1 to one of the addends, I make a doubles plus 1 fact.** Demonstrate on the chalkboard. **What is the sum of this fact?** 7 **What happened to the sum when I added 1 to an addend?** The sum got greater by 1.

Differentiated Instruction

Small Group Options

Option 1 Below/Approaching Level BL

VISUAL/SPATIAL

Materials: crayons or markers

- Write a list of doubles plus 1 facts for students.
- Have each student choose a fact and illustrate it with two groups of animal faces.
- Have students trade drawings and try to identify the doubles plus 1 fact from the drawing.
- **How many animals are in each group?**
- **How many more animals are in the larger group?**
- **Cross out 1 animal. What doubles fact does the drawing show now?**

Option 2 English Language Learners ELL

KINESTHETIC

Core Vocabulary: join, pairs, partners
Common Use Verbs: hold/is holding

Do Math This strategy reinforces kinesthetically doubles and doubles plus one vocabulary.

- Ask 6 students to come to the front of the room. Ask 1 other student to stand off to the side.
- Demonstrate Double 3s by telling 3 students to hold hands and make a line. The other 3 students repeat facing the first line. The two lines join hands across and turn to face the class.
- Say: "Each person has a **partner**. Count the **pairs**."
- Have students hold up the joined hands and count.
- Say: "There are 3 **pairs**. Are six students in 3 **pairs** a double or a double plus 1?"
- Repeat with another group of a different number of students. Have the class identify if groups are doubles or doubles plus 1.

Independent Work Options

Option 1 Early Finishers OL AL

LOGICAL

Materials: dominoes

- Spread faceup on a table.
- Have students pair dominoes that show doubles with the domino that shows that double plus 1.
- Have students write the facts for these dominoes.
- Repeat until all doubles have been found.

Option 2 Student Technology

Math Online macmillanmh.com

Math Songs, "The Addition Boogie" Track 11 • Math Adventures

Option 3 Learning Station: Language Arts (p. 313H)

Direct students to the Language Arts Learning Station for more opportunities to explore and extend the lesson concept.

Option 4 Problem-Solving Practice

Reinforce problem-solving skills and strategies with the Problem-Solving Practice worksheet.

Problem Solving (p. 14) BL OL AL

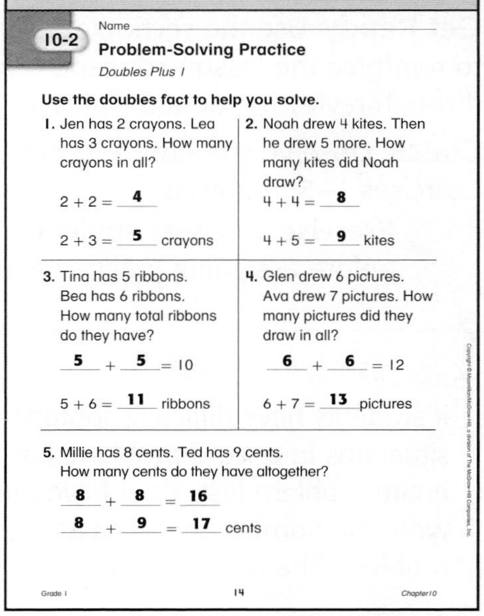

Name ____

10-2 **Problem-Solving Practice**
Doubles Plus 1

Use the doubles fact to help you solve.

1. Jen has 2 crayons. Lea has 3 crayons. How many crayons in all?
   2 + 2 = 4
   2 + 3 = 5 crayons

2. Noah drew 4 kites. Then he drew 5 more. How many kites did Noah draw?
   4 + 4 = 8
   4 + 5 = 9 kites

3. Tina has 5 ribbons. Bea has 6 ribbons. How many total ribbons do they have?
   5 + 5 = 10
   5 + 6 = 11 ribbons

4. Glen drew 6 pictures. Ava drew 7 pictures. How many pictures did they draw in all?
   6 + 6 = 12
   6 + 7 = 13 pictures

5. Millie has 8 cents. Ted has 9 cents. How many cents do they have altogether?
   8 + 8 = 16
   8 + 9 = 17 cents

Grade 1 14 Chapter 10

1 Introduce

Activity Choice 1 • Hands-On

- Choose eight students to stand at the front of the class in two groups of four. **Do these students show a doubles fact? How do you know? Which fact?** Yes; the groups have the same number; 4 + 4 = 8.
- Choose one student to join a group. **Is this a doubles fact? How do you know?** No; the groups do not have the same number.
- Have each group count off. **What is the difference between these groups?** One group has 1 more student.

Activity Choice 2 • Literature

Introduce the lesson with *Plant Fruits and Seeds* by David M. Schwartz. For additional support, see p. TR55.

2 Teach

- Give each student ten cubes of one color and one cube of a different color. Have them make two equal trains. **How many cubes are in each train?** 5 cubes
- Have students put the trains together. **How many cubes are in the long train?** 10 cubes **Write the addition sentence this shows.** 5 + 5 = 10
- Next have the students break the train into two 5-cube trains and attach one cube of a different color to one of the trains. **How many cubes are in each train?** 5 in one and 6 in the other
- Have students put the trains together to create a **doubles plus 1** fact. **How many cubes are in the long train?** 11 cubes **Write the addition sentence this shows.** 5 + 6 = 11

Get Ready Use the section at the top of p. 319 to reinforce the lesson concept. Guide students through reviewing doubles plus 1 facts.

Check Observe students as you work through Exercises 1–5 as a class.

Exercise 5 Assess student comprehension before assigning practice exercises.

COMMON ERROR!

If students have difficulty spotting doubles plus 1 situations in a word problem, have them read the entire problem first. Then have them go back and write the number sentence as they reread the problem. The doubles plus 1 will be apparent.

Name ______________________

Doubles Plus 1

Get Ready

Main Idea

I will add doubles plus one.

Review Vocabulary

doubles plus 1

You can use doubles plus 1 to help you add.

Check

Use the pattern to find the sums.

1. 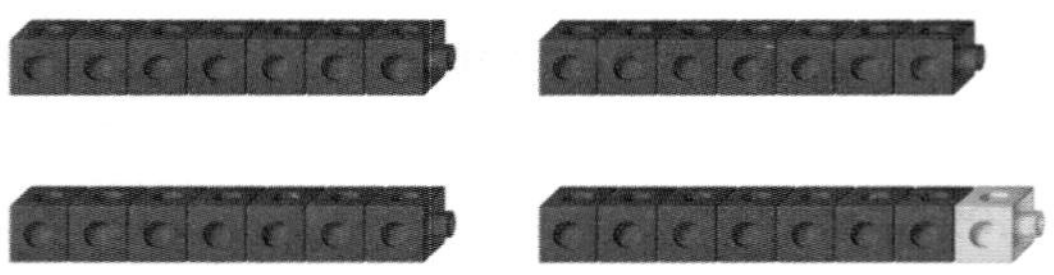
7 + 7 = **14**
7 + 8 = **15**

2. 
5 + 5 = 10
5 + 6 = 11

3. 4 + 4 = 8
4 + 5 = 9

4. 8 + 8 = 16
9 + 8 = 17

5. **Talk About It** How does knowing 4 + 4 help you find 4 + 5? Sample answer: 4 + 5 is one more than 4 + 4 so the sum is one more.

Reteach (p. 11) BL

10-2 Name ________

Reteach

Doubles Plus 1

You can use doubles to find the sum for doubles plus one.

Find the sum for the double. Add one to the sum of the double.

5 + 5 = 10   5 + 6 = 11

Add.

1. 4 + 4 = **8** sum
4 + 5 = **9** sum

2. 2 + 2 = **4** sum
2 + 3 = **5** sum

3. 3 + 3 = **6** sum
3 + 4 = **7** sum

4. 8 + 8 = **16** sum
8 + 9 = **17** sum

Grade 1   11   Chapter 10

Skills Practice (p. 12) OL

10-2 Name ________

Skills Practice

Doubles Plus 1

Use ▢ to find the sums. Circle the doubles facts.

1. (2 + 2) = **4**   (5 + 5) = **10**   2 + 3 = **5**
2. 5 + 4 = **9**   (4 + 4) = **8**   (3 + 3) = **6**
3. 6 + 7 = **13**   (7 + 7) = **14**   (6 + 6) = **12**
4. 4 + 5 = **9**   7 + 6 = **13**   3 + 2 = **5**
5. (8 + 8) = **16**   8 + 7 = **15**   7 + 8 = **15**
6. (9 + 9) = **18**   9 + 8 = **17**   8 + 9 = **17**

Solve. Show your work.

Write a doubles plus 1 fact to solve. What doubles fact can help you?

7. Ann has 6 rubber bands. Geri has 7. How many rubber bands do they have in all?
6 + 7 = **13** rubber bands
6 + **6** = 12

Grade 1   12   Chapter 10

Practice

Use the pattern to find the sums.

6. 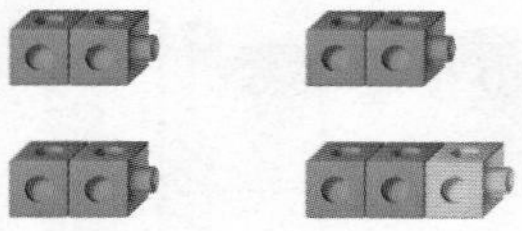

2 + 2 = 4 (2 + 2 is a doubles fact.)

2 + 3 = 5 (2 + 3 is a doubles plus one fact.)

Find the sums. Circle the doubles plus 1 facts.

7. 1 + 1 = 2   (1 + 2 = 3)

8. 8 + 8 = 16   (8 + 9 = 17)

9. 7 + 7 = 14   (7 + 8 = 15)

10. 3 + 3 = 6   (3 + 4 = 7)

11. 9 + 9 = 18   (9 + 10 = 19)

12. 6 + 6 = 12   (6 + 7 = 13)

13. 8 + 8 = 16   (8 + 9 = 17)

H.O.T. Problem

14. **Algebra** What are the missing numbers?

8 + 7 = 15

4 + 7 = 11

9 + 9 = 18

Math at Home Activity: Hold up 8 fingers. Have your child name the doubles fact (8+8) and what the doubles plus 1 fact (8+9) would be.

Enrich (p. 15) AL

10-2 Name

Enrich

Different Doubles

Add. Color the doubles facts orange.

Color the doubles plus 1 facts blue.

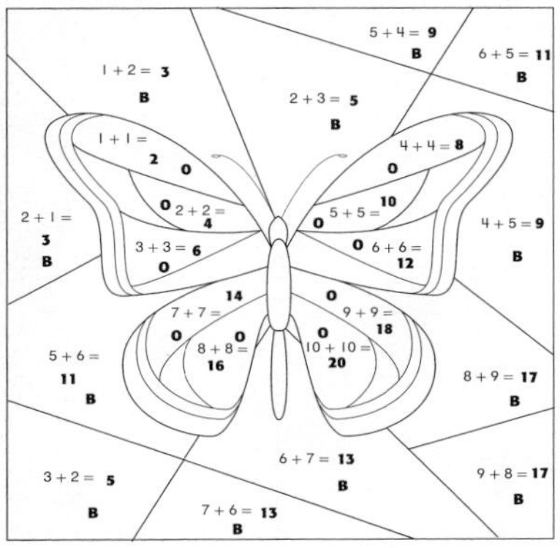

Grade 1   15   Chapter 10

Homework Practice (p. 13) OL

10-2 Name

Homework Practice

Doubles Plus 1

Use cubes to find the sums.

1. 6 + 6 = **12** ; so 6 + 7 = **13**
2. 4 + 4 = **8** ; so 4 + 5 = **9**
3. 7 + 7 = **14** ; so 7 + 8 = **15**
4. 1 + 1 = **2** ; so 1 + 2 = **3**

5. 5 + 5 = **10** | 5 + 6 = **11** | 6 + 6 = **12**
6. 9 + 9 = **18** | 9 + 10 = **19** | 10 + 10 = **20**
7. 8 + 8 = **16** | 8 + 9 = **17** | 8 + 7 = **15**

Write the missing numbers. Draw a picture to help.

8. Rani is baking pies. She baked 2 pies this morning. She will bake 5 pies in all. How many pies are left to bake?

2 + **3** = 5 pies

Grade 1   13   Chapter 10

BL Alternate Teaching Strategy

If students do not understand the concept of doubles plus 1 facts . . .

Then use one of the following reteach options.

1. CRM **Daily Reteach Worksheet** (p. 11)
2. **Grid Math** Give each student WorkMat 6: Grid. Have students illustrate doubles facts by coloring the same number of squares in two rows. Then have students use a different color to fill in one more square in the second row of the grid to illustrate doubles plus 1.

3 Practice

Differentiate practice using these leveled assignments for Exercises 6–14.

Level	Assignment
BL Below/ Approaching Level	Assist students by setting up the cubes for each exercise.
OL On Level	Complete the exercises independently.
AL Above/Beyond Level	Write a subtraction fact for each exercise.

4 Assess

Formative Assessment

- **Why are these facts called doubles plus 1?** Sample answer: The facts are doubles facts with 1 added.

WRITING IN MATH Have students write a word problem using a doubles plus 1 fact.

Quick Check **Are students continuing to struggle with learning doubles plus 1 facts?**

If Yes → Small Group Options (p. 319B)

If No → Independent Work Options (p. 319B)

CRM Skills Practice Worksheet (p. 12)

CRM Enrich Worksheet (p. 15)

Extra Practice

Review Lessons 10-1 to 10-2

Objective: Review and assess mastery of previous lessons' skills and concepts.

- Review with students the meaning of *doubles* and *doubles plus 1*.
- Students may want to use connecting cubes to find the sums.

Practice with Technology

Math Online Have students visit macmillanmh.com for additional practice with online activities, games, and quizzes.

Extra Practice

Name ______________________

Find each sum. Use doubles to help you add.

1. $8 + 8 = 16$ (circled) $8 + 9 = 17$ $9 + 8 = 17$

2.	$7 + 7 = 14$ (circled)	$7 + 8 = 15$	$8 + 7 = 15$
3.	$5 + 4 = 9$	$4 + 5 = 9$	$4 + 4 = 8$ (circled)
4.	$5 + 5 = 10$ (circled)	$6 + 5 = 11$	$5 + 6 = 11$
5.	$9 + 9 = 18$ (circled)	$8 + 9 = 17$	$9 + 8 = 17$
6.	$7 + 6 = 13$	$6 + 7 = 13$	$6 + 6 = 12$ (circled)

Now circle the doubles problem in each set.

Circle Up

Adding Doubles

You Will Need

Play with a partner.

- Take turns rolling the [number cube].
- Double the number you roll. If you are right, cover that number with a counter.
- If the number is already covered, take another turn.
- The player covering the most numbers wins.

Circle Up!

Math Concept:
Find Sums Using Doubles

Manipulatives: red number cube, two-colored counters

Introduce the game on p. 322 to students to play as a class, in small groups, or at a learning workstation to review concepts introduced in this chapter.

Instructions

- Students take turns rolling the red number cube.
- On his or her turn, a student doubles the number rolled and covers that number with a counter.
- If a student doubles the number rolled and finds that both of that number are already covered, the student takes another turn.
- Students play until every number is covered.

Extend the Game

Assign each student a color, yellow or red. If a player cannot cover his or her number, the player misses that turn. After every number is covered, the player who has more counters on the board is the winner.

Differentiated Practice

Use these leveling suggestions to differentiate the game for all learners.

Level	Assignment
BL **Below/Approaching Level**	Allow students to use connecting cubes to find the doubles.
OL **On Level**	Have students play the game with the rules as written.
AL **Above/Beyond Level**	Give students a red number cube. Have them find all the possible doubles for the red cube and modify the board so it is playable with those numbers.

LESSON 10-3

Make a 10 to Add

Lesson Planner

Objective
Use the strategy make a 10 to find sums.

Review Vocabulary
equals (=), sum

Resources
Materials: egg carton, WorkMat 1: Ten-Frame

Manipulatives: two-colored counters, connecting cubes

Literature Connection: *MATH-terpieces* by Greg Tang

Alternate Lessons: Adapt "Base Ten Unifix" *Patterns* on page 314 of *Math Their Way* for practice in addition to 10.
Use *IMPACT Mathematics*: Units B and H to provide practice with making a 10 to add.

Teacher Technology
TeacherWorks • Concepts in Motion • Math Tool Chest • Math Songs Track 11 Lesson Plan

Focus on Math Background
Making a 10 in order to add is the focus in this lesson. For an unfamiliar number fact, such as 9 + 4, students use a ten-frame to change one addend to a 10 by breaking apart the other addend—e.g. *to change 9 to 10, just take 1 from the 4.* In addition to strengthening students' familiarity with base-ten, this strategy also helps children develop flexibility and confidence with computation.

Daily Routine
Use these suggestions before beginning the lesson on p. 323.

5-Minute Check
(Reviews Lesson 10-2)

Find each sum.

1. 5 + 6 = 11	**2.** 4 + 5 = 9
3. 6 + 7 = 13	**4.** 3 + 4 = 7
5. 8 + 9 = 17	**6.** 8 + 7 = 15

Problem of the Day
Jenny has 8 fish in her fish tank. She bought 4 more fish at the pet store. How many fish does Jenny have altogether? 12 fish

LINE UP Ask four students to line up and count off.
- **There are 4 students in line. Double that number.** 8 **Add 1.** 9
- **How many students need to get in line to make 9?** 5 students Ask 5 students to join the line.
- **What doubles plus 1 fact does this show?** 4 + 5 = 9
- Repeat for other doubles plus 1 facts.

Review Math Vocabulary
- Write 3 + 4 on the board.
- **How do I finish this addition sentence?** Write =, or equals, 7. Finish the addition sentence.
- Circle the equals sign. **What is this called?** an equals sign **What does it mean?** It means that 3 + 4 is the same amount as 7.
- Circle the 7. **What is this called?** the sum

Visual Vocabulary Cards
Use Visual Vocabulary Cards 16 and 47 to reinforce the vocabulary reviewed in this lesson. (The Define/Example/Ask routine is printed on the back of each card.)

Spiral Review Chapters 1–10

Write each total. Then make the bar graph and answer the questions.

Favorite Color		
Subject	Tally	Total
Blue	卌 IIII	9
Green	卌	5
Orange	卌 II	7
Purple	II	2

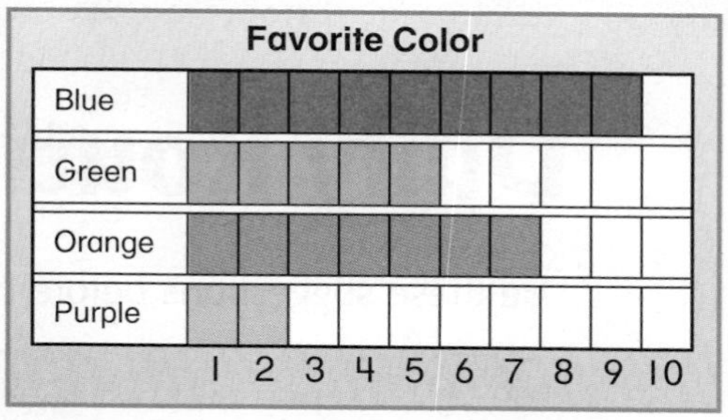

8. Which color is liked most? blue

9. Which color is liked least? purple

10. Do more students like green or orange? orange

Use the number line. Add.

0 1 2 3 4 5 6 7 8 9 10 11 12

11. 2 + 7 = 9 **12.** 1 + 4 = 5 **13.** 9 + 3 = 12

Write the time.

14. 

half past 3

15. 

10 : 30

16. 

half past 9

Spiral Review

Reviews Chapters 1 to 10

Objective: Review and assess mastery of skills and concepts from previous chapters.

Resources for Review

Based on student results, refer to these lessons for remediation.

- **Exercises 8–10: Lesson 4-6** (p. 137)
- **Exercises 11–13: Lesson 5-5** (p. 165)
- **Exercises 14–16: Lesson 7-3** (p. 217)

LESSON 10-5

Use Doubles to Subtract

Lesson Planner

Objective

Relate doubles addition facts to subtraction facts.

Review Vocabulary

subtraction sentence

Resources

Materials: string or masking tape, dominoes

Manipulatives: two-colored counters

Literature Connection: *Double the Ducks* by Stuart J. Murphy

Teacher Technology

TeacherWorks • Concepts in Motion • Math Songs Track 11 Lesson Plan

Focus on Math Background

This lesson focuses on helping students apply the doubles strategy to solve related subtraction facts. For example, if the students know that $4 + 4 = 8$, they can use this fact to calculate $8 - 4 = 4$. This type of understanding not only develops computational fluency and flexibility with numbers, but also fosters algebraic reasoning by helping students find patterns and relationships among number operations like addition and subtraction.

Daily Routine

Use these suggestions before beginning the lesson on p. 329.

5-Minute Check

(Reviews Lesson 10-4)

Draw a picture to solve.

Lisa has 5 books. Aldo has 15. How many more books does Aldo have? 10 books

Problem of the Day

Laura reads 5 pages every night before she goes to bed. How many days will it take her to finish a 40-page book? How did you find your answer?

8 days; count by fives: 5, 10, 15, 20, 25, 30, 35, 40

LINE UP As you prepare for recess, lunch, or dismissal, ask an even number of students to line up. Once the students are in line, have them split to form two equal lines.

- **What doubles subtraction sentence did you model?** Sample answer: $6 - 3 = 3$
- Repeat until all students are lined up.

Review Math Vocabulary

- Ask students to name an addition sentence with doubles. Write it on the board.
- **What is a subtraction sentence that uses the same numbers as this addition sentence?** See students' work.
- Explain that subtraction sentences are related to addition sentences. **Where is the greatest number in an addition sentence?** at the end **Where is the greatest number in a subtraction sentence?** at the beginning

Differentiated Instruction

Small Group Options

Option 1 LOGICAL

Gifted and Talented AL

Materials: blue number cube, connecting cubes

- Each student rolls a number cube and writes five missing number subtraction problems using that number.
- Students exchange papers and solve each other's problems, using patterns.
- Have students work together to check each answer by using addition. You may want to allow students to use connecting cubes to help with arithmetic.

8 - ___ = 6
8 - ___ = 2
8 - ___ = 8
8 - ___ = 3
8 - ___ = 4

Option 2 VISUAL/SPATIAL

English Language Learners ELL

Core Vocabulary: seek, behind, left
Common Use Verbs: hide

Do Math This lesson adapts "Hide and Seek" into "Seek and Hide" to engage students in using addition to help them subtract.

- Ask 8 students to come up to the front.
- Explain that each student seek (or look for) a partner and hold their hand.
- Show how 4 pairs make 8 in all. Write 4 + 4 = 8 on the board.
- Ask one student from each pair to hide behind their partner.
- Explain now there are only 4 students left.
- Model writing the number sentence on the board (8 – 4 = 4)
- Continue with "Seek and Hide" using other students or manipulatives.

Independent Work Options

Option 1 VISUAL/SPATIAL

Early Finishers OL AL

Materials: index cards, markers or crayons

Create a set of index cards that have a doubles addition fact and the related subtraction fact.

- Have each student choose a card.
- Students should copy and illustrate both facts on their own paper.

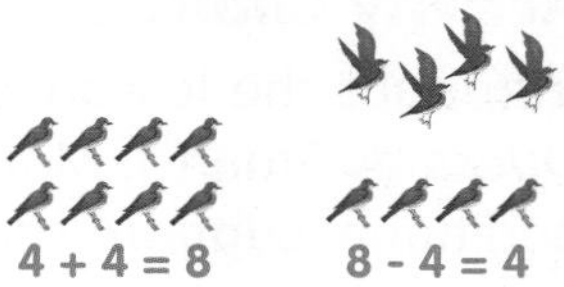

Option 2

Student Technology

Math Online macmillanmh.com

Math Songs, "The Addition Boogie" Track 11 • Math Adventures

Option 3

Learning Station: Science (p. 313H)

Direct students to the Science Learning Station for more opportunities to explore and extend the lesson concept.

Option 4

Problem-Solving Practice

Reinforce problem-solving skills and strategies with the Problem-Solving Practice worksheet.

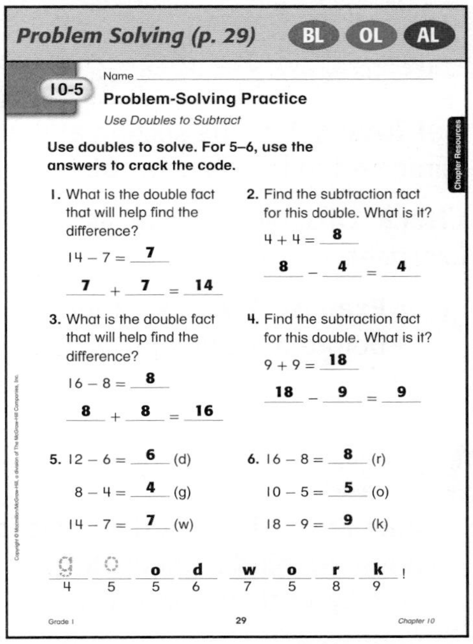

Problem Solving (p. 29) BL OL AL

10-5 Name ______________

Problem-Solving Practice
Use Doubles to Subtract

Use doubles to solve. For 5–6, use the answers to crack the code.

1. What is the double fact that will help find the difference?
   14 – 7 = **7**
   7 + **7** = **14**

2. Find the subtraction fact for this double. What is it?
   4 + 4 = **8**
   8 – **4** = **4**

3. What is the double fact that will help find the difference?
   16 – 8 = **8**
   8 + **8** = **16**

4. Find the subtraction fact for this double. What is it?
   9 + 9 = **18**
   18 – **9** = **9**

5. 12 – 6 = **6** (d)
   8 – 4 = **4** (g)
   14 – 7 = **7** (w)

6. 16 – 8 = **8** (r)
   10 – 5 = **5** (o)
   18 – 9 = **9** (k)

g	o	o	d	w	o	r	k	!
4	5	5	6	7	5	8	9	

Chapter Resources

Grade 1 29 Chapter 10

1 Introduce

Activity Choice 1 • Hands-On

Use string or masking tape to make two large circles on the floor at the front of the room. The circles should touch but not overlap.

- Call on four students to sit or stand in each circle.
- **How many students are there in all?** 8 students
- **What is the addition sentence?** 4 + 4 = 8
- Have four students leave a circle. **What subtraction sentence tells what happened?** 8 − 4 = 4

Activity Choice 2 • Literature

Introduce the lesson with *Double the Ducks* by Stuart J. Murphy. For additional support, see p. TR56.

2 Teach

Draw a blank domino frame on the overhead.

- Put three counters on one side of the domino and three counters on the other side. **How many counters are there in all?** 6 counters
- **What addition sentence does this model?** 3 + 3 = 6 Write the sentence on the overhead.
- Take three counters away. **There were 6 counters. I took 3 away. What subtraction sentence does this model?** 6 − 3 = 3 Write the sentence on the overhead.
- **How are the addition sentence and the subtraction sentence alike and different?** Sample answers: They have the same numbers; they both contain doubles. The greatest number is at the end of the addition sentence, but it is at the beginning of the subtraction sentence.

Get Ready Use the section at the top of p. 329 to reinforce the lesson concept.

Check Observe students as you work through Exercises 1–7 as a class.

Exercise 7 Assess student comprehension before assigning practice exercises.

COMMON ERROR!

There are addition and subtraction facts in this lesson. Remind students to read the problems carefully so they know which operation to use.

Name ______________________

Use Doubles to Subtract

Get Ready

Main Idea

I will use doubles facts to subtract.

You can use addition facts to help you subtract.

I think 6 + 6 = 12 so 12 − 6 = 6.

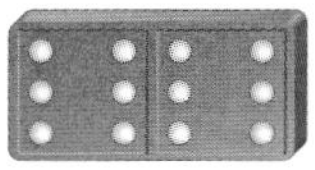

6 + 6 = **12**

12 − 6 = **6**

Check

7. Sample answer: If I know the addition fact then I also know the related subtraction fact.

Add the doubles facts. Then subtract.

1. 2 + 2 = **4**
   4 − 2 = **2**

2. 3 + 3 = 6
   6 − 3 = 3

3. 5 + 5 = 10 10 − 5 = 5

4. 1 + 1 = 2 2 − 1 = 1

5. 9 + 9 = 18 18 − 9 = 9

6. 7 + 7 = 14 14 − 7 = 7

7. Talk About It How can using addition help you subtract?

Reteach (p. 26) BL

10-5 Name ______

Reteach

Use Doubles to Subtract

Use doubles to help you subtract.

There are 8 gray counters and 8 white counters.

8 + 8 = **16**

Use the same doubles fact to subtract. Cross out 8 counters to subtract.

16 − 8 = **8**

Add the double. Then subtract.

1. 4 + 4 = **8** 8 − 4 = **4**
2. 7 + 7 = **14** 14 − 7 = **7**
3. 9 + 9 = **18** 18 − 9 = **9**
4. 6 + 6 = **12** 12 − 6 = **6**

Grade 1 26 Chapter 10

Skills Practice (p. 27) OL

10-5 Name ______

Skills Practice

Use Doubles to Subtract

Add or subtract. Then draw a line to match the related facts.

1. 4 + 4 = 8	2 − 1 = **1**
2. 7 + 7 = **14**	14 − 7 = **7**
3. 2 + 2 = **4**	8 − 4 = **4**
4. 1 + 1 = **2**	4 − 2 = **2**
5. 5 + 5 = **10**	6 − 3 = **3**
6. 9 + 9 = **18**	16 − 8 = **8**
7. 3 + 3 = **6**	12 − 6 = **6**
8. 8 + 8 = **16**	10 − 5 = **5**
9. 6 + 6 = **12**	18 − 9 = **9**

Grade 1 27 Chapter 10

Chapter Resources

Practice

Add the doubles facts. Then subtract.

8. 10 + 10 = 20
20 − 10 = 10

9. 4 + 4 = 8
8 − 4 = 4

10. 8 + 8 = 16 16 − 8 = 8

11. 6 + 6 = 12 12 − 6 = 6

Add or subtract.
Then draw a line to match the doubles fact.

12. 10 + 10 = 20	14 − 7 = 7
13. 9 + 9 = 18	16 − 8 = 8
14. 8 + 8 = 16	18 − 9 = 9
15. 7 + 7 = 14	20 − 10 = 10

Problem Solving

16. Number Sense A box has 12 crayons. You can only see 6. How many crayons are hidden in the box?

12 − 6 = 6 crayons

Math at Home Activity: Give your child a doubles fact. Have them give you a related subtraction fact.

Enrich (p. 30) AL

10-5 Name

Enrich
Amazing Doubles Facts!

Solve the subtraction sentences. Follow the doubles facts to win. Trace your path with a crayon.

START

14 − 7 = 7 15 − 4 = 11 11 − 5 = 6

16 − 6 = 10 4 − 2 = 2 13 − 6 = 7 16 − 8 = 8 16 − 8 = 8

12 − 6 = 6

6 − 3 = 3

18 − 9 = 9

20 − 2 = 18

WIN!

Grade 1 30 Chapter 10

Homework Practice (p. 28) OL

10-5 Name

Homework Practice
Use Doubles to Subtract

Add the double. Then subtract.

1. 4 + 4 = 8
8 − 4 = 4

2. 9 + 9 = 18
18 − 9 = 9

3. 8 + 8 = 16
16 − 8 = 8

4. 7 + 7 = 14
14 − 7 = 7

5. 3 + 3 = 6
6 − 3 = 3

6. 6 + 6 = 12
12 − 6 = 6

7. 5 + 5 = 10
10 − 5 = 5

8. 2 + 2 = 4
4 − 2 = 2

9. Fill in the domino. Write the related subtraction fact.

6 + 6 = 12
12 − 6 = 6

9 + 9 = 18
18 − 9 = 9

Grade 1 28 Chapter 10

BL Alternate Teaching Strategy

If students do not understand the concept of using doubles to subtract . . .

Then use one of the following reteach options.

1. CRM **Daily Reteach Worksheet** (p. 26)
2. **Find a Pattern** Help students answer Exercises 3–6. Then ask students to look for a pattern for the second and third numbers in the subtraction sentences. Ask if they see why these are called doubles subtraction facts.

3 Practice

Differentiate practice using these leveled assignments for Exercises 8–16.

Level	Assignment
BL Below/ Approaching Level	Complete with connecting cubes.
OL On Level	Complete the exercises independently.
AL Above/ Beyond Level	Write and answer the two doubles subtraction facts not given in the exercises.

4 Assess

Formative Assessment

- **Is there a doubles subtraction fact that starts with the number 15? Explain.** Sample answer: No, because there is no doubles addition fact with a sum of 15.

WRITING IN MATH Have students explain a doubles subtraction sentence in their own words. Ask students to use counters to justify their thinking.

Quick Check **Are students continuing to struggle with using doubles to subtract?**

If Yes → Strategic Intervention Guide (p. 90–93)

If No → Independent Work Options (p. 329B)
CRM Skills Practice Worksheet (p. 27)
CRM Enrich Worksheet (p. 30)

LESSON 10-6

Relate Addition and Subtraction

Lesson Planner

Objective

Identify patterns in related addition and subtraction sentences.

Review Vocabulary

pattern

Resources

Materials: number-sentence strips

Manipulatives: connecting cubes

Literature Connection: *Domino Addition* by Lynette Long, Ph.D.

Alternate Lessons: Use "Lift the Bowl" on pages 181 and 182 of *Math Their Way* to provide practice relating addition and subtraction facts.
Use *IMPACT Mathematics*: Unit B to provide practice with related addition and subtraction facts.

Teacher Technology

TeacherWorks • Concepts in Motion • Math Songs Track 11 Lesson Plan

Focus on Math Background

Relating addition to subtraction is the mathematical emphasis in this lesson. When students are able to explain and understand a relationship such as the following—"If 4 + 8 = 12 then 12 − 8 = 4"—they can instantaneously recall any subtraction fact to 20 by simply figuring out the related addition fact. By learning to recall subtraction facts in this way, students learn to make connections instead of relying solely on rote memorization.

Daily Routine

Use these suggestions before beginning the lesson on p. 331.

5-Minute Check

(Reviews Lesson 10-5)

Find the difference and write the related doubles addition fact:

1. 18 − 9 = _____ 9; 9 + 9 = 18
2. 8 − 4 = _____ 4; 4 + 4 = 8
3. 6 − 3 = _____ 3; 3 + 3 = 6

Problem of the Day

Mario picked 8 carrots from the garden on Tuesday. He picked 8 beets from the garden on Friday. How many vegetables did Mario pick in all? 16 vegetables

LINE UP As you prepare for recess, lunch, or dismissal, ask students to think of a number from 0 to 10. Begin with 0 and have each student in order add his or her number to the previous total. Help students find the next multiple of 10 and then add the remainder. After a student makes a mistake, begin at 0 with the next student.

Review Math Vocabulary

- Have students follow your **pattern.**
- Clap three times and snap your fingers twice. Wait for student response. **What was my pattern?** Clap 3 times and snap twice.
- Continue with other clap and snap patterns.
- Remind students that a pattern is an order that a set of objects or numbers follows over and over.

Visual Vocabulary Cards

Use Visual Vocabulary Card 33 to reinforce the vocabulary reviewed in this lesson. (The Define/Example/Ask routine is printed on the back of each card.)

pattern

Differentiated Instruction

Small Group Options

Option 1 Below Level (BL)

LINGUISTIC

Materials: colored construction paper, scissors

- Students will work together to make fact families.
- Assign a fact family with numbers from 0 to 20 to each small group.
- Have students write all the possible addition and subtraction sentences for the fact family.
- Groups then assemble the fact family by drawing and cutting out the numbers and the plus, minus, and equals signs from colored construction paper.

Option 2 English Language Learners (ELL)

LINGUISTIC

Materials: chart paper, marker, number cards 2–20, paper, pencil
Core Vocabulary: list, different ways, your own
Common Use Verb: make

Write Math This strategy helps students use graphic organizers and makes language comprehensible so they can solve problems.

- Post any number between 2–20. Brainstorm a list of ways to represent this number, with examples. List both on a chart.
- Prompt as necessary: (number) + (number) = (number); (number) – (number) = (number); tallies; ten-frames; coins, dominos; word for number; fact families; pictures.
- Say: "You are going to ***make* your own list**."
- Ask one person/pair to pull a number from the cards.
- Have partners work together writing five different ways to show this number on paper.

Independent Work Options

Option 1 Early Finishers (OL) (AL)

SPATIAL

Materials: markers or crayons, pattern blocks

- Have students write a subtraction sentence and trace pattern blocks to illustrate the sentence.
- Below their illustration students should write, "How many are left?"
- Have students write their answer next to the question.

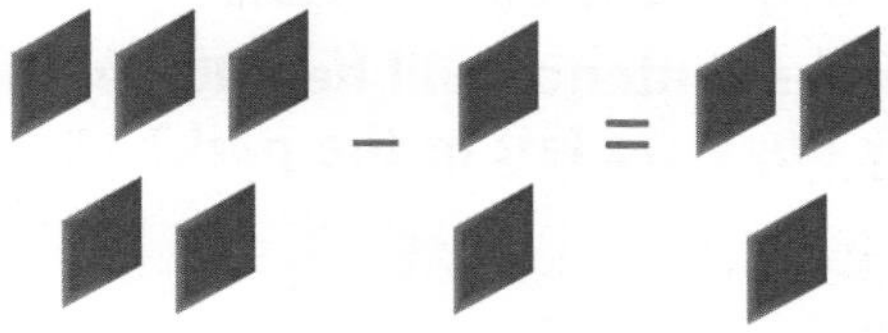

Option 2 Student Technology

Math Online macmillanmh.com

Option 3 Learning Station: Art (p. 313G)

Direct students to the Art Learning Station for more opportunities to explore and extend the lesson concept.

1 Introduce

Activity • Review

Read the following story aloud:

Rose watched some dogs playing in the park. Some of the dogs had to go home. Rose wants to know how many dogs are left in the park.

- **Will Rose add or subtract?** subtract **Use words to justify your thinking.** Sample answer: *Left* means to subtract.
- Ask students to act out the story in front of the class to confirm that subtraction is correct.

Now read this story aloud:

Rose saw 13 dogs playing in the park. Eight of the dogs had to go home. Rose wants to know how many dogs are left in the park.

- **What number sentence will help Rose find how many dogs are left in the park?** $13 - 8 = 5$

2 Teach

Have students read the problem on p. 333. Guide them through the problem-solving steps.

Understand Using the questions, review what students know and what they need to find.

Plan Have them discuss their strategy.

Solve Guide students to write a number sentence to solve the problem.

- **What do you know?** There are 18 students and 9 flowers.
- **Is this an addition or a subtraction?** subtraction **Use words to justify your thinking.** Sample answer: You have to find the difference between students and flowers.

Check Have students look back at the problem to make sure that the answers fit the facts given and is reasonable.

- **What does your answer tell?** The number of flowers she still needs

COMMON ERROR!

Students may incorrectly set up each number sentence. Remind students that the greatest number is always first in a subtraction sentence.

Name ____________________

Problem-Solving Investigation

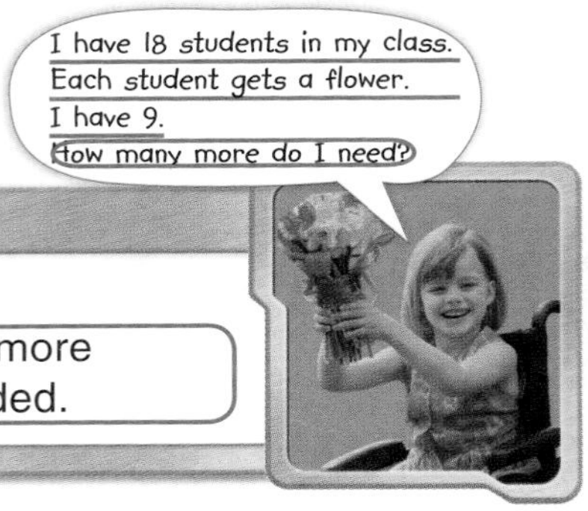

Main Idea

I will choose a strategy to solve a problem.

Your Mission:
Find how many more flowers are needed.

Understand

What do I know? Underline what you know.

What do I need to find? Circle it.

Plan

How will I solve the problem?

Solve

One way is to write a number sentence.

18 (−) 9 = 9

9 more flowers are needed.

Check

Look back.

Is my answer reasonable?

Check students' explanations.

Reteach (pp. 36–37) BL

10-7 Name ____________

Reteach (1)

Problem-Solving Investigation: Choose a Strategy

The lunchroom has 14 juice boxes.
19 students ask for juice boxes.
How many more juice boxes does the lunchroom need?

Step 1 **Understand**	**What do I know?** There are 14 juice boxes. 19 students want juice. **What do I need to find out?** How many more juice boxes are needed.
Step 2 **Plan**	**How will I find how many juice boxes are needed?** I can write a number sentence.
Step 3 **Solve**	**Write a number sentence.** 19 (−) 14 = 5 The lunchroom needs 5 more juice boxes.
Step 4 **Check**	**Look back.** Did I write a number sentence? yes Does my answer tell me how many more juice boxes are needed? yes

Grade 1 36 Chapter 10

Skills Practice (p. 38) OL

10-7 Name ____________

Skills Practice

Problem-Solving Investigation: Choose a Strategy

Choose a strategy. Solve.

Problem-Solving Strategies
- Choose the operation
- Draw a picture
- Write a number sentence

Show your work here.

1. 13 students are on the basketball team. 4 fewer students are on the volleyball team. How many students are on the volleyball team? 9 students
2. Stef has 8 pencils. Rich has 4 pencils. Todd has 2 pencils. How many total pencils do they have? 14 pencils
3. 20 students signed up for the Clean Up program. 6 students cleaned from 8:00 to 10:00. 4 students cleaned from 10:00 to 12:00. How many students cleaned? 10 students

Grade 1 38 Chapter 10

Mixed Problem Solving

Problem-Solving Strategies
- Write a number sentence
- Draw a picture
- Find a pattern

Choose a strategy. Solve.

1. Pablo has 5 leaves.
   Kaitlyn has 5 leaves.
   How many leaves do they have altogether?

10 leaves

2. Martin found 7 shells.
   Pam found 8 shells.
   How many shells did they find in all?

15 shells

3. Lina had 12 erasers.
   She gave her friends some of her erasers.
   Now she only has 6 erasers.
   How many erasers did she give away?

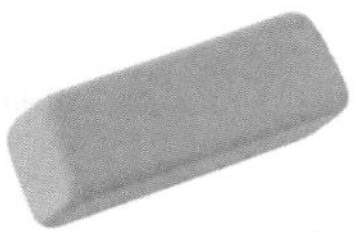

6 erasers

4. 14 bees were outside the hive.
   Then 7 bees went inside the hive.
   How many bees were left outside?

7 bees

Math at Home Activity: Take advantage of problem-solving opportunites during daily routines such as riding in the car, bedtime, doing laundry, putting away groceries, planning schedule, and so on.

Enrich (p. 40) AL

10-7 Name ____
Enrich
Follow the Chain

Follow the chain. Write your answer.

1. 12 +6 −0 +2 = 20
2. 10 +3 +5 −3 = 15
3. 13 −3 +2 +6 = 18
4. 9 +1 +10 −0 = 20
5. 8 +1 +1 +5 = 15
6. 15 −7 +3 −4 +7 = 14
7. 16 −9 +6 −4 +7 = 16
8. 7 +9 −8 +4 +6 = 18
9. 6 +5 −8 +9 +3 = 15
10. 14 −7 +8 −7 +5 = 13

Grade 1 40 Chapter 10

Homework Practice (p. 39) OL

10-7 Name ____
Homework Practice
Problem-Solving Investigation: Choose a Strategy

Choose a strategy. Solve.

Problem-Solving Strategies
- Choose the operation
- Draw a picture
- Write a number sentence

Show your work here.

1. Lisa earned 5 dollars. Zach earned 6 dollars. Jessie earned 4 dollars. How much did they earn altogether? 15 dollars
2. 18 birds sat in a tree. 9 of them flew away. How many birds are still in the tree? 9 birds
3. Nan can hold her breath for 20 seconds. Rudy can hold his breath for 17 seconds. How much longer can Nan hold her breath than Rudy? 3 seconds
4. 16 apples were on the tree. 8 fell off. How many apples are still on the tree? 8 apples

Grade 1 39 Chapter 10

BL Alternate Teaching Strategy

If students have trouble choosing a strategy . . .

Then use one of the following reteach options.

1. CRM **Daily Reteach Worksheet** (pp. 36–37)
2. **Get Organized** Have students list every step in the problem-solving process in their Math Journal. Discuss each step with students and give them an example to include in their journal.

3 Practice

Mixed Problem-Solving

Exercises 1–2 are best modeled with manipulatives.

Exercises 3–4 can be solved by drawing a picture or writing a number sentence.

4 Assess

Formative Assessment

Thirteen seagulls were on the beach. Six seagulls flew out to sea. **How many seagulls were left on the beach?** 7 seagulls

- **How did you solve the problem?** Sample answers: wrote an addition sentence; drew a picture
- **Why did you choose this strategy?** See students' work.

WRITING IN MATH Have students describe a situation in which they would use a number sentence to solve a problem.

Quick Check **Are students continuing to struggle with choosing a strategy?**

If Yes → Small Group Options (p. 333B)

If No → Independent Work Options (p. 333B)

CRM Skills Practice Worksheet (p. 38)

CRM Enrich Worksheet (p. 40)

LESSON 10-8

Fact Families

Lesson Planner

Objective

Identify patterns in fact families.

Review Vocabulary

fact family

Resources

Manipulatives: connecting cubes

Literature Connection: *One Moose, Twenty Mice* by Clare Beaton

Alternate Lesson: Use *IMPACT Mathematics*: Unit G to provide practice with fact families.

Teacher Technology

TeacherWorks • Concepts in Motion • Math Songs Track 12 Lesson Plan

Focus on Math Background

In this lesson, students focus on understanding fact families. Students will learn all of the ways that a set of related numbers, such as 4, 7, and 11, can be arranged into a family of facts—$4 + 7 = 11$, $7 + 4 = 11$, $11 - 7 = 4$, or $11 - 4 = 7$. This clustering method helps students more easily commit to memory an otherwise seemingly unrelated set of number facts.

Daily Routine

Use these suggestions before beginning the lesson on p. 335.

5-Minute Check

(Reviews Lesson 10-7)

Fifteen children were invited to a party. There were only 10 cups. How many more cups were needed?

1. What number sentence will help you solve the problem? $15 - 10 = 5$
2. What is the answer? 5 more cups

Problem of the Day

A survey shows that 8 students like to play basketball and 6 students like to play soccer. How many more students like to play basketball than soccer? 2 more students

LINE UP Have students wearing the same color, such as blue, line up. Count the students aloud. Then have students wearing a different color, such as red, line up.

- **What addition sentence did we make? What numbers are in this fact family? Name all the number sentences for this fact family.** See students' work.

Review Math Vocabulary

Draw a house on the board containing the three numbers from a **fact family.**

- Explain that these three numbers make a fact family. A fact family is addition sentences and subtraction sentences that use the same three numbers.
- Have students name a fact that is made up of the three numbers in the fact family's house.

Visual Vocabulary Cards

Use Visual Vocabulary Card 18 to reinforce the vocabulary introduced in this lesson. (The Define/Example/Ask routine is printed on the back of each card.)

fact family

Create the Book

Guide students to create their book.

- Have them fold the page in half.
- Ask them to write their name on page A.
- Explain that page A is the front cover and page D is the back cover. If necessary, have them practice flipping through the book in order.
- Guide them in reading the information and word problems on each of the pages.

Use the Student Pages

Have students work individually or in pairs to complete the problems on pages C–D.

Page C Students may not realize that this is a subtraction problem. Make sure a group of students act it out before attempting the problem.

Page D Have students count carefully. Tell them that one of the addends is the number of red stripes and the other addend is the number of white stripes.

WRITING IN MATH Have students write and answer a subtraction question about the stripes on the U.S. flag.

Extend the Activity

Have students use the Internet or the library to research one of the symbols. Gather the facts and create a poster.

Chapter Review/Test

FOLDABLES® Dinah Zike's Foldables

Use these lesson suggestions to incorporate the Foldables during the chapter. Students can then use their Foldable to review for the test.

Lesson 10-6 Discuss the relationship between addition and subtraction and record student observations and comments under the tab. Give specific examples.

Lesson 10-8 Under the Lesson 8 tab of the Foldable, write addition sentences and corresponding subtraction sentences.

Lesson 10-9 Show several different ways in which students can make the same number.

Vocabulary Review

Review chapter vocabulary using one of the following options.

- **Visual Vocabulary Card** (18)
- **eGlossary** at macmillanmh.com

Vocabulary Test

CRM **Chapter 10 Resource Masters** (p. 55)
Assess student comprehension of the chapter vocabulary with the Vocabulary Test.

Math Online **Chapter Test**
Alternative summative assessment options are available online at macmillanmh.com.

Name ____________________

Vocabulary

1. Circle the answer that shows a fact family.

(a.)	b.
7 + 4 = 11	6 + 5 = 11
4 + 7 = 11	5 + 6 = 11
11 − 4 = 7	4 + 6 = 11
11 − 7 = 4	6 + 4 = 11

Concepts

Draw the missing dots to show a double.
Write the doubles fact.

2. 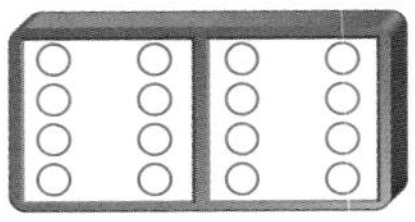

8 + 8 = 16

3. 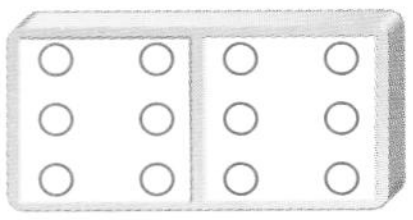

6 + 6 = 12

Draw the counters. Then add.

4. 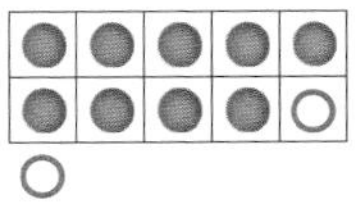

9 + 2 = 11, because
9 + 1 + 1 = 11 and
10 + 1 = 11

5. 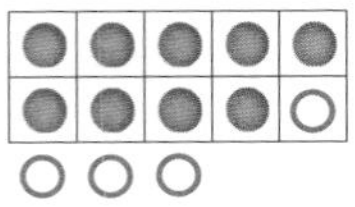

9 + 4 = 13, because
9 + 1 + 3 = 13 and
10 + 3 = 13

Chapter 10 Project

Addition Strategy Cards

Have students discuss the results of their completed chapter project as a class. Assess their work using the Chapter Project rubric found in Chapter 10 Resource Masters on p. 60.

Complete the fact family.

6.

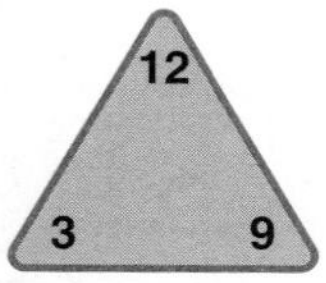

9 + 3 = 12   12 − 3 = 9

3 + 9 = 12   12 − 9 = 3

Add the doubles. Then subtract.

7. 7 + 7 = 14   14 − 7 = 7

8. 2 + 2 = 4

4 − 2 = 2

Find each missing number.

9. 12 − 5 = 7

5 + 7 = 12

10. 14 − 9 = 5

9 + 5 = 14

Write ways to make the number. Sample answers:

11.

Part	Part
6	9
Whole	
15	

Part	Part
9	6
Whole	
15	

Part	Part
7	8
Whole	
15	

Problem Solving

12. Adam hung 8 pictures in two rows.
He hung 4 pictures in the top row.
How many did he hang in the bottom row? 4

Summative Assessment

Use these alternate leveled chapter tests to differentiate assessment for the specific needs of your students.

Leveled Chapter 10 Tests			
Form	**Type**	**Level**	**CRM Pages**
1	Multiple Choice	BL	62–63
2A	Multiple Choice	OL	64–65
2B	Multiple Choice	OL	66–67
2C	Free Response	AL	68–69
2D	Free Response	AL	70–71

BL = below/approaching grade level
OL = on grade level
AL = above/beyond grade level

ExamView Assessment Suite Customize and create multiple versions of your Chapter Test and their test answer keys.

Data-Driven Decision-Making

Based on the results of the Chapter Review/Test, use the following to review concepts that continue to present students with problems.

Exercises	State/Local Standards	What's the Math?	Error Analysis	Resources for Review
1 **6** **9–10**		Identify fact families in order to solve addition and subtraction problems.	Does not understand addition and subtraction fact family.	Strategic Intervention Guide (p. 90) CRM Chapter 10 Resource Masters (Reteach Worksheets) **Math Online** Concepts in Motion Math Adventures
2–3 **7–8** **12**		Identify doubles and doubles plus 1 facts to solve addition and subtraction problems.	Does not understand doubles. Does not add or subtract correctly.	
4–5		Make a 10 to add.	Does not draw counters correctly. Does not add correctly.	
11		Make a number in different ways.	Does not write the correct fact families.	

Test Practice

Formative Assessment

- Use Student Edition pp. 345–346 as practice and cumulative review. The questions are written in the same style as many state tests.
- You can use these two pages to benchmark student progress, or as an alternative homework assignment.

Additional practice pages can be found in the Chapter 10 Resource Masters.

CRM Chapter 10 Resource Masters
Cumulative Test Practice
- Multiple Choice format (pp. 62–67, 72)
- Free Response format (pp. 68–71, 73)

ExamView Assessment Suite Create practice worksheets or tests that align to state standards.

Math Online
For additional standards practice, visit macmillanmh.com.

Name ______________________________

Listen as your teacher reads each problem.
Choose the correct answer.

1.

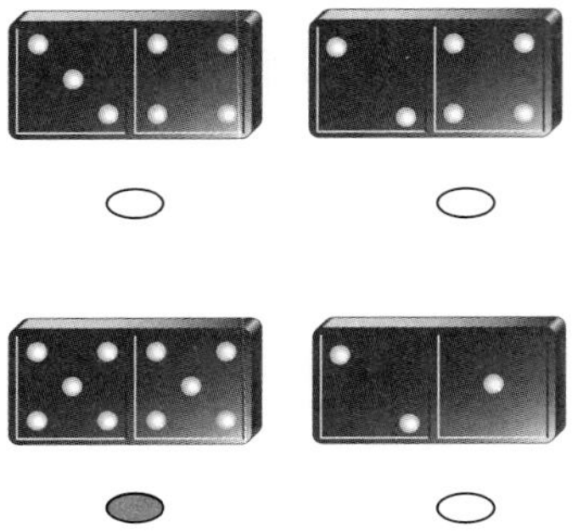

4. 7 + 5 = 12

7 − 5 = 2 ○ | 12 − 7 = 5 ● | 12 − 12 = 0 ○ | 5 − 2 = 3 ○

2. 11 − 7 = 4

11 − 4 = 7 ● | 7 − 4 = 3 ○ | 4 − 4 = 0 ○ | 11 − 0 = 11 ○

5. 3 + 7 = 10

6 + 4 ● | 11 − 2 ○ | 3 + 6 ○ | 5 + 4 ○

3. 16 36 12 24

○ 36 24 16 12
○ 16 36 12 24
● 12 16 24 36
○ 24 12 36 16

6. 30 40 50 60

61 ○ | 65 ○ | 70 ● | 80 ○

Test-Taking Tips

For the Teacher

- Preview the test or each section of a test with students before they begin working.
- Before collecting tests, it may be helpful to go through the completed tests as a class to teach students to proof their work.

For the Student

- Suggest that students take deep breaths or put their pencils down and wiggle their toes if they get nervous during a test.

7.

10.

8 + 4 = 12 ○ 6 + 6 = 12 ○

5 + 5 = 10 ○ 4 + 4 = 8 ●

8.

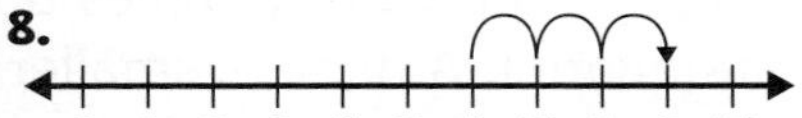

8 ○ 9 ● 10 ○ 12 ○

11. Ty found 6 shells.
Louis found 8 shells.
How many did they find in all?

14 shells

9.

$$\begin{array}{r} 3 \\ 7 \\ +\ 1 \\ \hline \end{array}$$

3 ○ 9 ○

10 ○ 11 ●

12. Jade has 13 stars.
She gave some to Kei.
Now she has 8 left.
How many stars did Jade give Kei?

5 stars

STOP

Test Directions for Teachers

Read the following direction to students before they begin. Then read each question followed by a pause to allow students time to work and choose an answer. The first test item can be worked as a class example.

- **Write your name at the top of the page.**
- **I am going to read each question to you. Listen carefully to the entire question before you choose an answer.**

Multiple Choice

1. Look at the group of dominoes. Which domino shows doubles?
2. Which subtraction fact is related to 11 − 7 = 4?
3. Look at the group of numbers. Which group shows the numbers in order?
4. Which subtraction fact is related to 7 + 5 = 12?
5. Look at the number sentence. Which shows another way to get 10?
6. Look at the group of numbers. What number comes next?

- **Turn the page over.**

7. Listen to the story. Beth started piano lessons at 4:00. Which clock shows 4:00?
8. Look at the number line. What is the sum?
9. Listen to the story. Paul went looking for insects. First, he saw 3 beetles. Next, he saw 7 ants. Last, he saw 1 caterpillar. How many insects did Paul see in all?
10. Look at the domino. Which addition sentence matches the domino?

Short Response

11. Ty found 6 shells. Louis found 8 shells. How many did they find in all?
12. Jade has 13 stars. She gave some to Kei and has 8 left. How many stars did Jade give Kei?

CHAPTER 11

Chapter Overview

Chapter-at-a-Glance

In Chapter 11, the emphasis is on identifying coins, finding the value of mixed sets of coins, counting money, making even exchanges of coins, and comparing the value of sets of coins to prices.

Lesson	Math Objective	State/Local Standards
11-1 **Pennies and Nickels** (pp. 351–352)	Identify by name and value pennies and nickels.	
11-2 **Pennies and Dimes** (pp. 353–354)	Identify by name and value dimes and pennies.	
11-3 **Pennies, Nickels, and Dimes** (pp. 355–356)	Find the value of a group of dimes, nickels, and pennies.	
11-4 **Counting Money** (pp. 357–358)	Count coins to find their total value.	
11-5 **Problem-Solving Strategy: Act It Out** (pp. 359–360)	Use the *act it out* strategy to solve problems.	
11-6 **Equal Amounts** (pp. 363–364)	Identify different combinations of coins that equal the same value.	
11-7 **Quarters** (pp. 365–368)	Identify the value of a quarter. Count groups of coins.	
11-8 **Problem-Solving Investigation: Choose a Strategy** (pp. 369–370)	Choose the best strategy to solve a problem.	
11-9 **Money Amounts** (pp. 371–372)	Find the value of a mixed set of coins. Compare the value of a set of coins with prices.	

Identify Coins

BIG Idea Mathematical reasoning and problem-solving occur when we purchase something, make change, or exchange one coin for another. One barrier to understanding how to count money is that the size of U.S. coins does not match their value. Twenty-five pennies do not fit inside the space of one quarter. A dime is smaller than a nickel.

Children must also learn how to count coins efficiently, starting with the coin of greatest value and ending with those of the least denomination. First graders need concrete and meaningful practice versus drill and memorization to accomplish these skills.

Algebra Readiness In Lesson 11-9, students prepare for Algebra by comparing the value of different coins. Describing the relationships among coins will introduce equation concepts for greater than, less than, and equal to.

Students prepare for Algebra by using addition when counting money in Lesson 11-4.

Focal Points and Connections

G1-FP4C *Number and Operations* **and** *Algebra:* Children use mathematical reasoning, including ideas such as commutativity and associativity and beginning ideas of tens and ones, to solve two-digit addition and subtraction problems with strategies that they understand and can explain. They solve both routine and nonroutine problems.

Skills Trace
Vertical Alignment

Kindergarten

In kindergarten, students learned to:

- Identify which set is equal to, more than, or less than the other.
- Count, recognize, and name a number of objects up to 30.

First Grade

During this chapter, students learn to:

- Find the total value of a group of dimes, nickels, and pennies.
- Identify the value of a quarter. Count groups of coins.
- Find the value of a mixed set of coins. Compare the value of a set of coins with prices.

After this chapter, students will learn to:

- Use place value with tens and ones. (Chapter 13)
- Read, write, compare, and order whole numbers to 99. (Chapter 13)
- Describe and identify two- and three-dimensional shapes. (Chapter 12)

Second Grade

In second grade, students will learn to:

- Model and solve problems by representing, adding, and subtracting amounts of money.
- Know and use the decimal notation and the dollar and cent symbols for money.
- Solve problems using a combination of coins and bills.

Backmapping and Vertical Alignment

McGraw-Hill's *Math Connects* program was conceived and developed with the final results in mind: student success in Algebra 1 and beyond. The authors, using the **NCTM Focal Points and Focal Connections** as their guide, developed this brand-new series by backmapping from Algebra 1 concepts, and vertically aligning the topics so that they build upon prior skills and concepts and serve as a foundation for future topics.

Math Vocabulary

The following math vocabulary words for Chapter 11 are listed in the glossary of the **Student Edition**. You can find interactive definitions in 13 languages in the **eGlossary** at macmillanmh.com.

cent (¢) (p. 351)

1¢ 1 cent

dime dime = 10¢ or 10 cents (p. 353)

nickel nickel = 5¢ or 5 cents (p. 351)

penny penny = 1¢ or 1 cent (p. 351)

quarter quarter = 25¢ or 25 cents (p. 363)

Visual Vocabulary Cards

Visual Vocabulary Cards Use Visual Vocabulary Cards 6, 15, 29, 34, and 40 to introduce and reinforce the vocabulary in this chapter. (The Define/Example/Ask routine is printed on the back of each card.)

Chapter 11 Chapter Planner

Suggested Pacing		
Instruction	Review and Assessment	TOTAL
9 days	2 days	**11 days**

Diagnostic Assessment
Are You Ready? (p. 348)

	Lesson 11-1 (Pacing: 1 day)	Lesson 11-2 (Pacing: 1 day)	Lesson 11-3 (Pacing: 1 day)
Lesson/ Objective	**Pennies and Nickels** (pp. 351–352) **Objective:** Identify by name and value pennies and nickels.	**Pennies and Dimes** (pp. 353–354) **Objective:** Identify by name and value dimes and pennies.	**Pennies, Nickels, and Dimes** (pp. 355–356) **Objective:** Find the value of a group of dimes, nickels, and pennies.
State/Local Standards			
Math Vocabulary	**cent (¢)**, **penny**, **nickel**	**dime**	
Lesson Resources	**Materials** paper cups, pencils **Manipulatives** coins (pennies, nickels) **Other Resources** CRM Leveled Worksheets (pp. 6–10) Daily Reteach • 5-Minute Check Problem of the Day	**Materials** pennies, dimes, and ten frame (class-size models or on overhead transparency); paper and markers **Manipulatives** coins (pennies, dimes) **Other Resources** CRM Leveled Worksheets (pp. 11–15) Daily Reteach • 5-Minute Check Problem of the Day	**Materials** class set of cards showing coin combinations **Manipulatives** coins (pennies, nickels, dimes) **Other Resources** CRM Leveled Worksheets (pp. 16–20) Daily Reteach • 5-Minute Check Problem of the Day
Technology Math Online	Math Song Track 16 Math Adventures	Math Song Track 16 Math Adventures	Math Song Track 16 Math Adventures
Reaching All Learners	Gifted/Talented, p. 351B AL English Learners, p. 351B ELL Early Finishers, p. 351B OL AL	Gifted/Talented, p. 353B AL English Learners, p. 353B ELL Early Finishers, p. 353B OL AL	Below Level, p. 355B BL English Learners, p. 355B ELL Early Finishers, p. 355B OL AL
Alternate Lessons	*Math Their Way*, pp. 332–333	*Math Their Way*, pp. 332–333	*Math Their Way*, pp. 332–333

KEY
BL Below/Approaching Level
OL On Level
AL Above/Beyond Level
ELL English Learners
SE Student Edition
TE Teacher Edition
CRM Chapter 3 Resource Masters
CD-Rom
Transparency
Flip Chart
Real-World Problem Solving Library

	Lesson 11-4 (Pacing: 1 day)	Lesson 11-5 (Pacing: 1 day)	Lesson 11-6 (Pacing: 1 day)
Lesson/ Objective	**Counting Money** (pp. 357–358) **Objective:** Count coins to find their total value.	**Problem-Solving Strategy** **Act It Out** (pp. 359–360) **Objective:** Use the *act it out* strategy to solve problems.	**Equal Amounts** (pp. 363–364) **Objective:** Identify different combinations of coins that equal the same value.
State/Local Standards			
Math Vocabulary			
Lesson Resources	**Materials** price tags, number line **Manipulatives** coins (dimes, nickels, pennies) **Other Resources** CRM Leveled Worksheets (pp. 21–25) Daily Reteach • 5-Minute Check Problem of the Day	**Manipulatives** coins (dimes, nickels, pennies) **Other Resources** CRM Leveled Worksheets (pp. 26–30) Daily Reteach • 5-Minute Check Problem of the Day *Following a Coin*	**Manipulatives** two-colored counters, coins (dimes, nickels, pennies) **Other Resources** CRM Leveled Worksheets (pp. 31–35) Daily Reteach • 5-Minute Check Problem of the Day
Technology Math Online	Math Songs Track 16 Math Adventures Concepts in Motion		Math Songs Track 16 Concepts in Motion
Reaching All Learners	Gifted/Talented, p. 357B AL English Learners, p. 357B ELL Early Finishers, p. 357B OL AL	Gifted/Talented, p. 359B AL English Learners, p. 359B ELL Early Finishers, p. 359B OL AL	Below Level, p. 363B BL English Learners, p. 363B ELL Early Finishers, p. 363B OL AL
Alternate Lessons	*Math Their Way*, p. 317		*Math Their Way*, pp. 332–333

Formative Assessment
- Mid-Chapter Check (p. 361)
- Spiral Review (p. 362)

Chapter 11 Planner

	Lesson 11-7 (Pacing: 1 day)	Lesson 11-8 (Pacing: 1 day)	Lesson 11-9 (Pacing: 1 day)
Lesson/ Objective	**Quarters** (pp. 365–368) Tech Link **Objective:** Identify the value of a quarter. Count groups of coins.	Problem-Solving Strategy **Choose a Strategy** (pp. 369–370) **Objective:** Choose the best strategy to solve a problem.	**Money Amounts** (pp. 371–372) **Objective:** Find the value of a mixed set of coins. Compare the value of a set of coins with prices.
State/Local Standards			
Math Vocabulary	**quarter**		
Lesson Resources	**Materials** overhead projector **Manipulatives** coins (quarters, dimes, nickels, pennies) **Other Resources** CRM Leveled Worksheets (pp. 36–40) Daily Reteach • 5-Minute Check Problem of the Day	**Manipulatives** coins (quarters, dimes, nickels, pennies) **Other Resources** CRM Leveled Worksheets (pp. 41–45) Daily Reteach • 5-Minute Check Problem of the Day *Following a Coin*	**Materials** toy store catalogs, paper, glue, markers, coin stamps or stickers **Manipulatives** coins (quarters, dimes, nickels, pennies) **Other Resources** CRM Leveled Worksheets (pp. 46–50) Daily Reteach • 5-Minute Check Problem of the Day
Technology Math Online	Math Songs Track 16 Math Tool Chest, Money Level 1 Math Adventures		Math Songs Track 16 Math Adventures
Reaching All Learners	Below Level, p. 365B BL English Learners, p. 365B ELL Early Finishers, p. 365B OL AL	Gifted/Talented, p. 369B AL English Learners, p. 369B ELL Early Finishers, p. 369B OL AL	Gifted/Talented, p. 371B AL English Learners, p. 371B ELL Early Finishers, p. 371B OL AL
Alternate Lessons	*Math Their Way*, pp. 332–333		*Math Their Way*, p. 225

Extra Practice (p. 373)
Game Time (p. 374)
Problem Solving in Social Studies (p. 375)

Summative Assessment
- Chapter Review/Test (p. 377)
- Test Practice (p. 379)

Assessment Options

Diagnostic Assessment

SE *Option 1:* Are You Ready? (p. 348)
Option 2: Online Quiz (macmillanmh.com)
CRM *Option 3:* Diagnostic Test (p. 52)
CRM *Option 4:* Chapter Pretest (p. 53)

Formative Assessment

TE Alternate Teaching Strategies (every lesson)
SE Talk About It (every lesson)
SE Writing in Math (every lesson)
SE Check (every lesson)
TE Line Up (every lesson)
SE Mid-Chapter Check (p. 361)
CRM Mid-Chapter Test (p. 54)

Summative Assessment

SE Chapter Review/Test (pp. 377–378)
SE Test Practice (pp. 379–380)
CRM Vocabulary Test (p. 55)
CRM Leveled Chapter Tests (pp. 62–71)
CRM Cumulative Test Practice (pp. 72–73)
CRM Listening Assessment (pp. 58–59)
CRM Oral Assessment (p. 57)
Exam*View*® Assessment Suite
Advance Tracker

Professional Development

Targeted professional development has been articulated throughout **McGraw-Hill's *Math Connects*** program. The **McGraw-Hill Professional Development Video Library** provides short videos that support the **NCTM Focal Points and Focal Connections**. For more information, visit macmillanmh.com.

Model Lessons

Instructional Strategies

What the Research Says . . .

Randell L. Drum and Wesley G. Petty Jr. (1999) encourage the use of proportionate models to teach children the value of coins:

"The teaching of monetary concepts and processes is necessary to prepare young children for experiences that they are probably already facing in the real world. Because coins are nonproportionate models in terms of the value they represent, they are abstract models for teaching purposes. To offer concrete experiences, teachers must use proportionate models that can be associated with each coin."

Reference: Drum, R. L., & Petty, W. G. (1999) Teaching the value of coins, *Teaching Children Mathematics*, 5, 264.

Teacher Notes

CHAPTER 11

Learning Stations

Cross-Curricular Links

Social Studies

group | LOGICAL, VISUAL/SPATIAL

The Presidents on Our Coins

- Look at the picture on the front of each coin. Which president is pictured there?
- Use a book about presidents to help you. Write your answers on your paper.
- President Abraham Lincoln is on the _____. cent or penny
- President Thomas Jefferson is on the _____. nickel
- President Franklin D. Roosevelt is on the _____. dime
- President George Washington is on the _____. quarter

Teacher Note: Visit the United States Mint's website or additional activities for students.

Materials:

- book about U.S. Presidents
- penny, nickel, dime, quarter
- paper and pencil

Art

individual | LOGICAL, VISUAL/SPATIAL

Design a Coin

- Many artists entered a contest. The winners' artwork was printed on our new quarters.
- Draw enough quarters to equal 75 cents.
- Design each quarter.
- Show your special quarters to classmates.

Materials:

- large circle drawn on paper
- colored pencils

Reading

group | LOGICAL, LINGUISTIC, SOCIAL

Coin Collecting

- Read a book about coin collecting.
- Use a magnifying glass to study real coins.
- Design your own coin. How much is it worth? What symbols or pictures will you put on it? Is it silver or copper?

Materials:

- magnifying glass
- real coins
- paper
- colored pencils
- books about coin collecting

Science

group | VISUAL/ SPATIAL, KINESTHETIC

Weigh In on Pennies

- Put a small object on one side of a balance scale.
- Add pennies to the other side of the scale.
- Stop when the sides of the scale are even.
- Make a chart. Draw a picture of each object you weigh. Write the number of pennies next to it.

Teacher Note: Provide items to weigh such as crayons, pencils, connecting cubes, and base-ten blocks. Challenge students to see if any combinations of coins have the same weight. For example, do two dimes weigh the same as one penny?

Materials:
- paper
- pencil
- pennies
- balance scale
- small objects to weigh

Language Arts

group | LINGUISTIC

Community Quarters

- The U.S. Mint is not an ice cream flavor! It is where money is made.
- Color the quarter for your state. Talk about what is on your state quarter. Talk about why that picture was chosen.
- What would you like to see on a quarter for your town or city? Why?
- Write about what you would put on a quarter for your community. Explain why you chose what you did.
- Draw the quarter.

Materials:
- paper
- pencil
- crayons

Calendar Time

Skip Counting with Coins

Distribute coins and student copies of the calendar for the current month. Have students do each of the following steps as you model them on the class calendar.

- Count by ones and place a penny on each date.
- Count by fives and place a nickel on each date that is a five.
- Count by tens and place a dime on each date that is a ten.

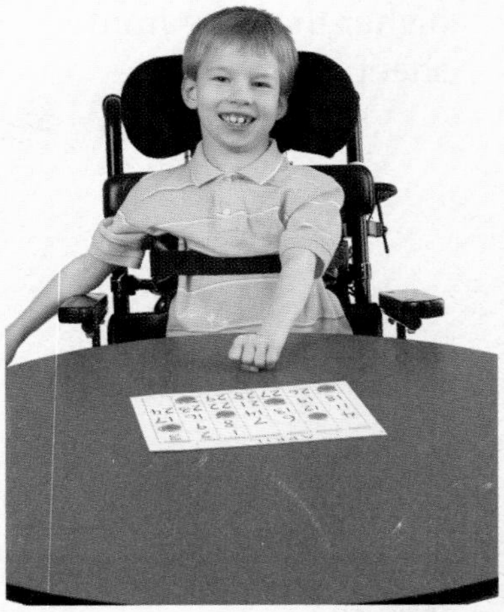

Introduce the Chapter

Real World: How Many?

Share with students that they are going to learn about kinds of coins and how to count money.

- Give students one quarter, one dime, one nickel, and one penny. Explain that people use money to buy things.
- Introduce each coin by name. **Each coin is worth a different number of cents. This is the symbol for cent.** Write ¢ on the chalkboard.
- Tell the value of each coin and have students find the coin and hold it up.

Have students turn to p. 347.

- **How much do the sunflowers cost?** 30 cents
- **Have you ever used money to buy something?** Sample answers: Yes; to buy lunch; to buy a gift

Key Vocabulary

Introduce the key vocabulary in the chapter using the routine below.

Define: A **dime** equals 10 cents.

Example: I used 1 dime to buy a marble.

Ask: What are some ways you have used a dime?

CHAPTER 11 **Identify Coins**

Key Vocabulary
penny 1¢
nickel 5¢
dime 10¢
quarter 25¢

Explore
Each flower costs 30¢. How much would 2 flowers cost?
60 ¢

Chapter 11 three hundred forty-seven 347

FOLDABLES® Study Organizer — Dinah Zike's Foldables

Guide students to create their Layered-Look Book Foldables for counting money.

1. Stack three 8½ × 11 sheets of paper so that the back sheet is one inch higher than the front sheet.

2. Bring the bottom of both sheets upward and align the edges so that all of the layers or tabs are the same distance apart.

3. When all tabs are an equal distance apart, fold the papers and crease well.

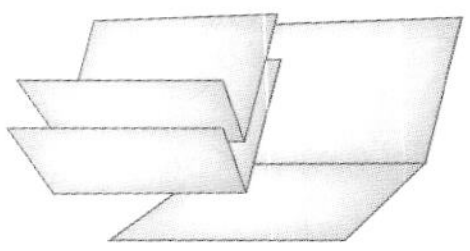

4. Open the papers and glue them together along the *valley* or inner center fold, or staple them along the mountain.

When to Use It *Lessons 11-1, 11-2, 11-3, 11-7 and 11-8. (Additional instructions for using the Foldable with these lessons are found on pp. 361 and 377.)*

Name ____________________

Math Online
Take the Chapter Readiness Quiz at macmillanmh.com.

Are You Ready for Chapter 11?

1. Skip count by 5s.

   5, 10, 15, 20, 25, 30

2. Skip count by 10s.

   10, 20, 30, 40, 50, 60

3. Circle all the pennies.
   Mark an X on the nickels.

4. Kimi is counting her gloves. She skip counts by twos. She counts up to 12. How many pairs of gloves does Kimi have? 6 pairs

5. There are 3 vases. Each vase has 10 flowers. How many flowers in all? 30 flowers

This page checks skills needed for Chapter 11.

Diagnostic Assessment

Check for students' prerequisite skills before beginning the chapter.

- **Option 1:** ***Are You Ready for Chapter 11?***
  SE Student Edition, p. 348
- **Option 2:** ***Online Assessment***
  Math Online macmillanmh.com
- **Option 3:** ***Diagnostic Test***
  CRM Chapter 11 Resource Masters, p. 52

RTI (Response to Intervention)

Apply the Results Based on the results of the diagnostic assessment on p. 348, use the chart below to address individual needs before beginning the chapter.

TIER 3 Intensive Intervention

If students miss four or more of the exercises:

Then use Chapters 3 and 5 of *Math Triumphs*, an intensive math intervention program from McGraw-Hill.

TIER 2 Strategic Intervention below/approaching grade level	TIER 1 On-Level	Above/Beyond Level
If students miss two or three in: **Exercises 1–5**	**If** students miss one in: **Exercises 1–5**	**If** students miss none in: **Exercises 1–5**
Then choose a resource:	**Then** choose a resource:	**Then** choose a resource:
Strategic Intervention Guide (p. 142)	TE Learning Stations (pp. 347G–347H)	TE Learning Stations (pp. 347G–347H)
CRM Chapter 8 Resource Masters (Reteach Worksheets)	TE Chapter Project (p. 349)	TE Chapter Project (p. 349)
Math Online Concepts in Motion	CRM Game: *Concentrate on Money*	Real-World Problem Solving: *Following a Coin*
	Math Adventures	Math Adventures
	My Math Zone Chapter 10	My Math Zone Chapters 10 and 11
	Math Online Fact Dash	Math Online Games

MATH at HOME

Before you begin Chapter 11:

- Read the Math at Home letter found on p. 349, with the class and have each student sign it.
- Send home copies of the Math at Home letter with each student.
- Use the Spanish letter on p. 350 for students with Spanish-speaking parents or guardians.

WRITING IN MATH

Starting the Chapter
Ask students to write about why it is important to save money rather than spend it all.

Read-Aloud Anthology
For an optional reading activity to introduce this chapter's math concepts, see the Read-Aloud Anthology on pp. TR36–TR37.

MATH at HOME

Dear Family,

Today my class started Chapter 11, **Identify Coins**. In this chapter, I will learn to identify and count coins. Here is an activity we can do and a list of books we can read together.

Love, ______________________

Activity

Set up a store. Put price tags on items around the house. Give your child coins to practice counting out the change to buy the items.

Key Vocabulary

penny 1¢

nickel 5¢

dime 10¢

quarter 25¢

Math Online Click on the eGlossary link at macmillanmh.com to find out more about these words. There are 13 languages.

Books to Read

The Three Silly Billies
by Margie Palatini
Simon & Schuster Children's Publishing, 2005.

The Penny Pot
by Stuart J. Murphy
Harper Trophy Publishers, 1998.

The Coin Counting Book
Rozanne Lanczak Williams
Charlesbridge Publishing, 2001.

Chapter 11 Project

Money Amounts

- As the students work through the chapter, have them use coin stamps and stamp pads to illustrate combinations of coins to show value.
- Provide students with pieces of 4 × 5 inch pieces of construction paper. Students will write a value at the top of each sheet of paper and stamp combinations of coins that equal the amount.
- Students may also include a coversheet with the stamp of each coin and name of the coin.
- Have students share their money amounts with the class and discuss other combinations of coins to make the same amount.

CRM *Refer to Chapter 11 Resource Masters, p. 60, for a rubric to assess students' progress on this project.*

MATEMÁTICAS en CASA

Estimada familia:

Hoy mi clase comenzó el Capítulo 11, **Identifica monedas.** En este capítulo, aprenderé a identificar y a contar monedas. A continuación, hay una actividad que podemos hacer y una lista de libros que podemos leer juntos.

Cariños, ______________________

Actividad

Organicen una tienda. Coloquen etiquetas de precios en objetos alrededor de la casa. Denle monedas a su hijo(a) a fin de que las cuente para comprar los objetos.

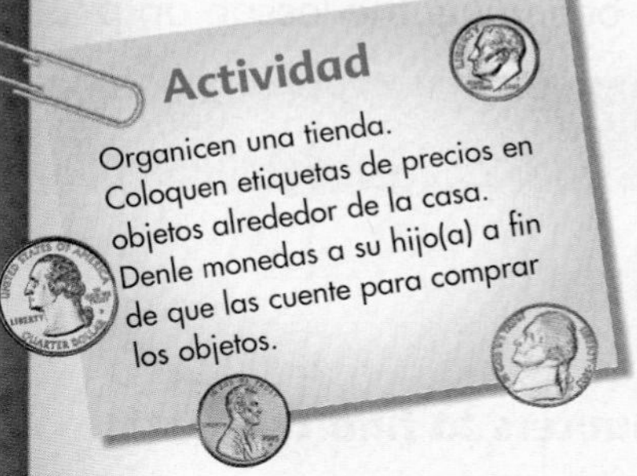

Vocabulario clave

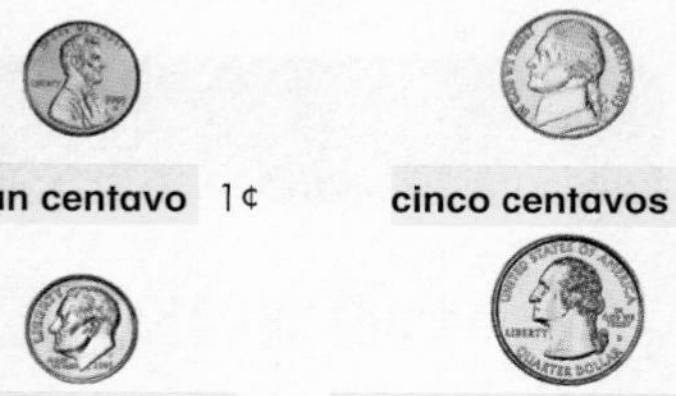

un centavo 1¢ **cinco centavos** 5¢

diez centavos 10¢ **veinticinco centavos** 25¢

Math Online Visiten el enlace eGlossary en macmillanmh.com para averiguar más sobre estas palabras, las cuales se muestran en 13 idiomas.

Libros recomendados

El gran negocio de francisca
de Russelll Hoban
Harper Trophy, 1996 .

De compras con mamá
de Mercer Mayer
Golden Books, 1997.

Matematicas y dinero
de Susan Ring
Yellow Umbrella Books, 2005.

350 three hundred fifty Chapter 11 Lesson 1

Chapter 11 Literature List

Lesson	Book Title
11-1	**Benny's Pennies** Pat Brisson
11-2	**Jelly Beans for Sale** Bruce McMillan
11-3	**The Coin Counting Book** Rozanne Lanczak Williams
11-4	**Twenty-Six Letters and Ninety-Nine Cents** Tana Hoban
11-5	**Bunny Money** Rosemary Wells
11-6	**The Penny Pot** Stuart J. Murphy
11-7	**The Penny Pot** Stuart J. Murphy
11-9	**The Big Buck Adventures** Shelley Gill and Deborah Tobola
Any	**The Three Silly Billies** Margie Palatini

ELL National ESL Standards Alignment for Chapter 11

Lesson, Page	ESL Standard	Modality	Level
11-1, p 351B	Goal 3, Standard 3, d	Linguistic, Kinesthetic	Intermediate
11-2, p 353B	Goal 3, Standard 1, e	Linguistic	Advanced
11-3, p 355B	Goal 3, Standard 2, d	Visual, Logical	Beginning
11-4, p 357B	Goal 1, Standard 1, f	Kinesthetic, Logical	Beginning
11-5, p 359B	Goal 1, Standard 3, k	Linguistic	Intermediate
11-6, p 363B	Goal 2, Standard 2, a	Visual/Spatial	Advanced
11-7, p 365B	Goal 2, Standard 2, m	Visual	Intermediate
11-8, p 369B	Goal 2, Standard 2, f	Intrapersonal	Beginning
11-9, p 371B	Goal 3, Standard 3, f	Visual, Auditory	Advanced

The National ESL Standards can be found in the Teacher Reference Handbook.

LESSON 11-1

Pennies and Nickels

Lesson Planner

Objective

Identify and find the value of a group of pennies and nickels.

Vocabulary

cent (¢), **penny**, **nickel**

Resources

Materials: paper cups, pencils

Manipulatives: coins (pennies, nickels)

Literature Connection: *Benny's Pennies* by Pat Brisson

Alternate Lesson: Use "Money" on pages 332 and 333 of *Math Their Way* to provide practice with values of nickels and pennies.

Teacher Technology

TeacherWorks • Math Songs Track 16 Lesson Plan

Focus on Math Background

In this lesson, students will count coin combinations consisting of pennies and nickels. Students must simultaneously consider the value of each coin and how to adjust the skip counting pattern as they calculate the cumulative value of the coins. First, students will determine the value of both coins by exchanging five pennies for one nickel. Then, students will learn that they should always start counting the coins with the greatest value (nickels) before proceeding to the pennies. Students will practice skip counting by fives. An even greater challenge for students in counting nickels and pennies is remembering when and how to stop skip counting by fives and begin counting by ones.

Daily Routine

Use these suggestions before beginning the lesson on p. 351.

5-Minute Check

(Reviews Lesson 10-9)

Use WorkMat 3 and counters to find two parts.

1. Whole 14 See students' work.

2. Whole 16 See students' work.

Problem of the Day

Frannie picks 10 apples each week. How many apples will she pick over 3 weeks? 30 apples

LINE UP As students line up, call out the name of a coin, either *penny* or *nickel*. When you call *penny*, have one student line up. When you call *nickel*, have five students line up.

Building Math Vocabulary

Write the vocabulary words **cent(¢)**, **penny**, and **nickel** on the board.

- Give five students a penny. Have them line up in front of the class. Explain that a penny equals 1 cent. Write ¢ and cent on the board. Explain that ¢ is a symbol for *cent*.
- Give one student a nickel. Explain that a nickel equals 5 cents.
- Have the student with the nickel take the place of the five students with pennies. Emphasize that one nickel equals 5 cents.

Visual Vocabulary Cards

Use Visual Vocabulary Cards 6, 29, and 34 to reinforce the vocabulary introduced in this lesson. (The Define/Example/Ask routine is printed on the back of each card.)

Differentiated Instruction

Small Group Options

Option 1 VISUAL/SPATIAL, SOCIAL

Gifted and Talented AL

Materials: blank charts, coins (pennies and dimes)

- Distribute pennies and dimes to students.
- Invite students to take turns showing the group an amount of money using only dimes.
- Have them challenge the rest of the group to show an equal amount of money using only pennies.
- Have students record on a picture chart the relationship of pennies and dimes with equal values.

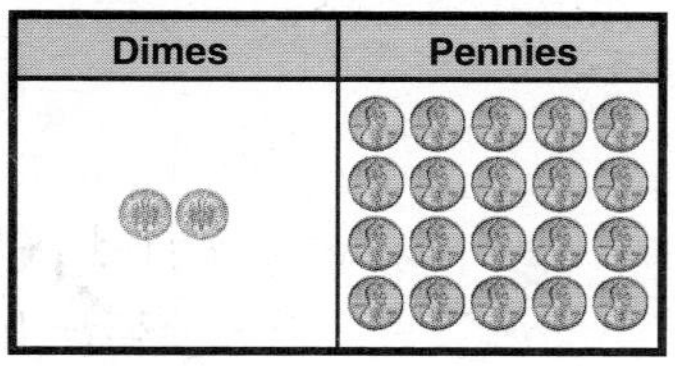

Option 2 LINGUISTIC

English Language Learners ELL

Materials: a penny, a dime, paper, pencil
Core Vocabulary: poem, to be worth, lines
Common Use Verb: describe

Write Math This strategy allows students to play with acquired vocabulary and math understanding of by writing poetry.

- Show a number line, students standing in a line, and a line of text.
- Say: "There are many types of lines." Explain the above examples.
- Say: "A poem is like a painting with words. Poems have lines. We are going to write a poem about a coin." Have the students examine a penny and a dime.
- The format for the coin poem is:

Type of coin, type of coin
What you like about the coin
Describe what the coin looks like
How much is the coin worth

- Model writing a poem. Have students repeat. If time permits, allow students to illustrate them.

Independent Work Options

Option 1 KINESTHETIC, SOCIAL

Early Finishers OL AL

Materials: six envelopes, coins (pennies and dimes)

- Fill envelopes with pennies in groups of ten, such as 10¢, 20¢, 30¢. Fill corresponding envelopes with dimes.
- Invite students to take turns counting one envelope of money. **How many dimes could you trade your pennies for? How many pennies could you trade your dimes for?** See students' work.

Option 2

Student Technology

Math Online macmillanmh.com

Math Songs, "How Many Pennies?" Track 16 • Math Adventures

Option 3

Learning Station: Science (p. 347H)

Direct students to the Science Learning Station for more opportunities to explore and extend the lesson concept.

Option 4

Problem-Solving Practice

Reinforce problem-solving skills and strategies with the Problem-Solving Practice worksheet.

Problem Solving (p. 14) BL OL AL

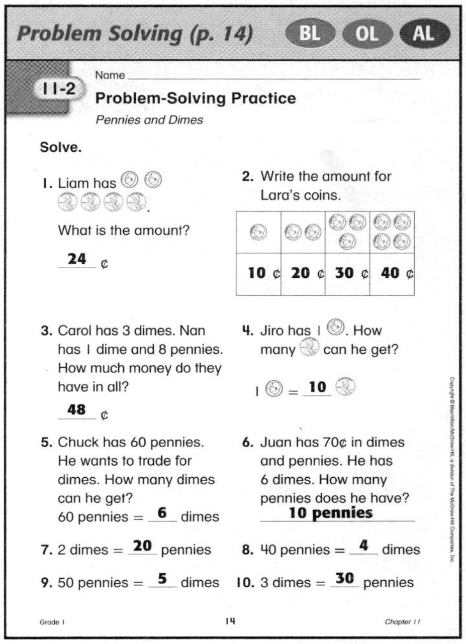

Name

11-2 **Problem-Solving Practice**
Pennies and Dimes

Solve.

1. Liam has [coins]. What is the amount? **24** ¢
2. Write the amount for Lara's coins.

[coin]	[coins]	[coins]	[coins]
10 ¢	20 ¢	30 ¢	40 ¢

3. Carol has 3 dimes. Nan has 1 dime and 8 pennies. How much money do they have in all? **48** ¢
4. Jiro has 1 [dime]. How many [pennies] can he get? 1 [dime] = **10** [pennies]
5. Chuck has 60 pennies. He wants to trade for dimes. How many dimes can he get? 60 pennies = **6** dimes
6. Juan has 70¢ in dimes and pennies. He has 6 dimes. How many pennies does he have? **10 pennies**
7. 2 dimes = **20** pennies
8. 40 pennies = **4** dimes
9. 50 pennies = **5** dimes
10. 3 dimes = **30** pennies

Grade 1 14 Chapter 11

11-2

1 Introduce

Activity Choice 1 • Hands-On

- Display a set of ten pennies. Explain that students could use one coin, a **dime**, that equals ten pennies instead of counting ten pennies one by one.
- Point to students one by one and have them say the next number in counting by tens. **How many students had to count before we reached 100?** 10 students
- Explain that counting dimes is like skip counting by tens.

Activity Choice 2 • Literature

Introduce the lesson with *Jelly Beans for Sale* by Bruce McMillan. For additional support, see p. TR57.

2 Teach

- Arrange ten pennies and one dime on the overhead. Explain that the value of ten pennies is equal to one dime.
- Arrange four dimes on the overhead. Have students count by tens to count the dimes.
- **How much?** 40¢
- **How many pennies are there in 40¢?** 40 pennies
- Add three pennies to the dimes.
- **Now how much is there?** 43¢

Get Ready Use the section at the top of p. 353 to reinforce the lesson concept. Help student determine the values of coins and price the objects.

Check Observe students as you work through Exercises 1–4 as a class.

Exercise 4 Assess student comprehension before assigning practice exercises.

COMMON ERROR!

Students may lose track of their counts when trading pennies for a dime. Provide a ten frame on which students can arrange sets of exactly 10 pennies before exchanging them for a dime.

Name ______________________

Pennies and Dimes

Get Ready

Main Idea

I will count pennies and dimes.

Vocabulary

dime

Count by tens to count dimes.

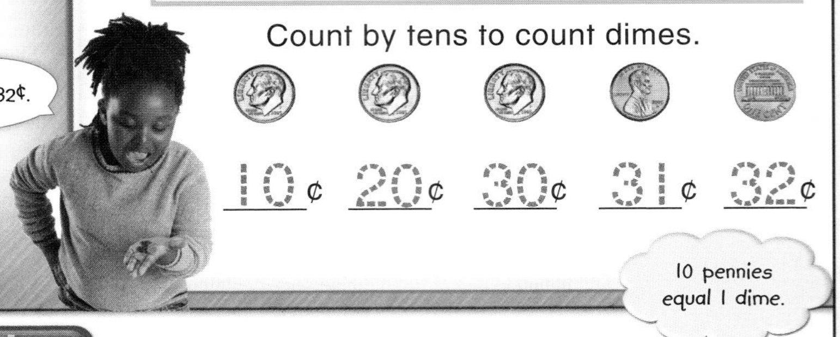

Check

Use [crayon] to circle the dimes. Count the coins. Write how much in all.

1. 
10 ¢ 20 ¢ 30 ¢ 30 ¢ in all

2. 
10 ¢ 20 ¢ 21 ¢ 21 ¢ in all

3. 
10 ¢ 20 ¢ 30 ¢ 31 ¢ 32 ¢ 33 ¢ 34 ¢ 34 ¢ in all

4. **Talk About It** How many dimes are the same as 50 pennies? 5

Reteach (p. 11) BL

11-2 Name ______________

Reteach

Pennies and Dimes

Ten pennies equal 10¢. One dime equals 10¢.

10¢ = 10¢

You can trade 10 pennies for 1 dime.
They are the same amount of money.

Use [penny] and [dime] to trade.
Count by tens to count dimes.

1. 20 [penny]
2. 30 [penny]
3. 50 [penny]
4. 40 [penny]

Skills Practice (p. 12) OL

11-2 Name ______________

Skills Practice

Pennies and Dimes

Trade pennies for as many dimes as you can. Draw dimes and pennies. Use [penny] and [dime] to help.

	Pennies You Start With	Trade for Dimes	Leftover Pennies	Total Amount
1.	36 [penny]	[3 dimes]	[6 pennies]	36 ¢
2.	44 [penny]	[4 dimes]	[4 pennies]	44 ¢
3.	51 [penny]	[5 dimes]	[1 penny]	51 ¢

Solve.

4. Tina has 40 pennies.
The machine only takes dimes.
What trade should she make? **4 dimes**

Practice

Use [crayon] to circle the dimes.
Count the coins. Write how much in all.

5. 1 ¢ 2 ¢ 3 ¢ — 3 ¢ in all

6. 10 ¢ 20 ¢ 30 ¢ 40 ¢ 50 ¢ 51 ¢ — 51 ¢ in all

7. 10 ¢ 11 ¢ 12 ¢ 13 ¢ — 13 ¢ in all

8. 10 ¢ 20 ¢ 30 ¢ 40 ¢ 50 ¢ 60 ¢ — 60 ¢ in all

9. 10 ¢ 20 ¢ 30 ¢ 40 ¢ 41 ¢ 42 ¢ — 42 ¢ in all

H.O.T. Problem

10. **Thinking Math**
You have 3 coins. They equal 20 cents.
Draw the coins you have. 1 dime and 2 nickels

Math at Home Activity: Give your child 3 dimes; ask him or her how many pennies that equals.

Enrich (p. 15) AL

11-2 Name ____
Enrich
Toy Shopping

**Look at the price of each toy.
Circle the coins needed to buy it.
Write how much money is left.**

1. 41¢ How much is left? **3** ¢
2. 64¢ How much is left? **0** ¢
3. 18¢ How much is left? **30** ¢
4. 82¢ How much is left? **2** ¢

Grade 1 15 Chapter 11

Homework Practice (p. 13) OL

11-2 Name ____
Homework Practice
Pennies and Dimes

Trade pennies for as many dimes as you can. Draw pennies and dimes. Use [penny] and [dime] to help.

	Pennies You Start With	Trade for Dimes	Leftover Pennies	Total Amount
1.	13 [penny]	[1 dime]	[3 pennies]	**13** ¢
2.	26 [penny]	[2 dimes]	[6 pennies]	**26** ¢
3.	41 [penny]	[4 dimes]	[1 penny]	**41** ¢

Solve.
4. Fred has 3 dimes and 27 pennies.
Can he trade his pennies for more dimes? **yes**
How many more dimes can he get? **2** dimes

Grade 1 13 Chapter 11

BL Alternate Teaching Strategy

If students have trouble skip counting by tens and changing to ones . . .

Then use one of the reteach options.

1. CRM **Daily Reteach Worksheet** (p. 11)
2. **Skip Counting on a Hundred Chart** Have students use a hundred chart and a combination of dimes and pennies.

   As students count the dimes, have them identify the value by shading in a row of ten, using a different color for each dime to represent the number of dimes. Next, have them color individual squares on the chart for each penny.

3 Practice

Differentiate practice using these leveled assignments for Exercises 5–10.

Level	Assignment
BL Below/Approaching Level	Guide students through the exercises. Use coins for support.
OL On Level	Complete the exercises independently, with coins for support if needed.
AL Above/Beyond Level	Complete the exercises independently.

4 Assess

Formative Assessment

Have students represent 23¢ with dimes and pennies. Have them use as many dimes as possible. 2 dimes and 3 pennies

WRITING IN MATH Ask students to draw and write about the kinds of coins they have studied. Have them tell the value of each coin.

Quick Check **Are students continuing to struggle with finding the value of dimes and pennies?**

If Yes → Strategic Intervention Guide (p. 114)
If No → Independent Work Options (p. 353B)
CRM Skills Practice Worksheet (p. 12)
CRM Enrich Worksheet (p. 15)

LESSON 11-3

Pennies, Nickels, and Dimes

Lesson Planner

Objective

Find the value of a group of dimes, nickels, and pennies.

Review Vocabulary

skip count

Resources

Materials: class set of cards showing coin combinations

Manipulatives: coins (pennies, nickels, dimes)

Literature Connection: *The Coin Counting Book* by Rozanne Lanczak Williams

Alternate Lesson: Use "Money" on pages 332 and 333 of *Math Their Way* to provide practice with values of pennies, nickels, and dimes.

Teacher Technology

TeacherWorks • Math Songs Track 16 Lesson Plan

Focus on Math Background

In this lesson, students will review the values of the penny, nickel, and dime, which were introduced in the previous two lessons. The instructional focus is on helping first graders develop an efficient strategy for deciding how and when to skip count by tens, fives, or ones in quantifying a collection of coins. Students will learn that they must first count the coin of the greatest denomination (the dime), followed by the coin with lesser value (the nickel), and ending with the most basic unit (the penny). Additional work will focus on comparing the coin equivalency among these three coins to make "fair trades."

Daily Routine

Use these suggestions before beginning the lesson on p. 355.

5-Minute Check

(Reviews Lesson 11-2)

Give the numbers of dimes and pennies that equal the amounts below.

1. 22¢ 2 dimes and 2 pennies

2. 14 ¢ 1 dime and 4 pennies

3. 33¢ 3 dimes and 3 pennies

4. A candy bar costs 54¢. How many dimes and pennies will buy 1 candy bar? 5 dimes and 4 pennies

Problem of the Day

Madeline wants to buy a barrette for 14¢. How many dimes and pennies does she need? 1 dime and 4 pennies

LINE UP Give each student one to nine dimes and three pennies. Call out the corresponding money amounts (13¢ to 93¢) in random order. Invite students to line up when you call out the value of the coins they hold.

Review Math Vocabulary

Materials: pennies, nickels, dimes or class-size coins

- Write the review vocabulary term **skip count** on the board. Display five nickels. Review that because a nickel equals 5 cents, students can skip count by fives to count nickels. Have students use skip counting by fives to count the nickels. **How much money is shown?** 25¢
- Repeat the activity with seven dimes. **What is the value of 7 dimes?** 70¢

Differentiated Instruction

Small Group Options

Option 1 KINESTHETIC, LOGICAL

Below/Approaching Level BL

Materials: paper bags, scrap paper, pencil, coins (pennies, dimes, nickels)

- Give one student a bag with five dimes, five nickels, and five pennies inside. Instruct the student to draw five coins from the bag.
- Choose one student in the group to count dimes by tens, another to count the nickels by fives, and a third to count the pennies by ones. Have the three students work together to the total value of the coins.
- Next, have students put the coins back in the bag, change roles, and repeat the activity.

Option 2 VISUAL, LOGICAL

English Language Learners ELL

Materials: A calender that starts on Monday, pennies, nickels, dimes

Core Vocabulary: working/days, are the same as, real life

Common Use Verb: learn/earn

See Math This strategy activates background knowledge to teach social studies and math concepts.

- Layout pennies on Monday through Friday. Say: "These are on working days. Students learn on working days."
- Say: "Five pennies are the same as a nickel." Count and trade pennies for a nickel. Place it on Saturday.
- Say: "These are playing days." Discuss vocabulary and how it connects to real life (parents work, and save or spend money, etc).
- Repeat for 2 weeks, trading 2 nickels for a dime placed on Sunday.

English Language Learners (p .25) ELL

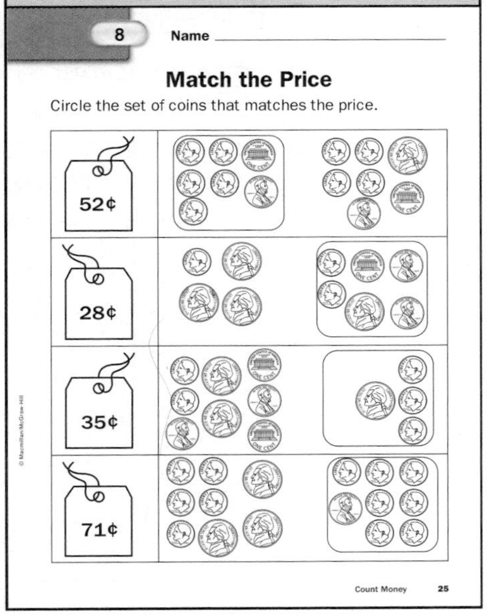

8 Name ____________

Match the Price

Circle the set of coins that matches the price.

52¢		
28¢		
35¢		
71¢		

© Macmillan/McGraw-Hill

Count Money 25

Use this worksheet to provide additional support for English Language Learners.

Independent Work Options

Option 1 VISUAL/SPATIAL, KINESTHETIC, SOCIAL

Early Finishers OL AL

Materials: paper bag, paper, pencil, coins (pennies, dimes, nickels)

- Place a collection of coins in a bag. Invite a student to pick four coins and name each one.
- Have students find the total value and record it. Invite students to compare quantities.

Option 2

Student Technology

Math Online macmillanmh.com

Math Songs, "How Many Pennies?" Track 16 • Math Adventures

Option 3

Learning Station: Social Studies (p. 347G)

Direct students to the Social Studies Learning Station for more opportunities to explore and extend the lesson concept.

Option 4

Problem-Solving Practice

Reinforce problem-solving skills and strategies with the Problem-Solving Practice worksheet.

Problem Solving (p. 19) BL OL AL

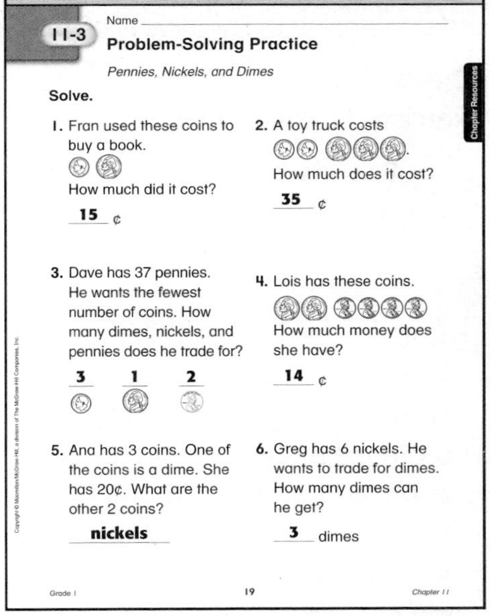

11-3 Name ____________

Problem-Solving Practice

Pennies, Nickels, and Dimes

Solve.

1. Fran used these coins to buy a book. How much did it cost? **15** ¢
2. A toy truck costs . How much does it cost? **35** ¢
3. Dave has 37 pennies. He wants the fewest number of coins. How many dimes, nickels, and pennies does he trade for? **3** **1** **2**
4. Lois has these coins. How much money does she have? **14** ¢
5. Ana has 3 coins. One of the coins is a dime. She has 20¢. What are the other 2 coins? **nickels**
6. Greg has 6 nickels. He wants to trade for dimes. How many dimes can he get? **3** dimes

Chapter Resources

Copyright © Macmillan/McGraw-Hill, a division of The McGraw-Hill Companies, Inc.

Grade 1 19 Chapter 11

1 Introduce

Activity Choice 1 • Hands-On

- Give each student one penny, one nickel, and one dime. Have student pairs take turns reviewing the names of each coin.
- Pose riddles and have students guess which coin each one describes.
- **I am larger in size than both a dime and a penny, but my value is less than 10¢. What am I?** a nickel

Activity Choice 2 • Literature

Introduce the lesson with *The Coin Counting Book* by Rozanne Lanczak Williams. For additional support, see p. TR57.

2 Teach

- Make a coin card for each student. Each card should show one of the following: 10 pennies, 5 pennies and 1 nickel; 2 nickels; 1 dime; 1 nickel; 5 pennies.
- Tell the students to find someone with a card that shows the same value as their card but different coins. Then students trade cards.
- Have students find another person with different coins but the same value.
- **Why did students with 1 nickel or 5 pennies find only one trading partner?** The only amount of money equal to 5 pennies is a nickel.

Get Ready Use the section at the top of p. 355 to reinforce the lesson concept. Help students determine a variety of ways to make ten cents.

Check Observe students as you work through Exercises 1–3 as a class.

Exercise 3 Assess student comprehension before assigning practice exercises.

COMMON ERROR!

Instead of counting on, some students may start counting from 0 each time they switch to a different type of coin. Have students use coins and a hundred chart to help them see that they are not starting over at the beginning, but rather building on.

Name ______________________

Hands-On Activity

Pennies, Nickels, and Dimes

Get Ready

Main Idea

I will count pennies, nickels, and dimes.

Pennies, nickels, and dimes have different values.

You can use different coins to make 10¢.		
1 dime	2 nickels	10 pennies

10¢ 20¢ 25¢ 26¢ 27¢ 28¢

Check

Use coins.

3. Sample answer: A dime or 2 nickels or 10 pennies are all 10 cents. A nickel is 5 cents or 5 pennies. A penny is 1 cent.

	You have these coins.	Draw the coins. Show how you count them.	How much money?
1.	1 3 1 	10¢ 5¢ 5¢ 5¢ 1¢ 10¢ 15¢ 20¢ 25¢ 26¢	26¢
2.	0 2 4 	5¢ 5¢ 1¢ 1¢ 1¢ 1¢ 5¢ 10¢ 11¢ 12¢ 13¢ 14¢	14¢

3. Talk About It Describe the relationship among a penny, a nickel, and a dime.

Reteach (p. 16) BL

11-3 Name ______________________

Reteach

Pennies, Nickels, and Dimes

One **penny** equals 1¢.
Count pennies by ones.

One **nickel** equals 5¢.
Count nickels by fives.

One **dime** equals 10¢.
Count dimes by tens.

Cut out the squares. Glue them to match the amount.

1. 27¢

2. 35¢

Grade 1 16 *Chapter 11*

Skills Practice (p. 17) OL

11-3 Name ______________________

Skills Practice

Pennies, Nickels, and Dimes

Draw the coins you have. Count them.

	Coins You Have	Draw Your Coins	How Much Money Do You Have?
1.	1 3 1	10¢ 5¢ 5¢ 5¢ 1¢	26¢
2.	2 3		**35** ¢
3.	3 1 1		**36** ¢
4.	1 4		**30** ¢

Solve.

5. Sara has 5 nickels.
Emily has 3 dimes.
Who has more money? **Emily**

Chapter Resources

Grade 1 17 *Chapter 11*

Practice

Use coins.

	You have these coins.	Draw the coins. Show how you count them.	How much money?
4.	4 0 2	(10¢) (10¢) (10¢) (10¢) (1¢) (1¢) 10 ¢ 20 ¢ 30 ¢ 40 ¢ 41 ¢ 42 ¢	42 ¢
5.	2 2 1	(10¢) (10¢) (5¢) (5¢) (1¢) 10 ¢ 20 ¢ 25 ¢ 30 ¢ 31 ¢	31 ¢
6.	5 1 0	(10¢) (10¢) (10¢) (10¢) (10¢) (5¢) 10 ¢ 20 ¢ 30 ¢ 40 ¢ 50 ¢ 55 ¢	55 ¢
7.	1 1 4	(10¢) (5¢) (1¢) (1¢) (1¢) (1¢) 10 ¢ 15 ¢ 16 ¢ 17 ¢ 18 ¢ 19 ¢	19 ¢

Problem Solving

8. Logical Reasoning You have pennies, nickels, and dimes.
You pick up 3 of those coins.
What is the greatest amount of money you could have? 30 ¢
What is the least amount of money you could have? 3 ¢

Math at Home Activity: Give your child some pennies, nickels, and dimes. Have him/her count the value of the group.

Enrich (p. 20) AL

11-3 Name ____

Enrich

How much? A riddle!

Count the coins. Use the key to solve the riddle.

1. **41** ¢
2. **37** ¢
3. **36** ¢
4. **19** ¢

H = 41¢
E = 19¢
O = 37¢
L = 36¢

What gets bigger the more you take away?

A **H** (1.) **O** (2.) **L** (3.) **E** (4.)!

Grade 1 20 Chapter 11

Homework Practice (p. 18) OL

11-3 Name ____

Homework Practice

Pennies, Nickels, and Dimes

Draw the coins you have. Count them.

	Coins You Have	Draw Your Coins	How Much Money Do You Have?
1.	3, 2		**40** ¢
2.	2, 2		**22** ¢
3.	3, 4		**19** ¢
4.	2, 2, 2		**32** ¢

Solve.

5. Sal has a dime, 2 nickels, and 3 pennies.
A rubber ball costs 25¢.
Does he have enough? **no**

Grade 1 18 Chapter 11

BL Alternate Teaching Strategy

If students do not understand how to find the value of dimes, nickels, and pennies . . .

Then use one of the reteach options.

1. CRM **Daily Reteach Worksheet** (p. 16)
2. **Review and Build** Have students first count the value of pennies, then nickels, and then dimes. Next have them count nickels and pennies, then dimes and pennies, and finally dimes and nickels.

3 Practice

Differentiate practice using these leveled assignments for Exercises 4–8.

Level	Assignment
BL Below/ Approaching Level	Guide students through the exercises with coins and a hundred chart for support.
OL On Level	Complete the exercises independently with coins for support.
AL Above/Beyond Level	Complete the exercises independently.

4 Assess

Formative Assessment

Display two dimes, two nickels, and two pennies. Ask students to find the total amount. Have them explain how they counted. 32¢; count dimes first, then nickels, then pennies.

WRITING IN ▸ MATH Ask students to write about why it is helpful to pay with nickels and dimes instead of with pennies. Sample answer: It is faster to count dimes and nickels, and you can carry fewer coins.

Quick Check

Are students continuing to struggle with counting dimes, nickels, and pennies?

If Yes → Small Group Options (p. 355B)
Strategic Intervention Guide (p. 114)

If No → Independent Work Options (p. 355B)
CRM Skills Practice Worksheet (p. 17)
CRM Enrich Worksheet (p. 20)

LESSON 11-4

Counting Money

Lesson Planner

Objective

Count coins to find their total value.

Review Vocabulary

doubles

Resources

Materials: price tags, number line

Manipulatives: coins (dimes, nickels, pennies)

Literature Connection: *Twenty-Six Letters and Ninety-Nine Cents* by Tana Hoban

Alternate Lesson: Use "The Store" on page 317 of *Math Their Way* to provide practice with counting money.

Teacher Technology

TeacherWorks • Concepts in Motion • Math Songs Track 16 Lesson Plan

Focus on Math Background

In this lesson, students will count out a specified amount of coins. To do this, a student must perform multiple tasks simultaneously. First, the student must tag each coin, then skip count according to the coin's value, and, finally, count on from the cumulative total. The student must also remember to stop at the specified number. Older students are able to recall certain coin combinations to facilitate this counting process—for example, "For 48¢, I need 4 dimes, 1 nickel, and 3 pennies." A first grader, however, will usually use trial and error to do this task, counting out and experimenting with different combinations of coins until finally arriving at the correct amount.

Daily Routine

Use these suggestions before beginning the lesson on p. 357.

5-Minute Check

(Reviews Lesson 11-3)

Find the total of the coins.

1. 3 dimes, 3 nickels, 4 pennies 49¢

2. 1 dime, 2 nickels, 3 pennies 23¢

3. 2 dimes, 1 nickel, 2 pennies 27¢

4. 4 dimes, 0 nickels, 1 penny 41¢

Problem of the Day

I am round and silver. I can be traded for 2 nickels, or for 1 nickel and 5 pennies, or for 10 pennies. What am I? a dime

LINE UP As students line up, have them look around the room for numbers to 99. Ask them to tell the coins they could use to represent those amounts.

Review Math Vocabulary

Materials: pennies, nickels, dimes or class-size coins

- Write the review vocabulary word **doubles** on the board. Display two dimes. Explain that adding two dimes, two nickels, or two pennies is the same as adding doubles because the two addends are the same number. Show students how adding two dimes is the same as 10 + 10 = 20.
- Repeat with adding two nickels and then two pennies.
- Give students two dimes, two nickels, and two pennies. Have them use doubles to find the total. 10 + 10 + 5 + 5 + 2 + 2 = 34¢

Differentiated Instruction

Small Group Options

Option 1 LINGUISTIC/KINESTHETIC, SOCIAL

Gifted and Talented AL

Materials: classroom items, price tags, coins

- Display items with price tags. Give students an amount to spend. Explain that the goal is to buy as many items as possible.
- Have students write the names of the items they would buy. Then have them write or draw pictures of the coins they would use to buy them.
- Invite students to explain why they bought the items they did.

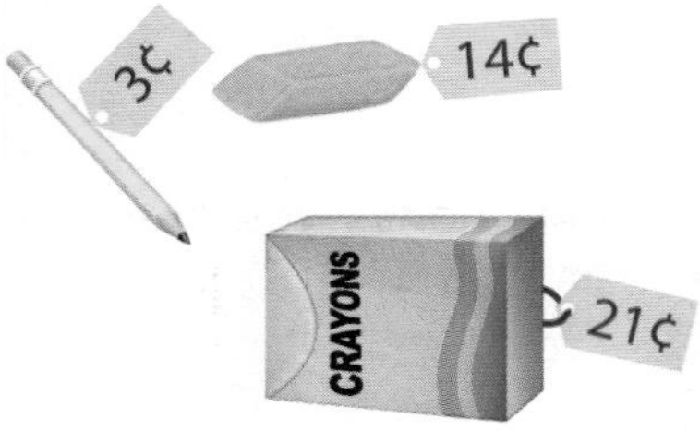

Option 2 KINESTHETIC/LOGICAL

English Language Learners ELL

Materials: sticky notes, playground
Core Vocabulary: playground, area, match
Common Use Verb: will play

Do Math This strategy integrates counting skills in a high interest situation.

- Pretend that the playground is an amusement park. Place post-it notes with money amounts on the various equipment.
- Give the students coins.
- Tell the students that they must count the coins and then find the area of the playground that matches the amount of coins they have. They will be playing in that section of the playground.
- Extend the activity by having students pay for their time on equipment until they run out of money. You may want to base their initial amount of money on completing an assignment or extra work.

Independent Work Options

Option 1 KINESTHETIC, SOCIAL, VISUAL/SPATIAL

Early Finishers OL AL

Materials: Money Bingo cards, two sets of game cards with each card showing an amount or picture of a coin combination from 1¢ to 99¢, two-colored counters

- First, have students play Money Bingo, with one student drawing and showing money cards and the others placing counters on Bingo cards. The winner becomes the caller.
- Then, have students use the money cards to play Concentration.

Option 2

Student Technology

Math Online macmillanmh.com

Math Songs, "How Many Pennies?" Track 16 • Math Adventures

Option 3

Learning Station: Social Studies (p. 347G)

Direct students to the Social Studies Learning Station for more opportunities to explore and extend the lesson concept.

Option 4

Problem-Solving Practice

Reinforce problem-solving skills and strategies with the Problem-Solving Practice worksheet.

Problem Solving (p. 24) BL OL AL

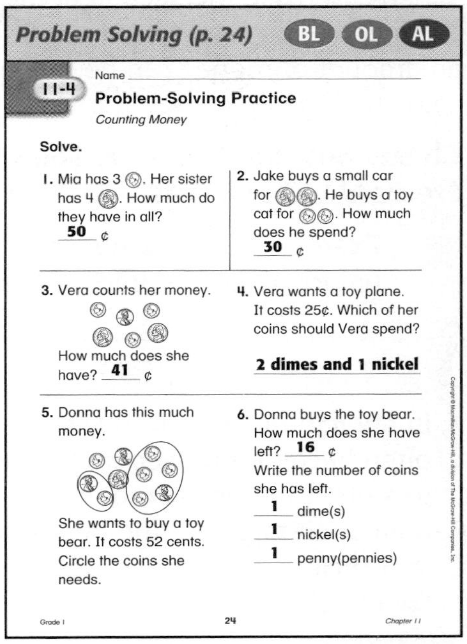

Name

11-4 **Problem-Solving Practice**
Counting Money

Solve.

1. Mia has 3 (coin). Her sister has 4 (coin). How much do they have in all? **50** ¢
2. Jake buys a small car for (coins). He buys a toy cat for (coins). How much does he spend? **30** ¢
3. Vera counts her money. How much does she have? **41** ¢
4. Vera wants a toy plane. It costs 25¢. Which of her coins should Vera spend? **2 dimes and 1 nickel**
5. Donna has this much money. She wants to buy a toy bear. It costs 52 cents. Circle the coins she needs.
6. Donna buys the toy bear. How much does she have left? **16** ¢ Write the number of coins she has left. **1** dime(s) **1** nickel(s) **1** penny(pennies)

Grade 1 24 Chapter 11

1 Introduce

Activity Choice 1 • Hands-On

- Make a price tag of less than 45¢ for each pair of students. Give pairs of students a handful of pennies, nickels, and dimes and a price tag.
- Ask students to use their coins to make that amount of money. Then have them describe other ways to make that amount of money. **Which way used the fewest coins?** See students' work. 4 dimes, 1 nickel

Activity Choice 2 • Literature

Introduce the lesson with *Twenty-Six Letters and Ninety-Nine Cents* by Tana Hoban. For additional support, see p. TR57.

2 Teach

- Write 26¢ on the overhead. Show several dimes, nickels, and pennies. Explain that you want to use the fewest coins to make 26¢.
- **Which coins will I use first?** dimes **Why?** They are worth more so you use fewer coins.
- **How many dimes can I use without having more than 26¢?** 2 dimes **Why?** Two dimes are worth 20¢; three dimes are worth 30¢, which is more than 26¢.
- Show two dimes on the overhead. **How many more cents do we need?** 6¢ **How can you make 6¢ with only two coins?** a nickel and a penny

Get Ready Use the section at the top of p. 357 to reinforce the lesson concept. Show students that an amount of money can be made with a variety of coin combinations.

Check Observe students as you work through Exercises 1–3 as a class.

Exercise 3 Assess student comprehension before assigning practice exercises.

! COMMON ERROR!

In finding the coins to buy something, students often become involved in counting and forget to stop at the price amount. Suggest that they mark their targeted number on a number line and circle each number they say as they skip count coins to that goal.

Name ____________________

Hands-On Activity

Counting Money

Get Ready

Main Idea

I will count mixed sets of coins.

When you count pennies, nickels, and dimes, start with the coin that has the greatest value.

Check

3. Sample answer: They are all worth 20 cents.

Circle how much money you need.
Use coins. Count.

1.

Draw how much money you need. Sample answer:

2.

10¢ 10¢ 5¢

3. Talk About It How are 20 pennies, 4 nickels, and 2 dimes alike?

Reteach (p. 21) BL

11-4 Name ____________________

Reteach

Counting Money

Counting coins is easier if you start with the coin that has the greatest value first.

Start by putting the coins in order from *greatest* to *least*. Then count.

10¢, 20¢, 25¢, 30¢, 31¢, 32¢, 33¢

Total = 33¢

Draw the coins from *greatest* to *least* value. Mark an X on the coin after you draw it. Then count. Write the total.

1. 10¢ 10¢ 10¢ 5¢ 5¢ 1¢

Total = **41** ¢

2. 10¢ 10¢ 5¢ 1¢ 1¢ 1¢

Total = **28** ¢

Chapter Resources

Grade 1 21 Chapter 11

Skills Practice (p. 22) OL

11-4 Name ____________________

Skills Practice

Counting Money

Circle how much money you need. Use coins.

1. 29¢

2. 60¢

3. 33¢

Solve. Use coins to help.

4. Marc has 5 coins in his pocket. They add up to 36¢. How many dimes, nickels, and pennies does he have?

3 dimes **1** nickels **1** pennies

Grade 1 22 Chapter 11

Practice

Circle how much money you need.

4.

Draw how much money you need.

5.

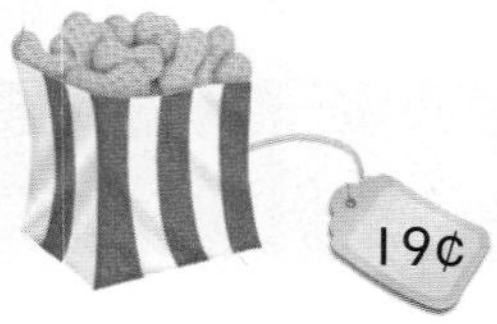

Sample answer: 10¢ 5¢ 1¢ 1¢ 1¢ 1¢

6.

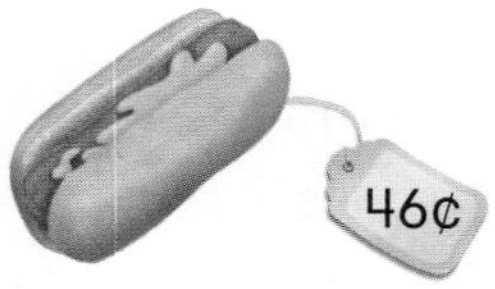

Sample answer: 10¢ 10¢ 10¢ 10¢ 5¢ 1¢

Problem Solving

7. **Logical Reasoning** A balloon costs 23¢. You have 2 dimes, 1 nickel, and 2 pennies. Do you have enough money? Explain.

Sample answer: Yes. I have 27¢, which is more than 23¢.

Math at Home Activity: Give your child a price (such as 33¢) and have him/her describe what combination of coins he/she could use to make that amount.

Enrich (p. 25) AL

11-4 Name ________
Enrich
Money Maze

Color the coins along the path to the bank.
Count the coins.

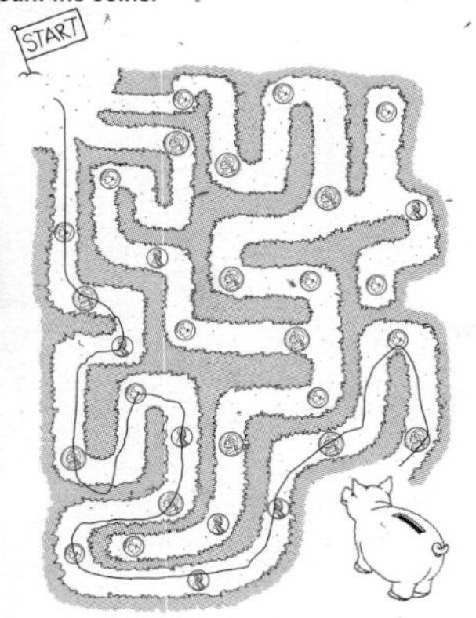

How much money did you color? **69¢**

Grade 1 25 Chapter 11

Homework Practice (p. 23) OL

11-4 Name ________
Homework Practice
Counting Money

Circle how much money you need. Use coins.

1.

2.

3.

Solve.

4. Cindy has 2 dimes and a penny. Sonia has a dime and 3 nickels. How much do they have altogether? **46** ¢

Grade 1 23 Chapter 11

BL Alternate Teaching Strategy

If students have difficulty skip counting while they count out change . . .

Then use one of the reteach options.

1 CRM **Daily Reteach Worksheet** (p. 21)

2 **Fair Trading** Allow students to first use pennies to make the targeted amount and then later exchange the pennies for other coins.

3 Practice

Differentiate practice using these leveled assignments for Exercises 4–7.

Level	Assignment
BL Below/ Approaching Level	Guide students through the exercises with coins for models.
OL On Level	Complete the exercises independently with coins for models.
AL Above/Beyond Level	Complete the exercises independently without models.

4 Assess

Formative Assessment

Have students use dimes, nickels, and pennies to count out the correct change to buy a 43¢ item. Ask them to use the fewest coins possible. 4 dimes, 3 pennies

WRITING IN MATH Have students write about something they could buy for less than 98¢ and the strategy they would use to pay for it with the fewest coins.

Quick Check **Are students continuing to struggle with counting coins to find the total value?**

If Yes → CRM Reteach Worksheet (p. 21)

If No → Independent Work Options (p. 357B)

CRM Skills Practice Worksheet (p. 22)

CRM Enrich Worksheet (p. 25)

11-5 Problem-Solving Strategy
Act It Out

Lesson Planner

Objective
Use the *act it out* strategy to solve problems.

Resources
Manipulatives: coins (dimes, nickels, pennies)
Literature Connection: *Bunny Money* by Rosemary Wells
Teacher Technology
TeacherWorks

Real-World Problem Solving Library
Math and Social Studies: *Following a Coin*

Use these leveled books to reinforce and extend problem-solving skills and strategies.

- OL On Level
- ELL Sheltered English
- SP Spanish

For additional support, see the Real-World Problem Solving Teacher Guide.

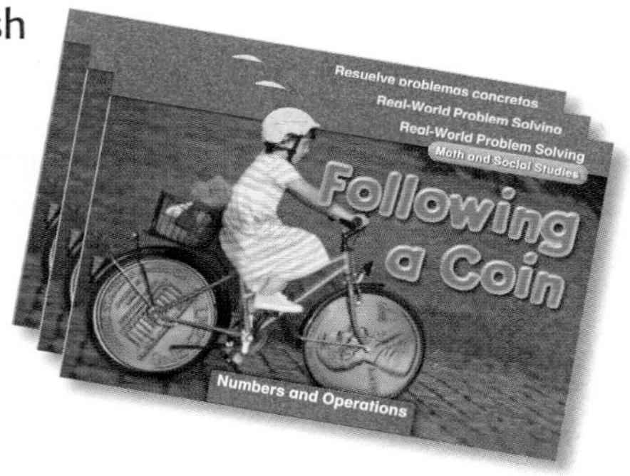

Daily Routine

Use these suggestions before beginning the lesson on p. 359.

5-Minute Check
(Reviews Lesson 11-4)

Count the money. Write the amount.

1. dime, nickel, penny 10, 15, 16; total 16¢
2. dime, dime, dime, nickel, nickel, penny 10, 20, 30, 35, 40, 41; total 41¢
3. dime, nickel, nickel, penny, penny, penny 10, 15, 20, 21, 22, 23; total 23¢
4. dime, dime, nickel, nickel, nickel, penny, penny, penny 10, 20, 25, 30, 35, 36, 37, 38; total 38¢

Problem of the Day
Are the number of letters in your first name greater than, less than, or equal to the number of letters in your last name? See students' work.

LINE UP **What are some ways to make 45¢?** Let each student who correctly gives a new combination of coins line up. Repeat with different amounts of money until all students are in line.

Differentiated Instruction

Small Group Options

LOGICAL, VISUAL/SPATIAL, SOCIAL

Option 1 Gifted and Talented AL

Materials: 10 envelopes, coins

- Write an amount in cents on the front of each envelope. Give each student four quarters, five dimes, ten nickels, and ten pennies.
- Have students count out the amount of money written on one of the envelopes and put the correct amount of coins inside the envelope.
- Have students exchange envelopes and see if the amount of money inside the envelope matches the amount written on the envelope.

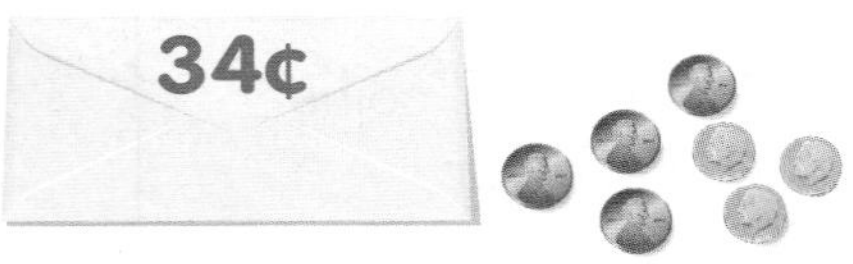

LINGUISTIC

Option 2 English Language Learners ELL

Materials: art supplies
Core Vocabulary: story problem, characters, represent
Common Use Verb: present

Write Math This strategy shelters writing addition stories in small groups.

- Write vocabulary on the board and call attention to the similarities in present and represent, and the different pronunciations of present (as a verb—to give, to act out or as a noun—a gift) and the names of coins.
- Place the students into groups and have them make hats to represent the characters in the story.
- Have the students act out the addition story in front of the class.
- The other students will need to write the addition problem down as the group is presenting it.
- Review the addition problem and discuss it using the target vocabulary. Restate student language as necessary.

Independent Work Options

KINESTHETIC, VISUAL/SPATIAL, LOGICAL

Option 1 Early Finishers OL AL

Materials: small items valued at less than $1 with price tags attached, paper, pencil, coins

- Have students shop in a class store. Ask them to make a shopping list by writing the name of each item they would like to buy and then listing the coins needed to purchase the item.
- Invite students to use pennies, nickels, and dimes to purchase items on their shopping list.

Option 2 Student Technology

Math Online macmillanmh.com

Option 3 Learning Station: Language Arts (p. 347H)

Direct students to the Language Arts Learning Station for more opportunities to explore and extend the lesson concept.

1 Introduce

Activity Choice 1 • Review

Write and read aloud the following:

Linda bought flowers for 89¢. She used the fewest coins possible. What coins did Linda use?

- **What do we know?** Linda bought flowers. She used the fewest coins possible. The flowers cost 89¢.
- **What do we need to find?** What coins did Linda use?
- **What strategy can we use to solve the problem?** *act it out*
- **What should we do?** Use coins to act out the problem. Model counting change to equal 89¢. 10¢, 20¢, 30¢, 40¢, 50¢, 60¢, 70¢, 80¢, 85¢, 86¢, 87¢, 88¢, 89¢; 8 dimes, 1 nickel, 4 pennies
- **Look back. Do the coins equal 89¢?** yes

Activity Choice 2 • Literature

Introduce the lesson with *Bunny Money* by Rosemary Wells. For additional support, see p. TR58.

2 Teach

Have students read the problems on page 359. Guide them through the problem-solving steps.

Understand Using the question, review what students know and what they need to find out.

Plan Have them discuss their strategy.

Solve Guide students to *act it out* to solve the problem.

- **If Peg has two nickels, how much does she have?** 10¢
- **Start with 10 and count on to 13. How much does Peg need to make 13¢?** 3¢

Check Have students look back at the problem to make sure that the answer fits the facts given.

- **What coins did Peg use?** 2 nickels and 3 pennies

! COMMON ERROR!

Students may have difficulty deciding which coins to count out. Remind them to count the coins with the greatest value first.

Name ______________________________

Problem-Solving Strategy

Act it Out

Main Idea

I will act it out to solve a problem.

Peg bought a box of pencils.
The pencils cost 13¢.
Peg has 2 nickels.
What other coins does she need?

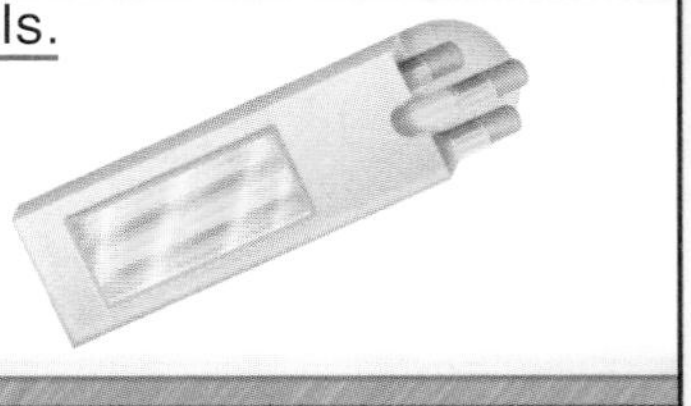

Understand

What do I know? Underline what you know.
What do I need to find? Circle the question.

Plan

How will I solve the problem?
I can use coins to act out the problem.

Solve

Act it out.

Show  .

Count and show the coins needed to make 13¢.

1¢ 1¢ 1¢

Check

Look back.
Is my answer reasonable? Check students' explanations.

Reteach (pp. 26–27) BL

11-5 Name ______________

Reteach (1)

Problem-Solving Strategy: Act It Out

Bob the Clown goes to the store.
He buys a [bird] for 5¢.
He buys a [hat] for 13¢.
How much money does Bob spend?

Step 1 **Understand**	**What do I know?** Bob spent 5¢. Bob spent 13¢. **What do I need to find out?** How much money Bob spends.
Step 2 **Plan**	**How will I find out how much he spent?** I can act it out.
Step 3 **Solve**	**Act it out.** Draw the coins for the [bird]. [nickel] or [5 pennies] Draw the coins for the [hat]. [dime, 3 pennies] Count all the coins. Bob spends **18** ¢.
Step 4 **Check**	Is my answer reasonable? yes

Grade 1 26 Chapter 11

Skills Practice (p. 28) OL

11-5 Name ______________

Skills Practice

Problem-Solving Strategy: Act It Out

Use coins to act out the problem. Solve.

1. Evan buys a [top] for 17¢. He buys a [ball] for 10¢. How much money does Evan spend altogether? Evan spends 27 ¢.
2. Jane buys a [rainbow] for 15¢. She buys a [heart] for 20¢. How much money does Jane spend in all? Jane spends **35** ¢.
3. Frank buys a toy car for 32¢. Then he buys a ball for 20¢. How much money does Frank spend? Frank spends **52** ¢.
4. Leon buys a [banana] for 24¢. Which coins did he use? Draw them. **Answers will vary.**

Grade 1 28 Chapter 11

Remember
Understand
Plan
Solve
Check

Try It

Act it out to solve.

1. Cliff wants to buy a hat.
   It costs 40¢. He has 25¢.
   What other coins does he need?

Cliff needs Sample answer: I dime and I nickel

2. Rina wants to buy a doll for 10 cents.
   Which coins could she use?

Rina could use Sample answer: I dime.

Your Turn

Act it out to solve.

3. Carla wants a fruit bar.
   The fruit bar costs 30 cents.
   Carla has I dime.
   How many more dimes does she need?

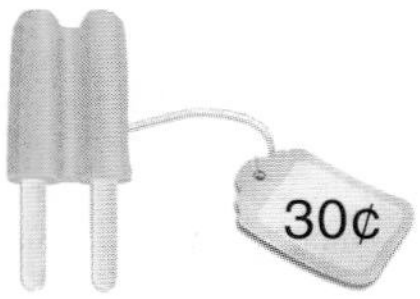

Carla needs 2 dimes.

4. Jeremy wants to buy 2 fish.
   The fish are 5 cents each.
   What coins could he use
   to buy the fish?

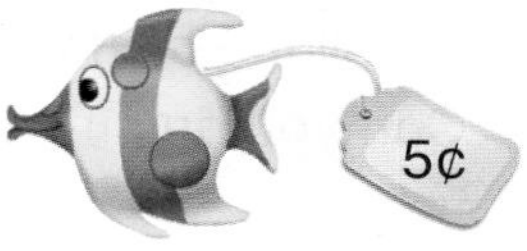

Jeremy could use Sample answer: 10 pennies.

Math at Home Activity: Use household items to set up a make believe store in your home. Put prices on each item. Give your child pennies, nickels, and dimes to use to buy items in the store.

Try It Observe students as you work through Exercises 1–2 as a class.

BL Alternate Teaching Strategy

If students have difficulty acting out money problems . . .

Then use one of the reteach options.

1. CRM **Daily Reteach Worksheet** (pp. 26–27)
2. **Use Tally Marks** Have students use tally marks and then find the coins that equal the tally marks. They should exchange one group of five tally marks for a nickel and two groups of five tally marks for a dime.

3 Practice

Your Turn

Exercises 3–4 Be sure students can read and understand the problems. Remind students to begin with the coin that has the greatest value.

4 Assess

Formative Assessment

Have students find the fewest possible coins that could be used to purchase a toy for 28¢. Have them explain how they counted the coins and why.
2 dimes, 1 nickel, 3 pennies

Enrich (p. 30) AL

11-5 Name ____

Enrich

How Much?

Use coins to help. Fill in the chart.

	How many? (penny)	How many? (nickel)	How many? (dime)
10¢ yo-yo	10	2	1
20¢ car	20	4	2
30¢ whistle	30	6	3

1. How many dimes for the car and the yo-yo?
   3 dimes
2. How many nickels for the whistle and the yo-yo?
   8 nickels
3. How many pennies for the car and the whistle?
   50 pennies

Grade 1 30 Chapter 11

Homework Practice (p. 29) OL

11-5 Name ____

Homework Practice

Problem-Solving Strategy: Act It Out

Chapter Resources

Solve. Use coins to help.

1. Geri buys a pen for 15¢. Which coins can she use? Draw them.

   Answers will vary.

2. Kara buys an apple for 35¢. Then she buys a can of juice for 10¢. How much does she spend?
   45 ¢
3. Robin has 3 dimes and 1 nickel. Rosa has 1 dime and 4 pennies. A poster costs 50¢. Do they have enough?
   no
4. Jacob buys a can of corn for 22¢. Which coins can he use? Draw them.

   Answers will vary.

5. Bob buys a peach for 43¢. Then he buys a bottle of water for 13¢. How much does he spend? **56** ¢

Grade 1 29 Chapter 11

Quick Check

Are students continuing to struggle with acting out money problems?

If Yes → CRM Reteach Worksheet (pp. 26–27)

If No → Independent Work Options (p. 359B)
CRM Skills Practice Worksheet (p. 28)
CRM Enrich Worksheet (p. 30)

Mid-Chapter Check

Lessons 11-1 to 11-5

Formative Assessment

Use the Mid-Chapter Check to assess student's progress in the first half of the chapter.

ExamView Assessment Suite Customize and create multiple versions of your Mid-Chapter Check and the test answer keys.

FOLDABLES Dinah Zike's Foldables

Use these suggestions to incorporate the Foldable during the first half of the chapter.

Lesson 11-1 Have students write an amount less than 50¢ on the first tab. On the second tab, have students draw pennies and nickels to make the amount written on the first tab.

Lesson 11-2 On the third tab, have students draw dimes and pennies to make the amount written on the first tab.

Lesson 11-3 On the fourth tab, have students draw dimes, nickels, and pennies to make the amount written on the first tab.

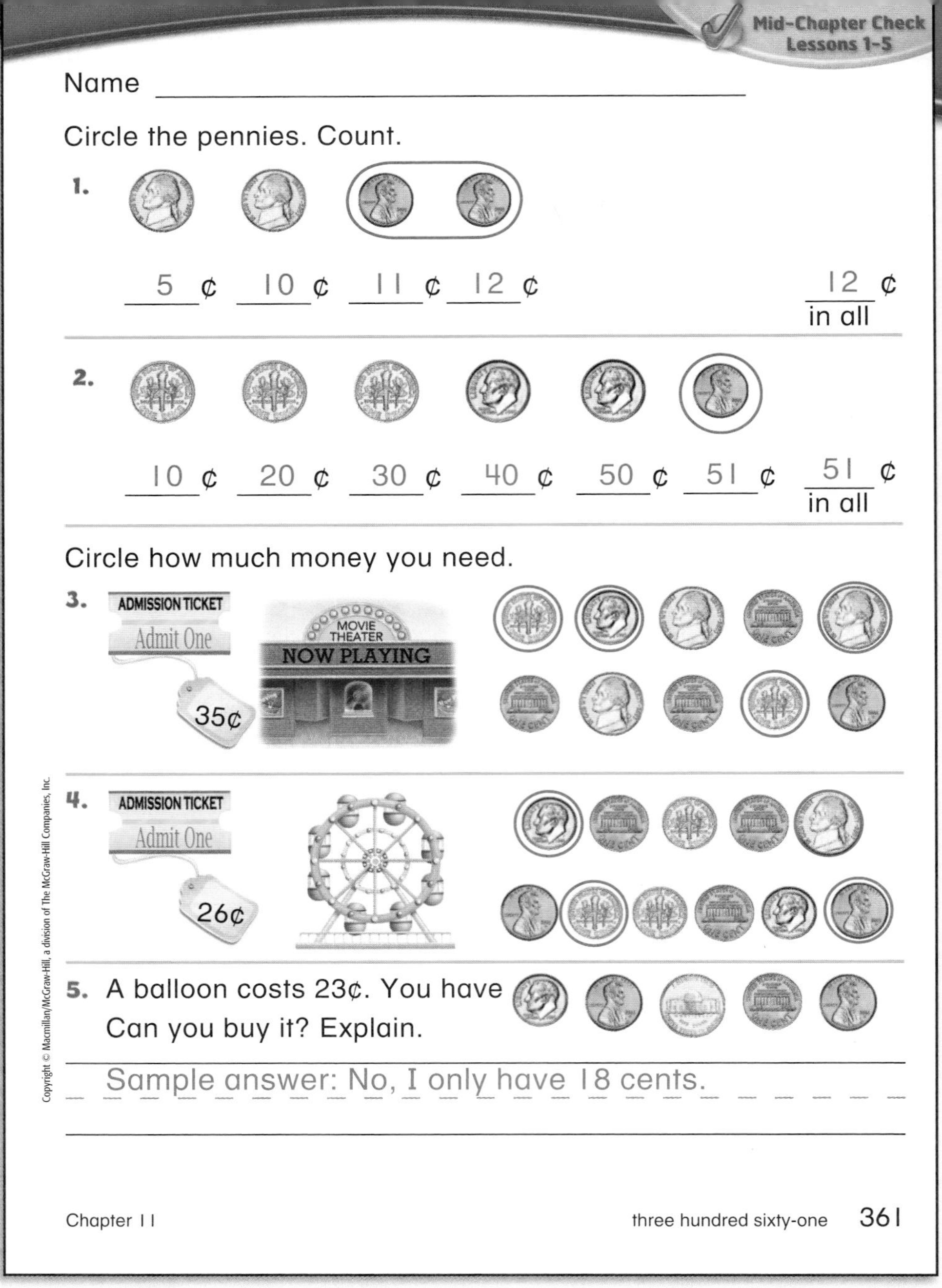

Mid-Chapter Check Lessons 1-5

Name ______

Circle the pennies. Count.

1. 5 ¢ 10 ¢ 11 ¢ 12 ¢ — 12 ¢ in all

2. 10 ¢ 20 ¢ 30 ¢ 40 ¢ 50 ¢ 51 ¢ — 51 ¢ in all

Circle how much money you need.

3. ADMISSION TICKET Admit One 35¢ — MOVIE THEATER NOW PLAYING

4. ADMISSION TICKET Admit One 26¢

5. A balloon costs 23¢. You have
Can you buy it? Explain.

Sample answer: No, I only have 18 cents.

Chapter 11 three hundred sixty-one 361

Data-Driven Decision Making

Based on the results of the Mid-Chapter Check, use the following resources to review concepts that continue to present students with problems.

Exercises	State/Local Standards	What's the Math?	Error Analysis	Resources for Review
1-2 Lesson 11-3		Identify and know the value of dimes, nickels, and pennies.	Does not count number of coins correctly. Does not add values of coins accurately.	Strategic Intervention Guide (p. 114) CRM Chapter 11 Resource Masters (Reteach Worksheets) Math Online Concepts in Motion Math Adventures
3-4 Lesson 11-4		Make precise calculations with pennies, nickels, and dimes to solve problems.	Does not add denominations of coins accurately.	
5 Lesson 11-5		Identify and know the value of coins to solve a problem.	Does not add denominations correctly. Does not write an explanation.	

Spiral Review Chapters 1–11

Put an X on the ones you take away.
Write how many are left.

6. 

10 take away 3 is 7.

7. 

9 take away 3 is 6.

Skip count by 2s or 5s.

8. 2, 4, 6, 8, 10, 12, 14

9. 5, 10, 15, 20, 25, 30

Use cube to measure.

10. 

about 2 cubes

11. 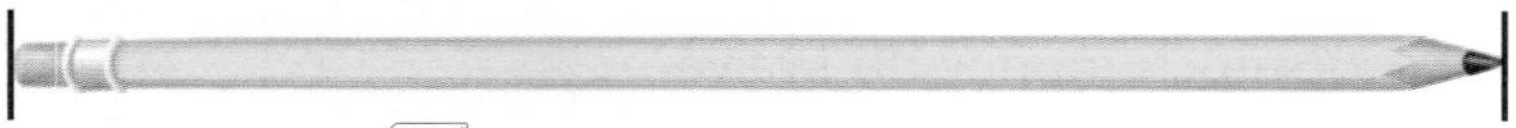

about 8 cubes

12. 

about 5 cubes

Spiral Review

Reviews Chapters 1 to 11

Objective: Review and assess mastery of skills and concepts from previous chapters.

Resources for Review

Based on student results, refer to these lessons for remediation.

- **Exercises 6–7: Lesson 3-2** (p. 89)
- **Exercises 8–9: Lesson 8-7** (p. 259)
- **Exercises 10–12: Lesson 9-2** (p. 279)

LESSON 11-6

Equal Amounts

Lesson Planner

Objective

Identify different combinations of coins that equal the same value.

Review Vocabulary

equal to

Resources

Manipulatives: counters, coins (pennies, nickels, dimes)

Literature Connection: *The Penny Pot* by Stuart J. Murphy

Alternate Lesson: Use "Money" on pages 332 and 333 of *Math Their Way* to provide practice identifying coin combinations.

Teacher Technology

TeacherWorks • Concepts in Motion • Math Songs Track 16 Lesson Plan

Focus on Math Background

Instruction in this lesson focuses on representing the same amount of money with different combinations of coins. To complete this task, students will draw upon their experience in decomposing numbers and their knowledge of coin values and exchanges. Up to this point, students have decomposed whole numbers into any combination of lesser numbers. When decomposing monetary values, however, students are restricted to using the monetary units. Using dimes, nickels, and pennies limits students to combinations that include only tens, fives, and ones. For example, instead of breaking 6 cents into 0 + 6, 1 + 5, 2 + 4, or 3 + 3, students find there are only two possibilities—1 nickel and 1 penny or 6 pennies.

Daily Routine

Use these suggestions before beginning the lesson on p. 363.

5-Minute Check

(Reviews Lesson 11-5)

Andrew is buying a pad of paper. It costs 75¢. What coins could Andrew use to buy the pad of paper? Sample answers: 7 dimes and 1 nickel; 5 dimes and 5 nickels

Problem of the Day

I have 2 dimes, 3 nickels, and 4 pennies. How much money do I have? 39¢

LINE UP As students line up, give them an amount. Have them tell you what coins they would use to equal that amount.

Review Math Vocabulary

Materials: pennies, nickels, dimes or class-size coins

- Write the review vocabulary term **equal to** on the board. Write 10¢ on the board. Ask students to show 10¢ using one coin. 1 dime Explain that one dime is equal to 10¢.
- Have students show 10¢ with two coins. 2 nickels Explain that two nickels are equal to one dime, or 10¢.
- Have students show 10¢ with two kinds of coins. 1 nickel and 5 pennies Make sure students understand that one nickel and five pennies are *equal to* one dime or two nickels. They are all equal to 10¢.

Differentiated Instruction

Small Group Options

Option 1 VISUAL/SPATIAL, KINESTHETIC, LOGICAL

Below Level BL

Materials: pictures of toys, coins (pennies, nickels, dimes)

- Display a picture of a toy with a price marked on it.
- Put out two different combinations of coins that each equal the price of the toy. Ask students which combination shows the fewest coins that could be used to purchase the item.
- Display another toy and have students select coins that they could use to buy the item. Ask if they can make any trades to use fewer coins.
- When students have the fewest number of coins possible, have them draw their combination.
- Ask students to explain the strategy they used. Sample answer: Starting with the coin of greatest value helps to find the fewest coins needed.

Option 2 VISUAL/SPATIAL

English Language Learners ELL

Materials: overhead and coins (pennies, nickels, dimes)
Core Vocabulary: draw, mix, different combinations
Common Use Verb: put together

See Math This strategy uses graphic organizers to help students create equal amounts.

- Give students a value.
- Show them different combinations of coins that equal this same value on a "is the same as" chart.
- Ask the students to determine how many different combinations they can come up with to arrive at that amount of money. They will need to draw pictures of the coins used for the combinations.
- Chart example:

$ .60	is the same as	6 nickels, 3 dimes
		6 dimes
		12 nickels

Independent Work Options

Option 1 LOGICAL, SOCIAL

Early Finishers OL AL

Materials: coins (pennies, nickels, dimes)

- Have students make as many combinations of coins as possible that equal 50¢.
- Invite them to use coins to model different combinations and then record each one.

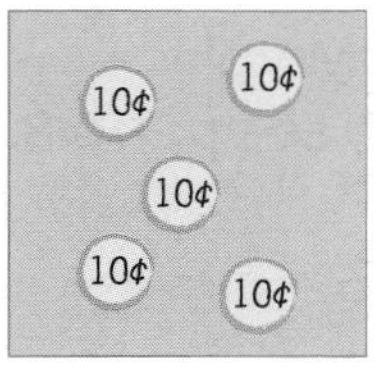

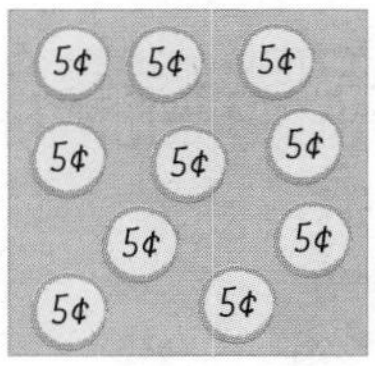

Option 2

Student Technology

Math Online macmillanmh.com

Math Songs, "How Many Pennies?" Track 16

Option 3

Learning Station: Science (p. 347H)

Direct students to the Science Learning Station for more opportunities to explore and extend the lesson concept.

Option 4

Problem-Solving Practice

Reinforce problem-solving skills and strategies with the Problem-Solving Practice worksheet.

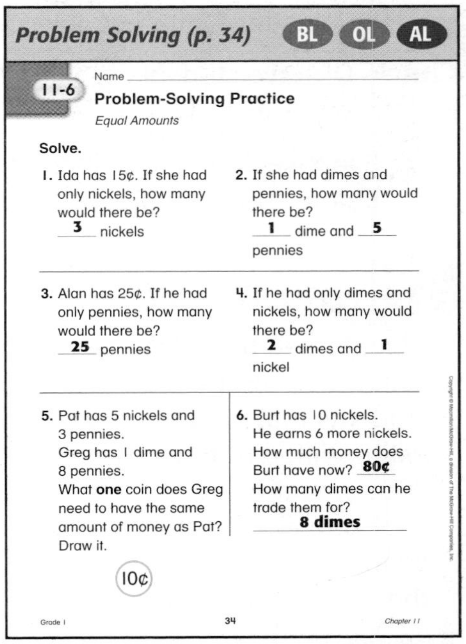

Problem Solving (p. 34) BL OL AL

11-6 Name ______

Problem-Solving Practice
Equal Amounts

Solve.

1. Ida has 15¢. If she had only nickels, how many would there be? **3** nickels
2. If she had dimes and pennies, how many would there be? **1** dime and **5** pennies
3. Alan has 25¢. If he had only pennies, how many would there be? **25** pennies
4. If he had only dimes and nickels, how many would there be? **2** dimes and **1** nickel
5. Pat has 5 nickels and 3 pennies. Greg has 1 dime and 8 pennies. What **one** coin does Greg need to have the same amount of money as Pat? Draw it. 10¢
6. Burt has 10 nickels. He earns 6 more nickels. How much money does Burt have now? **80¢** How many dimes can he trade them for? **8 dimes**

Grade 1 34 Chapter 11

11-6

1 Introduce

Activity Choice 1 • Hands-On

- Explain that addition facts can be different, yet equal. For example, 3 + 4 = 7 and 5 + 2 = 7.
- Have students use counters to explore and identify different addition facts that equal the same sum.
- Explain that different combinations of coins can also have equal value.

Activity Choice 2 • Literature

Introduce the lesson with *The Penny Pot* by Stuart J. Murphy. For additional support, see p. TR58.

2 Teach

- Give each student three dimes, four nickels, and ten pennies.
- **Is 1 dime equal to 2 nickels?** yes
- **Describe the relationship between 1 nickel and 5 pennies.** They are equal in value.
- **How many ways can you show 10¢?** 1 dime; 2 nickels; 1 nickel and 5 pennies; and 10 pennies
- **How many ways can you show 5¢?** 1 nickel; 5 pennies
- **How many ways can you show 17¢?** Sample answers: 17 pennies; 3 nickels and 2 pennies; 1 dime, 1 nickel, 2 pennies; 1 nickel and 12 pennies

Get Ready Use the section at the top of p. 363 to reinforce the lesson concept. Explore a variety of coin combinations with equal value.

Check Observe students as you work through Exercises 1–3 as a class.

Exercise 3 Assess student comprehension before assigning practice exercises.

COMMON ERROR!

When asked to match the value of a set of coins with another combination of coins, students may create a new combination but with a different total. Have students first show the amount using only pennies and then trade their pennies for other coins. Ask them to count their final combination and then count the original one again.

Name ______________________

Hands-On Activity

Equal Amounts

Get Ready

Main Idea

I will show different ways to make the same amount of money.

You can show the same amount of money in more than one way.

One Way

Another Way

Check

3. 4 ways; 1 dime, 2 nickels, 1 nickel and 5 pennies, 10 pennies

Use coins. Show each amount a different way.

1. Show 23¢.

One Way	Another Way Sample answer:
	10¢ 1¢ 5¢ 1¢ 5¢ 1¢

2. Show 18¢.

One Way	Another Way Sample answer:
	1¢ 5¢ 5¢ 5¢ 1¢ 1¢

3. Talk About It Tell the ways you can show 10¢.

Reteach (p. 31) BL

11-6 Name ______

Reteach

Equal Amounts

You can show the same amount in different ways.

20¢ =

20¢ =

20¢ =

20¢ =

Use or draw coins. Show the coin amount. Then show it a different way.

Amount	One Way	Another Way
15¢	**Answers will vary.**	**Answers will vary.**
10¢	**Answers will vary.**	**Answers will vary.**
17¢	**Answers will vary.**	**Answers will vary.**

Chapter Resources

Skills Practice (p. 32) OL

11-6 Name ______

Skills Practice

Equal Amounts

Use coins. Show each amount a different way.

1. Show 25¢. **sample answer** 10¢ 5¢ 5¢ 5¢
2. Show 40¢. **Answers will vary.**
3. Show 24¢. **Answers will vary.**
4. Show 17¢. **Answers will vary.**

Solve.

5. Jason has two dimes and a nickel. Luisa has one dime, a nickel, and five pennies. Do they have the same amount? **no**

Practice

Use coins. Show each amount a different way.

4. Show 37¢.

One Way	Another Way
	Sample answer: 10¢ 1¢ 1¢ 10¢ 10¢ 5¢

5. Show 40¢.

One Way	Another Way
	Sample answer: 10¢ 10¢ 10¢ 10¢

6. Show 51¢.

One Way	Another Way
	Sample answer: 10¢ 10¢ 10¢ 10¢ 1¢ 10¢

7. **WRITING IN MATH** Write a number story about these coins. Ask a friend to solve the problem.

Sample answer: Dad gave me a dime and a penny. Mom gave me 2 nickels. How much money do I have?

Math at Home Activity: Use coins to make an amount of money less than $1.00. Have your child make that same amount another way.

Enrich (p. 35) AL

11-6 Name ____
Enrich
Equal Amounts

You get to shop for new school supplies! Circle the group of coins that match the price. X the coins that do not.

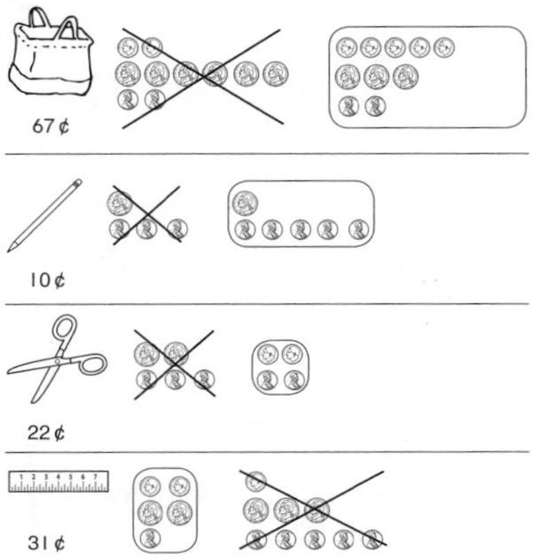

Grade 1 35 Chapter 11

Homework Practice (p. 33) OL

11-6 Name ____
Homework Practice
Equal Amounts

Use coins. Show each amount a different way.

1. Show 35¢. **Answers will vary.**
2. Show 41¢. **Answers will vary.**
3. Show 44¢. **Answers will vary.**
4. Show 28¢. **Answers will vary.**

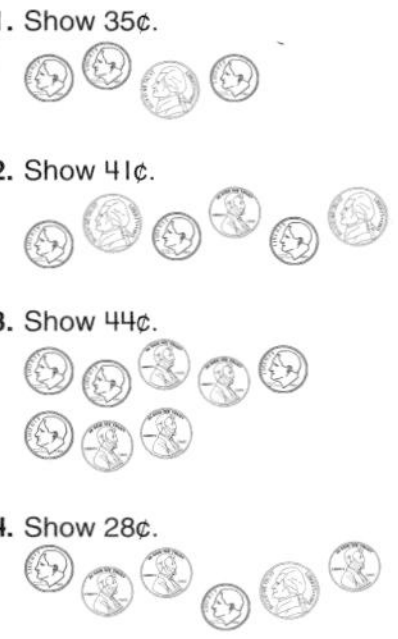

Solve. Use coins.

5. Sharon has 2 dimes, 2 nickels, and 5 pennies. Her dad has 3 dimes and a nickel. Do they have the same amount? **yes**

Grade 1 33 Chapter 11

BL Alternate Teaching Strategy

If students have difficulty identifying groups of coins with the same value . . .

Then use one of the reteach options.

1. CRM **Daily Reteach Worksheet** (p. 31)
2. **Provide Explicit Clues** Pair students. Have one partner make 16¢ with a combination of dimes and pennies. Have the other partner use nickels and pennies.

3 Practice

Differentiate practice using these leveled assignments for Exercises 4–7.

Level	Assignment
BL Below/Approaching Level	Guide students through the exercises with coins for support.
OL On Level	Complete the exercises independently with coins for support.
AL Above/Beyond Level	Complete the exercises independently without coins.

4 Assess

Formative Assessment

Have students show 14¢ using a combination of coins. When they have finished, have them show the same amount using a different combination. Sample answers: 1 dime, 4 pennies; 2 nickels, 4 pennies

WRITING IN MATH Have students write about how they can show the same amount of money using different combinations of coins. Sample answer: A nickel or 5 pennies can be used to show 5¢.

Quick Check **Are students continuing to struggle with recognizing equal value in different sets of coins?**

If Yes → Small Group Options (p. 363B)
If No → Independent Work Options (p. 363B)
CRM Skills Practice Worksheet (p. 32)
CRM Enrich Worksheet (p. 35)

LESSON
11-7 Quarters

Lesson Planner

Objective
Identify the value of a quarter. Count groups of coins.

Vocabulary
quarter

Resources
Materials: overhead projector

Manipulatives: coins (quarters, dimes, nickels, pennies)

Literature Connection: *The Penny Pot* by Stuart J. Murphy

Alternate Lesson: Use "Money" on pages 332 and 333 of *Math Their Way* to provide practice with the value of a quarter.

Teacher Technology

TeacherWorks • Math Songs Track 16 Lesson Plan

Focus on Math Background

In this lesson, students will learn that a quarter is worth 25 cents by equating its value with other coin combinations, such as by exchanging 25 pennies for 2 dimes and 1 nickel. To most first graders, 25 is a big number, especially if they must conserve its value when adding additional amounts to it or breaking it down into smaller units of tens, fives, and ones. Consequently, the most significant challenge in this lesson is counting amounts of money that contain one or more quarters in addition to coins of different values. To accomplish this task, students will learn that they must count on from 25 first and then skip count according to the value of the coin with the next greatest denomination—counting by tens for dimes, by fives for nickels, or by ones for pennies.

Daily Routine

Use these suggestions before beginning the lesson on p. 365.

5-Minute Check
(Reviews Lesson 11-6)

1. How can you show 50¢ with dimes? 5 dimes

2. How can you show 50¢ with nickels? 10 nickels

3. How can you show 50¢ with nickels and dimes? Sample answers: 4 dimes and 2 nickels; 3 dimes and 4 nickels

Problem of the Day
Alex is 5 years old. Laura is 10 years older than Alex. She is 5 years younger than Brett. How old are Laura and Brett? Laura is 15 years old; Brett is 20 years old.

LINE UP Display a combination of coins. Choose one student to tell the total value and then line up. Ask other students to name a different combination of coins that has equal value before they line up. Repeat with other combinations of coins.

Building Math Vocabulary
Materials: quarter

- Display a quarter. Write the word **quarter** on the board. Explain that a quarter equals 25 cents. Have students look at each side of a quarter and discuss what each side looks like. Explain the concept of *heads* and *tails*.
- Have students use different ways to show 25¢. Sample answers: 2 dimes and 1 nickel; 5 nickels; 25 pennies
- Display the different combinations of coins that equal 25¢.

Visual Vocabulary Cards
Use Visual Vocabulary Card 40 to reinforce the vocabulary introduced in this lesson. (The Define/Example/Ask routine is printed on the back of each card.)

Differentiated Instruction

Small Group Options

Option 1 VISUAL/SPATIAL, KINESTHETIC, LOGICAL, SOCIAL

Below/Approaching Level (BL)

Materials: toys with price tags attached, lunch bags, coins

- Display toys and a different price for each. For each toy, prepare a corresponding bag that contains a combination of coins equal to that item's price.
- Have students select a bag and count the coins.
- Challenge students to match the value of coins in their bag to the toy with that price.
- Invite students to talk about how they counted their coins and matched the amount to the toy.

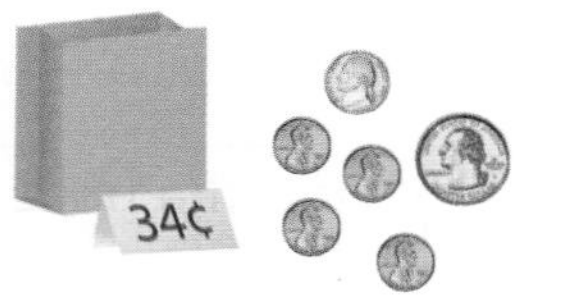

Option 2 VISUAL

English Language Learners (ELL)

Materials: pennies, nickels, dimes, and quarters in overhead coins
Core Vocabulary: pattern, money pyramid, replace
Common Use Verb: build

See Math This strategy helps students recognize quarters and the different ways to make 25¢.

- Place twenty-five pennies in a row on the overhead. Say: "25 pennies is the same as a quarter cents." Write "is the same as 25¢."
- On a row above the first, place a nickel and 20 pennies. Say: "Five pennies makes a nickel. A nickel and 20 pennies is the same as 25¢." Write "A nickel and 20 pennies is the same as 25¢."
- Repeat, placing only 1 coin per row until the pyramid reaches one quarter.
- Ask students to explain or describe the pattern.

Independent Work Options

Option 1 VISUAL/SPATIAL, KINESTHETIC, LOGICAL, SOCIAL

Early Finishers (OL) (AL)

Materials: paper, pencil, coins

- Have students select six coins.
- Instruct students to put their coins in order from greatest to least value. Then have them draw the row of coins.
- Have students count the coins to find the total amount.

Option 2

Student Technology

Math Online macmillanmh.com

Math Songs, "How Many Pennies?" Track 16 • Math Adventures

Option 3

Learning Station: Art (p. 347G)

Direct students to the Art Learning Station for more opportunities to explore and extend the lesson concept.

Option 4

Problem-Solving Practice

Reinforce problem-solving skills and strategies with the Problem-Solving Practice worksheet.

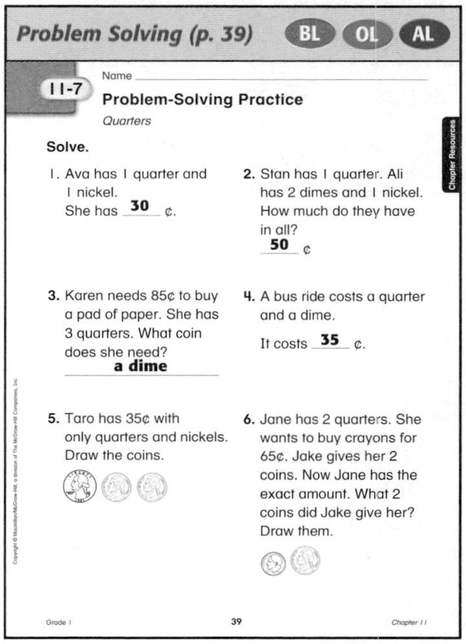

Problem Solving (p. 39) BL OL AL

Name

11-7 **Problem-Solving Practice**
Quarters

Solve.

1. Ava has 1 quarter and 1 nickel. She has **30** ¢.
2. Stan has 1 quarter. Ali has 2 dimes and 1 nickel. How much do they have in all? **50** ¢
3. Karen needs 85¢ to buy a pad of paper. She has 3 quarters. What coin does she need? **a dime**
4. A bus ride costs a quarter and a dime. It costs **35** ¢.
5. Taro has 35¢ with only quarters and nickels. Draw the coins.
6. Jane has 2 quarters. She wants to buy crayons for 65¢. Jake gives her 2 coins. Now Jane has the exact amount. What 2 coins did Jake give her? Draw them.

Grade 1 39 Chapter 11

11-7

1 Introduce

Activity Choice 1 • Hands-On

- Give pairs of students thirty play pennies, three dimes, and three nickels. On the overhead, show any combination of coins that equals 25¢, but do not say the amount. Have pairs work together to make the same combination.
- Tell students to make another combination of coins that equals 25¢. Ask students to tell what they did. Ask whether they know of a faster way to show 25¢.
- Show a **quarter** on the overhead, and tell students the name of the coin and that its value is 25¢.

Activity Choice 2 • Literature

Introduce the lesson with *The Penny Pot* by Stuart J. Murphy. For additional support, see p. TR58.

2 Teach

- Give pairs of students ten pennies, three dimes, three nickels, and two quarters.
- Write 37¢ on the board. Tell the students to figure out a way to show 37¢, and they must use a quarter.
- Then have one student from each pair draw the coins on the board while the other tells what to draw.

Get Ready Use the section at the top of p. 365 to reinforce the lesson concept. Guide students in identifying the values of coins.

Check Observe students as you work through Exercises 1–3 as a class.

Exercise 3 Assess student comprehension before assigning practice exercises.

! COMMON ERROR!

As they begin counting coin combinations with higher values, students may make errors in counting and keeping track of cumulative values. Allow students to track their counting on a hundred chart.

Name ______________________

Quarters

Get Ready

Main Idea

I will count pennies, nickels, dimes, and quarters.

Vocabulary

quarter

A **quarter** is worth 25 cents.

Count. Start with the quarter.

25 ¢ 35 ¢ 40 ¢ 41 ¢ 42 ¢

Check

Remember: Start counting with the coin of greatest value.

Count. Write the price.

1. 

25 ¢ 26 ¢ 27 ¢ 28 ¢ 29 ¢

Price 29 ¢

Draw coins to show the price.

2. 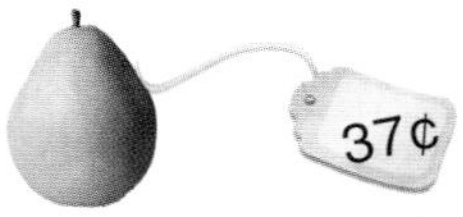

Sample answer: 25¢ 10¢ 1¢ 1¢

3. Talk About It Which is worth more: a quarter or 2 dimes? How do you know? quarter; a quarter is worth 25¢ and 2 dimes are worth 10¢

Reteach (p. 36) BL

11-7 Name ______________________

Reteach

Quarters

Twenty-five pennies equal 25¢. A quarter equals 25¢.

25¢ = 25¢

You can trade 2 dimes and 1 nickel for 1 quarter.

You can trade 1 dime, 2 nickels, and 5 pennies for 1 quarter.

Draw the coins you have. Count them.

Coins you have	Draw your coins	How much money do you have?
1 quarter, 3 dimes		55 ¢
2 quarters, 3 dimes, 1 nickel		85 ¢
3 quarters, 1 dime, 1 penny		86 ¢

Grade 1 36 Chapter 11

Skills Practice (p. 37) OL

11-7 Name ______________________

Skills Practice

Quarters

Count the coins. Write the price.

1. 53 ¢
2. 40 ¢
3. 70 ¢
4. 55 ¢

Solve.

5. Tani has 2 quarters, 1 dime, and 2 pennies. He says he has 67¢. Is he right? no

6. Ms. Cruz needs a new pen. It costs 80¢. She has [coins]. Does she have enough? no What coin does she need to buy the pen? a quarter

Grade 1 37 Chapter 11

Practice

Count. Write the price.

4\.

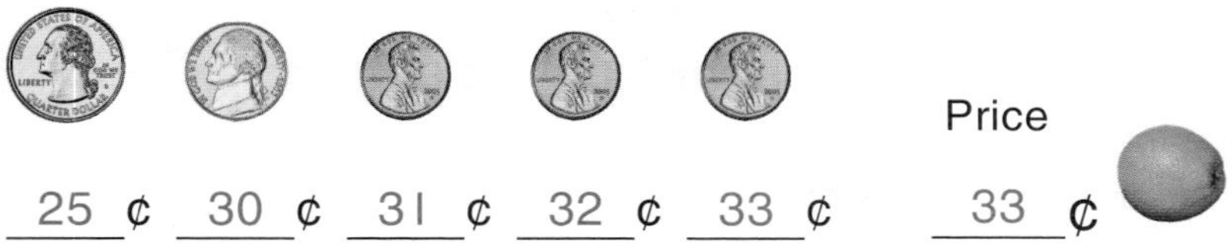

25 ¢ 30 ¢ 31 ¢ 32 ¢ 33 ¢ Price 33 ¢

5\.

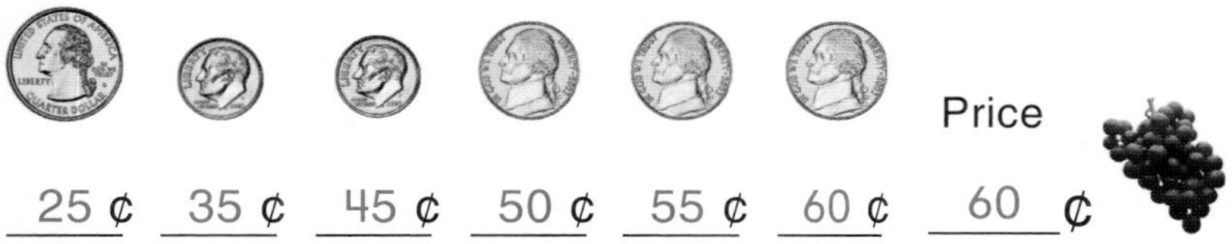

25 ¢ 35 ¢ 45 ¢ 50 ¢ 55 ¢ 60 ¢ Price 60 ¢

Draw coins to show the price.

6\. 52¢ Sample answer: (25) (25) (1) (1)

7\. 89¢ Sample answer: (25) (25) (25) (10) (1) (1) (1) (1)

8\. 93¢ Sample answer: (25) (25) (25) (10) (5) (1) (1) (1)

9\. 48¢ Sample answer: (25) (10) (10) (1) (1) (1)

GO on

Enrich (p. 40) AL

11-7 Name ______

Enrich

Quarters

Solve.

1\. TJ wants to buy a [yo-yo]. It costs 46¢.
TJ has (coins).
Does he have enough?
(yes) no
If he does not have enough, draw the coins he needs.

No coins are drawn.

2\. Rosa wants to buy a [hockey stick]. It costs 86¢.
Rosa has (coins).
Does she have enough?
yes (no)
If she does not have enough, draw the coins she needs.

Grade 1 40 Chapter 11

Homework Practice (p. 38) OL

11-7 Name ______

Homework Practice

Quarters

Count the coins. Write the price.

1\. 86 ¢

2\. 78 ¢

3\. 49 ¢

4\. 70 ¢

Solve.

5\. Lou has 3 quarters. A kite costs 75¢. Does he have enough money? **yes**

6\. Mario has 1 quarter, 3 dimes, and 2 nickels. A hat costs 70¢. Does he have enough money? **no**

Grade 1 38 Chapter 11

BL Alternate Teaching Strategy

If students have difficulty counting on by tens or fives from 25 . . .

Then use one of the reteach options.

1 CRM **Daily Reteach Worksheet** (p. 36)

2 **Make a Coin Line-Up** Have students line up their coins on a sheet of paper before counting them. Have students write under each coin the number they say as they add that coin's value to the count. Afterward, ask students to study the numbers they wrote and show where they stopped skip counting by twenty-fives and began counting by tens, and so on.

3 Practice

Differentiate practice using these leveled assignments for Exercises 4–9.

Level	Assignment
BL Below/Approaching Level	Guide students through the exercises, using coins and a hundred chart for support.
OL On Level	Complete the exercises independently, using coins, if needed.
AL Above/Beyond Level	Complete the exercises independently.

4 Assess

Formative Assessment

Provide coins and instruct students to select 1 quarter, 2 dimes, 1 nickel, and 3 pennies. Have them count their coins to determine the total value. 25¢, 35¢, 45¢, 50¢, 51¢, 52¢, 53¢

WRITING IN MATH Have students write about how they will remember the correct way to count a combination of different coins.

Quick Check **Are students continuing to struggle with counting quarters, dimes, nickels, and pennies?**

If Yes → Small Group Options (p. 365B)

If No → Independent Work Options (p. 365B)

CRM Skills Practice Worksheet (p. 37)

CRM Enrich Worksheet (p. 40)

Tech Link

Math Objective

Use technology to show the value of coins.

Resources

Math Tool Chest *(accessible in three ways)*

- **Math Online** macmillanmh.com
- StudentWorks Plus
- Math Tool Chest

Getting Started

- The activities and exercises on pp. 367–368 use the Level 1 Money Tool in Math Tool Chest. They may be completed as a class, in pairs, or individually.
- As a class, read and then work through the information and instructions on the top of p. 367.
- Guide students as they work through Exercises 10–11.

Using Math Tool Chest

Money The money tool in the Math Tool Chest program allows students to stamp out different amounts of coins.

- Students can experiment by stamping out many different combinations of coins to learn more about the value of money.
- Have students count as they stamp the coins shown in the example at the top of the page. They should count 25, 35, 45, 55, 65, 70, 75, 80. Students can click on the star at any time to check the value of the coins they have stamped so far.
- Once they have finished stamping, they can click on the question mark and enter the value of the coins. They can then click on the star to check their final answer.

Name ______________________

Tech Link

Practice with Technology

Quarters • Computer

Use the tool chest.
Click on Level 1.
Click on the open mat.

- Stamp out 1 quarter.
- Stamp out 4 dimes.
- Stamp out 3 nickels.

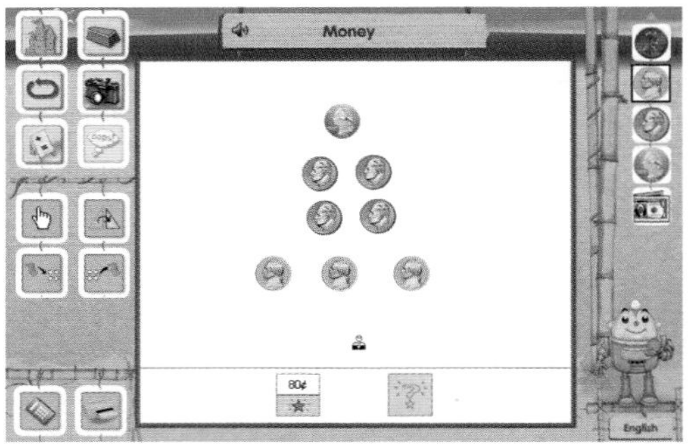

10. Draw the coins.
Write the amount.

25¢ 10¢ 10¢ 10¢ 10¢ 5¢ 5¢ 5¢

80 ¢

Use the tool chest.
Click on Level 1.
Click on the open mat.

- Stamp out 5 dimes.
- Stamp out 1 nickel.
- Stamp out 4 pennies.

11. Draw the coins. Write the amount.

10¢ 10¢ 10¢ 10¢ 10¢ 5¢ 1¢ 1¢ 1¢ 1¢

59 ¢

Money Buttons

Move Students click to move money on their mat. The cursor changes to a pointing finger. A red line hightlights each coin or bill as the cursor moves over it.

Flip Students click Flip and then click a coin or bill to see the opposite side.

Trade Up Trade Up exchanges coins for coins or bills of a higher denomination. Students click , click the coins they want to regroup, then click Trade Up again. The highest denomination students can trade up to is a $1 bill.

Trade Down Trade Down exchanges coins or bills for lower denominations. Students click and then click the bills or coins they want to exchange.

Sum Sum automatically totals all the money in the two sections of the Addition mat. Students click to find the total money amount.

Click on the tool chest. Click on Level 1.
Click on the open mat.

- Stamp out 2 quarters.
- Stamp out 1 nickel.
- Stamp out 4 pennies.

12. Draw the coins. Write the amount.

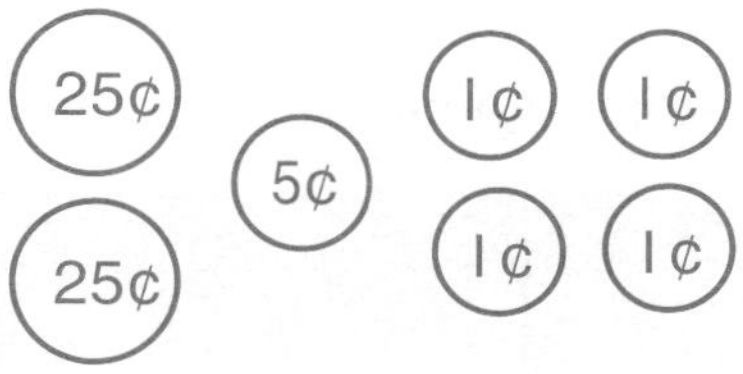

59 ¢

Data File

Every year New Jersey has a hot air balloon festival. The festival has music, games, and balloon rides.

13. Pretend you have these coins to spend.

How much money do you have? 87 ¢

Math at Home Activity: Find items under $1.00 in an advertisement. Have your child tell you the coins needed to buy each item.

Tech Link

Practice

Alone or in pairs, have students complete Exercise 12 as you observe their work.

Data File

Exercise 13 Use the Data File exercise to assess students' understanding of counting a mixed set of coins.

Extending the Link

To extend the link, have students complete the following activity:

- Click on the to erase everything on the mat.
- Divide students into pairs. Ask one student to choose a money amount that is less than $1.
- Have the other student stamp out coins to make the money amount.
- Ask students to print their work, so they have a record of one way to make the money amount.
- Then students can click on on to show the same amount in a different way.
- Ask students to switch roles and repeat the activity as time permits.

11-8 Problem-Solving Investigation
Choose a Strategy

Lesson Planner

Objective

Choose the best strategy to solve a problem.

Resources

Manipulatives: coins (quarters, dimes, nickels, pennies)
Teacher Technology
TeacherWorks

Real-World Problem Solving Library
Math and Social Studies: ***Following a Coin***

Use these leveled books to reinforce and extend problem-solving skills and strategies.

- OL On Level
- ELL Sheltered English
- SP Spanish

For additional support, see the Real-World Problem Solving Teacher Guide.

Daily Routine

Use these suggestions before beginning the lesson on p. 369.

5-Minute Check

(Reviews Lesson 11-7)

Find the total value of the coins.

1. quarter, dime, dime, nickel, penny, penny 52¢
2. quarter, quarter, dime, nickel, nickel, penny 71¢
3. quarter, dime, nickel, nickel, nickel 50¢
4. quarter, dime, dime, dime, nickel, penny 61¢

Problem of the Day

Cindy has 75¢. Pencils cost 10¢ each. She bought pencils for 6 friends. How much money does she have left? 15¢

LINE UP Give each student a quarter, dime, nickel, or penny. Have groups of approximately five students each find the total amount the group has. Have groups line up as they give you their correct total.

Differentiated Instruction

Small Group Options

Option 1 — LOGICAL, VISUAL/SPATIAL

Gifted and Talented BL

Materials: grocery store ads from the newspaper, coins

- Glue onto separate sheets of paper items cut from a grocery ad. On the back of each paper, write all the combinations of coins that can make up the cost of that item.
- Invite students to choose one of the ads. Ask them to use coins to find the combination they would use to purchase the item. Have them write or draw their answer.
- Have students look at the back of the ad to see if their answer is one of the possible answers listed.

Option 2 — INTRAPERSONAL

English Language Learners ELL

Materials: overhead, bingo grid, overhead cut into grid-size squares with problems written within each

Core Vocabulary: in a row, BINGO!, listen for

Common Use Verb: listen

Hear Math This strategy provides more practice decoding spoken number sentences.

- Pass out bingo supplies and ready overhead.
- Place a problem square somewhere on your grid.
- Students repeat, writing the problem in any square as you read it. (Move your square so students do not copy your placement.)
- Repeat until the grid is full. Turn the overhead off.
- Call problems. Remind the class to pay attention as problems are called. Use the overhead to verify problems.
- Reduce or increase the type or variety of vocabulary, or assign pairs to adjust the level of difficulty. Repeat as time permits.

Independent Work Options

Option 1 — LOGICAL, KINESTHETIC, VISUAL/SPATIAL

Early Finishers OL AL

Materials: bag, 1″ × 5″ grid strips, coins

- Prepare bags that each contain a set of five coins totaling less than $1. Write the number of coins and the total amount on the outside of the bag.
- Give each group of students a bag, some coins, and a grid strip. Explain that they will work together to figure out what coins are inside.
- Point out that students should place a coin in each square of the grid to make sure they use the correct number of coins. Have them try different combinations until they find the one that matches the total written on their bag.

Option 2

Student Technology

Math Online macmillanmh.com

Option 3

Learning Station: Social Studies (p. 347G)

Direct students to the Social Studies Learning Station for more opportunities to explore and extend the lesson concept.

11-8

1 Introduce

Activity • Review

Write and read aloud the following:

Karen and Kareem each had 36¢. Karen had three coins and Kareem had five coins. What three coins could Karen have?

- **Which problem-solving strategy can we use to solve this problem?** Sample answer: *guess and check*
- **How could we use *guess and check* to solve the problem?** Sample answer: Start with the coin that has the greatest value. See how many of these coins can be used. Then determine which coins equal the amount left over. Check to see that 3 coins were used. If not, try other combinations of coins.

2 Teach

Have students read the problem on p. 369. Guide them through the problem-solving steps.

Understand Using the question, review what students know and what they need to find.

Plan Have them discuss their strategy.

Solve Guide students to *guess and check* to solve the problem.

- Ask students to start with the coins that have the greatest value. 25¢, 35¢, 40¢, 41¢
- **Do we have 66¢ yet?** No, we have 41¢.
- **Do you need to add more coins or take away some? Explain.** We need to add more because 41¢ is less than 66¢.

Check Have students look back at the problem to make sure that the answer fits the facts given.

- **Did you guess and check to find which coins total 66¢?** yes
- **Does your solution show how many of each coin he has?** yes; 2 quarters, 1 dime, 1 nickel, and 1 penny

! COMMON ERROR!

Students who choose coins randomly for *guess and check* may become frustrated by the number of incorrect combinations. Remind them to start with the coins of greatest value.

Name ____________________

Problem-Solving Investigation

I have a pocket full of coins. They total 66 cents. I have at least 1 penny, 1 nickel, 1 dime, and 1 quarter. What coins do I have?

Main Idea

I will choose a strategy to solve a problem.

Your Mission: Find which coins total 66 cents.

Understand

What do I know? Underline what you know.

What do I need to find? Circle it.

Plan

How will I solve the problem?

One way is to guess and check.

Solve

I could have 1 penny, 1 nickel, 1 dime, and 1 quarter.
That is only 41¢, not 66¢.

I could have 1 penny, 1 nickel, 2 dimes, and 2 quarters.
That is 76¢, not 66¢.

I could have 1 penny, 1 nickel, 1 dime, and 2 quarters.
That is 66¢!

Check

Look back. Is my answer reasonable? Check students' explanations.

Reteach (pp. 41–42) BL

11-8 Name ____________________

Reteach (1)

Problem-Solving Investigation: Choose a Strategy

Dave has a lot of nickels.
They add up to 35¢.
How many nickels does he have?

Step 1 Understand
What do I know?
He has all nickels.
They add up to 35¢.
What do I need to find out?
How many nickels there are.

Step 2 Plan
How will I find out?
I can use a model. But I may not have coins to use.
I can guess and draw coins to find the answer.
I will guess and check.

Step 3 Solve
Guess and check.
There are 7 nickels.

Step 4 Check
Does my guess show how many nickels there are? yes
Did I choose the right strategy? **See students' work.**

Chapter Resources

Skills Practice (p. 43) OL

11-8 Name ____________________

Skills Practice

Problem-Solving Investigation: Choose a Strategy

Choose a strategy. Solve.

Problem-Solving Strategies
- Act it out
- Use a model
- Guess and check

1. Roy has 9 dimes. He spends 60¢. How many dimes does he have left? **3** dimes
2. Lisa has 14 pennies. She finds 25 pennies in the yard. She finds 8 pennies at school. How much money does she have? **47** ¢
3. Emil has 95¢. He gives 3 coins to his mom. Now he has 20¢. What 3 coins did he give? **3 quarters**

Shelly goes to the store. She wants to buy a present. She has 3 quarters.

4. How much money does Shelly have? **75** ¢
5. Can Shelly buy the horse? **yes**

Chapter Resources

Mixed Problem Solving

Problem-Solving Strategies
- Guess and check
- Act it out
- Make a table

Choose a strategy. Solve.

1. Edwin has all dimes in his piggy bank. He counted the money. It totals 50 cents. How many dimes does he have?

5 dimes

2. Larry and Ruthie each have 25 cents. Larry has a quarter. Ruthie has 3 coins. What coins does Ruthie have?

2 dimes, 1 nickel

3. Ivan has 2 quarters and 1 dime. How much money does he have?

60 cents

4. Turtles are 10 cents at the pet store. Derek wants 4 turtles. How much money does he need?

40 cents

Math at Home Activity: Take advantage of problem-solving opportunities during daily routines such as riding in the car, bedtime, doing laundry, putting away groceries, planning schedules, and so on.

Enrich (p. 45) AL

11-8 Name ______

Enrich

Can You Buy It?

Count the coins. Write the amount. Can you buy the object? Circle *yes* or *no* for your answer.

Amount	Price	Answer
12 ¢	15¢	Yes / (No)
22 ¢	25¢	Yes / (No)
25 ¢	20¢	(Yes) / No
18 ¢	10¢	(Yes) / No

Chapter Resources

Grade 1 45 Chapter 11

Homework Practice (p. 44) OL

11-8 Name ______

Homework Practice

Problem-Solving Investigation: Choose a Strategy

Choose a strategy. Solve.

Problem-Solving Strategies
- Act it out
- Use a model
- Guess and check

1. Pablo has 3 quarters. He spends 50¢. How many quarters does he have now? **1**
2. Mr. Bloom sells flowers for 40¢. Ms. Ito buys a flower. She spends 4 coins. What coins are they? **dimes**
3. Hakeem also buys a flower. He spends 3 coins. What coins are they? **1 quarter, 1 dime, 1 nickel**
4. Pat sells carrots for one penny. Chris buys 10 carrots. How many pennies does he need? **10 pennies**
5. Cora has [coins]. She says she has 60¢. Is she correct? **no**
6. Sharon has 6 dimes. She takes out 2 dimes and adds 1 quarter. Then she takes out another dime and adds 1 penny. How much money does she have? **56** ¢

Grade 1 44 Chapter 11

BL Alternate Teaching Strategy

If students have difficulty using the *guess and check* strategy . . .

Then use one of the following reteach options.

1. CRM **Daily Reteach Worksheet** (pp. 41–42)
2. **Up or Down?** Have students work in small groups to find three coins with a total of 60¢. Draw three squares on a sheet of paper and write the number 60, have students choose a coin to place in each square. Help them find the total value and write it next to 60.
   - **Does our total need to go up or down to equal 60¢?** Have students replace one of the coins, recalculate, and continue replacing one at a time until they total 60¢. 2 quarters, 1 dime

3 Practice

Mixed Problem Solving

Exercises 1–4 Be sure students can read and understand the problems. Remind students to think about the problem-solving strategies they have learned. Have them decide which strategy would best help them solve each problem.

4 Assess

Formative Assessment

Have students solve the following problem:

- **Mia has five coins that equal 46¢. What coins does Mia have?** 1 quarter,1 dime, 2 nickels, 1 penny Ask them to explain the steps they take in trying to find the answer.

Quick Check **Are students continuing to struggle with the *guess and check* strategy?**

If Yes → CRM Reteach Worksheet (pp. 41–42)

If No → Independent Work Options (p. 369B)

CRM Skills Practice Worksheet (p. 43)

CRM Enrich Worksheet (p. 45)

LESSON 11-9 Money Amounts

Lesson Planner

Objectives

Find the value of a mixed set of coins. Compare the value of a set of coins with prices.

Review Vocabulary

sum

Resources

Materials: toy store catalogs, paper, glue, markers, coin stamps or stickers

Manipulatives: coins (quarters, dimes, nickels, pennies)

Literature Connection: *The Big Buck Adventures* by Shelley Gill and Deborah Tobola

Alternate Lesson: Use "The Store" on page 225 of *Math Their Way* to provide practice with money amount combinations.

Teacher Technology

TeacherWorks • Math Songs Track 16 Lesson Plan

Focus on Math Background

In this lesson, students will continue to practice strategies they have learned for counting combinations of quarters, dimes, nickels, and pennies and will compare these money amounts to prices. To do this, students must understand *greater than* and *less than* and possess sufficient number sense to abstract the size of numbers beyond 30. For example, students demonstrate this degree of number sense when they can reason that 50 is greater than 39 but less than 71.

Daily Routine

Use these suggestions before beginning the lesson on p. 371.

5-Minute Check

(Reviews Lesson 11-8)

One dime equals 10¢. How much are 8 dimes worth? 80¢ What other coins show an equal amount? Sample answers: 3 quarters and 1 nickel, 7 dimes and 2 nickels

Problem of the Day

Al and Mark have 3 pennies each. Alicia has 5 pennies. Shawn has 6 pennies. Do the children have enough money to buy a pack of gum that costs 20¢? Explain. Sample answer: No; they only have 14¢

LINE UP Pose this question for partners to solve. Invite pairs who answer correctly to line up. **If I gave you a penny for each year of your age and you put your pennies together, what coins could you trade for?** Sample answer: Two 6-year-olds could trade for 1 dime and 2 pennies or 2 nickels and 2 pennies.

Review Math Vocabulary

- Write the word **sum** on the board. Remind students that a sum is the answer they get when they add numbers.
- Have students talk about how a sum and a total amount of coins are alike. Both are answers when you add numbers; a sum is the same thing as total amount.
- **What is the sum or total amount of 2 quarters, 1 dime, 1 nickel, and 2 pennies?** 67¢

Visual Vocabulary Cards

Use Visual Vocabulary Card 47 to reinforce the vocabulary reviewed in this lesson. (The Define/Example/Ask routine is printed on the back of each card.)

sum

Differentiated Instruction

Small Group Options

Option 1 Gifted and Talented AL

VISUAL/SPATIAL, KINESTHETIC, LOGICAL

Materials: index cards, crayons, pictures of toys, price tags

- Write a price on each tag, and attach it to a picture of a toy. Write the same money amount on an index card.
- Give each student a money index card. Challenge students to draw coins on a blank index card to show the value on the first index card.
- Have students shuffle the cards with pictures of coins and pass them out. Ask students to match the amount on their card with the correct toy.

Option 2 English Language Learners ELL

VISUAL, AUDITORY

Materials: index cards with money, cards with prices, overhead of lyrics and homonyms
Core Vocabulary: since, cents, sounds nearly the same
Common Use Verb: needs

Talk Math This strategy uses music to help integrate vocabulary and math skills.

- Say: "Words can sound the same or alike." Pantomime meanings of "cents," "sense" "scents" and "since." Say "Since" sounds nearly the same as the others." Practice saying them.
- Pass out cards. Sing the following chorally to the tune of The Farmer in the Dell:

  The girl (or boy) **needs** 50 **cents**, repeat), who has 50 **cents**? the girl **needs** 50 cents. 50 **cents**.
- Prompt the holder of the 50 cents to sing:

  I have 50 **cents**! (repeat) I can give her (or him) 50 cents **since** I have 50 cents.

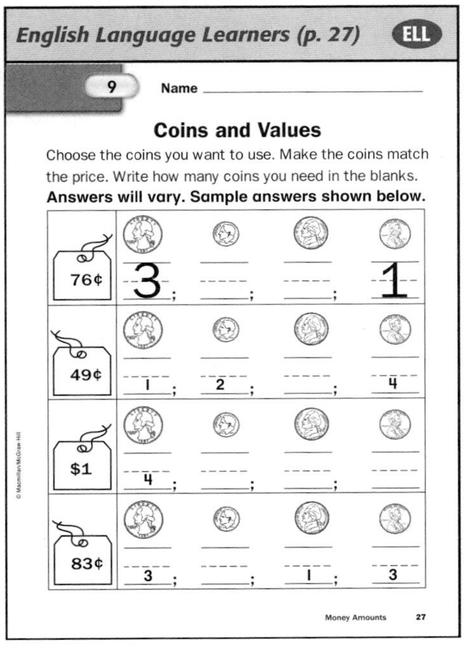

English Language Learners (p. 27) ELL

9 Name ____________

Coins and Values

Choose the coins you want to use. Make the coins match the price. Write how many coins you need in the blanks.
Answers will vary. Sample answers shown below.

76¢	3			1
49¢	1	2		4
$1	4			
83¢	3		1	3

© Macmillan/McGraw-Hill

Money Amounts 27

Use this worksheet to provide additional support for English Language Learners.

Independent Work Options

Option 1 Early Finishers OL AL

VISUAL/SPATIAL, KINESTHETIC, SOCIAL

Materials: drawing paper, crayons

- Have students draw an item and its price.
- Have students write a problem that can be solved with information from the picture. For example: *Jack wants to buy a new baseball. He has 3 dimes, 1 nickel, and 2 pennies. Can he buy the ball?*
- Have students work together to solve the problems.

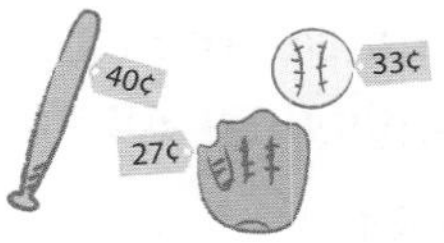

Option 2 Student Technology

Math Online macmillanmh.com

Math Songs, "How Many Pennies?" Track 16 • Math Adventures

Option 3 Learning Station: Reading (p. 347G)

Direct students to the Reading Learning Station for more opportunities to explore and extend the lesson concept.

Option 4 Problem-Solving Practice

Reinforce problem-solving skills and strategies with the Problem-Solving Practice worksheet.

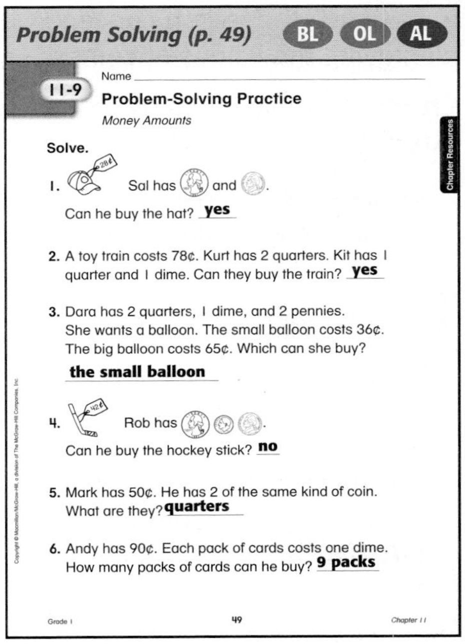

Problem Solving (p. 49) BL OL AL

11-9 Name ____________

Problem-Solving Practice

Money Amounts

Chapter Resources

Solve.

1. 28¢ Sal has (quarter) and (nickel).
   Can he buy the hat? **yes**
2. A toy train costs 78¢. Kurt has 2 quarters. Kit has 1 quarter and 1 dime. Can they buy the train? **yes**
3. Dara has 2 quarters, 1 dime, and 2 pennies. She wants a balloon. The small balloon costs 36¢. The big balloon costs 65¢. Which can she buy?
   the small balloon
4. 42¢ Rob has (quarter) (dime) (nickel).
   Can he buy the hockey stick? **no**
5. Mark has 50¢. He has 2 of the same kind of coin. What are they? **quarters**
6. Andy has 90¢. Each pack of cards costs one dime. How many packs of cards can he buy? **9 packs**

Copyright © Macmillan/McGraw-Hill, a division of The McGraw-Hill Companies, Inc.

Grade 1 49 Chapter 11

1 Introduce

Activity Choice 1 • Hands-On

- Have students cut out a picture of their favorite item from a toy catalog and glue it onto a sheet of paper.
- Write a price less than 99¢ below the picture. Then have students use coin stamps, stickers or draw pictures to show a combination of coins that equals the item's value.
- Collect the pictures to create a class catalog.

Activity Choice 2 • Literature

Introduce the lesson with *The Big Buck Adventures* by Shelley Gill and Deborah Tobola. For additional support, see p. TR58.

2 Teach

Have students show one quarter, two dimes, one nickel, and four pennies. **Which coin should you start counting first? Why?** the quarter, because it is worth the most

- Have students count to determine the total value of the coins. 54¢
- Ask the class to count in unison to check their answer. 25, 35, 45, 50, 51, 52, 53, 54
- Inform students that the price of a pencil is 49¢. **Does everyone have enough money to buy a pencil? How do you know?** Yes, 54¢ is more than 49¢.

Get Ready Use the section at the top of p. 371 to reinforce the lesson concept. Guide students in identifying the values of coins.

Check Observe students as you work through Exercises 1–3 as a class.

Exercise 3 Assess student comprehension before assigning practice exercises.

COMMON ERROR!

When comparing a collection of coins to a price or another collection, students may leave out a step in the problem-solving process. Teach them the following 1-2-3 checklist and display it in the room or on students' desks: **1-Order** the coins; **2-Count** and keep track; **3-Compare** the totals.

Name ______________________

Money Amounts

Get Ready

Main Idea

I will compare the value of a set of coins with prices.

Counting coins helps you know if you have enough money to buy something.

Here are your coins:

How much money did you count? 42 ¢

Do you have enough money? (Yes) No

Check

	Look at the price	Count the coins	Do you have enough money?
1.	 37¢		Yes / (No)
2.	 53¢		(Yes) / No

3. Talk About It A ride costs 50¢. Manuel has 3 quarters. Nadine has 4 dimes. Who has enough money for the ride? Explain? Manuel; he has 75¢ which is more than 50¢.

Reteach (p. 46) BL

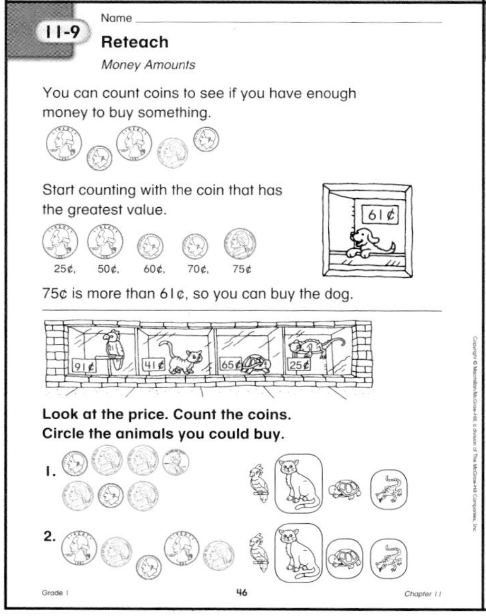
11-9 Name
Reteach
Money Amounts

You can count coins to see if you have enough money to buy something.

Start counting with the coin that has the greatest value.

25¢, 50¢, 60¢, 70¢, 75¢

75¢ is more than 61¢, so you can buy the dog.

Look at the price. Count the coins. Circle the animals you could buy.

1.

2.

Grade 1 46 Chapter 11

Skills Practice (p. 47) OL

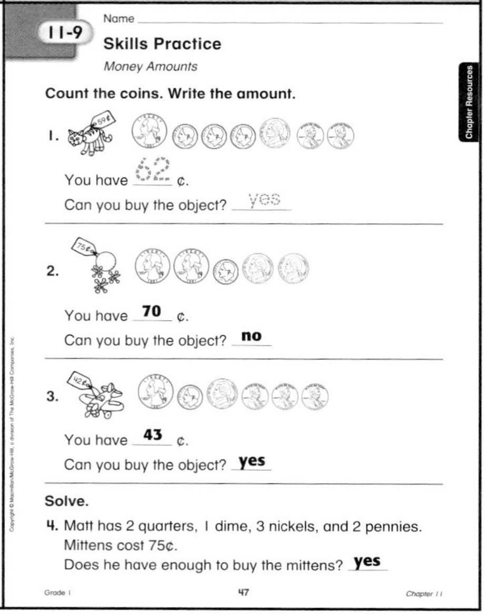
11-9 Name
Skills Practice
Money Amounts

Count the coins. Write the amount.

1. You have 62 ¢. Can you buy the object? yes

2. You have 70 ¢. Can you buy the object? no

3. You have 43 ¢. Can you buy the object? yes

Solve.

4. Matt has 2 quarters, 1 dime, 3 nickels, and 2 pennies. Mittens cost 75¢. Does he have enough to buy the mittens? yes

Grade 1 47 Chapter 11

Practice

	Look at the price	Count the coins	Do you have enough money?
4.			(Yes) No
5.			Yes (No)
6.			Yes (No)
7.			(Yes) No

Problem Solving

8. **Logical Reasoning** Ling has 50¢. He has 2 of the same kind of coin in his hand. What coin does he have? quarter

Math at Home Activity: Find an item in the store that costs less then $1.00. Have your child describe two combinations of coins that could be used to buy that item.

Enrich (p. 50) AL

11-9 Name

Enrich

What to buy?

You have 82¢ to spend at the grocery store.

50¢ 25¢ 35¢

Draw pictures of what you will buy.

Answers will vary.

Draw how much money you have left.

Answers will vary.

Grade 1 50 Chapter 11

Homework Practice (p. 48) OL

11-9 Name

Homework Practice

Money Amounts

Count the coins. Write the amount.

1. You have **50** ¢. Can you buy the object? **no**

2. You have **46** ¢. Can you buy the object? **yes**

3. You have **38** ¢. Can you buy the object? **no**

Solve.

4. Lori has 1 quarter, 1 dime, 1 nickel, and 1 penny. Cans of juice cost 39¢ each. Does she have enough to buy a can? **yes**

Grade 1 48 Chapter 11

BL Alternate Teaching Strategy

If students cannot successfully compare the value of a set of coins to a price . . .

Then use one of the reteach options.

1. CRM **Daily Reteach Worksheet** (p. 46)
2. **Greater or Less Than** Write 55¢ on the board. Have students count out one quarter and two dimes (45¢).

- **Is the value of your coins greater than or less than 55¢?** less than (45¢) Have them add a dime to their collection and count again.
- **How does your amount compare to 55¢ now?** It is equal to 55¢.

3 Practice

Differentiate practice using these leveled assignments for Exercises 4–8.

Level	Assignment
BL Below/ Approaching Level	Guide students through the exercises with manipulatives.
OL On Level	Complete the exercises independently with manipulatives.
AL Above/Beyond Level	Complete the exercises independently

4 Assess

Formative Assessment

Give students one quarter, three dimes, two nickels, and three pennies. Ask them if they can buy a poster that costs 75¢. No; 68¢ is less than 75¢.

WRITING IN MATH Have students write and solve a problem similar to Exercise 8.

Quick Check **Are students continuing to struggle with comparing the value of coins with prices?**

If Yes → CRM Reteach Worksheet (p. 46)

If No → Independent Work Options (p. 371B)
CRM Skills Practice Worksheet (p. 47)
CRM Enrich Worksheet (p. 50)

Extra Practice

Reviews Lesson 11-9

Objective: Review and assess mastery of previous lessons' skills and concepts.

- Review with students how to count money and compare the value of a set of coins with prices.
- Explain that students will have to count money beginning with the coin(s) that have the greatest value. Then they will have to find the toy(s) with a price less than or equal to the value of their coins.
- Students may wish to use coins for support.

Practice with Technology

Math Online Have students visit macmillanmh.com for additional practice with online activities, games, and quizzes.

Extra Practice

Name ____________________

Count the coins. Circle all of the toys you have enough money to buy.

1.  kite plane yo-yo

2.  kite plane yo-yo

3.  kite plane yo-yo

4.  kite plane yo-yo

5.  kite plane yo-yo

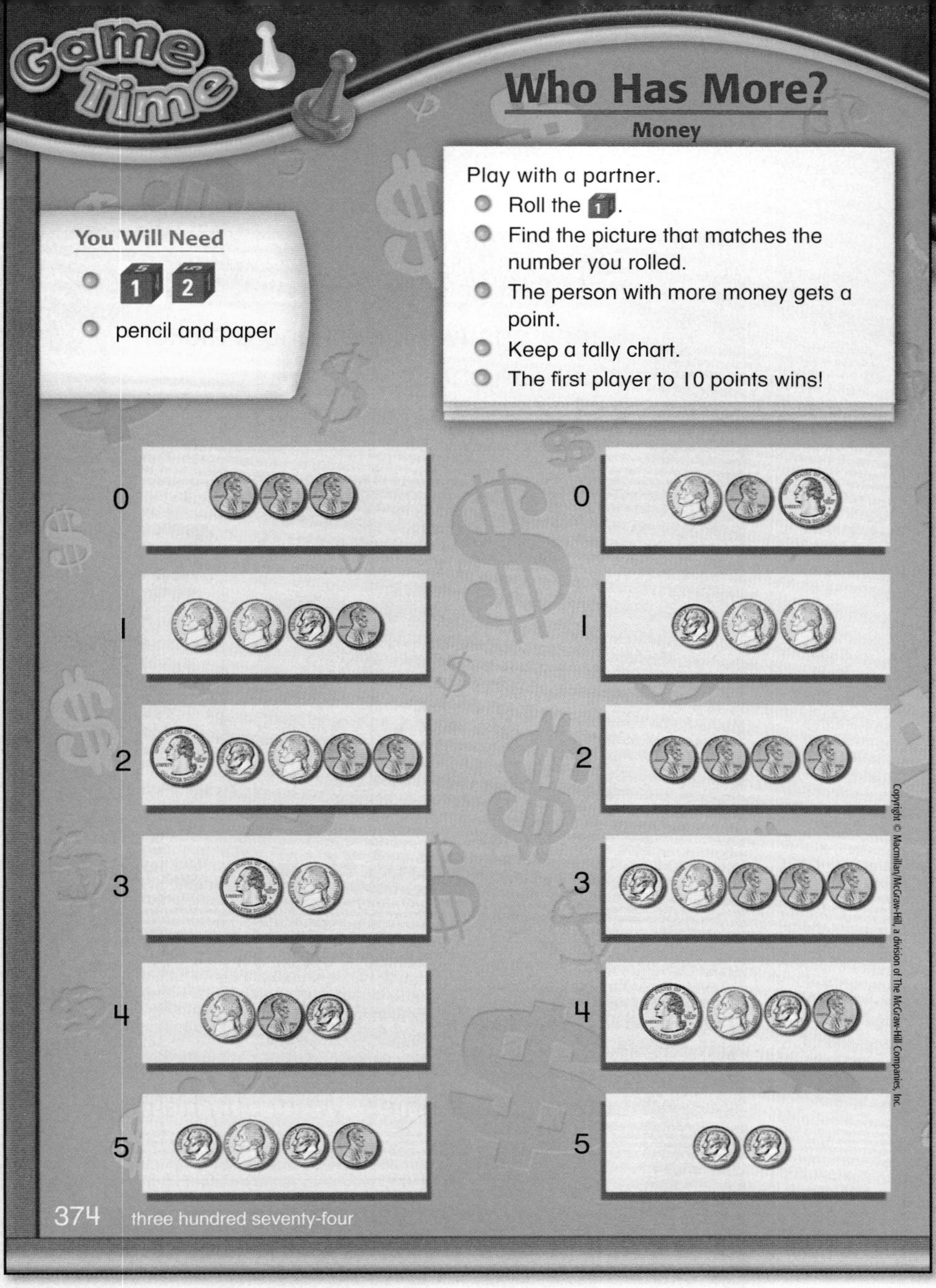

Game Time

Who Has More?

Money

You Will Need

- 1 2
- pencil and paper

Play with a partner.

- Roll the 1.
- Find the picture that matches the number you rolled.
- The person with more money gets a point.
- Keep a tally chart.
- The first player to 10 points wins!

0 0

1 1

2 2

3 3

4 4

5 5

Who Has More?

Math Concept:
Counting Money

Manipulatives: two red number cubes

Introduce the game on p. 374 to students to play with a partner or at a learning workstation to review concepts introduced in this chapter.

Instructions

- Have partners roll their number cubes and find the picture that matches the number they rolled.
- The player with the picture that shows more money scores 1 point.
- Have students use a tally chart to keep track of points. The first player to score 10 points wins.

Extend the Game

Have students who score a point tell how much more money they have than their partner.

Differentiated Practice

Use these leveled suggestions to differentiate the game for all learners.

Level	Assignment
BL Below/Approaching Level	Have students work with a partner as a team playing against another team of two students. Allow each team to work together to count the coins.
OL On Level	Have students play the game with the rules as written.
AL Above/Beyond Level	Have students play the game with the rules as written, but partners must also determine how much money they have together on each turn.

Lesson Planner

Objective

Compare the value of different coins to solve problems in real-life situations.

National Standards

Social Studies

Students should know economic wants are desires that can be satisfied by consuming a good, service, or leisure activity.

Activate Prior Knowledge

Before you turn students' attention to the pages, discuss garage sales.

- **What is a garage sale?** A garage sale is a sale where people sell used things.
- Talk to your class about community activities and how they bring neighbors closer together.
- **In what ways would a garage sale be a good community activity?** Sample answer: The money could be used to help someone in need or for a community project. Neighbors could buy and sell things to each other rather than throwing things away.

Create the Book

Guide students to create their book.

- Have them fold the page in half.
- Ask them to write their name on page A.
- Explain that page A is the front cover and page D is the back cover. If necessary, have them practice flipping through the book in order.
- Guide them in reading the information and word problems on each of the pages.

Extend the Activity

Have students organize a "classroom sale" of books or toys they no longer use to raise money for buying library books. Help students make price tags for their items and make posters inviting students from the school to come to the sale.

Use the Student Pages

Have students work individually or in pairs to solve the word problems on pages B–D.

Page B Students may have problems comparing the value of coins with prices. Suggest that students use coins for support.

Page C Students may have difficulty knowing whether the value of coins is enough to purchase something. Remind students that the total value of the coins must be greater than or equal to the cost of an item if they want to buy an item.

WRITING IN MATH Have students write about activities they know of in their community.

Chapter Review/Test

FOLDABLES Dinah Zike's Foldables

Use these lesson suggestions to incorporate the Foldable during the chapter. Students can use their Foldables to review for the test.

Lesson 11-7 On the fifth tab, have students use quarters, nickels, and pennies to make the amount written on the first tab.

Lesson 11-8 On the sixth tab, have students use quarters, dimes, and pennies to make the amount written on the first tab.

Vocabulary Review

Review chapter vocabulary using one of the following options.

- **Visual Vocabulary Cards (6, 15, 29, 34, and 40)**
- **eGlossary** at macmillanmh.com

Vocabulary Test

CRM **Chapter 11 Resource Masters** (p. 55)
Assess student comprehension of the chapter vocabulary with the Vocabulary Test.

Math Online **Chapter Test**
Alternate summative assessment options are available online at macmillanmh.com.

Name ____________________

Vocabulary

Circle the picture that matches the word.

1. cent

¢ $

2. penny

3. nickel

4. dime

5. quarter

Concepts

Count to find each price. Write each price on the tag.

6.

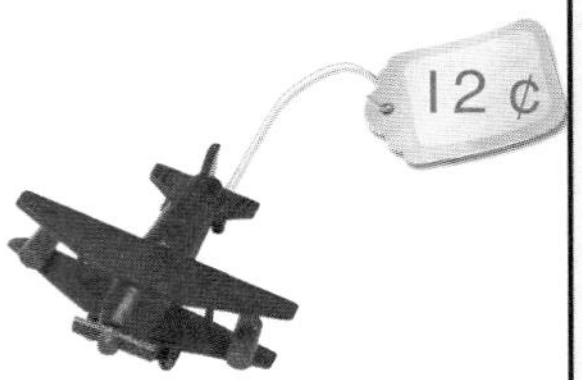

5 ¢ 10 ¢ 11 ¢ 12 ¢

7.

10 ¢ 15 ¢ 16 ¢ 17 ¢ 18 ¢ 19 ¢

Chapter 11 Project

Money Amounts

Have students discuss the results of their completed chapter project as a class. Assess their work using the Chapter Project rubric found in Chapter 11 Resource Masters on p. 60.

Circle how much money you need.

8.

Show the same amount of money a different way.

9. Show 27¢.

One Way	Another Way
	Sample answers: 1 quarter and 2 pennies; 2 dimes, 1 nickel, and 2 pennies; 5 nickels and 2 pennies

10. Count the coins to find the price.
Write the price.

25 ¢ 30 ¢ 31 ¢ 32 ¢ 33 ¢ Price 33 ¢

Problem Solving

11. How can you make 40¢ using the fewest coins? Explain.

Sample answer: 1 quarter, 1 dime, and 1 nickel.

Summative Assessment

Use these alternate leveled chapter tests to differentiate assessment for the specific needs of your students.

Leveled Chapter 11 Tests			
Form	**Type**	**Level**	**CRM Pages**
1	Multiple Choice	BL	62–63
2A	Multiple Choice	OL	64–65
2B	Multiple Choice	OL	66–67
2C	Free Response	AL	68–69
2D	Free Response	AL	70–71

BL = below/approaching grade level
OL = on grade level
AL = above/beyond grade level

ExamView Assessment Suite Customize and create multiple versions of your Chapter Test and their test answer keys.

Data-Driven Decision Making

Based on the results of the Chapter Review/Test, use the following to review concepts that continue to present students with problems.

Exercises	State/Local Standards	What's the Math?	Error Analysis	Resources for Review
1–5		Identify and know value of coins up to a dime. Count and add dimes, nickels and pennies.	Adds incorrectly. Uses wrong values of coins.	Strategic Intervention Guide (p. 114) CRM Chapter 11 Resource Masters (Reteach Worksheets) Math Online Concepts in Motion Math Adventures
6–8 10		Count and group coins. Add coins.	Does not count accurately. Does not count multiples of a nickel or dime.	
9		Identify and know the value of coins and show different combinations of coins that equal the same value.	Does not draw correct number of coins for different sums.	
11		Create and solve number sentences that express addition relationships of coins.	Assigns wrong value to coins. Adds coins incorrectly. Does not write explanation or draw correct number of coins.	

Test Practice

Formative Assessment

- Use Student Edition pp. 379–380 as practice and cumulative review. The questions are written in the same style as many state tests.
- You can use these two pages to benchmark student progress, or as an alternative homework assignment.

Additional practice pages can be found in the Chapter 11 Resource Masters.

CRM Chapter 11 Resource Masters
Cumulative Test Practice

- Multiple Choice format (pp. 62–67, 72)
- Free Response format (pp. 68–71, 73)

ExamView Assessment Suite Create practice worksheets or tests that align to state standards.

Math Online
For additional standards practice, visit macmillanmh.com.

Name ______________________________

Listen as your teacher reads the problem.
Choose the correct answer.

1.

2.

3¢ 11¢ 21¢ 30¢

3.

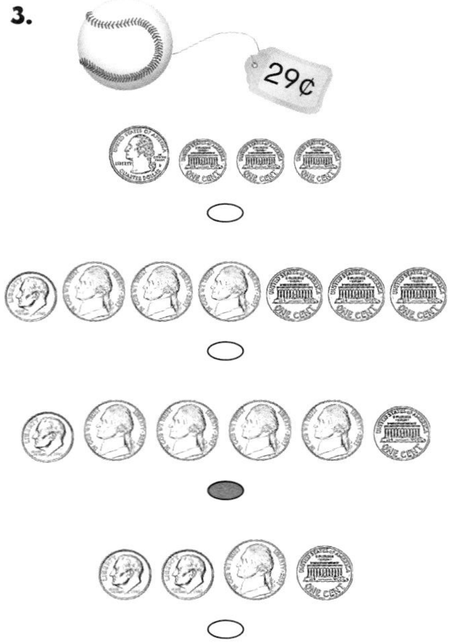

4.

Test-Taking Tips

For the Teacher

- Make sure each student understands the directions before beginning the test.
- Read at a moderate pace so as to hold the students' attention while assuring they clearly hear each word.

For the Student

- Eliminate answers that you know are incorrect.
- Be sure to have an extra pencil.

5. 6 + 4 = 10

10 − 6 = 10 (marked) | 6 − 2 = 4 | 6 − 4 = 2 | 4 + 6 = 10

8.

21	22	23	24	25	26	27	28	29	30
31	32	33	34	35	36	37	38	39	40
41	42	43	44	45	46	47	48	49	50

24 | 33 (marked) | 34 | 40

6. 18 (marked) | 20 | 22 | 27

9. Tanya has 70¢ in dimes and pennies. She has 6 dimes. How many pennies does she have?

10 pennies

7. 

4¢ | 8¢ | 12¢ (marked) | 20¢

10. Carmen has 2 dimes. Nick has 1 dime and 2 pennies. How much money do they have in all?

32 ¢

STOP

Test Directions for Teachers

Read the following directions to students before they begin. Then read each question followed by a pause to allow students time to work and choose an answer. The first test item can be worked as a class example.

- **Write your name at the top of the page.**
- **I am going to read each question to you. Listen carefully to the entire question before you choose an answer.**

Multiple Choice

1. Listen to the story. Emily practiced the piano at 4:00. Which clock shows 4:00?
2. Look at the coins. The coins show how much a ring costs. How much does the ring cost?
3. Listen to the number story. Jenny wants to buy a ball that costs 29¢. Which coins show enough money to buy the ball?
4. Look at the coins. Mark the coin that has a value of 25¢.

- **Turn the page over.**

5. Look at the addition fact. Which is a related subtraction fact for 6 + 4 = 10?
6. What number comes before 19?
7. Look at the group of coins. Count the coins to find how much money is shown. Mark the amount that shows how much money is shown.
8. Look at the chart. Find 23. What number is 10 more than 23?

Short Response

9. Tanya has 70¢ in dimes and pennies. She has 6 dimes. How many pennies does she have?
10. Carmen has 2 dimes. Nick has 1 dime and 2 pennies. How much money do they have in all?

CHAPTER 12

Chapter Overview

Chapter-at-a-Glance

In Chapter 12, the emphasis is on identifying and classifying common three-dimensional figures and two-dimensional figures and using position words to tell where objects are.

Lesson		Math Objective	State/Local Standards
12-1	**Three-Dimensional Figures** (pp. 385–386)	Identify common three-dimensional figures and relate them to real-world objects.	
12-2	**Faces and Corners** (pp. 387–388)	Describe and identify three-dimensional figures according to number of faces and corners.	
12-3	**Problem-Solving Strategy: Look for a Pattern** (pp. 389–390)	Use the *look for a pattern* strategy to solve problems.	
12-4	**Two- and Three-Dimensional Figures** (pp. 391–392)	Use faces of three-dimensional figures to compose two-dimensional figures.	
12-5	**Two-Dimensional Figures** (pp. 395–396)	Identify, describe, and compare attributes of two-dimensional figures.	
12-6	**Problem-Solving Investigation: Choose a Strategy** (pp. 399–400)	Choose the best strategy to solve a problem.	
12-7	**Position** (pp. 401–404)	Use position words to tell where objects are.	
12-8	**Make New Figures** (pp. 405–406)	Use pattern blocks to make new figures.	
12-9	**Give and Follow Directions** (pp. 407–408)	Give and follow directions to find locations.	

Identify Geometric Figures

BIG Idea Students have worked extensively with shapes by first grade. As kindergarteners, students used shapes to sort, create patterns, add, and subtract. In first grade, geometry is taken a step further. In this chapter, students are asked to identify and describe both two-dimensional and three-dimensional figures, classify figures according to the number of faces and corners, and arrange figures according to position.

Algebra Readiness In Lesson 12-9, students prepare for Algebra by finding and describing the location of objects on a coordinate plane.

Geometry Readiness In Lesson 12-1, students prepare for Geometry by identifying and describing common three-dimensional figures. In Lesson 12-5, students prepare for Geometry by identifying and describing two-dimensional figures.

Focal Points and Connections

G1-FP3 *Geometry:* **Composing and decomposing geometric shapes**

Children compose and decompose plane and solid figures (e.g., by putting two congruent isosceles triangles together to make a rhombus), thus building an understanding of part-whole relationships as well as the properties of the original and composite shapes. As they combine figures, they recognize them from different perspectives and orientations, describe their geometric attributes and properties, and determine how they are alike and different, in the process developing a background for measurement and initial understandings of such properties as congruence and symmetry.

Skills Trace
Vertical Alignment

Kindergarten

In kindergarten, students learned to:
- Identify and describe common geometric objects.
- Compare two- and three-dimensional figures using common attributes.

First Grade

During this chapter, students will learn to:
- Identify common three-dimensional figures and classify them by common attributes.
- Identify, describe, and compare attributes of two-dimensional figures.
- Use position words to tell where objects are.

Second Grade

In second grade, students will learn to:
- Describe and classify two- and three-dimensional figures according to the number and shape of faces and vertices.
- Put shapes together and take them apart to compose and decompose two- and three-dimensional figures.

Backmapping and Vertical Alignment

McGraw-Hill's *Math Connects* program was conceived and developed with the final results in mind: student success in Algebra 1 and beyond. The authors, using the **NCTM Focal Points and Focal Connections** as their guide, developed this brand-new series by backmapping from Algebra 1 concepts, and vertically aligning the topics so that they build upon prior skills and concepts and serve as a foundation for future topics.

Math Vocabulary

The following math vocabulary words for Chapter 12 are listed in the glossary of the ***Student Edition.*** You can find interactive definitions in 13 languages in the ***eGlossary*** at macmillanmh.com.

circle a closed round figure (p. 395)

cone a round three-dimensional figure that narrows to a point (p. 385)

corner the point where lines, edges, or sides of a shape meet (p. 387)

cube a square block (p. 385)

cylinder a three-dimensional figure shaped like a can (p. 385)

face the flat part of a three-dimensional figure (p. 387)

pyramid a three-dimensional figure with a square base and triangular-shaped faces (p. 385)

rectangle a shape with four sides and four corners (p. 395)

rectangular prism a three-dimensional shape (p. 385)

side the flat surface of a three-dimensional figure (p. 395)

sphere a three-dimensional figure that has the shape of a round ball (p. 385)

square a rectangle that has four equal sides (p. 395)

triangle a shape with three sides (p. 395)

Visual Vocabulary Cards Use Visual Vocabulary Cards 7–11, 39, 41, 42, 44, 45, and 49 to introduce and reinforce the vocabulary in this chapter. (The Define/Example/Ask routine is printed on the back of each card.)

CHAPTER 12

Chapter Planner

Suggested Pacing		
Instruction	**Review and Assessment**	**TOTAL**
9 days	2 days	**11 days**

Diagnostic Assessment
Are You Ready? (p. 382)

	Lesson 12-1 (Pacing: 1 day)	Lesson 12-2 (Pacing: 1 day)	Lesson 12-3 (Pacing: 1 day)
Lesson/ Objective	**Three-Dimensional Figures** (pp. 385–386) **Objective:** Identify common three-dimensional figures and relate them to real-world objects.	**Faces and Corners** (pp. 387–388) **Objective:** Describe and identify three-dimensional figures in order to sort them according to number of faces and corners.	**Problem-Solving Strategy** **Look for a Pattern** (pp. 389–390) **Objective:** Use the *look for a pattern* strategy to solve problems.
State/Local Standards			
Math Vocabulary	**pyramid**, **cone**, **cube**, **cylinder**, **sphere**, **rectangular prism**	**face**, **corner**	
Lesson Resources	**Manipulatives** geometric solids **Other Resources** CRM Leveled Worksheets (pp. 6–10) Daily Reteach • 5-Minute Check Problem of the Day	**Materials** chart paper **Manipulatives** geometric solids **Other Resources** CRM Leveled Worksheets (pp. 11–15) Daily Reteach • 5-Minute Check Problem of the Day	**Materials** pencils, crayons, drawing paper **Manipulatives** connecting cubes **Other Resources** CRM Leveled Worksheets (pp. 16–20) Daily Reteach • 5-Minute Check Problem of the Day *Shapes in Nature*
Technology	Math Song Track 3		
Reaching All Learners	Below Level, p. 385B BL English Learners, p. 385B ELL Early Finishers, p. 385B OL AL	Below Level, p. 387B BL English Learners, p. 387B ELL Early Finishers, p. 387B OL AL	Below Level, p. 389B BL English Learners, p. 389B ELL Early Finishers, p. 389B OL AL
Alternate Lessons	*Math Their Way*, pp. 70–71 *IMPACT Mathematics:* Unit I	*Math Their Way*, pp. 76–77 *IMPACT Mathematics:* Unit I	

KEY

- BL Below/Approaching Level
- OL On Level
- AL Above/Beyond Level
- ELL English Learners
- SE Student Edition
- TE Teacher Edition
- CRM Chapter 12 Resource Masters
- CD-Rom
- Transparency
- Flip Chart
- Real-World Problem Solving Library

	Lesson 12-4 (Pacing: 1 day)	Lesson 12-5 (Pacing: 1 day)	Lesson 12-6 (Pacing: 1 day)
Lesson/ Objective	**Two- and Three-Dimensional Figures** (pp. 391–392) **Objective:** Use faces of three-dimensional figures to compose two-dimensional figures.	**Two-Dimensional Figures** (pp. 395–396) **Objective:** Identify, describe, and compare attributes of two-dimensional figures.	Problem-Solving Investigation **Choose a Strategy** (pp. 399–400) **Objective:** Choose the best strategy to solve a problem.
State/Local Standards			
Math Vocabulary		**triangle**, **square**, **side** **rectangle**, **circle**	
Lesson Resources	**Materials** modeling clay **Manipulatives** pattern blocks, geometric solids **Other Resources** CRM Leveled Worksheets (pp. 21–25) Daily Reteach • 5-Minute Check Problem of the Day	**Materials** paper cut-outs of two-dimensional shapes, magazines, books **Manipulatives** attribute blocks **Other Resources** CRM Leveled Worksheets (pp. 26–30) Daily Reteach • 5-Minute Check Problem of the Day	**Materials** paper, crayons **Manipulatives** pattern blocks, geometric solids **Other Resources** CRM Leveled Worksheets (pp. 31–35) Daily Reteach • 5-Minute Check Problem of the Day *Shapes in Nature*
Technology Math Online	Concepts in Motion	Math Adventures	
Reaching All Learners	Below Level, p. 391B BL English Learners, p. 391B ELL Early Finishers, p. 391B OL AL	Gifted and Talented, p. 395B AL English Learners, p. 395B ELL Early Finishers, p. 395B OL AL	Below Level, p. 399B BL English Learners, p. 399B ELL Early Finishers, p. 399B OL AL
Alternate Lesson	*Math Their Way*, pp. 72–73 *IMPACT Mathematics:* Units I and J	*IMPACT Mathematics:* Unit J	

Extra Practice (p. 393)
Game Time: Corners (p. 394)

Formative Assessment
- Mid-Chapter Check (p. 397)
- Spiral Review (p. 398)

CHAPTER 12

Chapter Planner

	Lesson 12-7 Pacing: 1 day	Lesson 12-8 Pacing: 1 day	Lesson 12-9 Pacing: 1 day
Lesson/ Objective	**Position** (pp. 401–404) **Objective:** Use position words to tell where objects are.	**Make New Figures** (pp. 405–406) **Objective:** Use pattern blocks to make new figures.	**Give and Follow Directions** (pp. 407–408) **Objective:** Give and follow directions to find locations.
State/Local Standards			
Math Vocabulary	**position**		
Lesson Resources	**Materials** magnets, construction paper **Other Resources** CRM Leveled Worksheets (pp. 36–40) Daily Reteach • 5-Minute Check Problem of the Day	**Manipulatives** pattern blocks **Other Resources** CRM Leveled Worksheets (pp. 41–45) Daily Reteach • 5-Minute Check Problem of the Day	**Materials** masking tape **Other Resources** CRM Leveled Worksheets (pp. 46–50) Daily Reteach • 5-Minute Check Problem of the Day
Technology Math Online	Math Adventures		Concepts in Motion
Reaching All Learners	Below Level, p. 401B BL English Learners, p. 401B ELL Early Finishers, p. 401B OL AL	Below Level, p. 405B BL English Learners, p. 405B ELL Early Finishers, p. 405B OL AL	Below Level, p. 407B BL English Learners, p. 407B ELL Early Finishers, p. 407B OL AL
Alternate Lessons			*Math Their Way,* p. 82

Problem-Solving in Art (p. 409)

Summative Assessment
- Chapter Review/Test (p. 411)
- Test Practice (p. 413)

Assessment Options

Diagnostic Assessment

- SE *Option 1:* Are You Ready? (p. 382)
- *Option 2:* Online Quiz macmillanmh.com
- CRM *Option 3:* Diagnostic Test (p. 52)
- CRM *Option 4:* Chapter Pretest (p. 53)

Formative Assessment

- TE Alternate Teaching Strategies (every lesson)
- TE Line Up (every lesson)
- SE Talk About It (every lesson)
- SE Writing in Math (every lesson)
- SE Check (every lesson)
- SE Mid-Chapter Check (p. 397)
- CRM Mid-Chapter Test (p. 54)

Summative Assessment

- SE Chapter Review/Test (p. 411)
- SE Test Practice (p. 413)
- CRM Vocabulary Test (p. 55)
- CRM Leveled Chapter Tests (pp. 62–71)
- CRM Cumulative Test Practice (pp. 72–73)
- CRM Listening Assessment (pp. 58–59)
- CRM Oral Assessment (pp. 56–57)
- Exam*View*® Assessment Suite
- Advance Tracker

Professional Development

Targeted professional development has been articulated throughout **McGraw-Hill's *Math Connects*** program. The **McGraw-Hill Professional Development Video Library** provides short videos that support the **NCTM Focal Points and Focal Connections**. For more information, visit macmillanmh.com.

Model Lessons

Instructional Strategies

Assessment Tips

Vocabulary is an essential part of geometry and it requires students to be able to "say it," "read it," "write it," "define it," and "draw it."

- Have students create vocabulary cards for each word in the chapter.
- Conduct a vocabulary interview each day with a couple of different students.
- Ask them to tell you all about one of their vocabulary cards, providing the word, definition, and drawing.
- Probe for their understanding of the vocabulary words and record your observations on index cards that can be put in their file folders.

Teacher Notes

CHAPTER 12

Learning Stations

Cross-Curricular Links

Reading

pairs | VISUAL/ SPATIAL, LINGUISTIC

Make Your Own Book

- Read *Captain Invincible and the Space Shapes* by Stuart J. Murphy aloud to your partner.
- Each time Captain Invincible comes upon a geometric object, place the tracing paper over the book and trace the object.
- Write the name of the shape.
- After you have traced all the objects, make your own version of the book. Cut out the tracings and paste them into a notebook.
- Color the pages and create your own in the story.

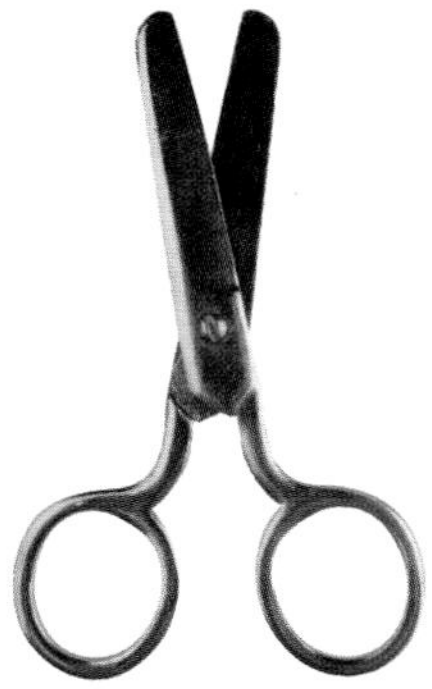

Materials:

- *Captain Invincible and the Space Shapes* by Stuart J. Murphy
- tracing paper
- crayons
- scissors

Art

individual | VISUAL/ SPATIAL

Beautiful Shapes

- Take a geometric solid and trace around one face of the object.
- Write the name of the shape that you drew and the name of the solid you used.
- Make a pattern by adding smaller shapes similar to the first one you drew.
- Decorate your pattern.
- Display your completed drawing with your classmates' drawings.

Teacher Note: Help students find the face of the solids.

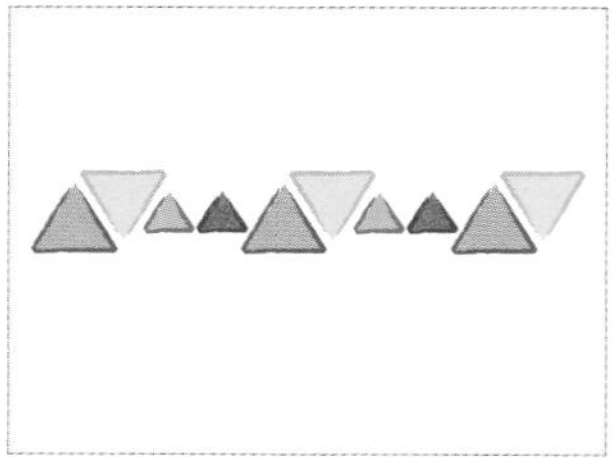

Materials:

- construction paper
- geometric solids
- decorating materials
- crayons or markers

Language Arts

pairs | SOCIAL, LINGUISTIC

Draw a Map

- Write a story about how you got to school today. Make sure to write directions.
- Switch papers with your partner. Draw a map from your partner's house to school by reading the story.
- After you are both finished, talk about the maps. Is your map correct? Did you label the right directions? What else could you have put in your story to help your partner draw a better map?

Teacher Note: If a road map between home and school is too complicated, have students choose two places within school, such as the cafeteria and their classroom.

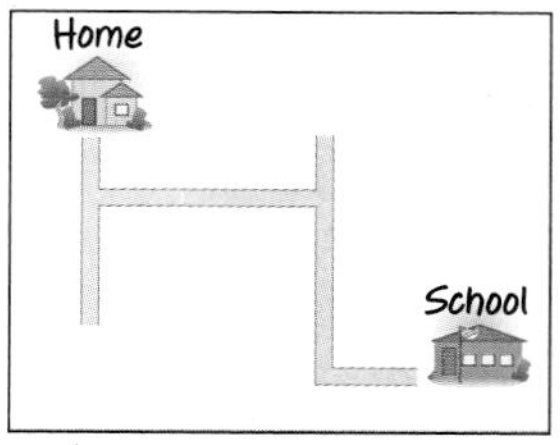

Materials:

- paper
- crayons, pencils, or markers

Science

individual | VISUAL/SPATIAL

Two- and Three-Dimensional Figures

- Trace each pattern block 6 times on a sheet of cardboard.
- Cut out your shapes.
- Try to build each of the geometric solids using your shapes. Use tape to hold them in place. Are there any three-dimensional figures you cannot build?
- Make a chart for your three-dimensional figures like the one on this card. Tell each figure's name and how many of each shape you used to build it.

Solid	Circles	Triangles	Squares	Rectangles
Pyramid	0	4	1	0

Materials:
- pattern blocks
- geometric solids
- cardboard
- tape

Social Studies

individual | INTRAPERSONAL

Shape of the World

- Look in an atlas and choose a country.
- On a sheet of paper, use pattern blocks to build a picture that looks like the country.
- Trace the outline of the country around the pattern blocks.
- Write the country's name. Draw and color the country's flag.
- Repeat the activity for two other countries.
- Put all the class's pages together to make an atlas.

Teacher Note: Adjust the times to meet your students' needs.

Materials:
- pattern blocks
- atlas
- paper
- crayons or markers

Calendar Time

Shapes and Days

- Ask volunteers to come up to the calendar and trace a shape on a specific day of the week. Use prompts such as the following:
- **Trace a triangle on Tuesday. What date is that?**
- **Trace a square on the following Friday.**
- **Trace a circle on the 15th. What day of the week is that?**

Introduce the Chapter

Real World: How Many?

Share with students that they are going to study figures. Explain that three-dimensional figures are also referred to as three-dimensional shapes or solid shapes. Two-dimensional figures are also referred to as two-dimensional shapes or plane shapes.

- Have students call out figures they know and list them on the board.
- Then ask for volunteers to tell what they know about some of the figures.
- **Where have you seen these figures before?**
- Have students draw pictures using the figures they know.

Have students turn to page 381.

- **Can you name any of the figures in the picture?**

Key Vocabulary

Introduce the key vocabulary in the chapter using the routine below.

Define: A **three-dimensional figure** is a figure that is solid. It has length, width, and depth.
Example: A desk is a three-dimensional figure because we can measure it in 3 ways: length, width, and height.
Ask: What is another three-dimensional figure in the classroom? In what ways can it be measured?

CHAPTER 12

Identify Geometric Figures

Key Vocabulary
- sphere
- rectangular prism
- face
- corner

Explore
Find objects in the classroom that look like these figures.
Check students' answers.

FOLDABLES® Study Organizer **Dinah Zike's Foldables**

Guide students to create their Three-Tab Venn Diagram Foldables for identifying geometric figures.

1. Fold a sheet of paper like a hot dog.

2. With the paper horizontal, and the fold of the hot dog up, fold the right side toward the center, trying to cover half of the paper.

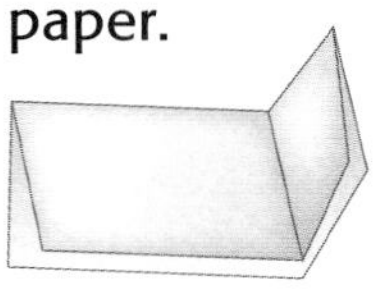

3. Fold the left side over the right side to make a book with three folds.

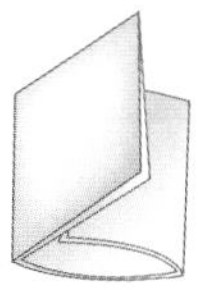

4. Open the folded book. Place your hands between the two thicknesses of paper and cut up the two valleys on one side only. This will form three tabs.

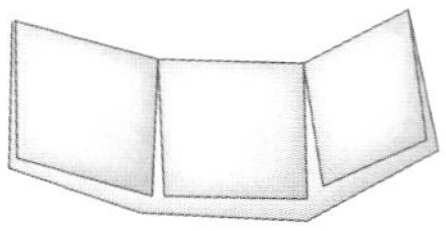

5. Draw overlapping circles on the three tables to make a Venn Diagram.

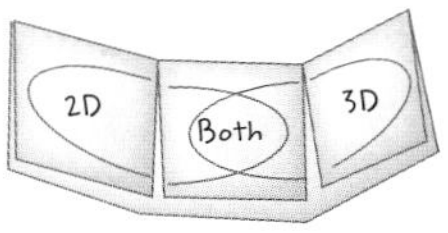

When to Use It *Lessons 12-1, 12-2, 12-4, and 12-5. (Additional instructions for using the Foldable with these lessons are found on pp. 397 and 411.)*

Name ____________________

Math Online
Take the Chapter Readiness Quiz at macmillanmh.com.

Are You Ready for Chapter 12?

Circle the ▢ figure.
Underline the △ figure.
Put an X on the ◯ figure.

1.

Put an X on the same figure.

2.

3.

4.

5.

6. Put an X on the figure that is inside the box.

This page checks skills needed for Chapter 12.

Diagnostic Assessment

Check for students' prerequisite skills before beginning the chapter.

- **Option 1:** ***Are You Ready for Chapter 12?***
  SE Student Edition, p. 382
- **Option 2:** ***Online Assessment***
  Math Online macmillanmh.com
- **Option 3:** ***Diagnostic Test***
  CRM Chapter 12 Resource Master, p. 52

RTI (Response to Intervention)

Apply the Results Based on the results of the diagnostic assessment on student p. 382, use the chart below to address individual needs before beginning the chapter.

TIER 3 Intensive Intervention

If students miss four or more of the exercises:

Then use Chapters 7 and 8 of *Math Triumphs*, an intensive math intervention program from McGraw-Hill.

TIER 2 Strategic Intervention below/approaching grade level	TIER 1 On-Level	Above/Beyond Level
If students miss two or three in: **Exercises 1–6**	**If** students miss one in: **Exercises 1–6**	**If** students miss none in: **Exercises 1–6**
Then choose a resource:	**Then** choose a resource:	**Then** choose a resource:
Strategic Intervention Guide (p. 118) TE Smart Start 4: Geometry (p. 9) Math Online Concepts in Motion	TE Learning Stations (pp. 381G–381H) TE Chapter Project (p. 383) CRM Game: *Shaping Faces* Math Adventures My Math Zone Chapter 11 Math Online Fact Dash	TE Learning Stations (pp. 381G–381H) TE Chapter Project (p. 383) Real-World Problem Solving: *Shapes in Nature* My Math Zone Chapters 11 and 12 Math Online Games

MATH at HOME

Before you begin Chapter 12:

- Read the Math at Home letter found on p. 383 with the class and have each student sign it.
- Send home copies of the Math at Home letter with each student.
- Use the Spanish letter on p. 384 for students with Spanish-speaking parents or guardians.

WRITING IN MATH

Starting the Chapter
Have students describe at least three street signs they see on the way to or from school. In particular, students should describe the signs' shapes and colors and any words or pictures on the signs.

Read-Aloud Anthology
For an optional reading activity to introduce this chapter's math concepts, see the Read-Aloud Anthology on p. TR38.

MATH at HOME

Dear Family,

Today my class started Chapter 12, **Identify Geometric Figures**. In this chapter, I will learn about three-dimensional and two-dimensional figures. I will also learn how to locate objects. Here is an activity we can do and a list of books we can read together.

Love, ______________________

Activity

Have your child tell you the shape of road signs while you are driving. Look for triangles, rectangles, squares, and circles.

Key Vocabulary

corner point where lines, edges, or sides of a shape meet

position tell where an object is

Math Online Click on the eGlossary link at macmillanmh.com to find out more about these words. There are 13 languages.

Books to Read

Cubes, Cones, Cylinders, and Spheres
by Tana Hoban
Greenwillow, 2000.

If You Were a Preposition
by Nancy Loewen
Picture Willow Books, 2006.

Shapes, Shapes, Shapes
by Tana Hoban
Greenwillow, 1986.

Chapter 12 Project

Geometric Mural

- Have students build a geometric mural. Post a large piece of butcher paper on the wall for students to draw on.
- Explain to students that they will create a large drawing of their town using geometric figures.
- As students learn each figure, have them add it to the mural. For example, a rectangular mailbox or triangular street sign.
- Check that students are drawing figures correctly.

CRM *Refer to Chapter 12 Resource Masters, p. 60, for a rubric to assess students' progress on this project.*

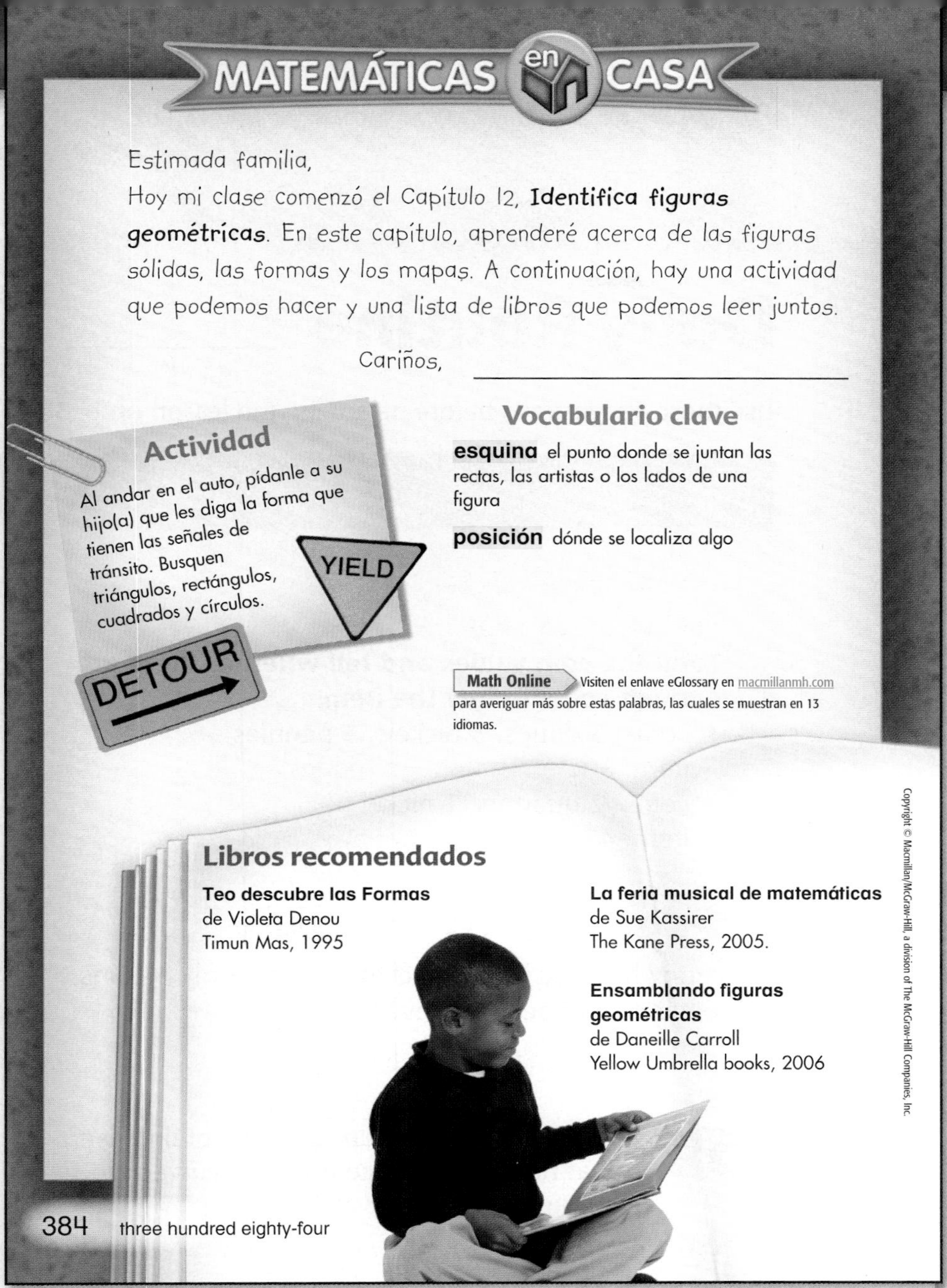

MATEMÁTICAS en CASA

Estimada familia,

Hoy mi clase comenzó el Capítulo 12, **Identifica figuras geométricas**. En este capítulo, aprenderé acerca de las figuras sólidas, las formas y los mapas. A continuación, hay una actividad que podemos hacer y una lista de libros que podemos leer juntos.

Cariños, ______________________

Actividad

Al andar en el auto, pídanle a su hijo(a) que les diga la forma que tienen las señales de tránsito. Busquen triángulos, rectángulos, cuadrados y círculos.

Vocabulario clave

esquina el punto donde se juntan las rectas, las aristas o los lados de una figura

posición dónde se localiza algo

Math Online Visiten el enlace eGlossary en macmillanmh.com para averiguar más sobre estas palabras, las cuales se muestran en 13 idiomas.

Libros recomendados

Teo descubre las Formas
de Violeta Denou
Timun Mas, 1995

La feria musical de matemáticas
de Sue Kassirer
The Kane Press, 2005.

Ensamblando figuras geométricas
de Daneille Carroll
Yellow Umbrella books, 2006

Chapter 12 Literature List

Lesson	Book Title
12-1	**Captain Invincible and the Space Shapes** Stuart J. Murphy
12-2	**Captain Invincible and the Space Shapes** Stuart J. Murphy
12-3	**Counting Penguins** Betsey Chessen
12-4	**When a Line Bends . . . A Shape Begins** Rhonda Gowler Greene
12-5	**Math Counts: Shapes** Henry Pluckrose
12-7	**The Greatest Gymnast of All** Stuart J. Murphy
12-8	**Three Pigs, One Wolf, and Seven Magic Shapes** Grace Maccarone
12-9	**Three Pigs, One Wolf, and Seven Magic Shapes** Grace Maccarone
Any	**Cubes, Cones, Cylinders, and Spheres** Tana Hoban
Any	**If You Were a Preposition** Nancy Loewen
Any	**Shapes, Shapes, Shapes** Tana Hoban

ELL National ESL Standards Alignment for Chapter 12

Lesson, Page	ESL Standard	Modality	Level
12-1, p 385B	Goal 1, Standard 3, b	Logical, Auditory	Beginning
12-2, p 387B	Goal 1, Standard 3, c	Logical	Beginning
12-3, p 389B	Goal 2, Standard 1, f	Intrapersonal, Linguistic	Advanced
12-4, p 455B	Goal 2, Standard 2, g	Linguistic	Intermediate
12-5, p 461B	Goal 1, Standard 3, k	Linguistic, Visual	Intermediate
12-6, p 463B	Goal 2, Standard 3, i	Intrapersonal, Linguistic	Advanced
12-7, p 465B	Goal 1, Standard 1, a	Spatial, Auditory	Intermediate
12-8, p 449B	Goal 2, Standard 2, j	Visual/Spatial	Intermediate
12-9, p 451B	Goal 2, Standard 2, a	Linguistic	Intermediate

The National ESL Standards can be found in the Teacher Reference Handbook.

LESSON 12-1

Three-Dimensional Figures

Lesson Planner

Objective

Identify common three-dimensional figures and relate them to real-world objects.

Vocabulary

pyramid, **cube**, **sphere**, **cone**, **cylinder**, **rectangular prism**

Resources

Manipulatives: geometric solids

Literature Connection: *Captain Invincible and the Space Shapes* by Stuart J. Murphy

Alternate Lessons: Adapt "Read My Mind" on pages 70 and 71 of *Math Their Way* to provide practice with identification of three-dimensional figures.
Use *IMPACT Mathematics:* Unit 1 to provide practice with identifying three-dimensional figures.

Teacher Technology

TeacherWorks • Math Songs Track 3 Lesson Plan

Focus on Math Background

This lesson introduces students to formal geometric vocabulary for labeling and describing three-dimensional figures. In the lesson, students identify three-dimensional figures, including the pyramid, cube, sphere, cone, cylinder, and rectangular prism; and then classify these figures by common attributes. By discussing how these three-dimensional shapes are alike and different, students begin to make generalizations and discover relationships that lay the foundation for future work with proofs in high school geometry.

Daily Routine

Use these suggestions before beginning the lesson on p. 385.

5-Minute Check

(Reviews Lesson 11-9)

Total the coin values and tell whether there are enough coins to buy the item.

1. coins: 3 dimes, 3 nickels, 3 pennies 48¢
item: 50¢ not enough money

2. coins: 2 quarters, 1 nickel 55¢
item: 47¢ enough money

Problem of the Day

Jenny has 50¢ in her pocket. She has only 5 coins. What coins does she have? Sample answer: 5 dimes

LINE UP When students line up, give this brainteaser: What has one flat face and one curved side? a cone

Building Math Vocabulary

- Display examples of a **cube**, **sphere**, **pyramid**, **cylinder**, **rectangular prism**, and **cone**. Introduce each figure and write the name on the board.
- Pick up the objects to demonstrate that they are three-dimensional figures—they have height, depth and width.

Visual Vocabulary Cards

Use Visual Vocabulary Cards 8, 10, 11, 39, 42, and 44 to reinforce the vocabulary introduced in this lesson. (The Define/Example/Ask routine is printed on the

Differentiated Instruction

Small Group Options

Option 1 KINESTHETIC

Below Level BL

Materials: paper or cloth bag, geometric solids (but not the hemisphere)

Put the geometric solids in a bag so they cannot be seen.

- Each student in the group takes a turn reaching into the bag and grasping one solid. Without taking the solid from the bag, the student guesses its name and then pulls the solid out of the bag to check the answer.
- The student then returns the shape to the bag so another student may take a turn. Students take turns until each solid has been guessed once or all students have had a turn.

Option 2 LOGICAL, AUDITORY

English Language Learners ELL

Materials: three-dimensional figures

Core Vocabulary: pointed, round, flat side

Common Use Verb: sticks out

See Math This strategy activates background knowledge and introduces three-dimensional figures.

- Show your hand. Say: "This is my hand." Show your hand flat on the table. Say "My hand is now flat."
- Repeat for "now rounded" and "now pointed," each time restarting the first sentence before you introduce the new figure. Repeat with students.
- Post three-dimensional figures. Describe them using their names and the vocabulary.
- Walk around the room and identify the various shapes of the items in the classroom.
- Choose a figure and ask students to point to an item that sticks out in the same way.
- When the student places the item with the picture, ask the student to verbally describe the item.

Independent Work Options

Option 1 KINESTHETIC, LOGICAL

Early Finishers OL AL

Materials: index card, chart paper, geometric solids

Prepare two sets index cards. Write pad of paper, building, evergreen tree, hat, piece of fruit, on two cards.

- Have students ask, "what real-world object does each figure look like?" Let students place the appropriate index card or cards with the figure.
- Then have students create a chart to show identify each geometric figure.

Option 2

Student Technology

Math Online macmillanmh.com

Math Songs, "Geometric Shapes" Track 3

Option 3

Learning Station: Art (p. 381G)

Direct students to the Art Learning Station for more opportunities to explore and extend the lesson concept.

Option 4

Problem-Solving Practice

Reinforce problem-solving skills and strategies with the Problem-Solving Practice worksheet.

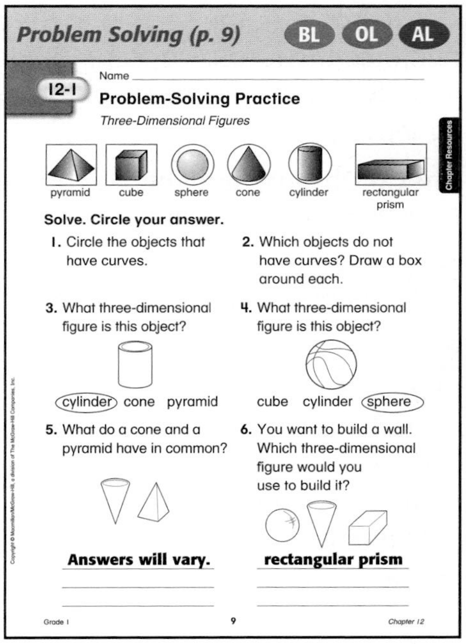

Problem Solving (p. 9) BL OL AL

Name

12-1 **Problem-Solving Practice**

Three-Dimensional Figures

pyramid cube sphere cone cylinder rectangular prism

Chapter Resources

Solve. Circle your answer.

1. Circle the objects that have curves.
2. Which objects do not have curves? Draw a box around each.
3. What three-dimensional figure is this object?
   cylinder cone pyramid
4. What three-dimensional figure is this object?
   cube cylinder sphere
5. What do a cone and a pyramid have in common?
   Answers will vary.
6. You want to build a wall. Which three-dimensional figure would you use to build it?
   rectangular prism

Grade 1 9 Chapter 12

1 Introduce

Activity Choice 1 • Hands-On

Display a **sphere**, **pyramid**, **cylinder**, **cube**, **rectangular prism**, and **cone**. Ask six volunteers to choose an object and examine it carefully.

- Tell the students something about one of the objects, and if the description fits, they should stand near you. Anyone whose object does not fit the description should stay with or go back to the original group.
- **Which three-dimensional figure looks like a soup can?** cylinder **Which three-dimensional figure looks like a cereal box?** rectangular prism **Which three-dimensional figure looks like baseball?** sphere
- Continue with other geometric figures.

Activity Choice 2 • Literature

Introduce the lesson with *Captain Invincible and the Space Shapes* by Stuart J. Murphy. For additional support, see p. TR58.

2 Teach

Write the names of the three-dimensional figures on the chalkboard. Lead a brainstorming session about real-world objects that have the shape of each solid. Keep manipulatives nearby for reference.

- Circle *cylinder* and *sphere*. **How are these geometric figures alike?** They have curved parts.

Get Ready Use the section at the top of p. 385 to reinforce the lesson concept. Guide students as they identify the characteristics of three-dimensional figures.

Check Observe students as you work through Exercises 1–5 as a class.

Exercise 5 Assess student comprehension before assigning practice exercises.

COMMON ERROR!

Students may not realize that objects can be the same shape but different sizes. Show them a variety of objects in one shape and different sizes.

Name ____________________

Three-Dimensional Figures

Get Ready

Main Idea

I will identify three-dimensional figures.

Vocabulary

pyramid
cube
sphere
cone
cylinder
rectangular prism

Solid shapes are also called three-dimensional figures.

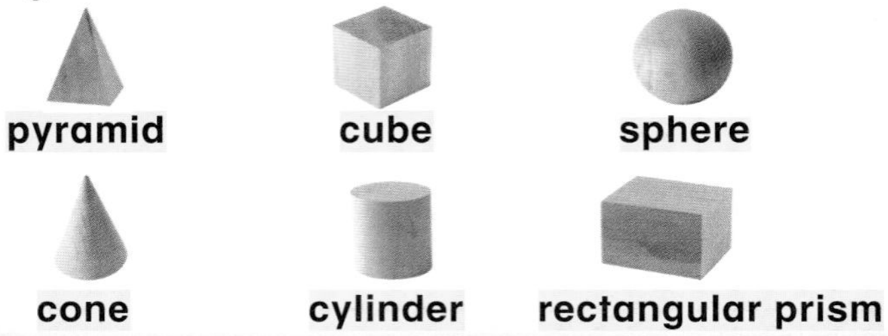

Check They are both the same three-dimensional figure. They each have 6 sides.

Look at the three-dimensional figure. Circle the objects with the same shape.

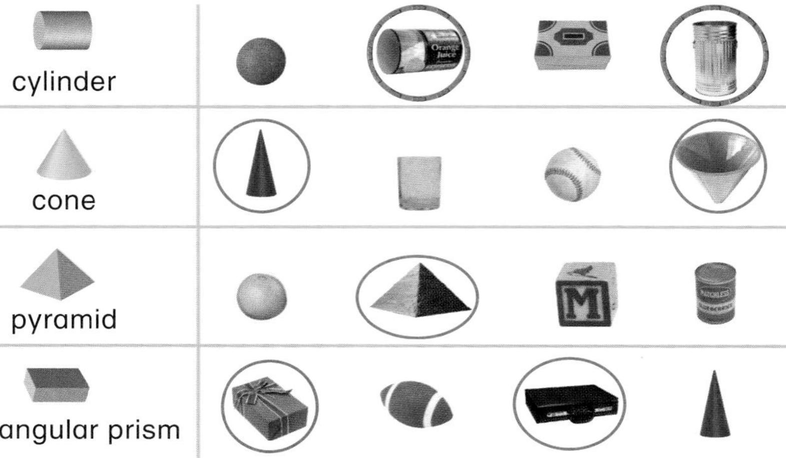

5. **Talk About It** How is a rectangular prism like your math book?

Reteach (p. 6) BL

12-1 Name ____

Reteach

Three-Dimensional Figures

Draw lines from the three-dimensional figures to the matching objects.

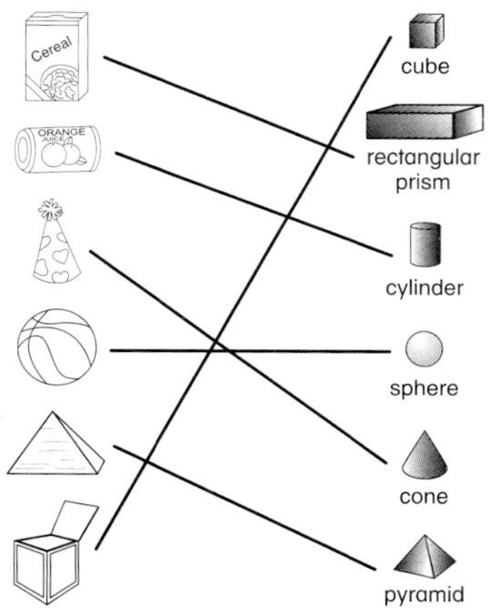

Grade 1 6 Chapter 12

Skills Practice (p. 7) OL

12-1 Name ____

Skills Practice

Three-Dimensional Figures

Color the figures.

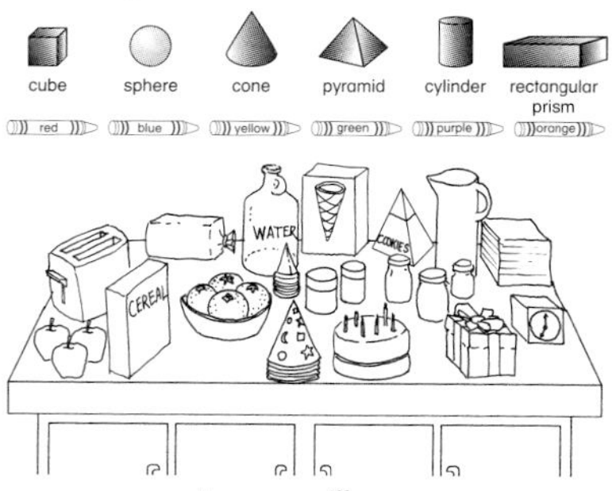

Solve. **Answers will vary.**

Sort the objects into two groups. Circle each object in one group. Underline each object in the other group.

Answers will vary.

Grade 1 7 Chapter 12

Practice

6–11. Check students' drawings.

Find an object in your classroom that matches each three-dimensional figure. Draw the object.

6. 
rectangular prism

7. 
cylinder

8. 
cone

9. 
sphere

10. 
cube

11. 
pyramid

12. **WRITING IN MATH** Sort the objects into two groups. Circle each object in one group green. Circle each object in the other group blue. See students' answers.

Explain your sorting rule.

Sample answer: objects that are round and objects that are not round

Math at Home Activity: Have your child find objects at home that have the same shape as the three-dimensional figures above.

Enrich (p. 10) AL

12-1 Name ____

Enrich

Three-Dimensional Figures All Around You

Look at the picture below. Draw a line to match a three-dimensional figure with an object in the picture.

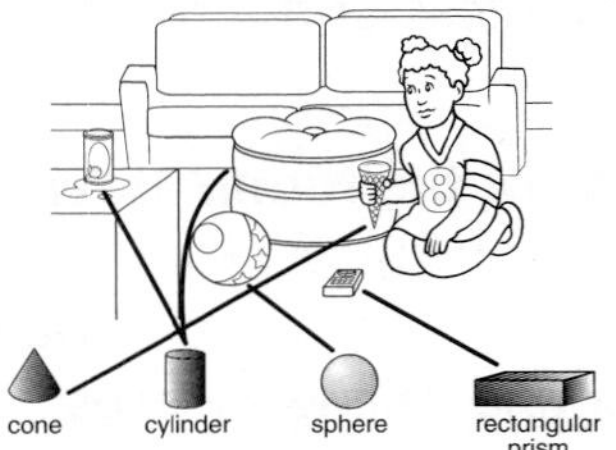

Now draw some figures from your own room. Write what three-dimensional figures they match.

Answers will vary.

Grade 1 10 *Chapter 12*

Homework Practice (p. 8) OL

12-1 Name ____

Homework Practice

Three-Dimensional Figures

Circle the objects that match the three-dimensional figure.

1. 

2. 

Find an object that matches the figure. Draw it. Answers will vary.

3. 
4. 

Grade 1 8 *Chapter 12*

BL Alternate Teaching Strategy

If students have trouble identifying three-dimensional figures . . .

Then use one of the following reteach options.

1. CRM **Daily Reteach Worksheet** (p. 6)
2. **Treasure Hunt** Give a group of students the set of geometric solids and have them search the classroom to find one object that has the shape or that contains the shape of each solid. Check their answers.

3 Practice

Differentiate practice using these leveled assignments for Exercises 6–12.

Level	Assignment
BL Below/Approaching Level	Allow students to refer to the geometric solids manipulatives.
OL On Level	Complete independently.
AL Above/Beyond Level	Draw and name two or three objects for each practice exercise.

4 Assess

Formative Assessment

- Place the six geometric solids from the lesson on the table. Have the students write and place a label correctly in front of each one.

WRITING IN MATH Have students describe similarities and differences between a cylinder and a cone.

Quick Check **Are students continuing to struggle with identifying common solid figures?**

If Yes → Small Group Options (p. 385B)
Strategic Intervention Guide (p. 118)

If No → Independent Work Options (p. 385B)
CRM Skills Practice Worksheet (p. 7)
CRM Enrich Worksheet (p. 10)

LESSON 12-2

Faces and Corners

Lesson Planner

Objectives

Describe and identify three-dimensional figures in order to sort them according to the number of faces and corners.

Vocabulary

face, **corner**

Resources

Materials: chart paper

Manipulatives: geometric solids

Literature Connection: *Captain Invincible and the Space Shapes* by Stuart J. Murphy

Alternate Lessons: Adapt "Tiptoe: A Sorting Game" on pages 76 and 77 of *Math Their Way* to provide practice with classifying shapes by faces and corners.
Use *Impact Mathematics:* Unit 1, to provide practice with identifying and describing three-dimensional figures.

Teacher Technology
TeacherWorks

Focus on Math Background

In this lesson, students will describe and identify key features of three-dimensional figures, including faces and corners (vertices). Identifying the faces on geometric solids provides a natural segue for connecting three-dimensional figures to two-dimensional representations. For example, a pyramid has a square base with four triangular faces. Be aware, though, that students will likely use the word "corners" to describe points on geometric solids. However, the correct geometric term is "vertices."

Daily Routine

Use these suggestions before beginning the lesson on p. 387.

5-Minute Check

(Reviews Lesson 12-1)

Name an object that has the shape of each figure.

1. cone _______ Sample answer: party hat
2. rectangular prism _______ Sample answer: book
3. cylinder _______ Sample answer: soda can
4. sphere _______ Sample answer: ball

Problem of the Day

Go on a shape hunt in your classroom. Find a sphere, a cube, and a rectangular prism. Draw what you found. See students' work.

LINE UP When students line up, have them point to and name three-dimensional objects in the room.

Building Math Vocabulary

- Write the lesson vocabulary words on the board.
- Explain that vertex is the same as **corner**.
- **Where are the vertices of the room? How many vertexes are there?** Answers will vary depending on the shape of the classroom. Help students find the vertices of the room around the ceiling.
- **Where are the flat parts of the room? How many faces are there?** Answers will vary depending on the shape of the classroom. Help students name the floor and ceiling as faces.

Visual Vocabulary Cards

Use Visual Vocabulary Card 9 to reinforce the vocabulary introduced in this lesson. (The Define/Example/Ask routine is printed on the back of each card.)

Differentiated Instruction

Small Group Options

Option 1 LOGICAL, KINESTHETIC

Below Level BL

Materials: pattern blocks, paper, pencils

- Have students work individually with a pencil, paper, and two triangle, two square, and one hexagon pattern blocks.
- Each student will take the pattern blocks and make as many different shape patterns as they can using all or just some of the blocks that they were given.
- After they have made a pattern, they need to record their pattern onto the paper either by writing out the names, tracing the blocks, or drawing the shapes and the pattern on their own.
- The students will exchange their papers with other students to compare answers.

Option 2 INTRAPERSONAL, LINGUISTIC

English Language Learners ELL

Materials: chart containing 4 columns
Core Vocabulary: look again, hidden, suggest
Common Use Verb: hunt for

Do Math This strategy allows students to internalize the properties of shapes.

- Give a student a shape to hide and have him describe it while the remaining students hunt for it. Make sure the student keeps the shape hidden, so seekers must rely on listening skills.
- When students think they have found the shape, they may ask the caller if it is correct. If not, the caller will show a pattern that uses his or her hidden shape, then say: "I suggest you look again."
- If the class has still not found the hidden shape, remove one or more shapes that matches the caller's hidden shape from the caller's pattern.
- Have students identify the pattern and hunt for the missing shape or shapes.

Independent Work Options

Option 1 VISUAL SPATIAL

Early Finishers OL AL

Materials: pattern blocks

- Have students work in pairs. Direct the first partner to make a pattern using two colors and two shapes.
- Then have the second partner continue the pattern.
- Invite students to switch roles and repeat the activity. If time allows, invite them to take turns making other more complicated patterns.

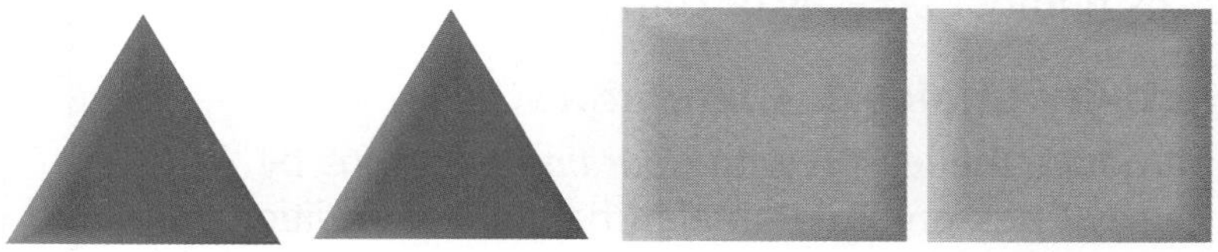

Option 2

Student Technology

Math Online macmillanmh.com

Option 3

Learning Station: Art (p. 381G)

Direct students to the Art Learning Station for more opportunities to explore the lesson concept.

1 Introduce

Activity Choice 1 • Review

- **What are some three-dimensional figures we have learned to describe and identify?** spheres, rectangular prisms (including cubes), pyramids, cylinders, and cones.
- **How can we sort them?** We can sort them according to the number of faces and corners.
- Ask students to help you list attributes on the board various ways to sort three-dimensional figures.
- Have students choose a geometric figure to draw. Have the students label their figure and write down one or more of its attributes such as its number of faces or corners.

Activity Choice 2 • Literature

Introduce the lesson with *Counting Penguins* by Betsey Chessen and Pamela Chanko. For additional support, see p. TR59.

2 Teach

Understand Using the questions, review what students know and need to find.

Plan Have them discuss their strategy.

Solve Guide students to use the *look for a pattern* strategy to solve the problem.

- **What pattern do you see?** red rectangular prism, red cube, yellow rectangular prism
- **What color should come next?** red **What shape should come next?** rectangular prism **What is the missing block?** red rectangular prism

Check

- **Did you follow the pattern? Did you look at both the figure and the color of each block?** See students' explanations.

COMMON ERROR!

Students may only look at one attribute when looking for a pattern. Encourage students to describe patterns in as many ways as possible. Use attribute blocks for practice with creating and identifying patterns.

Name ____________________

Problem-Solving Strategy
Look for a Pattern

Main Idea

I will look for a pattern to solve a problem.

Marcus made a pattern with his blocks. Which block is missing?

Understand

What do I know?
Underline what you know.
What do I need to find?
Circle the question.

Plan

How will I solve the problem?

I will look for a pattern.

Solve

Look for a pattern.
Circle the pattern unit.
Draw the block that is missing.

student should draw a red rectangular prism

Check

Look back.
Is my answer reasonable?

Check students' explanations.

Reteach (pp. 16–17) BL

12-3 Name ____________________

Reteach (1)

Problem-Solving Strategy: Look for a Pattern

Melita made a pattern with her blocks.

Which block is missing?

Step 1 Understand	**What do I know?** Melita made a pattern. 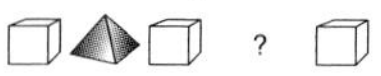 **What do I need to find out?** Which block is missing?
Step 2 Plan	**Plan: How will I find which shape is in the middle?** I will look for a pattern.
Step 3 Solve	**Look for a pattern.** Hint: What is the pattern unit?
Step 4 Check	**Look back.** Is my answer reasonable? yes

Grade 1 16 Chapter 12

Copyright © Macmillan/McGraw-Hill, a division of The McGraw-Hill Companies, Inc.

Skills Practice (p. 18) OL

12-3 Name ____________________

Skills Practice

Problem-Solving Strategy: Look for a Pattern

Look for a pattern to solve. Draw your answers.

Show your work here.

1. Marcy draws a pattern with shapes. Which shape is missing?

2. Nicole makes a pattern with her blocks. Which shape is missing?

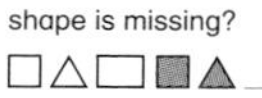

3. Toby draws a pattern with shapes. Which shape is missing?

Grade 1 18 Chapter 12

Copyright © Macmillan/McGraw-Hill, a division of The McGraw-Hill Companies, Inc.

Remember
Understand
Plan
Solve
Check

Try It

Look for a pattern to solve.

1. June made a line of blocks. Draw the block that is missing. student should draw an orange triangle

2. These are Quinn's blocks. Draw the block that is missing. student should draw a green square

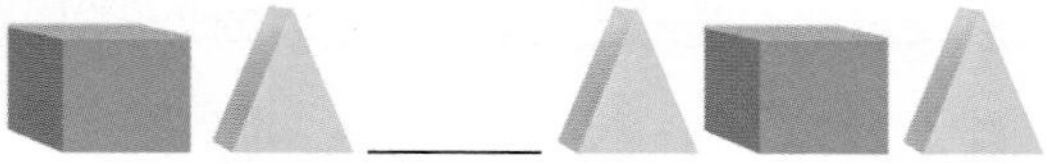

Your Turn

Look for a pattern to solve.

3. Ayden made a line of blocks. Draw the block that is missing. student should draw a red triangle

4. Grace is making a line of blocks. She needs 2 more blocks to finish. Draw the blocks that are missing. student should draw a green triangle and an orange rectangle

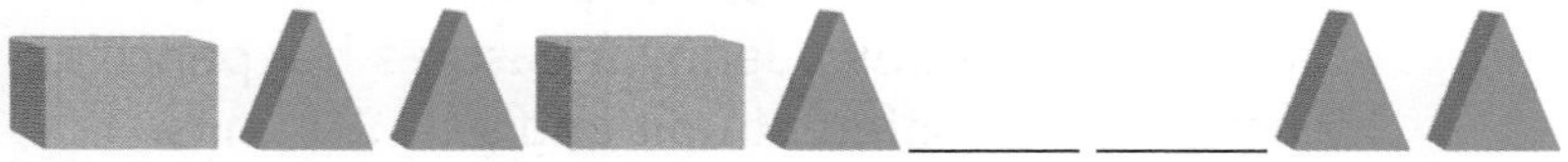

Math at Home Activity: Look for patterns on the boxes and cans of food items. Ask your child what comes next.

Enrich (p. 20) AL	Homework Practice (p. 19) OL

12-3 Name ______
Enrich
Making Patterns

Draw your own pattern. Use any shapes you like.

Look back at the pattern you made. Write or draw your answers below.

1. How many different shapes are in your pattern?
Answers will vary.
2. What is your pattern unit? Draw it.
Drawings will vary.
3. Can you make another pattern with your shapes? Draw it.
Drawings will vary.

Grade 1 20 Chapter 12

12-3 Name ______
Homework Practice
Problem-Solving Strategy: Look for a Pattern

Look for a pattern to solve. Draw your answers.

Show your work here.

1. Ms. King draws a pattern with shapes. Which shape is missing?
○○△○ ___ △ ○
2. Tani makes a pattern with his blocks. Which shape is missing?
3. Karen draws a pattern with shapes. Which shape is missing?

Grade 1 19 Chapter 12

Try It Observe students as you work through Exercises 1 and 2 as a class.

BL Alternate Teaching Strategy

If students do not understand how to look for a pattern . . .

Then use one of the following reteach options.

1. CRM **Daily Reteach Worksheet** (pp. 16–17)
2. **Connecting Cubes** Have students work with partners to create and describe number and color patterns.
3. **TechLink** Have students use Math Tool Chest to help coplete the problem-solving exercises.

3 Practice

Your Turn

Exercises 3–4 Make sure students can read and understand the problems. Make sure students understand that they need to look at both color and shape in the patterns.

4 Assess

Formative Assessment

- **How can we solve problems by *looking for a pattern?* Use words or cubes to justify your thinking.** Sample answer: Find the pattern unit. Then to add on to extend the pattern or fill in missing spaces to complete the pattern.

WRITING IN MATH Draw a picture to show a pattern using yellow squares and red triangles.

Quick Check **Are students continuing to struggle with finding a pattern to solve problems?**

If No → Small Group Options (p. 389B)
If Yes → Independent Work Options (p. 389B)
CRM Skills Practice Worksheet (p. 18)
CRM Enrich Worksheet (p. 20)

LESSON 12-4 Two- and Three-Dimensional Figures

Lesson Planner

Objective

Use faces of three-dimensional figures to make two-dimensional figures.

Review Vocabulary

cone, cylinder

Resources

Materials: modeling clay

Manipulatives: pattern blocks, geometric solids

Literature Connection: *When a Line Bends . . . A Shape Begins* by Rhonda Gowler Greene

Alternate Lessons: Adapt "Sorting and Classifying Walks" on pages 72 and 73 of *Math Their Way* for practice with describing, identifying, and comparing two-dimensional figures.
Use *IMPACT Mathematics:* Units I and J to provide practice with using the faces of three-dimensional figures to make two-dimensional figures.

Teacher Technology
TeacherWorks • Concepts in Motion

Focus on Math Background

Students will discover relationships between two- and three-dimensional figures in this lesson. By observing the faces on geometric solids, children will see two-dimensional outlines, or plane figures, such as squares, rectangles, circles, and triangles. Students should focus on the exterior lines that enclose the interior of two-dimensional figures in order to concentrate on properties and attributes, such as straight, slanted, and curved, versus what these plane figures resemble—e.g., a ball or roof top.

Daily Routine

Use these suggestions before beginning the lesson on p. 391.

5-Minute Check

(Reviews Lesson 12-3)

Match the three-dimensional figure with its name.

1.  c   a. sphere

2.  b   b. cube

3.  a   c. pyramid

Problem of the Day

Hiromi and Jenny have pencils that are the same length. Hiromi measures her pencil's length in one unit and gets 8 units. Jenny measures her pencil's length using a different unit and gets 10 units. Who used the longer unit to measure? Hiromi

LINE UP As you prepare for recess, lunch, or dismissal, hold up pattern blocks. **Which three-dimensional figure has this plane figure as a face?** If more than one figure can be correct, prompt additional students to answer. Students who answer correctly get in line.

Review Math Vocabulary

- Review **cone** and **cylinder** shapes with students.
- Hold up a geometric solid of a cone and cylinder. **How are these figures different?** Sample answer: A cone has 1 face and 1 corner, and a cylinder has 2 faces and 0 corners.
- Explain that a cylinder has two flat sides and one curved side, but a cone has only one flat side and one curved side that comes to a point.

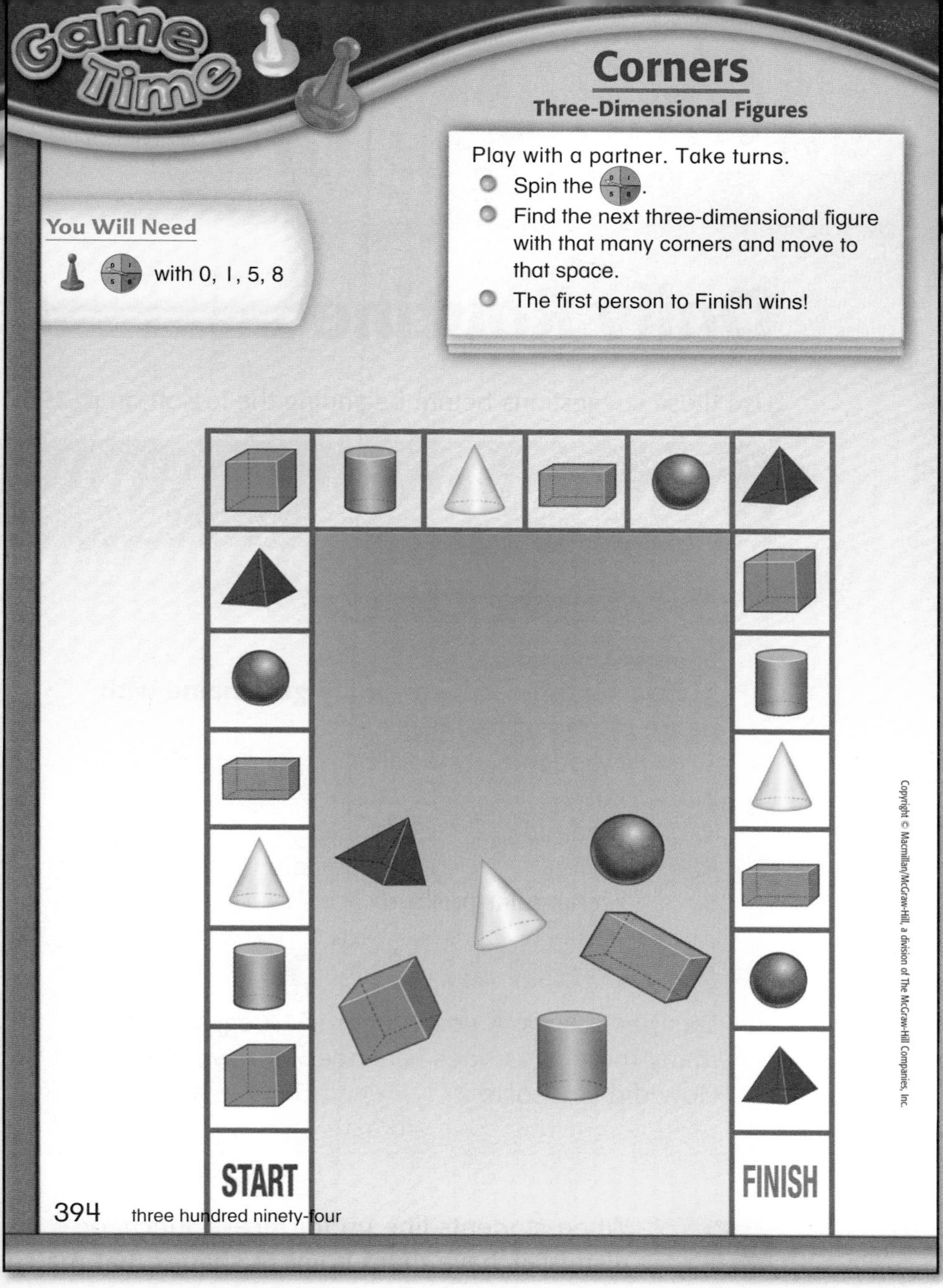
Game Time

Corners

Three-Dimensional Figures

Play with a partner. Take turns.

- Spin the spinner.
- Find the next three-dimensional figure with that many corners and move to that space.
- The first person to Finish wins!

You Will Need

game piece, spinner with 0, 1, 5, 8

Game Time

Corners

Math Concept:

Identify and Count the Corners of Three-Dimensional Figures

Materials: game pieces

Manipulatives: transparent spinner with the numbers 0, 1, 5, and 8

Introduce the game on page 394 to students to play as a class, in small groups, or at a learning workstation to review concepts introduced in this chapter.

Instructions

- Assign each player a game piece. Students begin at *Start.*
- Players take turns spinning the spinner and finding the next figure with that number of corners.
- When a player finds the figure, the player moves his or her game piece to that space.
- The first player to reach *Finish* wins!

Extend the Game

Change the numbers in the spinner to 1, 2, 5, and 6. Students must now find a figure with that number of faces.

Differentiated Practice

Use these leveling suggestions to differentiate the game for all the learners.

Level	Assignment
BL Below/Approaching Level	Allow students to use the geometric solids manipulatives to count corners.
OL On Level	Have students play the game with the rules as written.
AL Above/Below Level	Students must name the figure and state the number of straight edges.

LESSON 12-5 Two-Dimensional Figures

Lesson Planner

Objective

Identify, describe, and compare attributes of two-dimensional figures.

Vocabulary

triangle, **rectangle**, **square**, **circle**, **side**

Resources

Materials: paper cut-outs of two-dimensional figures, magazines, books

Manipulatives: attribute blocks

Literature Connection: *Math Counts: Shapes* by Henry Pluckrose

Alternate Lesson: Use *IMPACT Mathematics:* Unit J to provide practice identifying, describing, and comparing two-dimensional figures.

Teacher Technology

TeacherWorks

Focus on Math Background

In this lesson, students focus exclusively on two-dimensional figures. The students will describe and name the attributes of two-dimensional figures in order to sort the shapes by common features. Students might classify triangles, squares, and rectangles as figures with straight lines. Students must understand the difference between straight and curved lines before they can use the concept and terminology of *polygon* and *nonpolygon* in classifying two-dimensional figures. By comparing and contrasting two-dimensional figures, students begin to see relationships and make generalizations, such as understanding that a square is a special type of rectangle.

Daily Routine

Use these suggestions before beginning the lesson on p. 395.

5-Minute Check

(Reviews Lesson 12-4)

Match the three-dimensional figure name with name of one of its faces.

1.	cylinder a	a. circle
2.	cube b	b. square
3.	pyramid c, b	c. triangle
4.	cone a	d. rectangle
5.	rectangular prism d	

Problem of the Day

Lars has 2 eggs. A dozen eggs is 12 eggs. How many more eggs does Lars need to have a dozen? How did you solve it? 10 eggs; Sample answer: I used connecting cubes to act it out.

LINE UP When students line up for recess, lunch, or dismissal, have them point to shapes that match riddles about shapes:

- **I have 3 corners and 3 sides.** triangle
- **I have 4 equal-length sides.** square
- **I have no corners, and I am a nonpolygon.** circle

Building Math Vocabulary

Draw and label a **circle**, a **rectangle**, a **square**, and a **triangle** at the top of the board.

- Lead students to the definition of each figure by asking questions. Focus on the number of **sides** and corners.
- Then ask students to classify each shape as a polygon or nonpolygon.

Visual Vocabulary Cards

Use Visual Vocabulary Cards 7, 41, 45, and 49 to reinforce the vocabulary introduced in this lesson. (The Define/Example/Ask routine is printed on the back of each card.)

Differentiated Instruction

Small Group Options

Option 1 KINESTHETIC, VISUAL/SPATIAL

Gifted and Talented AL

Materials: construction paper, marker, ruler, scissors

- Help students use a marker and ruler to draw a three-inch square on construction paper.
- Have students cut out their squares.
- Students fold their square in a way they think will create another figure. Have students mark the line along the fold.
- Students name the figures created and discuss their work with the group.
- **Can anyone think of a way to create a circle from the square?**

Option 2 LINGUISTIC, VISUAL

English Language Learners ELL

Materials: a variety of paper shapes, poster of each shape with a sentence describing its properties (A square has 4 equal sides and 4 corners, etc.).
Core Vocabulary: sort by, corner, side
Common Use Verb: paste

See Math This strategy allows students to vocalize the properties of plane figures as they sort them.

- Describe the number of corners and sides of each type of shape as you pass them out.
- Have students vocalize the properties of each as they place them in like groups. Encourage them to use the poster to help them remember the language.
- Review their work as you walk the room. If they have them correct, have them paste the shapes onto that page.
- As time permits, allow students to sit in a circle. Give each student a shape.
- Have students say the name of their shape (simultaneously, for practice, not accuracy) and pass the shape to the right. Repeat.

Independent Work Options

Option 1 VISUAL/SPATIAL, INTRAPERSONAL

Early Finishers OL AL

Materials: magazines, poster board, scissors, glue

- Have students work independently to find geometric figures in magazine pictures.
- Have each student try to find two different pictures that show each figure, cut out the pictures, and glue them onto the poster board to make a new picture.
- Students should label the sets with the figure represented.

Option 2

Student Technology

Math Online macmillanmh.com

Math Adventures

Option 3

Learning Station: Social Studies (p. 381H)

Direct students to the Social Studies Learning Station for more opportunities to explore and extend the lesson concept.

Option 4

Problem-Solving Practice

Reinforce problem-solving skills and strategies with the Problem-Solving Practice worksheet.

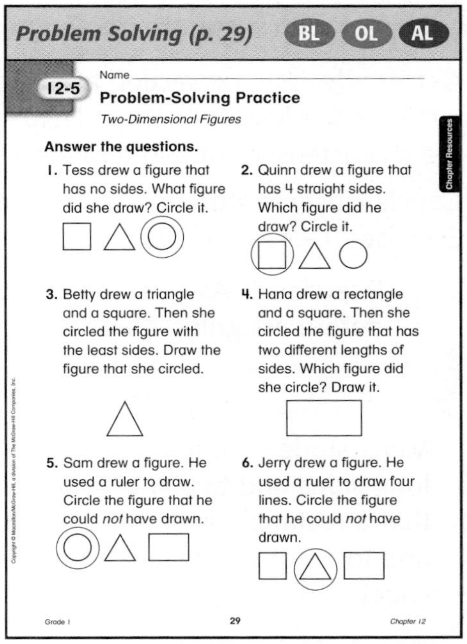
Problem Solving (p. 29) BL OL AL

12-5 Name ______

Problem-Solving Practice

Two-Dimensional Figures

Chapter Resources

Answer the questions.

1. Tess drew a figure that has no sides. What figure did she draw? Circle it.
2. Quinn drew a figure that has 4 straight sides. Which figure did he draw? Circle it.
3. Betty drew a triangle and a square. Then she circled the figure with the least sides. Draw the figure that she circled.
4. Hana drew a rectangle and a square. Then she circled the figure that has two different lengths of sides. Which figure did she circle? Draw it.
5. Sam drew a figure. He used a ruler to draw. Circle the figure that he could *not* have drawn.
6. Jerry drew a figure. He used a ruler to draw four lines. Circle the figure that he could *not* have drawn.

Grade 1 29 Chapter 12

12-5

1 Introduce

Activity Choice 1 • Hands-On

Provide students with paper cut-outs of two-dimensional figures. Have students look through magazines, cut out two-dimensional figures that match.

- **What two-dimensional figures did you find?** See students' work.
- Have the students sort their two-dimensional figures according to straight and curved **sides**.
- **Which of these two-dimensional figures are polygons? Which ones are nonpolygons?** See students' work.
- Now ask the students to sort their two-dimensional figures according to the number of sides.
- **Which figure has three sides?** triangle **What objects did you find that are triangles?** See students' work.

Activity Choice 2 • Literature

Introduce the lesson with *Math Counts: Shapes* by Henry Pluckrose
For additional support, see p. TR59.

2 Teach

- Have the students trace with their fingers around a triangular attribute block as you do on an overhead. Tell students to start in one corner and trace the sides. Model and describe what you are doing; for example, one line going to the side, turning a corner, another line going down, and so on. Identify the figure.
- Repeat with a **square**, **rectangle**, and **circle**.

Get Ready Use the section at the top of p. 395 to reinforce the lesson concept. Help students identify the characteristics of two-dimensional figures.

Check Observe students as you work through Exercises 1–5 as a class.

Exercise 5 Assess student comprehension before assigning practice exercises.

COMMON ERROR!

Many students think that a rectangle has two long sides and two short sides. Tell students that a rectangle is any shape with four sides and four corners that are like corners on a sheet of paper. Is a square a rectangle?

Name ____________________

Two-Dimensional Figures

Get Ready

Main Idea

I will identify and describe two-dimensional figures.

Vocabulary

triangle
rectangle
square
circle
side

Review Vocabulary

corner

Flat figures are called two-dimensional figures. Some two-dimensional figures have straight sides and corners.

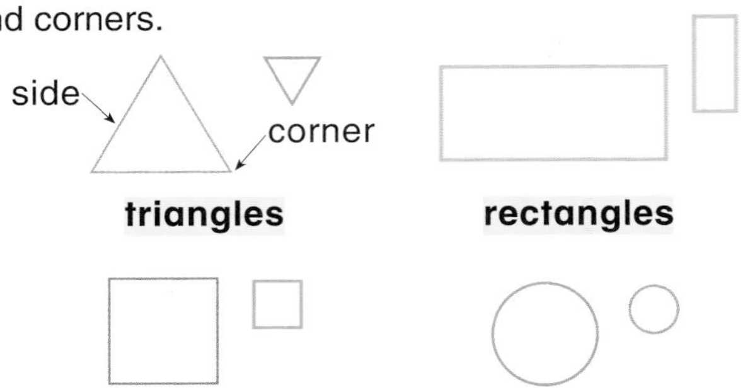

Check

Write how many.

1. 0 sides, 0 corners
2. 4 sides, 4 corners
3. 4 sides, 4 corners
4. 3 sides, 3 corners

5. **Talk About It** What objects in your classroom are the shape of a circle? Sample answer: clock, table top, paint jar lid

---

Reteach (p. 26) BL

12-5 Name ____________________

Reteach

Two-Dimensional Figures

Two-dimensional figures are figures that are flat.

circle triangle square rectangle

Name as many objects that are shaped like each two-dimensional figure as you can.

1. (circle) plate, clock, coins
2. (triangle) **Answers will vary.**
3. (square) **Answers will vary.**
4. (rectangle) **Answers will vary.**

Grade 1 26 Chapter 12

Skills Practice (p. 27) OL

12-5 Name ____________________

Skills Practice

Two-Dimensional Figures

1. Draw a robot. Use at least one (square), one (circle), one (triangle), and one (rectangle). **Answers will vary.**
2. Color all (square) orange.
3. Color all (circle) blue.
4. Color all (triangle) red.
5. Color all (rectangle) brown.

Solve.

6. Jay is drawing the faces of a cube. Will he draw more than one kind of shape? Explain. **No; all of the faces are the same size squares.**

Chapter Resources

Grade 1 27 Chapter 12

Practice Check students' drawings

Remember
Squares, circles, triangles, and rectangles can be different sizes.

6. Draw a picture. Use □, ○, △, and ▭.

Color □ crayon   Color ○ crayon

Color △ crayon   Color ▭ crayon

H.O.T. Problem

7. **Explaining Math** How is a square different from a rectangle?

Sample answer: A square has 4 equal sides. The sides of a rectangle are not all the same length.

Math at Home Activity: Have your child identify and describe two-dimensional figures in your home or neighborhood.

BL Alternate Teaching Strategy

If students struggle with identifying two-dimensional figures . . .

Then use one of the following reteach options.

1. CRM **Daily Reteach Worksheet** (p. 26)
2. **Real World** Have students identify two-dimensional geometric figures throughout the classroom. Have them write down the shape and where they found it so they can refer to it later.

3 Practice

Differentiate practice using these leveled assignments for Exercises 6–7.

Level	Assignment
BL Below/ Approaching Level	Arrange pattern blocks to create a playground. Then draw your playground on the page.
OL On Level	Complete the exercises independently.
AL Above/Beyond Level	Label each shape with its correct name.

4 Assess

Formative Assessment

- **How is a triangle different from a rectangle?** A triangle has three sides; a rectangle has four sides.
- **How is a square different from a rectangle?** A square has four equal-length sides.

WRITING IN MATH Have students explain how they will remember the difference between a square and a rectangle.

Quick Check **Are students continuing to struggle identifying two-dimensional figures?**

If Yes → CRM Reteach Worksheet (p. 26)
If No → Independent Work Options (p. 381B)
CRM Skills Practice Worksheet (p. 27)
CRM Enrich Worksheet (p. 30)

Enrich (p. 30) AL

12-5 Name
Enrich
Two-Dimensional Figures

circle square rectangle triangle

Read the directions. Draw a picture. Label the figures you used.

1. Make a picture using 1 figure with no corners, 1 figure that has 3 corners, and 1 figure with 4 equal sides.
Answers will vary.

2. Make a picture using 2 figure with no corners, 1 figure with 4 corners, and 1 figure with 3 corners.
Answers will vary.

Grade 1 30 Chapter 12

Homework Practice (p. 28) OL

12-5 Name
Homework Practice
Two-Dimensional Figures

Draw the following two-dimensional figures.

1. Draw a circle.
2. Draw a square.
3. Draw a triangle.
4. Draw a rectangle.

Write how many.

5. 4 sides, 4 corners
6. 3 sides, 3 corners
7. 4 sides, 4 corners
8. 0 sides, 0 corners

Grade 1 28 Chapter 12

Mid-Chapter Check

Lessons 12-1 to 12-5

Formative Assessment

Use the Mid-Chapter Check to assess student's progress in the first half of the chapter.

ExamView Assessment Suite Customize and create multiple versions of your Mid-Chapter Check and the test answer keys.

FOLDABLES Dinah Zike's Foldables

Use these lesson suggestions to incorporate the Foldable during the chapter.

Lesson 12-1 On the inside top section of the 3-D tab, record what students learn about common three-dimensional figures and classify them by common attributes. Include labeled pictures of the following: pyramid, cube, sphere, cone, cylinder, rectangle, and rectangular prism.

Lesson 12-2 On the inside bottom section of the 3-D tab, record what students learn about the classification of three-dimensional figures by observing the number of faces and corners. Demonstrate how different attributes, such as faces and corners, can be used to classify three-dimensional figures.

Lesson 12-4 Under the 2-D tab, record what students learn about the attributes of plane shapes including triangles, rectangles, squares, and circles.

Lesson 12-5 Under the "Both" tab of the Foldable, illustrate how to use faces of three-dimensional figures to make two-dimensional shapes.

Name ______________________________

Draw an object that matches each three-dimensional figure.

1.

rectangular prism

Check students' drawings.

2.

cylinder

Check students' drawings.

Circle all the three-dimensional figures that match the rule.

3. 8 **corners**

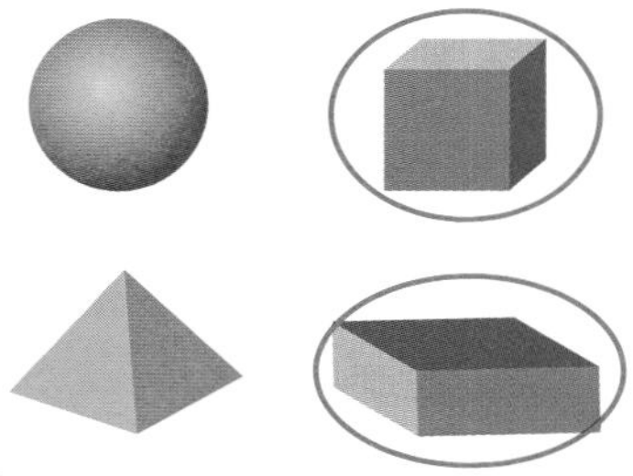

4. 5 **faces**

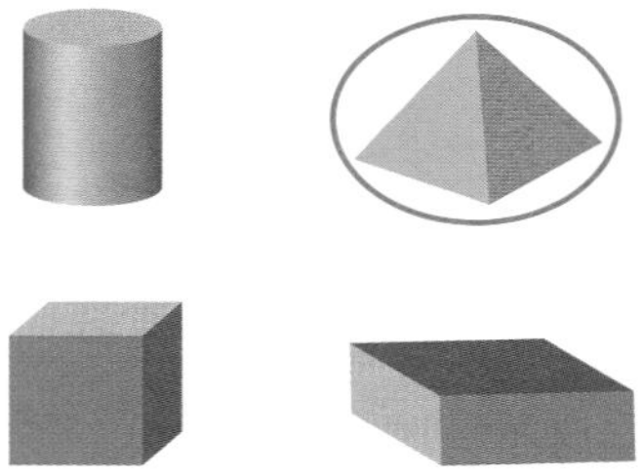

Circle the object that has a face with the same shape. Look at the two-dimensional shape.

5.

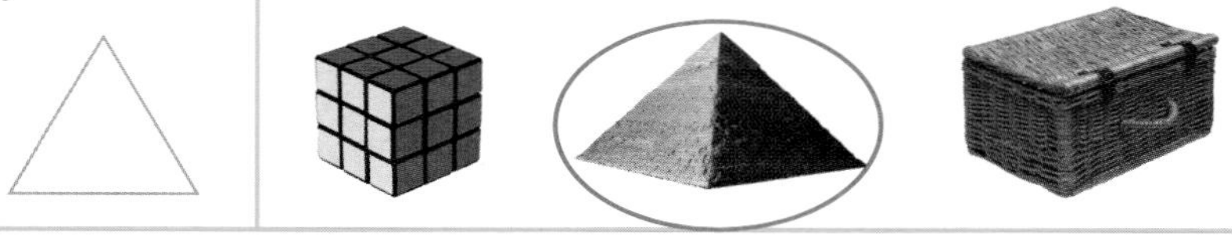

Circle the answer.

6. I have 4 corners.
I have 2 long sides
and 2 short sides.
What am I?

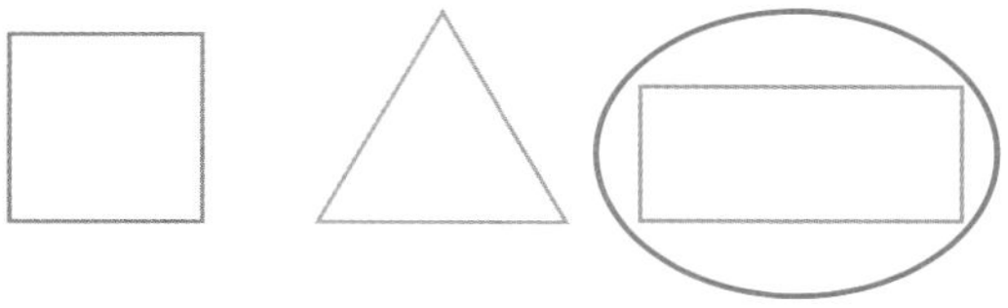

Data-Driven Decision Making

Based on the results of the Mid-Chapter Check, use the following resources to review concepts that continue to give students problems.

Exercises	State/Local Standards	What's the Math?	Error Analysis	Resources for Review
1–2 Lesson 12-1		Draw geometric figures.	Does not follow directions.	Strategic Intervention Guide (p. 118) CRM Chapter 12 Resource Masters (Reteach Worksheets) Math Online Concepts in Motion Math Adventures
3–4 Lesson 12-2		Identify geometric figures and explain which attributes are being used for classification.	Does not circle all objects matching description.	
5 Lesson 12-4		Match the faces of two- and three-dimensional figures.	Does not choose correct real-world object.	

Spiral Review Chapters 1–12

Write each missing number.

7. 11 − 6 = 5
 6 + 5 = 11

8. 13 − 5 = 8
 5 + 8 = 13

9. 12 − 5 = 7
 5 + 7 = 12

10. Show 39¢.

Sample answer:
3 dimes, 9 pennies

Add.

11. 2 + 6 = 8

12. 8 + 2 = 10

13. 1 + 4 = 5

14. 3 + 6 = 9

15. Circle the activity that takes the least amount of time.

half hour

four hours

one hour

Spiral Review

Reviews Chapters 1 to 12

Objective: Review and assess mastery of skills and concepts from previous chapters.

Resources for Review

Based on student results, refer to these lessons for remediation:

- **Exercises 7–9: Lesson 10-8** (p. 335)
- **Exercise 10: Lesson 11-9** (p. 371)
- **Exercises 11–14: Lesson 2-3** (p. 55)
- **Exercise 15: Lesson 7-6** (p. 227)

Problem-Solving Investigation

Choose a Strategy

Lesson Planner

Objective

Choose the best strategy to solve a problem.

Resources

Materials: paper, crayons

Manipulatives: pattern blocks, geometric solids

Teacher Technology

TeacherWorks

Real-World Problem Solving Library
Math and Science: *Shapes in Nature*
Use these leveled books to reinforce and extend problem-solving skills and strategies.

Leveled for:

- OL On Level
- ELL Sheltered English
- SP Spanish

For additional support, see the Real-World Problem Solving Teacher Guide.

Daily Routine

Use these suggestions before beginning the lesson on p. 399.

5-Minute Check

(Reviews Lesson 12-5)
Draw the face of an animal or a person. Use at least 1 circle, 1 rectangle, 1 square, and 1 triangle.

Problem of the Day

Mrs. Behouse's class has 20 students. She needs to put her class into groups of 10 for a project. Count by tens to find how many groups her class will have. 2 groups
For another project, she needs to put her class into groups of 5. Count by fives to find out how many groups her class will have. 4 groups

LINE UP Have each student choose a pattern block.

- **If you have a figure with three corners, line up. What figure is it?** a triangle
- **If you have a figure with four equal-length sides, line up. What figure is it?** a square
- **If you have a figure with four sides, line up. What figure is it?** a rectangle
- **If you have a figure with no corners, line up. What figure is it?** a circle

Differentiated Instruction

Small Group Options

Option 1 — LOGICAL, KINESTHETIC

Below Level BL

Materials: paper, pencil

Have students copy this list from the board: *sphere, triangle, pyramid, cube, cylinder, rectangular prism, and square.*

- Have students go on a shape hunt in the classroom. They should search the room for the shapes on their list.
- When they find a shape, they should write down where they found it and draw a picture of it.
- Students can refer back to their lists throughout the lesson.

Option 2 — INTRAPERSONAL, LINGUISTIC

English Language Learners ELL

Materials: paper, crayons

Core Vocabulary: in the center, underneath, above

Common Use Verb: draw

Hear Math This strategy allows students to integrate their understanding of shapes with their listening skills.

- Pass out paper and say: "Listen closely. I will say a shape and tell you where to draw it."
- Read the following: "Draw a triangle **in the center** of your paper. Draw 2 small circles **above** the triangle. Draw a rectangle **underneath** the triangle. Draw a large circle around everything you have drawn so far."
- Show your papers. If students have followed your directions, they should have a funny looking face on the paper.
- Reduce the complexity of directions according to the level of your group or repeat the strategy a second time, modeling the placement at each step. Emphasize target vocabulary.

Independent Work Options

Option 1 — INTRAPERSONAL

Early Finishers OL AL

Materials: a paper or cloth bag, pattern blocks

Place several of each pattern block in a bag so that students cannot see the blocks.

- Students should take turns reaching into the bag and feeling a pattern block without pulling it from the bag.
- After students feel the shape, they will draw the figure they felt. Students may then look at their figure to see if their drawing matches it.
- If a student does not draw the correct figure, the group should discuss why or how he or she was fooled.

Option 2

Student Technology

Math Online macmillanmh.com

Option 3

Learning Station: Reading (p. 381G)

Direct students to the Reading Learning Station for more opportunities to explore and extend the lesson concept.

1 Introduce

Activity • Review

Write this problem on the board:

Timmy the baker has 12 loaves of bread. On Saturday he sells 5 loaves. On Sunday he sells 6 loaves. How many loaves are left?

- **What problem-solving strategies can we use to solve this problem?** Sample answers: Write a number sentence; draw a picture; make a model.
- Tell students you will model drawing a picture.
- Draw twelve loaves of bread. **How many loaves did Timmy sell on Saturday?** 5 loaves Cross out five loaves. **How many loaves did Timmy sell on Sunday?** 6 loaves Cross out six loaves.
- **How many loaves are left?** 1 loaf

2 Teach

Have students read the problem on p. 399. Guide them through the problem-solving steps.

Understand Using the questions, review what students know and what they need to find.

- **What do you know?** The window has 4 sides and 4 corners. Each side is the same length.
- **Could the window be a triangle? Explain.** No, a triangle has 3 sides. Have students draw a picture to justify their thinking.

Plan Have them discuss their strategy.

Solve Guide students to *draw a picture* to solve the problem.

Check Have students look back at the problem to make sure that the answer fits the facts given.

COMMON ERROR!

Drawing three-dimensional figures is challenging even for bright students. Show students a step-by-step process for drawing a pyramid, a rectangular prism, and a square.

Name ______________________________

Problem-Solving Investigation

Main Idea

I will choose a strategy to solve a problem.

The window in my room has 4 sides and 4 corners. Each side is the same length. What shape is the window?

Your Mission:
Find the shape that is described.

Understand

What do I know?
Underline what you know.
What do I need to find?
Circle it.

Plan

How will I solve the problem?
One way is to draw a picture.

Remember the window has 4 sides.

Solve

Draw a picture.
Use the clues to draw a picture.

See students' drawings.

Check

Look back.
Is my answer resonable?

Check students' explanations.

Reteach (pp. 31–32) BL

Name

12-6 **Reteach (1)**
Problem-Solving Investigation: Choose a Strategy

Mark has a can of peas. It has 2 faces.
1 face is the shape of a circle.
What is the other face?

Step 1 Understand	**What do I know?** Mark has a can of peas. It has 2 faces. 1 face is a circle. **What do I need to find out?** What the other face is.
Step 2 Plan	**How will I find what the face is?** I can draw a picture.
Step 3 Solve	**Draw a picture.** The faces are a circle and a circle.
Step 4 Check	**Look back.** Did I draw a picture of a can? yes Does my answer show what shape the other face is? yes

Grade 1 31 Chapter 12

Skills Practice (p. 33) OL

Name

12-6 **Skills Practice**
Problem-Solving Investigation: Choose a Strategy

Choose a strategy. Solve.

Problem-Solving Strategies
- Find a pattern
- Use logical reasoning
- Draw a picture

1. Sofia looks at a postcard. The postcard has 4 corners. Its sides are not the same length. She says her postcard is a rectangle. Is she right? **yes**

Show your work here.

Strategies will vary.

2. Dave draws patterns. He draws a cube, a square, a rectangle, a cube, and a square. What will the 8th shape be? **square**

3. Earl camps. His tent has 4 faces that are triangles. He says the floor of his tent is a circle. Is he right? **no**

Grade 1 33 Chapter 12

Mixed Problem Solving

Choose a strategy. Solve.

Problem-Solving Strategies
- Draw a picture
- Find a pattern
- Use logical reasoning

1. Ramón's toy box is a rectangular prism. How many corners does it have? 8 corners

2. LaToya is buying a picture frame. She wants the frame to have 4 corners and all the sides the same length. What should the shape of the frame be? square

3. Katie first puts a red bead, then a blue bead, and then a yellow bead on a string. She starts with a square bead. The next bead is a triangle. What color is the triangle? blue

4. Beatriz is drawing a pattern. The first triangle points up, the next points down, the third points up, the next points down. Which way is the 8th triangle pointing? down

Math at Home Activity: Take advantage of problem-solving opportunities during daily routines such as riding in the car, bedtime, doing laundry, putting away groceries, planning schedules, and so on.

Enrich (p. 35) AL

12-6 Name ______

Enrich

Sitting and Shapes

Write or draw your answers.

1. When you and your friends sit around a campfire, you sit in a circle. How would you and your family sit around your dinner table? **Answers may vary.**
2. How would you and your friends sit during lunch? **Answers may vary.**
3. How would you and your friends sit in class? **Answers may vary.**
4. Think of the last time you sat in a circle. Draw a picture to show it. **Answers may vary.**

Chapter Resources

Grade 1 35 Chapter 12

Homework Practice (p. 34) OL

12-6 Name ______

Homework Practice

Problem-Solving Investigation: Choose a Strategy

Choose a strategy. Solve.

Problem-Solving Strategies
- Find a pattern
- Use logical reasoning
- Draw a picture

1. Jake drinks a can of juice. The can has two faces. The side of the can is curved. He says it is a cylinder. Is he right? **yes** — Show your work here. **Strategies may vary.**
2. Jerome puts a stamp on his letter. The stamp has 4 corners. Each side is the same length. He says it is a cube. Is he right? **no**
3. Lisa makes a banner. She puts a triangle, circle, triangle, and circle on the banner. What will the 8th shape be? **circle**

Grade 1 34 Chapter 12

BL Alternate Teaching Strategy

If students are having trouble choosing a problem-solving strategy . . .

Then use one of the following reteach options.

1. CRM **Daily Reteach Worksheet** (pp. 31–32)
2. **Review** List the problem-solving strategies on the board. Have volunteers explain or provide an example of each one. Keep the list on the board for students to refer to as they work.

3 Practice

Mixed Problem Solving

Exercises 1–2 Students must be familiar with two- and three-dimensional figures to answer these problems. Have manipulatives available.

Exercises 3–4 Students can draw pictures to solve these problems.

4 Assess

Formative Assessment

Ask students to guess which three-dimensional figure you are describing. **It has 6 faces with edges that are not of equal length. Which figure is it? How will you solve this problem?** Sample answer: I will use logical reasoning. A cube and a rectangular prism have 6 faces. But a cube has edges with equal lengths. So the three-dimensional figure must be a rectangular prism.

WRITING IN MATH Have students describe how to draw a triangle.

Quick Check **Are students continuing to struggle with choosing a problem-solving strategy?**

If Yes → Small Group Options (p. 399B)

If No → Independent Work Options (p. 399B)

CRM Skills Practice Worksheet (p. 33)

CRM Enrich Worksheet (p. 35)

LESSON 12-7 Position

Lesson Planner

Objective
Use position words to tell where objects are.

Vocabulary
position

Resources
Materials: prepared poster for "Little Yellow Star"

Literature Connection: *The Greatest Gymnast of All* by Stuart J. Murphy

Teacher Technology
TeacherWorks

Focus on Math Background

This lesson develops students' spatial awareness by focusing on the concept of position. In this lesson, the students arrange and describe objects in space by proximity (near or far), position (below, above, up, down, behind, in front of, or next to) and direction (left or right). First, students will need to develop a strong understanding of positional and directional terms such as below, above, left, and right. Then students will be ready to practice using the words north, south, east, and west to describe location and movement. Being able to navigate distances and points in space lays the foundation for future work with coordinate geometry and transformations, such as rotations, translations, and reflections.

Daily Routine

Use these suggestions before beginning the lesson on p. 401.

5-Minute Check
(Reviews Lesson 12-6)
Shantel is making a necklace out of shapes. First she adds a small triangle and then a small square. Next she adds a small circle and a small rectangle. Then Shantel starts the pattern over. What are the next 3 shapes she will add to her necklace? a small triangle, a small square, and a small circle

Problem of the Day
Look at a number line. Start at the number 3. What number is 5 more? 8 What addition fact did you show on the number line? $3 + 5 = 8$

LINE UP When students line up for recess, lunch, or dismissal, have them form two lines. Ask questions about their positions in line. For example: **Who is next to Carlita? Who is far from Roger? Who is in front of Nelson? Who is behind Jason?**

Building Math Vocabulary
- Write **position** on the board. Write *above* above *position, below* below *position, left* left of *position,* and *right* right of *position*. Below this, write a sentence frame: _______ is ______ position.
- Tell students that an object's position is where the object is. Position words to tell the position of each word on the board in relation to the word *position*.
- Ask the position of each word on the board. **What is the position of *above*?** *Above* is above *position*. **Where is *left*?** *Left* is left of *position.*

Differentiated Instruction

Small Group Options

Option 1 — KINESTHETIC, LINGUISTIC

Below/Approaching Level BL

- Play a game of Follow the Leader. Ask group members to listen to your directions. As you describe different actions, perform them and have students follow you.
- Use words related to position. For example: **Put both hands under your chin. Put one hand over your head.**
- Vary the game by giving directions that involve specific students, such as: **Carlos, stand in front of Mary. John, stand next to Liza.**

Option 2 — SPATIAL, AUDITORY

English Language Learners ELL

Materials: list of classroom items, paper, pencil
Core Vocabulary: hot/cold, warmer/colder, you're getting
Common Use Verb: don't know

Hear Math This strategy helps students kinesthetically and auditorily understand the concept of position and proximity.

- Introduce hot and cold. Say: "I am thinking of something in the room. You ***don't know*** where it is. "As you get closer, I will say: **"you're getting warmer."** If you are getting further away, I will say: **"you're getting colder."** (farther away) until you find it."
- Divide students into pairs and encourage them to look for the target.
- Use clues until they find the object.
- Repeat with other pairs as time permits. Encourage classmates to chorally respond **colder/warmer** with you. Add *hot/cold* and *freezing* as appropriate for the group.

Independent Work Options

Option 1 — KINESTHETIC, LOGICAL

Early Finishers OL AL

- Pair students and have each one write directions to a place in the classroom. The directions explain where to start, but do not name the destination.
- Have partners exchange directions and follow them. Students should continue until they find their partner's destination.

Option 2

Student Technology

Math Online macmillanmh.com

Math Adventures

Option 3

Learning Station: Language Arts (p. 381G)

Direct students to the Language Arts Learning Station for more opportunities to explore and extend the lesson concept.

Option 4

Problem-Solving Practice

Reinforce problem-solving skills and strategies with the Problem-Solving Practice worksheet.

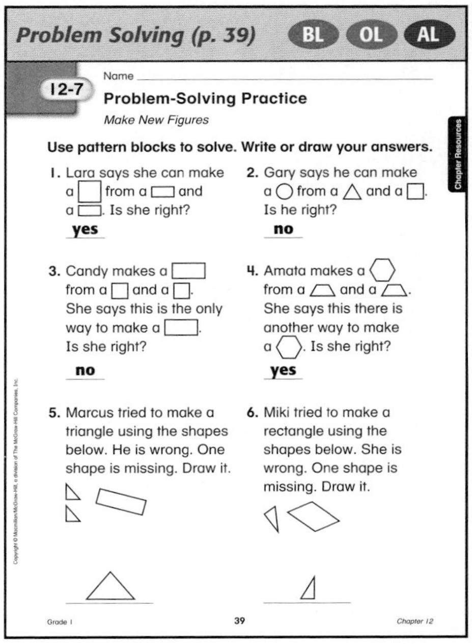

Problem Solving (p. 39) BL OL AL

Name ______

12-7 **Problem-Solving Practice**
Make New Figures

Chapter Resources

Use pattern blocks to solve. Write or draw your answers.

1. Lara says she can make a □ from a ▭ and a ▭. Is she right? **yes**
2. Gary says he can make a ○ from a △ and a □. Is he right? **no**
3. Candy makes a ▭ from a □ and a □. She says this is the only way to make a ▭. Is she right? **no**
4. Amata makes a ⬡ from a ⏢ and a ⏢. She says this there is another way to make a ⬡. Is she right? **yes**
5. Marcus tried to make a triangle using the shapes below. He is wrong. One shape is missing. Draw it.
6. Miki tried to make a rectangle using the shapes below. She is wrong. One shape is missing. Draw it.

Grade 1 39 Chapter 12

1 Introduce

Activity Choice 1 • Hands-On

Use magnets to hold construction paper shape cut-outs on the board. Arrange a circle, a square, and a triangle in a vertical line.

- **Where is the triangle?** below the square
- **Where is the circle?** above the square
- Explain that *below* and *above* are words that describe position.
- Continue with the shapes in other positions.

Once students have a strong understanding of the positional words *above* and *below*, introduce *north*, *south*, *east*, and *west*.

- Label each wall accordingly with a sign reading *north*, *south*, *east*, and *west*.
- As you call out a directional term, have students point in that direction.
- Then point in a specific direction and have students state the appropiate directional term.

Activity Choice 2 • Literature

Introduce the lesson with *the Greatest Gymnast of All* by Stuart J. Murphy for additional support, see p. TR59.

Name ______________________

Position

Get Ready

Main Idea

I will use position words to tell where objects are.

Vocabulary

position

Position words tell where objects are.

Reteach (p. 36) BL

12-7 Name ______

Reteach

Make New Figures

You can use two-dimensional figures to make other two-dimensional figures.

Two squares make a rectangle.

Use pattern blocks. Find another way to make a rectangle. Draw the figures you used.

Drawings will vary.
Sample answer:

Grade 1 36 Chapter 12

Check

5. Yes. Sample answer: an object can be next to something and also be in front of something else.

Use the position words to draw. 1–4. Check students' work.

1.  in front of 

2.  left of 

3.  above 

4.  near 

5. **Talk About It** Can an object have more than one position word that tells where it is? Give an example.

GO on 

Skills Practice (p. 37) OL

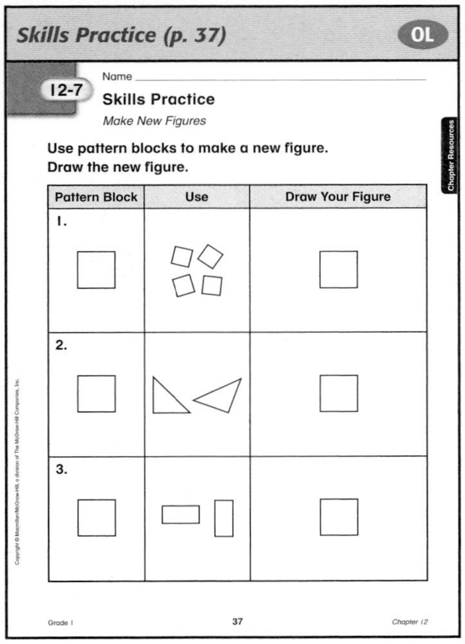

12-7 Name ____________

Skills Practice

Make New Figures

Use pattern blocks to make a new figure.
Draw the new figure.

Pattern Block	Use	Draw Your Figure
1.		
2.		
3.		

Grade 1 37 Chapter 12

2 Teach

- Draw a large square on the chalkboard containing four rows of four evenly spaced dots. Draw a square, a rectangle, a circle, and a triangle on four of the dots.
- Ask for descriptions of the **position** of the shapes. For example: **Can you tell where the circle is?** Sample answer: The circle is on the bottom corner.
- Ask for several different descriptions of the positions of each shape. Listen to students' language as they say things like, "The triangle is to the right of the square."

Get Ready Use the section at the top of p. 401 to reinforce the lesson concept. Guide students in correctly using the position words.

Check Observe students as you work through Exercises 1–5 as a class.

Exercise 5 Assess student comprehension before assigning practice exercises.

BL Alternate Teaching Strategy

If students struggle with using position words . . .

Then use one of the following reteach options.

1. CRM **Daily Reteach Worksheet** (p. 36)
2. **Act It Out** The best way to teach position words is kinesthetically. Help students act out the words *above, below, left, right, north, south, east, west, in front, behind, up, down, near,* and *far* with their hands. Reinforce with a game of position Simon Says.

COMMON ERROR!

The most difficult position concepts to understand are *right* and *left*. Show students that the thumb and first finger on the left hand make an *L* for *left*. For right-handed students, use the mnemonic "I write with my right."

3 Practice

Differentiate practice using these leveled assignments for Exercises 6–13.

Level	Assignment
BL Below/ Approaching Level	Pair students and have them act out each exercise.
OL On Level	Complete the exercises independently.
AL Above/Beyond Level	Write a sentence about each exercise, using another position word.

Name ______________________

Practice

Look at the picture. Circle the position word.

6. 

The  goes ____ the .

up (down)

7. 

The  is to the ____ of the .

left (right)

8. 

The  is ____ the .

behind (in front of)

9. 

The  is ____ the .

(above) below

Enrich (p. 40) AL

12-7 Name ______________

Enrich

Shapes in the Park

Look at the picture. How many shapes can you find? Write them.

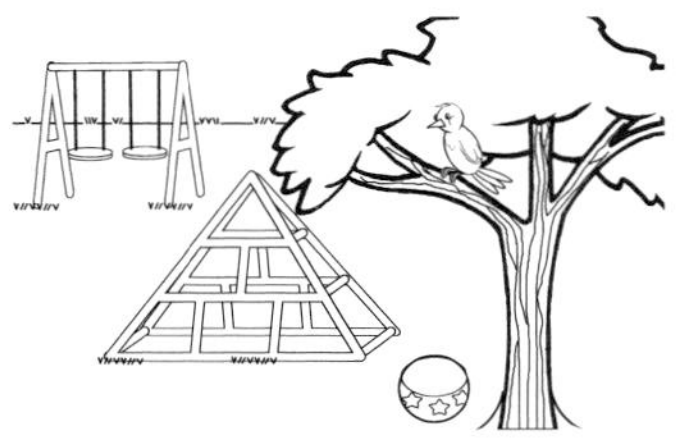

Answers will vary. Sample answers: triangle,

circle, pyramid, sphere, rectangle.

Grade 1 40 Chapter 12

Problem Solving

Visual Thinking Follow the directions.

10. In the middle of the page, draw a green △ in the middle of a □.

11. Draw a ▭ to the right of the □.

12. Draw a red △ above the □.

13. Draw a ○ on top of the red △.

See students' drawings.

Math at Home Activity: Choose an object and have your child guess what it is by answer position clues such as: It is above the television, it is behind the curtain.

Homework Practice (p. 38) OL

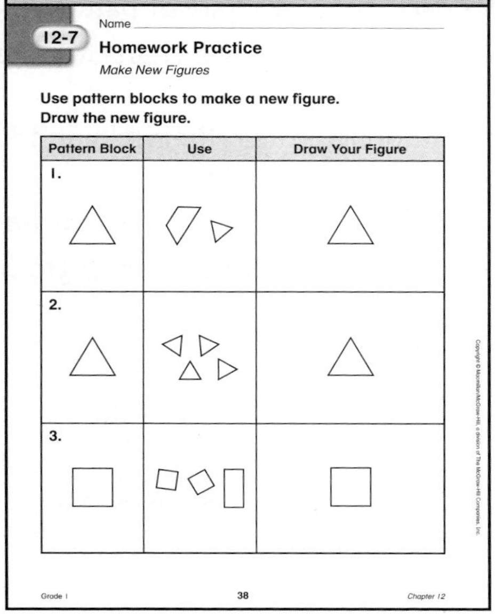
Name ______

12-7 **Homework Practice**

Make New Figures

Use pattern blocks to make a new figure. Draw the new figure.

Pattern Block	Use	Draw Your Figure
1. △		△
2. △		△
3. □		□

4 Assess

Formative Assessment

Ask students to draw some clouds above a building. **Tell the position of the building in relation to the clouds.** The building is below the clouds.
Add to the picture using other position words.

WRITING IN MATH Have students explain where they sit in the classroom. Encourage them to use as many position words as possible.

Quick Check **Are students continuing to struggle with using position words?**

If Yes → Small Group Options (p. 401B)

If No → Independent Work Options (p. 401B)

CRM Skills Practice Worksheet (p. 37)

CRM Enrich Worksheet (p. 40)

LESSON

12-8 Make New Figures

Lesson Planner

Objectives

Use concrete objects such as pattern blocks to make new geometric figures.

Review Vocabulary

rectangle, triangle

Resources

Manipulatives: pattern blocks
Literature Connection: *Three Pigs, One Wolf, and Seven Magic Shapes* by Grace Maccarone
Teacher Technology
TeacherWorks

Daily Routine

Use these suggestions before beginning the lesson on p. 405.

5-Minute Check

(Reviews Lesson 12–7)

Look around the classroom to fill in the blanks.

1. The clock is above the _____.
2. I am sitting in front of _____.
3. _____ sits beside me.
4. The _____ are to the left of _____.

1–4. See students' work.

Problem of the Day

Is 19 an even number or an odd number? Explain.
odd; Sample answers: 19 ends with 9; if you count by 2s there is one left over.

LINE UP Name geometric figures and have students hold up fingers to show the number of sides the figure has. For each figure you name, match the number of students you ask to line up to the number of sides the figure has.

Reviewing Math Vocabulary

- Give each student a pile of pattern blocks.
- Remind students of the characteristics of **rectangles** and **triangles**.
- Have students search their pile and find all the rectangles and triangles.
- **How many sides does a triangle have?** 3 sides
- **How many sides does a rectangle have?** 4 sides

Visual Vocabulary Cards

Use Visual Vocabulary Card(s) 41 and 49 to reinforce the vocabulary in this lesson. (The Define/Example/Ask routine is printed on the back of each card.)

Differentiated Instruction

Small Group Options

Option 1 Below Level BL

KINESTHETIC

Materials: pattern blocks, paper, pencil.

- Have each student choose twelve pattern blocks and make a new shape out of all twelve pattern blocks.
- Students should record on paper how many of each shape was used to make the larger shape.
- Students should then repeat the activity using fifteen, twenty, and twenty-four pattern blocks.

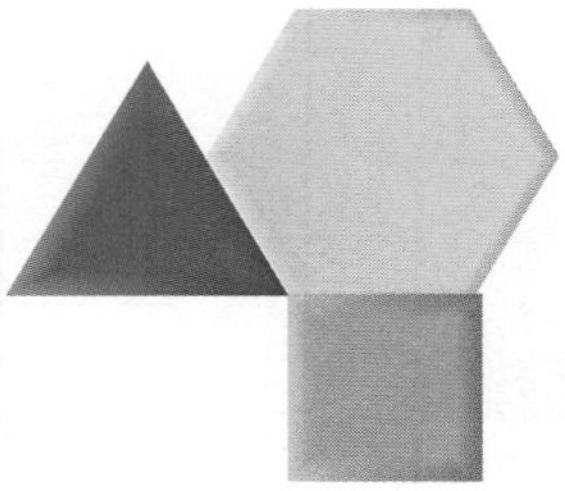

Option 2 English Language Learners EL

VISUAL, SPATIAL

Materials: overhead with a folder screening it, common objects: scissors, pencil, crayon, coin
Core Vocabulary: shape, appears to be, only see the outline
Common Use Verb: imagine

See Math This strategy helps students visualize the shape of common objects.

- Place scissors on the overhead projector. Turn it on. Say: "You can **only see the outline**. What does it **appear to be**?" Have students guess the projected shape from the outline.
- Repeat with other objects.
- Place coin on projector. Say, "Some things can **appear to be** like others. What do you ***imagine*** this is?"
- After students guess, show the coin.
- As students demonstrate understanding, begin to show two shapes together (triangle over a square like a house). Allow students to guess what shapes you used to create the house.

Independent Work Options

Option 1 Early Finishers AL OL

VISUAL/SPATIAL

Materials: pencils, crayons, paper, pattern blocks

- Invite students to combine concrete models such as pattern blocks to make the shape of a real-world object, such as a house, a car, an animal, etc.
- Invite students to record their creations by tracing and coloring the shapes on drawing paper.

Option 2 Student Technology

Math Online macmillanmh.com

Option 3 Learning Station: Science (p. 381H)

Direct students to the Science Learning Station for more opportunities to explore the lesson concept.

Option 4 Problem-Solving Practice

Reinforce problem-solving skills and strategies with the Problem-Solving Practice worksheet.

Problem Solving (p. 44) BL OL AL

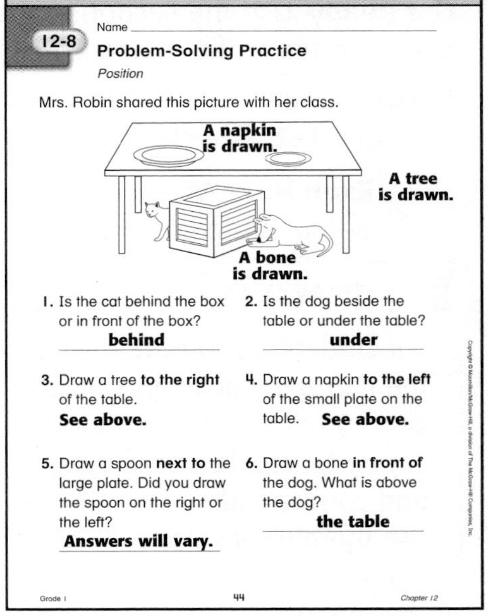

12-8 Name ______

Problem-Solving Practice

Position

Mrs. Robin shared this picture with her class.

1. Is the cat behind the box or in front of the box? **behind**
2. Is the dog beside the table or under the table? **under**
3. Draw a tree **to the right** of the table. **See above.**
4. Draw a napkin **to the left** of the small plate on the table. **See above.**
5. Draw a spoon **next to** the large plate. Did you draw the spoon on the right or the left? **Answers will vary.**
6. Draw a bone **in front of** the dog. What is above the dog? **the table**

Grade 1 44 Chapter 12

1 Introduce

Activity Choice 1 • Hands-On

- Distribute pattern blocks to students.
- **How many triangles do I need to form a trapezoid?** 3 triangles
- Demonstrate with pattern blocks by arranging three triangles on top of a trapezoid. Have students do the same.
- **How many trapezoids do I need to form a hexagon?** 2 trapezoids
- Demonstrate and have students follow your model.

Activity Choice 2 • *Literature*

Introduce the lesson with *Three Pigs, One Wolf, and Seven Magic Shapes* by Grace Maccarone.
For additional support, see p. TR60.

2 Teach

- Show students that they can use pattern blocks to make new figures. Allow them time to explore the relationships between the different pattern blocks.
- **What did you notice as you explored with the pattern blocks?** See students' work.
- Invite students to share relationships they found between the different pattern block shapes. Sample answer: 2 triangles can be arranged in a parallelogram; 6 triangles can make a hexagon.

Get Ready Use the section at the top of student p. 405 to teach the lesson concept.

Check Observe students as you work through Exercises 1–3 as a class.

Exercise 3 Assess student comprehension before assigning practice exercises.

COMMON ERROR!

For students who have difficulty remembering the name of each figure, keep a visual reference chart on display in the classroom. For further support, provide a set of geometric figure cards and corresponding name cards. Have students use them to practice matching figures and names.

Name ______________________________

Hands-On Activity

Make New Figures

Get Ready

Main Idea

I will use pattern blocks to make new figures.

You can make new figures by putting other figures together.

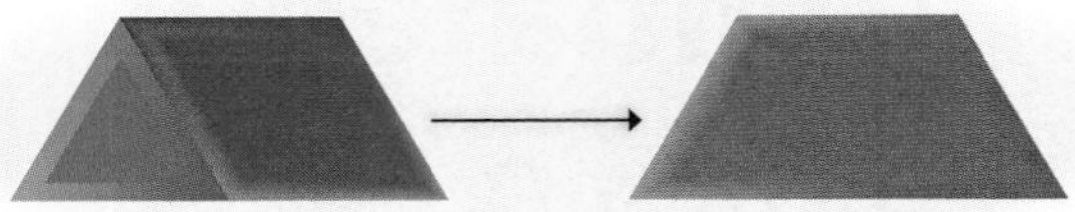

Check

Use pattern blocks to make a new figure. Draw the new figure.

Figure	Use	Draw your figure.
1.  hexagon	 trapezoid	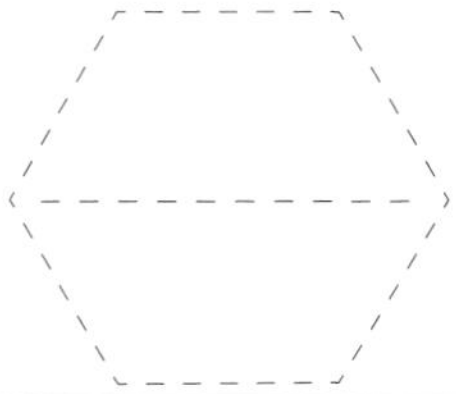
2.  trapezoid	 triangle	1–2. Check student's drawings.

3. Talk About It How can you find out which figures are needed to make a new figure? Students answers may vary.

Reteach (p. 41) BL

12-8 Name ______________________________

Reteach

Position

Position words tell you where something is.

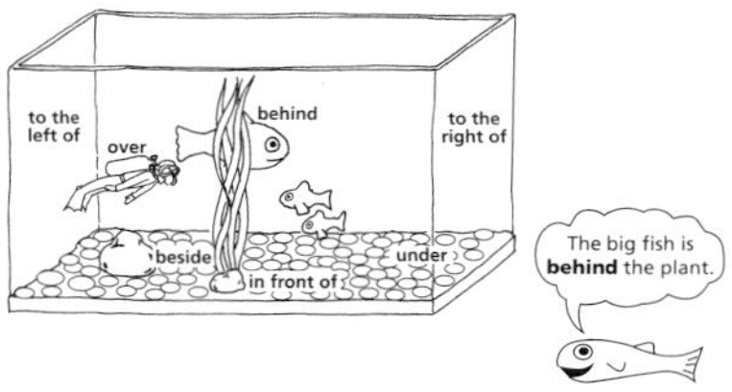

Look at the picture. Use position words to fill in the blanks. Possible answers given.

1. The small rock is in front of the plant.
2. The little fish are **to the right of** the plant.
3. The big fish is **to the left of** the little fish.
4. The big rock is **beside** the plant.
5. The toy diver is **over or above** the big rock.
6. The toy diver is **to the left of** the plant.
7. The plant is **in front of** the big fish.
8. The plant is **behind** the small rock.

Chapter Resources

Skills Practice (p. 42) OL

12-8 Name ______________________________

Skills Practice

Position

Position words tell where objects are.

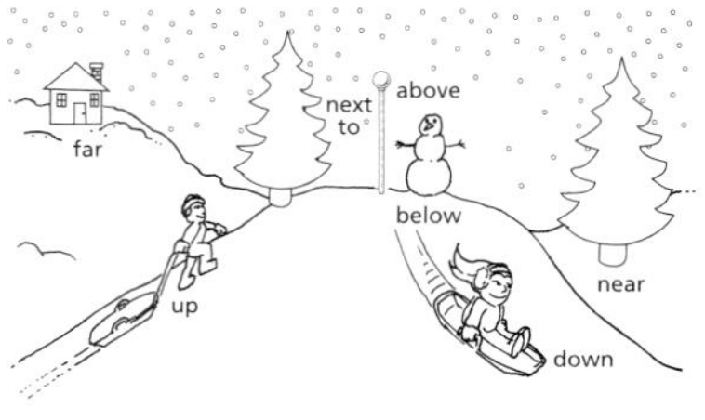

Draw here or on another sheet of paper.
Answers will vary.

1. going up
2. going down
3. below
4. near
5. left of
6. right of

Practice

Use pattern blocks to make a new figure.
Draw the new figure. 4–5. Check students drawings.

Figure	Use	Draw your figure.
4.  parallelogram	 triangle	
5.  hexagon	 parallelogram 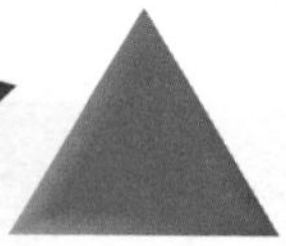 triangle  trapezoid	

H.O.T. Problem

6. **Make It Right** Paul tried to use these figures to make a trapezoid. Tell why Paul is wrong. Make it right. Draw the missing figure.

Student drawing of triangle.

He cannot make a trapezoid with a square and parallelogram. He could use the parallelogram and a triangle.

Math at Home Activity: Go on a shape scavenger hunt! While driving or walking, draw attention to doors and windows in the shape of rectangles, road signs in the shape of triangles, and roofs in the shape of trapezoids.

BL Alternate Teaching Strategy

If students have difficulty using concrete two-dimensional figures to make new geometric figures . . .

Then one of the following reteach options.

1 CRM **Daily Reteach Worksheet** (p. 41)

2 **Use Pattern Blocks** Draw a geometric figure, such as a hexagon, on a piece of paper. Draw dotted lines to show how smaller geometric figures, such as a two trapezoids, can form the larger one. Have students use pattern blocks to follow the model and cover the larger shape.

3 Practice

Differentiate practice using these leveled assignments for Exercises 4, 5.

Level	Assignment
BL Below/ Approaching Level	Guide students through the exercises. Use pattern blocks for support.
OL On Level	Complete exercises with pattern blocks for support if needed.
AL Above/Beyond Level	Complete exercises independently.

4 Assess

Formative Assessment

Have students trace a hexagon pattern block on a piece of paper and show how different pattern blocks can be used to make a hexagon. Sample answers: 1 hexagon; 2 trapezoids; 6 triangles

Quick Check **Are students continuing to make new figures?**

If Yes → Small Group Options (p. 405B)
If No → Independent Work Options (p. 405B)
CRM Skills Practice Worksheet (p. 42)
CRM Enrich Worksheet (p. 45)

Enrich (p. 45) AL

Name
12-8 **Enrich**
Shapes and Positions

Look at the picture. Fill in the blanks. Use the word box to help.

sphere	pyramid	triangle
over	rectangle	near
behind	next to	far

Sample answers given.

1. The sphere is **next to** the tree.
2. The bird is over the **sphere**.
3. The swings are behind the **pyramid**.
4. Can you find any triangles? Use position words to write where they are.

Answers will vary.

Grade 1 45 Chapter 12

Homework Practice (p. 43) OL

Name
12-8 **Homework Practice**
Position

Use the position words to draw.

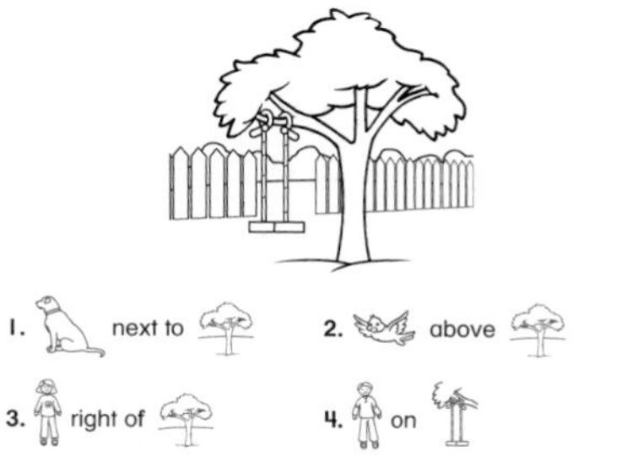

1. next to
2. above
3. right of
4. on

Circle your answer.

5. Danni's bedroom was on the first floor in her old house. Her new bedroom is on the second floor. Danni's new bedroom is ______ her old bedroom.
(above) below
6. Dave's swing set is in the backyard. His swing set is ______ the house.
in front of (behind)

Grade 1 43 Chapter 12

LESSON 12-9 Give and Follow Directions

Lesson Planner

Objective
Give and follow directions to find locations.

Review Vocabulary
unit

Resources
Materials: masking tape

Literature Connection: *Three Pigs, One Wolf, and Seven Magic Shapes* by Grace Maccorone

Alternate Lesson: Adapt *Geoboard Arrow Games* on page 82 of *Math Their Way* for practice with following directions to find locations.

Teacher Technology

TeacherWorks • Concepts in Motion

Focus on Math Background

Giving and following directions is the mathematical emphasis in this lesson. In this lesson, students will continue to build their spatial awareness by describing relationships of objects using proximity, position, and direction. Students will follow and formulate directions to move or place an object. Students will use this spatial knowledge to navigate distances and landmarks on maps as well as to describe the movements that generate transformations, such as rotating a triangle clockwise around one of its points.

Daily Routine

Use these suggestions before beginning the lesson on p. 407.

5-Minute Check

(Reviews Lesson 12-7)

Use more than one pattern block to make each figure.

1.

2.

Problem of the Day

Start with 12 squares. Subtract some. Write a subtraction sentence to show how many you subtracted and how many are left. Sample answer: $12 - 10 = 2$

LINE UP When students line up for recess, lunch, or dismissal, ask several students to tell the number of steps they took in each direction to get in line.

Review Math Vocabulary

Remind students that a **unit** is what is used to measure something. Give five paper clips to each student.

- Model laying the paper clips end to end.
- Show students how to measure a finger and a textbook using the paper clips as units.
- Draw a 4 x 4 grid on the board.
- Tell students that a grid is made up of many small squares. In math problems, grids can help for drawing or giving directions. The side of each square is 1 unit. **Which directions do the units go?** left and right, up and down

Use the Student Pages

Have students work individually or in pairs to solve the word problems on pages B–D.

Page B Students may have trouble counting the circles among the other shapes in the illustration. Suggest that students cross out the circles as they count them so they do not count a circle twice.

Page C This problem requires a good understanding of problem-solving strategies. Guide students to use the "understand, plan, solve, and check" routine. Students will need to find missing information from the picture and then may write a number sentence.

Extend the Activity

Have students create their own picture of the classroom by coloring or cutting and gluing construction paper. Discuss how to draw the classroom.

- **How many desks will you draw? What figures will you use to draw objects?** See students' work.

WRITING IN MATH Have students write and answer a story problem about Steve's drawing on page B.

Chapter Review/Test

FOLDABLES Dinah Zike's Foldables

If students have not completed their Foldables, guide them to create and fill in the appropriate information using the instructions on pp. 381 and 397.

You may choose to use the Foldable to help students review the concepts presented in this chapter and as a tool for studying for the Chapter Test.

Vocabulary Review

Review chapter vocabulary using one of the following options.

- **Visual Vocabulary Cards** (7–11, 39, 41, 42, 44, 45, and 49)
- **eGlossary** at macmillanmh.com

Vocabulary Test

CRM **Chapter 12 Resource Masters** (p. 55)
Assess Student comprehension of the chapter vocabulary with the Vocabulary Test.

Math Online **Chapter Test**
Alternative summative assessment options are available online at macmillanmh.com.

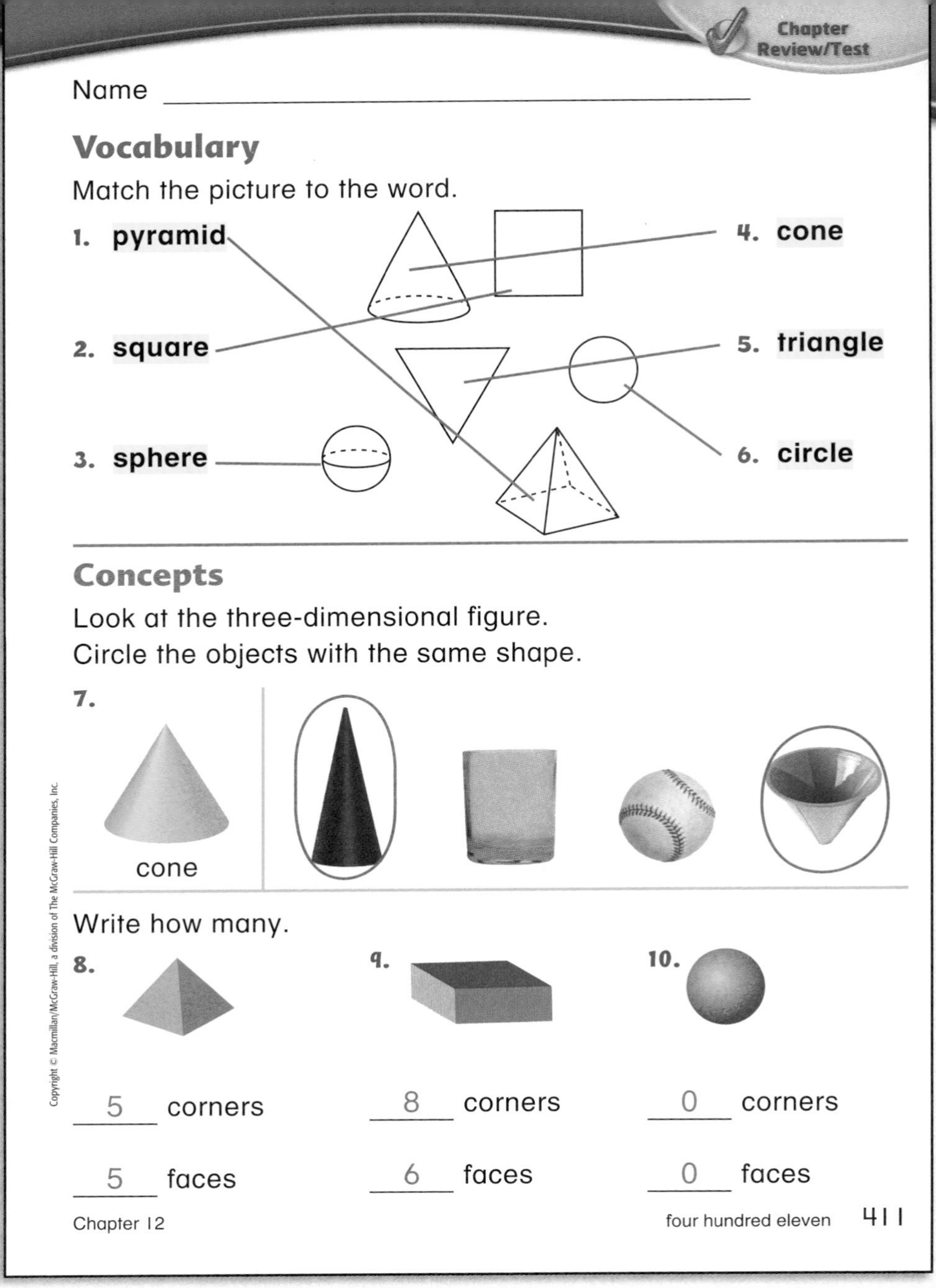
Chapter Review/Test

Name ______________________

Vocabulary

Match the picture to the word.

1. pyramid
2. square
3. sphere
4. cone
5. triangle
6. circle

Concepts

Look at the three-dimensional figure.
Circle the objects with the same shape.

7. cone

Write how many.

8. 5 corners, 5 faces
9. 8 corners, 6 faces
10. 0 corners, 0 faces

Chapter 12 Project

Geometric Mural

Have students discuss the results of their completed chapter project as a class. Assess their work using the Chapter Project rubric found in Chapter 12 Resource Masters on p. 60.

7.

20 45 33 28

28 45 33 20 ○ | 20 28 33 45 ●

45 33 28 20 ○ | 33 45 20 28 ○

10.

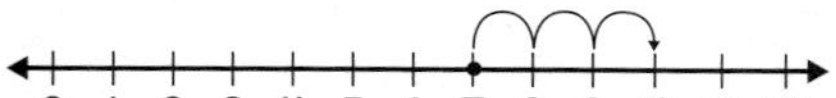

6 + 3 = 9 ○ | 10 − 7 = 3 ○

7 + 3 = 10 ● | 3 + 4 = 7 ○

8.

11. Alvin has 60 pennies. He wants to trade for dimes. How many dimes can he get?

6 dimes

9.

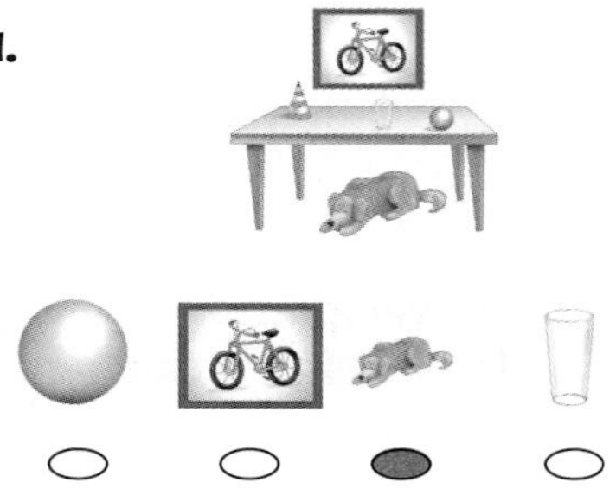

12. Tito had 10 cards. Kela took some of the cards. Now Tito has only 6 cards. How many cards did Kela take?

4 cards

STOP

Test Directions for Teachers

Read the following directions to students before they begin the test. Then read each question followed by a pause to allow students time to work on the problem and choose an answer. The first item can be worked as a class example.

- **Write your name at the top of the page.**
- **I am going to read each question to you. Listen carefully to the entire question before you choose your answer.**

Multiple Choice

1. Look at the party hat. Now look at the figures below the party hat. Mark the figure that is the same shape as the party hat.
2. Look at the triangle. Now look at the figures below the triangle. Mark the figure that has a face the shape of a triangle.
3. I have 8 corners and 6 faces. What am I? Mark the figure that has 8 corners and 6 faces.
4. Look at the figure. Now look at the objects below the figure. Mark the object that has a face that shape.
5. Mark the figure that has two faces.
6. Look at the group of coins. Count the coins. How much money is shown?

- **Turn the page over.**

7. Look at the numbers. Which group below shows the numbers in order?
8. Look at the clocks. Mark the clock that shows what time it will be a half hour after 4:00.
9. Find the object that is below the table. Mark the object that is below the table.
10. Look at the number line. Which problem does the number line show?

Short Response

11. Alvin has 60 pennies. He wants to trade for dimes. How many dimes can he get?
12. Tito has 10 cards. Kela took some of the cards. Now Tito has only 6 cards. How many cards did Kela take?

CHAPTER 13

Chapter Overview

Chapter-at-a-Glance

In Chapter 13, the emphasis is on students learning place value.

Lesson	Math Objective	State/Local Standards
13-1 Tens (pp. 419–422)	Create sets of tens and use concrete objects to describe whole numbers.	
13-2 Tens and Ones (pp. 423–424)	Create sets of tens and ones to describe whole numbers.	
13-3 Problem-Solving Strategy: Guess and Check (pp. 427–428)	Use the *guess and check* strategy to solve problems.	
13-4 Numbers to 50 (pp. 429–432)	Learn to show numbers to 50 using tens and ones.	
13-5 Numbers to 100 (pp. 433–436)	Learn different ways to show a number.	
13-6 Estimate Numbers (pp. 439–440)	Learn to estimate numbers.	
13-7 Problem-Solving Investigation: Choose a Strategy (pp. 441–442)	Choose the best strategy to solve a problem.	
13-8 Compare Numbers to 100 (pp. 443–444)	Compare whole numbers using sets of concrete objects.	
13-9 Order Numbers to 100 (pp. 445–446)	Order whole numbers using concrete objects and pictorial models.	

Understand Place Value

BIG Idea Students must develop an understanding of place value before they can master any other area of mathematics, including addition and subtraction.

- Learning the concept of tens and ones is the first step in being able to identify and read numbers of any size.
- Understanding place value will help students in learning to use decimals and money and will aid them in the proper placement of decimal points and commas.

Algebra Readiness In Lesson 13-3, students prepare for Algebra by using the *guess and check* strategy to solve division problems.

Focal Points and Connections

G1-FP2 *Number and Operations:* **Developing an understanding of whole number relationships, including grouping in tens and ones**

Children compare and order whole numbers (at least to 100) to develop an understanding of and solve problems involving the relative sizes of these numbers. They think of whole numbers between 10 and 100 in terms of groups of tens and ones (especially recognizing the numbers 11 to 19 as 1 group of ten and particular numbers of ones). They understand the sequential order of the counting numbers and their relative magnitudes and represent numbers on a number line.

Skills Trace

Vertical Alignment

Kindergarten

In kindergarten, students learned to:

- Know that the larger numbers describe sets with more objects in them than the smaller numbers have.
- Order, count, recognize, represent, and name a number of objects up to 30.

First Grade

During this chapter, students learn to:

- Count, read, and write whole numbers to 100.
- Estimate to find *about* how many.
- Use concrete objects to create sets of ones and tens.
- Compare and order whole numbers to 100 by using the symbols for less than, equal to, or greater than ($<$, $=$, $>$).

After this chapter, students learn to:

- Separate a whole into two, three, or four equal parts. (Chapter 14)
- Use appropriate language to describe part of a set. (Chapter 14)

Second Grade

In second grade, students learn to:

- Count, read, and write whole numbers to 1,000 and identify the place value for each digit.
- Use words, models, and expanded forms to represent numbers to 1,000.
- Order and compare whole numbers to 1,000 by using the symbols $<$, $=$, and $>$.

Math Vocabulary

The following math vocabulary words for Chapter 13 are listed in the glossary of the ***Student Edition.*** You can find interactive definitions in 13 languages in the ***eGlossary*** at macmillanmh.com.

after to follow in place or time (p. 445)

before Example: The letter *A* comes before the letter *B*. (p. 445)

between Example: The letter *B* is between the letter *A* and the letter *C*. (p. 445)

compare to look at objects, shapes, or numbers and see how they are alike or different. (p. 443)

estimate to find a number close to an exact amount (p. 439)

equal to having the same value as or is the same as (p. 443)

greater than when being compared, a number that is larger than the other; example: $7 > 2$; seven is greater than two. (p. 443)

less than when being compared, a number that is smaller than the other; example: $3 < 8$; eight is less than three (p. 443)

ones a place value of a number; example: In the number 23, the 3 is in the ones place. (p. 423)

regroup to take apart a number to write it in a new way; example: 12 ones = 1 ten 2 ones (p. 423)

tens a place value of a number; example: In the number 23, the 2 is in the tens place. (p. 419)

Visual Vocabulary Cards Use Visual Vocabulary Cards 24 and 32 to introduce the vocabulary in this chapter. (The Define/Example/Ask routine is printed on the back of each card.)

Backmapping and Vertical Alignment

McGraw-Hill's *Math Connects* program was conceived and developed with the final results in mind: student success in Algebra 1 and beyond. The authors, using the **NCTM Focal Points and Focal Connections** as their guide, developed this brand-new series by backmapping from Algebra 1 concepts, and vertically aligning the topics so that they build upon prior skills and concepts and serve as a foundation for future topics.

CHAPTER 13

Chapter Planner

Suggested Pacing		
Instruction	Assessment and Practice	TOTAL
9 days	2 days	**11 days**

Diagnostic Assessment
Are You Ready? (p. 416)

	Lesson 13-1 (Pacing: 1 day)	Lesson 13-2 (Pacing: 1 day)	Lesson 13-3 (Pacing: 1 day)
Lesson/ Objective	**Tens** (pp. 419–422) **Objective:** Create sets of tens and use concrete objects to describe whole numbers.	**Tens and Ones** (pp. 423–424) **Objective:** Create sets of tens and ones to describe whole numbers.	**Problem-Solving Strategy** **Guess and Check** (pp. 427–428) **Objective:** Use the *guess and check* strategy to solve problems.
State/Local Standards			
Math Vocabulary	**tens**	**regroup**	
Lesson Resources	**Materials** music (tape recorder and cassette or CD player and CD), hundred chart **Manipulatives** connecting cubes **Other Resources** CRM Leveled Worksheets (pp. 6–10) Daily Reteach • 5-Minute Check Problem of the Day	**Materials** WorkMat 7: Tens and Ones Chart, hundred chart **Manipulatives** spinners, connecting cubes, two-colored counters **Other Resources** CRM Leveled Worksheets (pp. 11–15) Daily Reteach • 5-Minute Check Problem of the Day	**Manipulatives** two-colored counters, connecting cubes, base-ten blocks **Other Resources** CRM Leveled Worksheets (pp. 16–20) Daily Reteach • 5-Minute Check Problem of the Day *How Fast, How Far?*
Technology Math Online	Math Adventures	Math Adventures Concepts in Motion	
Reaching All Learners	Below Level, p. 419B BL English Learners, p. 419B ELL Early Finishers, p. 419B OL AL	Gifted and Talented, p. 423B AL English Learners, p. 423B ELL Early Finishers, p. 423B OL AL	Gifted and Talented, p. 427B AL English Learners, p. 427B ELL Early Finishers, p. 427B OL AL
Alternate Lessons	*Math Their Way,* p. 314 *IMPACT Mathematics:* Unit H	*Math Their Way,* p. 315 *IMPACT Mathematics:* Unit H	

Extra Practice (p. 425)
Math Game (p. 426)

KEY
BL Below/Approaching Level — OL On Level — AL Above/Beyond Level — ELL English Learners
SE Student Edition — TE Teacher Edition — CRM Chapter 13 Resource Masters — CD-Rom
Transparency — Flip Chart — Real-World Problem Solving Library

	Lesson 13-4 (Pacing: 1 day)	Lesson 13-5 (Pacing: 1 day)	Lesson 13-6 (Pacing: 1 day)
Lesson/ Objective	**Numbers to 50** (pp. 429–432) **Objective:** Learn to show numbers to 50 using tens and ones.	**Numbers to 100** Tech Link (pp. 433–436) **Objective:** Learn different ways to show a number.	**Estimate Numbers** (pp. 439–440) **Objective:** Learn to estimate numbers.
State/Local Standards			
Math Vocabulary			
Lesson Resources	**Materials** WorkMat 7: Tens and Ones Chart, number line **Manipulatives** connecting cubes, base-ten blocks **Other Resources** CRM Leveled Worksheets (pp. 21–25) Daily Reteach • 5-Minute Check Problem of the Day	**Materials** WorkMat 7: Tens and Ones Chart **Manipulatives** connecting cubes, base-ten blocks **Other Resources** CRM Leveled Worksheets (pp. 26–30) Daily Reteach • 5-Minute Check Problem of the Day	**Materials** coins, rocks, buttons, or other small items **Other Resources** CRM Leveled Worksheets (pp. 31–35) Daily Reteach • 5-Minute Check Problem of the Day
Technology Math Online	Math Adventures	Math Song Track 13 Math Adventures Concepts in Motion	
Reaching All Learners	Below Level, p. 429B BL English Learners, p. 429B ELL Early Finishers, p. 429B OL AL	Gifted and Talented, p. 433B AL English Learners, p. 433B ELL Early Finishers, p. 433B OL AL	Below Level, p. 499B BL English Learners, p. 499B ELL Early Finishers, p. 499B OL AL
Alternate Lessons	*Math Their Way*, p. 310 *IMPACT Mathematics:* Unit H	*Math Their Way*, pp. 308–309 *IMPACT Mathematics:* Unit H	*IMPACT Mathematics:* Unit H

Formative Assessment
- Mid-Chapter Check (p. 437)
- Spiral Review (p. 438)

CHAPTER 13

Chapter Planner

	Lesson 13-7 (Pacing: 1 day)	Lesson 13-8 (Pacing: 1 day)	Lesson 13-9 (Pacing: 1 day)
Lesson/ Objective	Problem-Solving Investigation **Choose a Strategy** (pp. 441–442) **Objective:** Choose the best strategy to solve a problem.	**Compare Numbers to 100** (pp. 443–444) **Objective:** Compare whole numbers using sets of concrete objects.	**Order Numbers to 100** (pp. 445–446) **Objective:** Order whole numbers using concrete objects and pictorial models.
State/Local Standards			
Math			
Lesson Resources	**Manipulatives** connecting cubes, two-colored counters **Other Resources** CRM Leveled Worksheets (pp. 36–40) Daily Reteach • 5-Minute Check Problem of the Day *How Fast, How Far?*	**Materials** number cards 20–80, hundred charts, translucent counters **Manipulatives** connecting cubes, base-ten blocks **Other Resources** CRM Leveled Worksheets (pp. 41–45) Daily Reteach • 5-Minute Check Problem of the Day	**Materials** number cards 1–20, WorkMats 4–5: Number Lines **Manipulatives** two-colored counters **Other Resources** CRM Leveled Worksheets (pp. 46–50) Daily Reteach • 5-Minute Check Problem of the Day
Technology		Math Adventures	Math Adventures
Reaching All Learners	Below Level, p. 441B BL English Learners, p. 441B ELL Early Finishers, p. 441B OL AL	Below Level, p. 443B BL English Learners, p. 443B ELL Early Finishers, p. 443B OL AL	Below Level, p. 445B BL English Learners, p. 445B ELL Early Finishers, p. 445B OL AL
Alternate Lessons		*Math Their Way*, p. 320 *IMPACT Mathematics:* Unit H	*Math Their Way*, p. 248 *IMPACT Mathematics:* Unit H

Problem Solving in Science (p. 447)

Summative Assessment
- Chapter Review/Test (p. 449)
- Test Practice (p. 451)

Assessment Options

Diagnostic Assessment

- SE *Option 1:* Are You Ready? (p. 416)
- *Option 2:* Online Quiz macmillanmh.com
- CRM *Option 3:* Diagnostic Test (p. 52)
- CRM *Option 4:* Chapter Pretest (p. 53)

Formative Assessment

- TE Alternate Teaching Strategies (every lesson)
- TE Line Up (every lesson)
- SE Talk About It (every lesson)
- SE Writing in Math (every lesson)
- SE Check What You Know (every lesson)
- SE Mid-Chapter Check (p. 437)
- CRM Mid-Chapter Test (p. 54)

Summative Assessment

- SE Chapter Review/Test (p. 449)
- SE Test Practice (p. 451)
- CRM Vocabulary Test (p. 55)
- CRM Leveled Chapter Tests (pp. 62–71)
- CRM Cumulative Test Practice (pp. 72–73)
- CRM Listening Assessment (pp. 58–59)
- CRM Oral Assessment (pp. 56–57)
- ExamView® Assessment Suite
- Advance Tracker

McGraw-Hill Professional Development

Targeted professional development has been articulated throughout **McGraw-Hill's *Math Connects*** program. The **McGraw-Hill Professional Development Video Library** provides short videos that support the **NCTM Focal Points and Focal Connections**. For more information, visit macmillanmh.com.

Model Lessons

Instructional Strategies

Assessment Tips

Place value of whole numbers can be difficult for students to grasp, so be very clear regarding the objectives you want them to master.

- Come up with four or five specific objectives you want to observe during this chapter.
- Create a class checklist which includes these four or five objectives.
- As students master a specific objective, check it off.
- Add comments where appropriate.

Teacher Notes

CHAPTER 13

Learning Stations

Cross-Curricular Links

Reading

pair | SPATIAL

Hungry Groups of Ants

- With a partner, read aloud *One Hundred Hungry Ants*.
- As you read, count the number of ants on each page.
- Write the number of groups of ten you can make with each number.

Materials:

- *One Hundred Hungry Ants* by Elinor Pinczes

Art

individual | KINESTHETIC

Wearable Math

- Sort beads by color. Then string 10 beads of one color on yarn.
- Choose another color. Add 10 of those beads to your necklace. Continue the pattern. Put 10 beads of each color.
- Have your teacher tie the necklace around your neck.

Teacher Note: Prepare in advance for each student a 16 inch length of yarn on a large plastic threading needle.

Materials:

- yarn
- colored beads

Language Arts

individual | LINGUISTIC

Silly Sentences

- Write silly sentences.
- Use place value in your sentences.
- Draw pictures to match your sentence.

Materials:

- paper
- pencil
- crayons

Name ______________________

Math Online
Take the Chapter Readiness Quiz at macmillanmh.com.

Are You Ready for Chapter 13?

Circle to make groups of 10.

1.

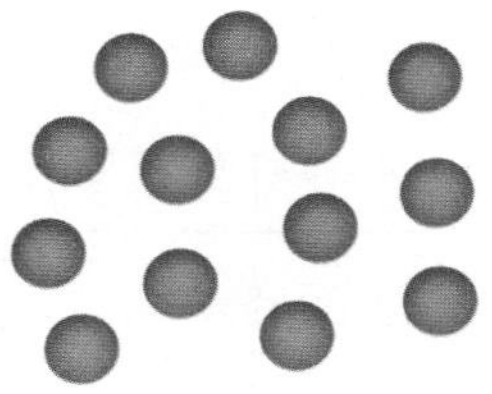

Check students' work.

2. Check students' work.

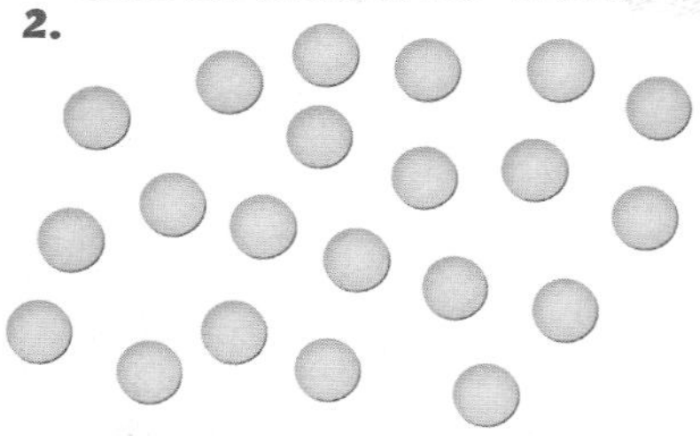

3. Say and write the missing numbers.

1	2	3	4	5	6	7	8	9	10
11	12	13	14	15	16	17	18	19	20
21	22	23	24	25	26	27	28	29	30

Circle groups of 10. Count. Write the number.

4.

Check students' work.

16 frogs

5. There are 4 boxes on the floor.
Each box has 10 red balls in it.
How many balls in all? 40 balls

This page checks skills needed for Chapter 13.

Diagnostic Assessment

Check for students' prerequisite skills before beginning the chapter.

- **Option 1:** ***Are You Ready for Chapter 13?***
  SE Student Edition, p. 416
- **Option 2:** ***Online Assessment***
  Math Online macmillanmh.com
- **Option 3:** ***Diagnostic Test***
  CRM Chapter 13 Resource Master, p. 52

RTI (Response to Intervention)

Apply the Results Based on the results of the diagnostic assessment on student p. 416, use the chart below to address individual needs before beginning the chapter.

TIER 3 Intensive Intervention

If students miss four or more of the exercises:

Then use Chapter 5 of *Math Triumphs*, an intensive math intervention program from McGraw-Hill

TIER 2 Strategic Intervention below/approaching grade level	TIER 1 On-Level	Above/Beyond Level
If students miss two or three in: **Exercises 1–5**	**If** students miss one in: **Exercises 1–5**	**If** students miss none in: **Exercises 1–5**
Then choose a resource:	**Then** choose a resource:	**Then** choose a resource:
Strategic Intervention Guide (p. 98) CRM Chapter 8 Resource Masters (Reteach Worksheets) Math Online Concepts in Motion	TE Learning Stations (pp. 415G–415H) TE Chapter Project (p. 417) CRM Game: *Number Skipping* Math Adventures My Math Zone Chapter 12 Math Online Fact Dash	TE Learning Stations (pp. 415G–415H) TE Chapter Project (p. 417) Real-World Problem Solving: *How Fast, How Far?* My Math Zone Chapters 12 and 13 Math Online Game

MATH at HOME

Before you begin Chapter 13:

- Read the Math at Home letter found on p. 417 with the class and have each student sign it.
- Send home copies of the Math at Home letter with each student.
- Use the Spanish letter on p. 418 for students with Spanish-speaking parents or guardians.

WRITING IN MATH

Starting the Chapter
Ask students to think about sets of items they have in their bedrooms at home (toys, games, articles of clothing).

- **What do you have 10 of?**
- **What do you have 20 of? More than 20?**

Have students write their responses.

Read-Aloud Anthology
For an optional reading activity to introduce this chapter's math concepts, see the Read-Aloud Anthology on p. TR39.

MATH at HOME

Dear Family,
Today my class started Chapter 13, **Understand Place Value**. In this chapter, I will learn to count, read, write, and compare numbers to 100. Here is an activity we can do and a list of books we can read together.

Love, ______________________

Activity

Write fifteen different numbers that are less than 100 on separate pieces of paper. Put the numbers in a sack. Both of you draw a number. Ask your child to tell who has the greater number.

Key Vocabulary

tens this number has 2 tens

regroup to take apart a number to write it in a new way

Math Online Click on the eGlossary link at macmillanmh.com to find out more about these words. There are 13 languages.

Books to Read

Betcha!
by Stuart J. Murphy
HarperCollins Children's Books, 1997.

100th Day Worries
by Margery Cuyler
Simon & Schuster Books for Young Readers, 2005.

Coyotes All Around
by Stuart J. Murphy
HarperCollins Children's Books, 2003.

four hundred seventeen 417

Chapter 13 Project

Guess and Check

Have students bring from home cereal, cotton balls, buttons, or other small items. Ask students to choose one type of item, count out any number from 40–100, and put the items in a sandwich bag.

- Have students trade bags. Ask them to arrange the items from the bag into groups of tens, count the tens and ones, and record the amount.
- **Which bag has the most? the least?** Answers will vary. Hold up two bags that have similar numbers of items. **Does it look like these two bags contain the same amount? Why or why not?** Sample answer: No; the objects are different sizes.
- Each day have students choose a new bag.

CRM *Refer to Chapter 13 Resource Masters, p. 60, for a rubric to assess students' progress on this project.*

MATEMÁTICAS en CASA

Estimada familia:

Hoy mi clase comenzó el Capítulo 13, **Comprende el valor de posición**. En este capítulo, aprenderé a contar, a leer, a escribir y a comparar números hasta 100. A continuación, hay una actividad que podemos hacer y una lista de libros que podemos leer juntos.

Cariños, ____________________

Actividad

Escriban quince números diferentes menores de 100 en hojas de papel separadas. Coloquen los números en una bolsa. Saquen juntos un número. Pregúntenle a su hijo quién tiene el número menor.

Vocabulario clave

decenas este número tiene 2 decenas

reagrupar reordenar los números en partes más simples

Math Online Visiten el enlace eGlossary en macmillanmh.com para averiguar más sobre estas palabras, las cuales se muestran en 13 idiomas.

Libros recomendados

Valor posicional
de Dinaielle Carroll
Yellow Umbrella Books, 2006.

Hacer decenas: grupos de gollyluvas
de John Burstein
Weekly Reader Early Learning Library, 2006

Chapter 13 Literature List

Lesson	Book Title
13-1	**Counting is for the Birds** Frank Mazzola, Jr.
13-2	**The King's Commissioners** Aileen Friedman
13-3	**Ten Black Dots** Donald Crews
13-4	**Zin! Zin! Zin! A Violin** Lloyd Moss
13-5	**100 Days of School** Trudy Harris
13-6	**Get Up and Go!** Stuart J. Murphy
13-8	**Out for the Count: A Counting Adventure** Kathryn Cave
13-9	**Elevator Magic** Stuart J. Murphy
Any	**Betcha! Estimating** Stuart J. Murphy
Any	**100th Day Worries** Margery Cuyler
Any	**Coyotes All Around** Stuart J. Murphy

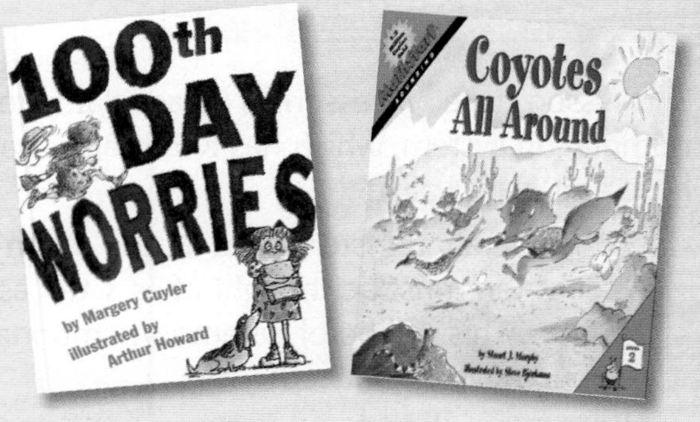

ELL National ESL Standards Alignment for Chapter 13

Lesson, Page	ESL Standard	Modality	Level
13-1, p 419B	Goal 2, Standard 1, d	Intrapersonal, Linguistic	Beginning
13-2, p 423B	Goal 1, Standard 3, g	Visual, Kinesthetic	Beginning
13-3, p 427B	Goal 2, Standard 2, m	Intrapersonal	Advanced
13-4, p 429B	Goal 2, Standard 2, i	Linguistic, Intrapersonal	Intermediate
13-5, p 433B	Goal 1, Standard 3, k	Linguistic, Intrapersonal	Intermediate
13-6, p 439B	Goal 2, Standard 2, j	Visual/Spatial, Logical	Advanced
13-7, p 441B	Goal 2, Standard 1, g	Logical, Linguistic	Intermediate
13-8, p 443B	Goal 2, Standard 1, a	Visual, Kinesthetic	Intermediate
13-9, p 445B	Goal 2, Standard 3, e	Spatial, Kinesthetic	Intermediate

The National ESL Standards can be found in the Teacher Reference Handbook.

LESSON 13-1

Tens

Lesson Planner

Objective

Create sets of tens and use concrete objects to describe whole numbers.

Vocabulary

tens

Resources

Materials: music (tape recorder and cassette or CD player and CD), hundred chart

Manipulatives: connecting cubes

Literature Connection: *Counting is for the Birds* by Frank Mazzola, Jr.

Alternate Lessons: Adapt "Base Ten Unifix Patterns" on page 314 of *Math Their Way* for practice with tens. Use *IMPACT Mathematics:* Unit H to provide practice with creating sets of tens.

Teacher Technology

TeacherWorks

Focus on Math Background

This lesson develops essential ideas related to our base ten numeration system, which has two major characteristics: base and place value.

- Our numeration system uses a base of ten for grouping. A set of ten must be thought of as 1 ten as well as 10 ones. This will be of paramount importance when regrouping is introduced.
- Place value, the idea that the position of digits in numbers determines their value, follows the concept of grouping by tens and will be introduced in the next lesson.

Daily Routine

Use these suggestions before beginning the lesson on p. 419.

5-Minute Check

(Reviews Lesson 12-9)

Place a pencil below your desk. Place a folder to the right of the pencil. Place an eraser on the right side of your desk. Place a crayon behind your chair. What is to the left of the folder?

the pencil

Problem of the Day

Draw a picture of a house, using at least one square, triangle, circle, and rectangle.

See students' work.

LINE UP Ask one student to name a number that ends in a zero and then line up. Tell students they will count by tens from that number to 100, and then count back down to 0 by tens. Each student you point to should say the next number in the count and then line up.

Building Math Vocabulary

Review counting dimes to introduce counting by tens.

- Show students a line of four dimes.
- **How many dimes do we have?** 4 dimes
- Remind students that they can find the value of dimes by counting **tens**.
- Have children find the value of the dimes by counting tens. 10, 20, 30 40
- **What is the value of the dimes?** 40¢
- Have students practice counting by tens with different groups of dimes.

Differentiated Instruction

Small Group Options

Option 1 SPATIAL

Below Level BL

Materials: yarn, scissors, connecting cubes

- Have small groups of students sort large containers of connecting cubes into 10 sets of ten.
- After students finish sorting their cubes into sets of ten, have them cut pieces of yarn to circle their sets of ten.
- After the cubes are circled with yarn, have students practice counting by tens by counting the sets.

Option 2 INTERPERSONAL, LINGUISTIC

English Language Learners ELL

Materials: a diagram with various sets of tens
Core Vocabulary: Let's make sure, Can we make 10?, We can make 10!
Common Use Verb: look

Write Math This strategy reinforces ways to make 10 and allows students to practice acquired language.

- Give students 1 to 9 cubes and write vocabulary phrases on the board.
- Say: "Walk around with your set of cubes. **Look** at a classmate. Ask your classmate **"Can we make 10?"**
- Say: "Look at the sets. **Let's make sure** we have ten."
- Model finding someone with a match. Demonstrate the language for checking a match. Say "Look at the sets. Let's make sure we have 10." Model counting the sets.
- Say: "After you have counted them, if you have 10, hold hands and say **'We can make ten!'** Write your number sentence on the board with your names."
- Say: "If you can't make 10, find someone else and try again."
- Allow student to repeat as time permits or until all sets have found a match.

Independent Work Options

Option 1 KINESTHETIC/LINGUISTIC

Early Finishers OL AL

Materials: two-colored counters

- Have students work together to make three sets of ten two-colored counters.
- Ask students to count by 10s and tell how many counters there are.
- Have students repeat the activity making five, seven, and nine rows of counters.

Option 2

Student Technology

Math Online macmillanmh.com

Math Adventures

Option 3

Learning Station: Reading (p. 415G)

Direct students to the Reading Learning Station for more opportunities to explore and extend the lesson concept.

Option 4

Problem-Solving Practice

Reinforce problem-solving skills and strategies with the Problem-Solving Practice worksheet.

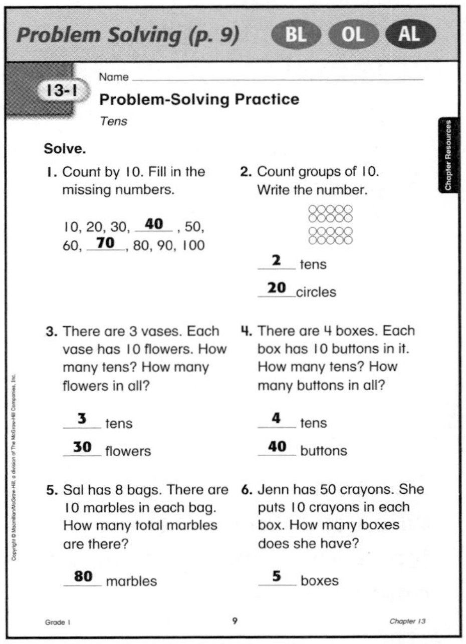

Problem Solving (p. 9) BL OL AL

13-1 Name ______

Problem-Solving Practice
Tens

Solve.

1. Count by 10. Fill in the missing numbers.
10, 20, 30, **40**, 50, 60, **70**, 80, 90, 100

2. Count groups of 10. Write the number.
2 tens
20 circles

3. There are 3 vases. Each vase has 10 flowers. How many tens? How many flowers in all?
3 tens
30 flowers

4. There are 4 boxes. Each box has 10 buttons in it. How many tens? How many buttons in all?
4 tens
40 buttons

5. Sal has 8 bags. There are 10 marbles in each bag. How many total marbles are there?
80 marbles

6. Jenn has 50 crayons. She puts 10 crayons in each box. How many boxes does she have?
5 boxes

Grade 1 9 Chapter 13

1 Introduce

Activity Choice 1 • Hands-On

Write the word *ten* on the chalkboard. Beside it, write the numeral 10. Review with students that a *ten* is a set of ten objects.

- Using connecting cubes, have students build a ten-train. Have them check their accuracy by comparing their ten-train to a classmates.
- Give students time to explore the classroom. **What other objects can you group into tens?** Sample answers: pennies, beads, counters, crayons
- After a minute or two of exploration time, have students list their ideas on the chalkboard. Select a few ideas to model grouping into ten with the class.

Activity Choice 2 • Literature

Introduce the lesson with *Counting Is for the Birds* by Frank Mazzola, Jr.
For additional support, see p. TR60.

COMMON ERROR!

Students may count by tens instead of ones when counting things out to make groups of ten. Remind them that they must first count by ones to make a ten.

Name ____________________

Tens

Hands-On Activity

Get Ready

Main Idea
I will count groups of ten.

Vocabulary
tens

Check

Use [cube]. Make groups of ten. Say and write the number.

1. 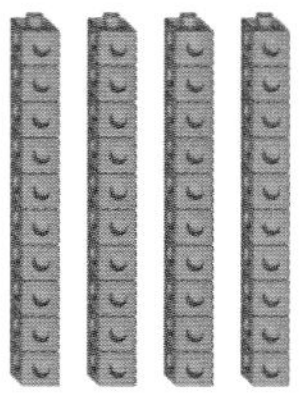

4 tens 40

Say: forty

2. 

7 tens 70

Say: seventy

Reteach (p. 6) BL

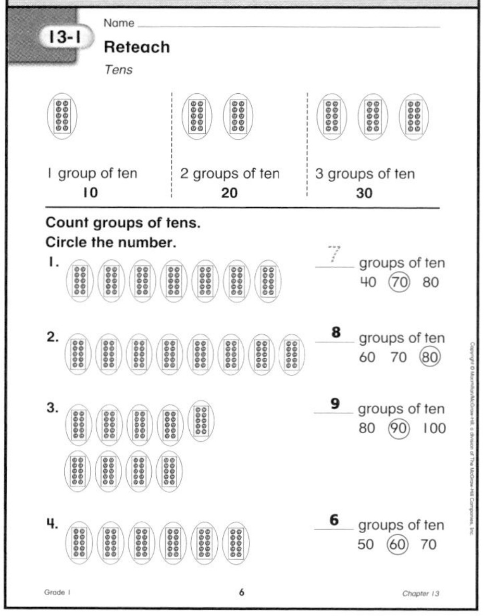
13-1 Name
Reteach
Tens

1 group of ten 10 | 2 groups of ten 20 | 3 groups of ten 30

Count groups of tens. Circle the number.

1. 7 groups of ten — 40 (70) 80
2. 8 groups of ten — 60 70 (80)
3. 9 groups of ten — 80 (90) 100
4. 6 groups of ten — 50 (60) 70

Grade 1 6 Chapter 13

Use [cube]. Make groups of ten. Say and write the number.

3.
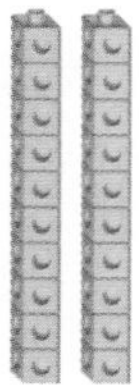

2 tens 20
Say: twenty

4.

8 tens 80
Say: eighty

5.

5 tens 50
Say: fifty

6.
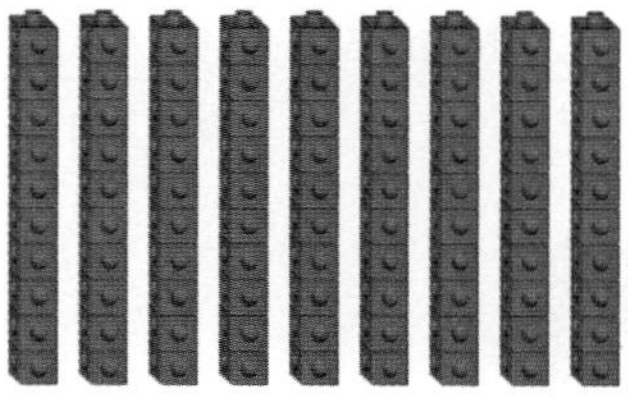

9 tens 90
Say: ninety

7.
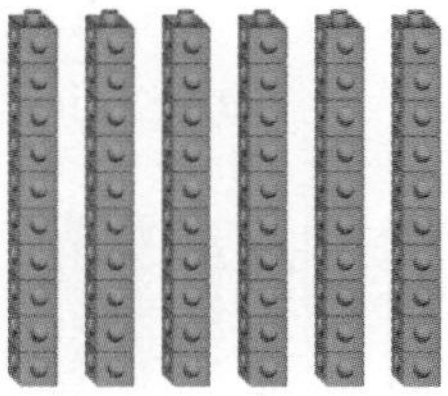

6 tens 60
Say: sixty

8.

3 tens 30
Say: thirty

Sample answer: I would make 10 ten-trains.

9. Talk About It How would you use cubes to model the number 100?

GO on

Skills Practice (p. 7) OL

13-1 Name ____

Skills Practice

Tens

Count groups of ten. Write the number.

1. 3 tens 30 thirty

2. 4 tens 40 forty

3. 6 tens 60 sixty

Write your answers.

4. Gwen has 5 vases with 10 flowers in each vase.
How many groups of ten does she have? 5
How many flowers are there in all? 50 flowers

5. Mark, Juan, Carla, and Ben each have 10 marbles.
How many groups of ten are there? 4
How many marbles do they have in all? 40
Carla goes home and takes her marbles with her.
How many marbles are there now? 30 marbles

Grade 1 7 Chapter 13

2 Teach

Give each student a pile of connecting cubes.

- **How do you make a ten-train?** Connect 10 cubes together. Have each student make one ten-train.
- Explain to students that you are going to play some music and they will create ten-trains until the music stops.
- **How many trains did you make?** See students' work.
- Have students count their trains. **What number did you make?** See students' work. **What is the easiest/fastest way to count the number of cubes each person has?** Count the trains by tens rather than counting the cubes one by one.
- Discuss the idea of "ten more than" and "ten less than." Make the connection with counting tens (i.e., ten before is "ten less than," ten after is "ten more than").

Get Ready Use the section at the top of p. 419 to reinforce the lesson concept. Guide students as they count by tens.

Check Observe students as you work through Exercises 1–9 as a class.

Exercise 9 Assess student comprehension before assigning practice exercises.

BL Alternate Teaching Strategy

If students have trouble counting by tens . . .

Then use one of the following reteach options.

1. CRM **Daily Reteach Worksheet** (p. 6)
2. **Use Manipulatives** Help students find the tens column on a hundred chart and discuss the patterns they see in that set of numbers. Then invite students to use the chart as a reference whenever they count by ten.

13-1

3 Practice

Differentiate practice using these leveled assignments for Exercises 10–20.

Level	Assignment
BL Below/ Approaching Level	Guide students through the exercises and have them make ten-trains of connecting cubes to use in counting.
OL On Level	Complete independently.
AL Above/Beyond Level	After students have identified the number asked for, ask them to double the number by counting out the same number again.

Name ______________________

Practice

Use [cube]. Make groups of ten. Say and write the number.

10.

4 tens 40
Say: forty

11.

1 ten 10
Say: ten

12.

2 tens 20
Say: twenty

13.

3 tens 30
Say: thirty

14.

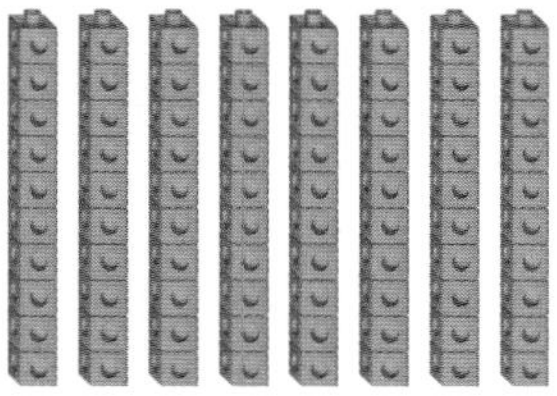

8 tens 80
Say: eighty

15.

9 tens 90
Say: ninety

Enrich (p. 10) AL

13-1 Name ______

Enrich

Baseball Card Bonanza

There are 10 baseball cards in every pack.
Read each question.
Write how many each person has.

1. Leroy buys 4 packs of cards. How many cards does he have in all? **40**

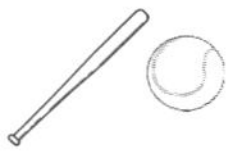

2. Katie buys 6 packs. How many cards does she have? **60**
3. Josh and Joe buy 8 packs of cards. They each take half. How many cards do each of them have? **40**
4. Arnie buys 3 packs of cards. The next week, he buys 5 more. How many cards does Arnie buy in all? **80**
5. Sonya buys 2 packs of cards. She gets 3 more packs for her birthday. How many cards does Sonya have? **50** If Sonya gives 2 packs to her brother, how many cards will she have? **30**

Grade 1 10 Chapter 13

Use [cube]. Make groups of ten. Say and write the number.

16.
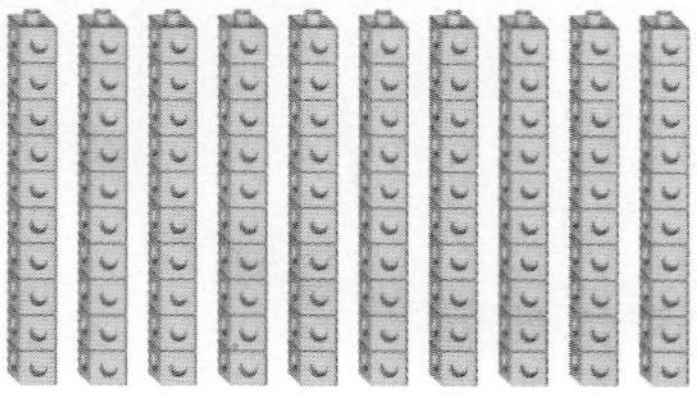

10 tens 100
Say: one hundred

17.
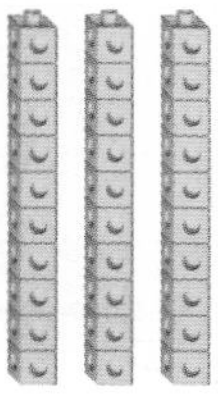

3 tens 30
Say: thirty

18.

5 tens 50
Say: fifty

19.
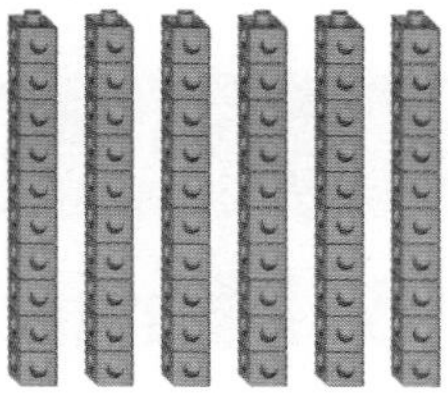

6 tens 60
Say: sixty

H.O.T. Problem

20. Make It Right Rob says there are 20 pennies. Tell why Rob is wrong. Make it right.

Sample answer: One of Rob's group of pennies only has 7 pennies. Make it right by adding three more pennies so there are two groups of ten pennies.

Math at Home Activity: Give your child several small items (buttons, pennies) to count. Help your child make groups of ten and then count by tens.

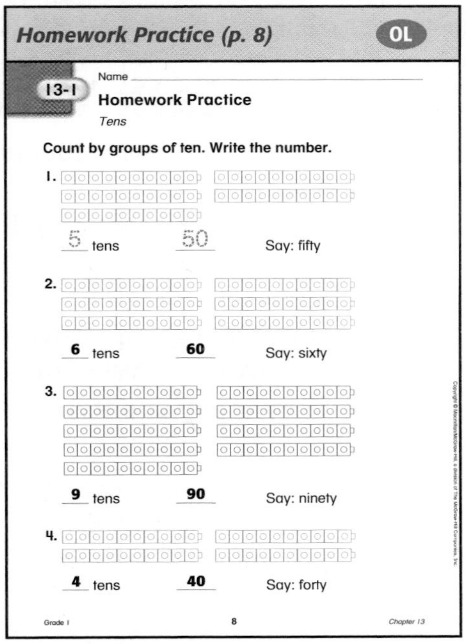
Homework Practice (p. 8) OL

13-1 Name ______
Homework Practice
Tens

Count by groups of ten. Write the number.

1. 5 tens 50 Say: fifty
2. 6 tens 60 Say: sixty
3. 9 tens 90 Say: ninety
4. 4 tens 40 Say: forty

Grade 1 8 Chapter 13

4 Assess

Formative Assessment

Have students draw 21 Xs on a sheet of paper. Have them count the groups of ten and circle them.

WRITING IN ▶ MATH Have students write a word problem that involves counting by tens. Suggest that students invite a classmate to try to solve the problem.

Quick Check **Are students continuing to struggle with counting by tens?**

If Yes → Small Group Options (p. 421B)

If No → Independent Work Options (p. 421B)

CRM Skills Practice Worksheet (p. 7)

CRM Enrich Worksheet (p. 10)

LESSON 13-2

Tens and Ones

Lesson Planner

Objective

Create sets of tens and ones using sets of concrete objects.

Vocabulary

regroup

Resources

Materials: WorkMat 7: Tens and Ones Chart, hundred chart

Manipulatives: spinners, connecting cubes, two-colored counters

Literature Connection: *The King's Commissioners* by Aileen Friedman

Alternate Lessons: Adapt "Perimeters" on page 315 of *Math Their Way* for practice with tens and ones. Use *IMPACT Mathematics:* Unit H to provide practice with creating sets of tens and ones.

Teacher Technology

TeacherWorks • Concepts in Motion

Focus on Math Background

This lesson introduces the concept of describing and labeling quantities by sets of tens and ones. Grouping numbers into units of tens and ones is a procedure fundamental to understanding place value. Students also use place labeling as a way to indicate how the digit in the tens place stands for the number of tens units and the numeral in the ones place represents how many ungrouped items remain.

Daily Routine

Use these suggestions before beginning the lesson on p. 423.

5-Minute Check

(Reviews Lesson 13-1)

Use connecting cubes to make groups of 10 to show each number. Count how many.

1. 30

2. 50

3. 10

Problem of the Day

Explain why 7 + 8 = 15 and 15 − 8 = 7 are in the same fact family, but 3 + 9 = 12 and 12 − 4 = 8 are not. Sample answer: The first two problems use the same numbers for the two number sentences. The last two problems use different numbers, so they cannot be part of the same fact family.

LINE UP Have students count off in line to find how many students are present. **How many tens are there? How many ones are left over?** Have students get into groups of tens and ones to demonstrate.

Building Math Vocabulary

Distribute counters and have students count out 14, one by one.

- Tell students that they are going to **regroup** the counters into 1 ten and some ones. Have them put 10 counters in one group and the rest of the counters in another group. **How many groups of ten do you have?** 1 **How many ones do you have?** 4 **How many counters are there in all?** 14
- Explain to students that *regroup* means to name a number a different way. Explain that they did that by regrouping 14 ones into 1 ten and 4 ones.
- Repeat using the numbers 15, 17, and 9.

Differentiated Instruction

Small Group Options

Option 1 LINGUISTIC, AUDITORY

Gifted and Talented AL

Materials: paper, pencil

- Have students work with a partner. Have one partner create a number riddle. For example: *I am thinking of a number that has 3 tens and 16 ones. What is my number?* 46
- Have the other partner solve the riddle and give a different way to describe the same number.
- Partners switch roles and repeat.

I am thinking of a number that has 3 tens and 16 ones. What is my number?

Option 2 VISUAL, KINESTHETIC

English Language Learners ELL

Materials: connecting cubes, a diagram with columns of 2-digit number, = sign , blank space, plus sign, blank space. The = and + signs should look like dividing lines and the blank spaces should have a picture of a rod and cube respectively so that each line, when filled in, looks like the following: 24 = 20 + 4.

Core Vocabulary: rebuild, sets of 10, what was in it?

Common Use Verb: take apart

Do Math This strategy helps students learn that numbers can be divided by 10's and ones by decomposing sets.

- Post the diagram. Model taking a set of cubes, counting them and writing the number in the first column.
- Connect sets of ten and show them. Say: "2 **sets of ten** is __?". Prompt and write 20 after the = sign.
- Count the leftovers and write "4" after the + sign.
- Have students repeat, writing the numbers on the chart.
- Discuss what was in each set and if they see a pattern.
- Have students draw or write out their explanation as time permits.

Independent Work Options

Option 1 LOGICAL, LINGUISTIC

Early Finishers OL AL

Materials: index cards, markers

- Have pairs of students create a set of cards for numbers 30 to 40 written as tens and ones.
- Have one partner close his or her eyes. Have the other partner arrange four cards in order, but with one missing.
- Have the first partner tell which card is missing.

3 tens and 4 ones	3 tens and 5 ones	3 tens and 6 ones		3 tens and 8 ones

Option 2

Student Technology

Math Online macmillanmh.com

Math Adventures

Option 3

Learning Station: Art (p. 415G)

Direct students to the Art Learning Station for more opportunities to explore and extend the lesson concept.

Option 4

Problem-Solving Daily Practice

Reinforce problem-solving skills and strategies with the Leveled Problem-Solving worksheet.

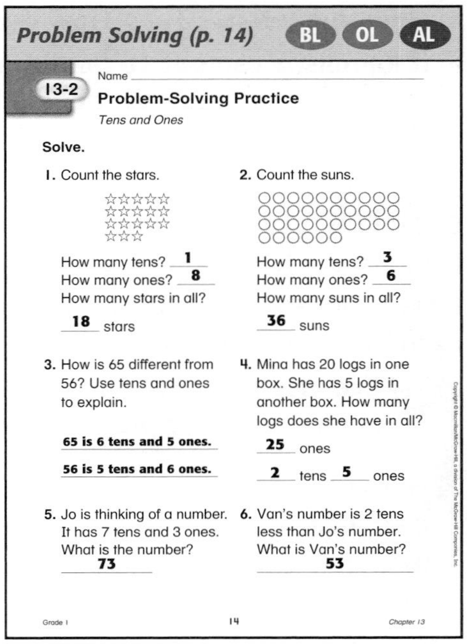
Problem Solving (p. 14) BL OL AL

13-2 Name ____

Problem-Solving Practice

Tens and Ones

Solve.

1. Count the stars.

How many tens? **1**
How many ones? **8**
How many stars in all?
18 stars

2. Count the suns.

How many tens? **3**
How many ones? **6**
How many suns in all?
36 suns

3. How is 65 different from 56? Use tens and ones to explain.

65 is 6 tens and 5 ones.
56 is 5 tens and 6 ones.

4. Mina has 20 logs in one box. She has 5 logs in another box. How many logs does she have in all?

25 ones
2 tens **5** ones

5. Jo is thinking of a number. It has 7 tens and 3 ones. What is the number?
73

6. Van's number is 2 tens less than Jo's number. What is Van's number?
53

Copyright © Macmillan/McGraw-Hill, a division of The McGraw-Hill Companies, Inc.

Grade 1 14 Chapter 13

1 Introduce

Activity Choice 1 • Hands-On

Give small groups of students a ten-section spinner and a pile of connecting cubes.

- Have each student spin the spinner and connect that number of cubes together.
- **Can you create a 10-train with one spin? Explain.** No, the number 10 is not on the spinner.
- **How many 10-trains can your group create if you put all your cubes together?** Ask one person from each group to share the results. See students' work.

Activity Choice 2 • Literature

Introduce the lesson with *The King's Commissioners* by Aileen Friedman. For additional support, see p. TR60.

2 Teach

Give sixteen connecting cubes and WorkMat 7: Tens and Ones Chart to each student.

- Tell the students that the cubes show how many books Kameisha has to put on bookshelves. Tell the students to put all their cubes on the ones side of the mat.
- Kameisha can put ten books on each shelf. **Do you need to regroup to make 10?** yes
- Have students regroup by making a 10-train and moving it to the tens column on the workmat.
- **How many tens?** 1 ten **How many ones?** 6 ones
- **If Kameisha can put 10 books on each shelf, how many shelves will she need?** 2 shelves **Why?** Sample answer: She has 1 ten and 6 ones. Ten will go on one shelf; six will go on a second shelf.

Get Ready Use the section at the top of p. 423 to reinforce the lesson concept.

Check Observe students as you work through Exercises 1–5 as a class.

Exercise 5 Assess student comprehension before assigning practice exercises.

! COMMON ERROR!

If students read numbers backward, remind them that we read numbers the same way we read words—start on the left and go to the right.

Name ____________________

Hands-On Activity

Tens and Ones

Get Ready

Main Idea

I will make groups of tens and ones.

Vocabulary

regroup

You can show a number as tens and ones.
You can **regroup** 10 ones as 1 ten.

16 ones = 1 ten and 6 ones or 16

Check

Use [cube]. Make groups of tens and ones.
Write how many.

1. 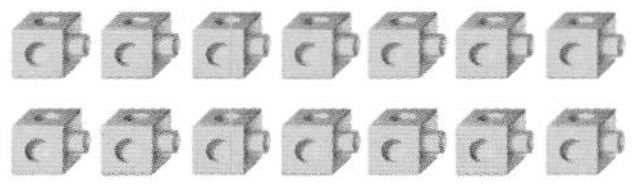
14 ones = 1 ten and 4 ones 14

2. 
18 ones = 1 ten and 8 ones 18

3. 21 ones = 2 tens and 1 one 21

4. 52 ones = 5 tens and 2 ones 52

5. Talk About It How would you regroup 20 ones? Sample answer: 2 groups of ten, or 2 tens 0 ones

---

Reteach (p. 11) BL

13-2 Name ____________________

Reteach

Tens and Ones

32 = 32 ones   32 ones = 3 tens 2 ones

Write how many ones.
Count the groups of ten.
Write how many tens and ones.

1. 43 = **43** ones   **4** tens **3** ones
2. 31 = **31** ones   **3** tens **1** one
3. 16 = **16** ones   **1** ten **6** ones
4. 25 = **25** ones   **2** tens **5** ones

Skills Practice (p. 12) OL

13-2 Name ____________________

Skills Practice

Tens and Ones

Use [cube]. Make groups of tens and ones.
Write how many.

1. 26 twenty-six
26 ones
2 tens **6** ones

2. 31 thirty-one
31 ones
3 tens **1** one

3. 22 twenty-two
22 ones
2 tens **2** ones

4. 13 thirteen
13 ones
1 ten **3** ones

Write your answer.

5. How can you use tens and ones to show that 23 is different than 32? **23 has 2 tens and 3 ones. 32 has 3 tens and 2 ones.**

6. Pat is thinking of a number.
It has 5 tens and 4 ones.
What is the number? **54**

Practice

Use [cube]. Make groups of tens and ones.
Write how many.

6. 

13 ones = 1 ten and 3 ones 13

7. 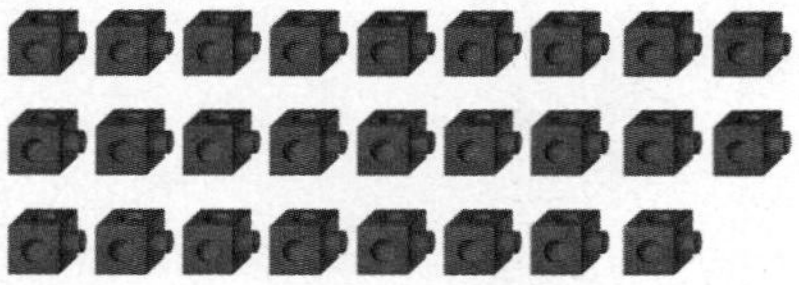

26 ones = 2 tens and 6 ones 26

8. 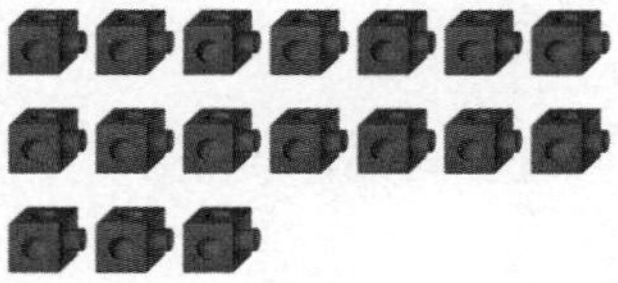

17 ones = 1 ten and 7 ones 17

9. 35 ones = 3 tens and 5 ones 35
10. 46 ones = 4 tens and 6 ones 46
11. 67 ones = 6 tens and 7 ones 67
12. 29 ones = 2 tens and 9 ones 29

13. **WRITING IN MATH** Explain how to regroup 51 ones as tens and ones.

Sample answer: Make groups of ten; 5 tens and 1 one

Math at Home Activity: Ask your child to regroup 83 as tens and ones.

Enrich (p. 15) AL

13-2 Name ______

Enrich

Number Race

Play with a partner. You need 2 [number cube].

- Roll the [number cube]. Use this number for the tens place.
- Roll the [number cube] again. Use this number for the ones place.
- Write the numbers on the chart.
- You cannot repeat any numbers.
- Go as fast as you can. The first player to fill in the chart wins! **Answers will vary.**

Player 1	Player 2
___ ___ tens ones = ___	___ ___ tens ones = ___
___ ___ tens ones = ___	___ ___ tens ones = ___
___ ___ tens ones = ___	___ ___ tens ones = ___
___ ___ tens ones = ___	___ ___ tens ones = ___
___ ___ tens ones = ___	___ ___ tens ones = ___
___ ___ tens ones = ___	___ ___ tens ones = ___
___ ___ tens ones = ___	___ ___ tens ones = ___
___ ___ tens ones = ___	___ ___ tens ones = ___
___ ___ tens ones = ___	___ ___ tens ones = ___
___ ___ tens ones = ___	___ ___ tens ones = ___

Homework Practice (p. 13) OL

13-2 Name ______

Homework Practice

Tens and Ones

Write the numbers.

1. 16 ones = **1** ten and **6** ones = **16**
2. 22 ones = **2** tens and **2** ones = **22**
3. 33 ones = **3** tens and **3** ones = **33**
4. 41 ones = **4** tens and **1** one = **41**
5. 30 ones = **3** tens and **0** ones = **30**
6. 58 ones = **5** tens and **8** ones = **58**
7. 77 ones = **7** tens and **7** ones = **77**
8. 69 ones = **6** tens and **9** ones = **69**

Write your answer.

9. Maria has 30 pencils in one box.
She has 2 pencils in another box.
How many pencils does Maria have in all?
32 ones = **3** tens **2** ones

10. Carl is thinking of a number.
It has 6 tens and 4 ones.
What is the number? **64**

BL Alternate Teaching Strategy

If students have trouble understanding how to count numbers by tens and ones . . .

Then use one of the following reteach options.

1. CRM **Daily Reteach Worksheet** (p. 11)
2. **Use a Hundred Chart** Have students look at a hundred chart. Select random numbers and have students tell you how many ones and sets of ten are in each number. Then have them check their answer by modeling the number with connecting cubes or base-ten blocks.

3 Practice

Differentiate practice using these leveled assignments for Exercises 6–13.

Level	Assignment
BL Below/Approaching Level	Allow students to use manipulatives to help count, if necessary.
OL On Level	Complete the exercises independently.
AL Above/Beyond Level	Have students add a hundreds place value and name how many hundreds, tens, and ones.

4 Assess

Formative Assessment

Give students a handful of counters. Have them put the counters into groups of tens, tell how many tens and ones, and then name the total amount.

WRITING IN MATH Explain how 13 and 31 are different. Use cubes to justify your thinking.

Quick Check **Are students continuing to struggle with counting tens and ones?**

If Yes → CRM Reteach Worksheet (p. 11)

If No → Independent Work Options (p. 423B)
CRM Skills Practice Worksheet (p. 12)
CRM Enrich Worksheet (p. 15)

Extra Practice

Review Lessons 13-1 to 13-2

Objective: Review and assess mastery of previous lessons' skills and concepts.

- Review with students how to build tens with connecting cubes. Encourage them to do this as they complete the extra practice.
- Review with students how to count the extras as ones.
- If students lose track counting pictures on the page, have them make a tally mark for each picture or have them match each picture to a connecting cube before assembling them into tens.

Practice with Technology

Math Online Have students visit macmillanmh.com for additional practice with online activities, games, and quizzes.

Name ____________________

Count the objects in the picture.

1. How many trees are there? 13
   How many tens? 1
   How many ones? 3

2. How many dogs are there? 10
   How many tens? 1
   How many ones? 0

3. How many flowers are there? 25
   How many tens? 2
   How many ones? 5

4. How many dogs with red collars? 3
   How many tens? 0
   How many ones? 3

Game Time

Lizzie the Lizard

Making Ten

You Will Need

Play with a partner. Take turns.
- Choose a . Place it on START.
- Roll the .
- Decide how many you would add to that number to make 10.
- Move that many foot prints.
- The first person to FINISH wins.

Lizzie the Lizard

Math Concept:
Adding Ones to Make a Set of Ten

Materials: game pieces

Manipulatives: number cube

Introduce the game on page 426 to students to play as a class, in small groups, or at a learning workstation to review concepts introduced in this chapter.

Instructions

- Have students use their finger to follow the path of footprints. This will ensure that students know how to move from *Start* to *Finish*.
- Choose a game piece.
- Roll the number cube.
- Decide how many ones you would need to add to that number to get 10.
- Move that many spaces on the board.
- The first person to *Finish* wins.

Extend the Game

Have students state the addition problem they have made to equal 10. Then have them state the reverse fact, using 10 minus the number rolled. If they cannot state the subtraction fact, have them go back two spaces.

Differentiated Practice

Use these leveling suggestions to differentiate the game for all learners.

Level	Assignment
BL Below/Approaching Level	Allow students to use connecting cubes to help them get a total of 10.
OL On Level	Have students play the game with the rules as written.
AL Above/Beyond Level	Have students write the addition problem they have created to equal 10 before they can move their game piece.

13-3 Problem-Solving Strategy

Guess and Check

Lesson Planner

Objective

Use the *guess and check* strategy to solve problems.

Resources

Manipulatives: two-colored counters, connecting cubes, base-ten blocks

Literature Connection: *Ten Black Dots* by Donald Crews

Teacher Technology

TeacherWorks

Real-World Problem Solving Library
Math and Science: *How Fast, How Far?*
Use these leveled books to reinforce and extend problem-solving skills and strategies.

Leveled for:

- OL On Level
- ELL Sheltered English
- SP Spanish

For additional support, see the Real-World Problem Solving Teacher Guide.

Daily Routine

Use these suggestions before beginning the lesson on p. 427.

5-Minute Check

(Reviews Lesson 13-2)

Write the tens and ones.

1. 31 ones = _____ tens and _____ ones 3; 1
2. 17 ones = _____ tens and _____ ones 1; 7
3. 6 ones = _____ tens and _____ ones 0; 6
4. 78 ones = _____ tens and _____ ones 7; 8
5. 22 ones = _____ tens and _____ ones 2; 2

Problem of the Day

Awil has a tennis ball, a pencil box, and a can of juice. What three-dimensional figures are the objects? a sphere, a rectangular prism, and a cylinder

LINE UP Have students line up in groups of ten. Count how many groups of ten there are, how many ones are left, and what the total number of students is. Repeat by adding or taking away students from the line.

Differentiated Instruction

Small Group Options

Option 1 LOGICAL

Gifted and Talented AL

Materials: Workmat 7: Tens and Ones Chart, base-ten blocks (mat, rods, units), spinners

- Distribute blocks, a mat, and a spinner to each pair of students.
- Have one partner spin for the number of tens. Have the other partner spin for the number of ones.
- Explain that partners should then use blocks to build their number on WorkMat 7: Tens and Ones Chart.
- Ask students to tell the value of each digit (example: 3 tens = 30) and name their total number (example: 3 tens and 2 ones = 32).
- Have partners switch roles and repeat the activity.

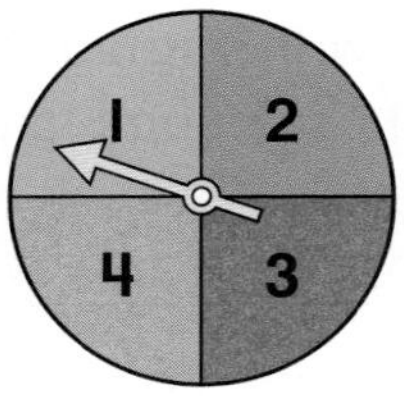

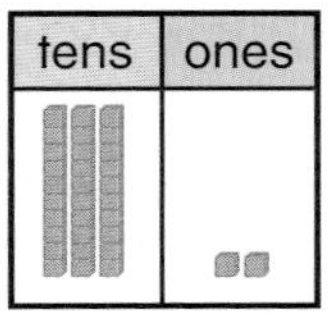

Option 2 INTRAPERSONAL

English Language Learners ELL

Core Vocabulary: steals, a point, if wrong
Common Use Verb: earn

Do Math This strategy helps students integrate the math knowledge with listening skills.

- Line the class up into teams. Say: "I will say 2 numbers. The first student in line to write the sum will get **a point** for their team. The other team checks the problem and **steals a point if** the first team was **wrong**. The first team to ***earn*** 20 points wins!"
- Use a ten multiple and a single digit number as addends, mixing the order throughout.
- Have students discuss their strategy for solving the problems mentally with their teammates.
- At the end of the game, have the winning team explain their strategy to the other groups as time permits.

Independent Work Options

Option 1 LOGICAL

Early Finishers OL AL

Materials: 15 number cards with numbers to 100, penny

- Ask students to mix up the number cards and place them face down.
- Have students take turns flipping the penny. Heads represents ones and tails represents tens.
- Ask the student to choose a card and say the number. If heads, have the student say the value of the number in the ones place. If tails, have the student say the value of the number in the tens place.
- Students continue the activity until all cards have been used.

Option 2

Student Technology

Math Online macmillanmh.com

Option 3

Learning Station: Art (p. 415G)

Direct students to the Art Learning Station for more opportunities to explore and extend the lesson concept.

1 Introduce

Activity Choice 1 • Review

Write and read aloud the following:

Eight children want to check out a book about George Washington. The library has only five books about Washington. How many students will not get a book about Washington?

- **What do we know?** There are 8 children in the library who want books about George Washington. There are only 5 books.
- **What do we want to find?** The number of children that will not get a book. Help students use counters to model, if necessary.
- **Which operation should we use?** subtraction
- **What is the number sentence?** 8 – 5 = 3

Activity Choice 2 • Literature

Introduce the lesson with *Ten Black Dots* by Donald Crews. For additional support, see p. TR60.

2 Teach

Have students read the problem on p. 427. Guide them through the problem-solving steps.

Understand Using the questions, review what students know and what they need to find.

Plan Have them discuss their strategy.

Solve Guide students to *guess and check*.

- Have students use connecting cubes.
- **How many cubes do you need?** 15 cubes
- **How can you *guess and check*?** Separate the cubes into three piles. Try to make equal piles.
- **How many cubes are in each pile if they have same amount?** 5 cubes

Check Have students look back at the problem to make sure that the answers fit the facts given.

! COMMON ERROR!

Students may forget that they need to separate the cubes into 3 equal piles. Encourage students to draw 3 long lines on a piece of paper to represent the 3 shelves. Have them line the cubes up on the shelves as they separate them into equal groups.

Name ____________________

Problem-Solving Strategy

Guess and Check

Main Idea

I will guess and check to solve a problem.

Raj has 15 toy cars to put on 3 shelves. He wants to put the same number of cars on each shelf. How many cars go on each shelf?

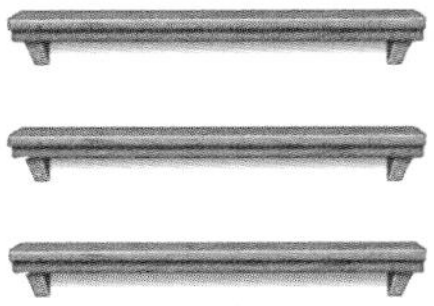

Understand

What do I know?

Underline what you know.

What do I need to find?

Circle the question.

Plan

How will I solve the problem?

I will use cubes to guess and check.

Solve

Put 4 cubes on each shelf.

Count the cubes. Only 12 cubes in all.

Try 5.

Check

Look back.

Is my answer reasonable? Check students' explanations.

Reteach (pp. 16–17) BL

13-3 Name ____________________

Reteach (1)

Problem-Solving Strategy: Guess and Check

Beth has 12 shirts to put in 3 drawers.
She wants the same number of shirts in each drawer.
How many shirts go in each drawer?

Step 1 Understand — **What do I know?**
Beth has 12 shirts.
There are 3 drawers.
She wants the same number of shirts in each drawer.
What do I need to find out?
How many shirts in each drawer?

Step 2 Plan — **How will I find the reasonable answer?**
I will guess and check.

Step 3 Solve — **Guess and check.**
Guess the number. Use cubes to check.
Guess **4** shirts in each drawer.
Put **4** cubes in 3 groups.
Count the cubes. How many? **12**

Step 4 Check — Is my answer reasonable? **yes**
How did I check my guess? **I used cubes.**

Grade 1 16 Chapter 13

Skills Practice (p. 18) OL

13-3 Name ____________________

Skills Practice

Problem-Solving Strategy: Guess and Check

Use guess and check to solve.

1. Greg has 13 cents. He says he can give the same amount of money to 3 friends. Is he right? Show how you know.
   no
   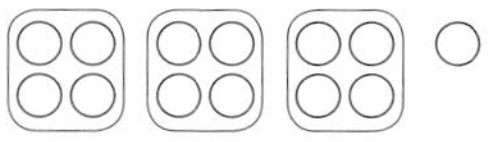
2. Sue Ellen is planning a trip. She wants to visit 8 places in 16 days. She wants to spend the same number of days at each place. How many days can she visit each place?
   2 days
3. Ron is at a parade. He sees 30 people in each band. He sees 3 bands. How many people does Ron see?
   90 people
4. Ms. White has 4 shelves. She has 9 plates on each shelf. How many total plates does Ms. White have?
   36 plates

Grade 1 18 Chapter 13

Remember
Understand
Plan
Solve
Check

Try It

Guess and check to solve.

1. Brianna puts 12 pears into 2 bowls. She wants to put the same number of pears in each bowl. How many pears go in each bowl?

6 pears

2. There are 3 stacks of pennies. There are 10 pennies in each stack. How many pennies are there in all?

30 pennies

Your Turn

Guess and check to solve.

3. Ms. Kim has 18 balloons. She wants to give Rae and Doug the same number of balloons. How many balloons does she give each person?

9 balloons

4. There are 4 spelling bee teams. Each team is made up of 5 students How many students are there altogether?

20 students

Math at Home Activity: Give your child 40, 50, or 60 pennies. Ask your child to guess and check to figure out how many equal stacks can be made.

Try It Observe students as you work through Exercises 1–2 as a class.

BL Alternate Teaching Strategy

If students have trouble using the *guess and check* strategy to solve a problem . . .

Then use one of the following reteach options.

1. CRM **Daily Reteach Worksheet** (pp. 16–17)
2. **Use Coins** Give each student a handful of pennies. Have students guess how many groups of ten they can make with the pennies. Ask students to check their guess by dividing the pennies into groups of ten. Repeat activity as time permits.

3 Practice

Your Turn

Exercises 3–4 Have students use connecting cubes for each problem to help them work out the answer.

4 Assess

- Pose the following problem to students and write it on the board.
  Keith planted 14 rows of flowers in his garden. Eight rows had tulips. The rest of the rows had daisies. How many rows of daisies were there?
  6 rows of daisies
- **What strategy did you use to solve this problem?** Sample answers: guess and check; write a number sentence; draw a picture

Enrich (p. 20) AL

13-3 Name

Enrich

What Number Am I?

Use guess and check. Write your answer.

1. I am less than half of 18. I am more than 7. What number am I? **8**
2. I am 3 more than 6 doubled. What number am I? **15**
3. I am 4 and 6 and 13 in all. What number am I? **23**
4. I was 35. Now, I am 14 less. What number am I? **21**
5. I was 20 less than 30. But now I am 4 more than that. What number am I? **14**

Grade 1 20 Chapter 13

Homework Practice (p. 19) OL

13-3 Name

Homework Practice

Problem-Solving Strategy: Guess and Check

Use guess and check to solve.

1. There are 5 swim teams. Each team has 4 students. How many total students are there? **20** students
2. There are 4 piles of books. There are 7 books in each pile. How many books are there in all? **28** books
3. Meg has 22 game cards. She wants to give her 2 friends the same number of cards. How many cards does she give to each friend? **11** cards
4. The mail carrier gives 40 letters to 8 homes. She gives the same number of letters to each home. How many letters does she give to each home? **5** letters

Chapter Resources

Grade 1 19 Chapter 13

Quick Check

Are students continuing to struggle with using the *guess and check* strategy to solve problems?

If Yes → CRM Reteach Worksheet (pp. 16–17)

If No → Independent Work Options (p. 427B)
CRM Skills Practice Worksheet (p. 18)
CRM Enrich Worksheet (p. 20)

LESSON 13-4

Numbers to 50

Lesson Planner

Objective

Learn to show numbers to 50 using tens and ones.

Review Vocabulary

greater than

Resources

Materials: WorkMat 7: Tens and Ones Chart, number line

Manipulatives: connecting cubes, base-ten blocks

Literature Connection: *Zin! Zin! Zin! A Violin* by Lloyd Moss

Alternate Lessons: Adapt "Counting Jars of Objects" on page 310 of *Math Their Way* for practice in counting numbers to 50.
Use *IMPACT Mathematics:* Unit H to provide practice modeling numbers to 50.

Teacher Technology
TeacherWorks

Focus on Math Background

In this lesson students apply their understanding of place value concepts to label and quantify numbers to 50. Students can appreciate how the process of counting large amounts like 50 one-by-one is a tedious and inefficient strategy. Grouping items into sets of tens and ones, however, provides students with a way to arrange large amounts so that the objects are easier to count and quantify.

Daily Routine

Use these suggestions before beginning the lesson on p. 429.

5-Minute Check

(Reviews Lesson 13-3)

Solve.

1. There are 5 stacks of dimes. There are 10 dimes in each stack. How many dimes in all? 50 dimes

2. There are 3 kickball teams. Each team has 5 players. How many players in all? 15 players

Problem of the Day

Write a number story that shows the following addition sentence: 8 + 8 = 16. Sample answer: On Monday 8 ducks were on the pond. On Tuesday 8 more ducks join them. Altogether there were 16 ducks.

LINE UP Ask all students whose name begins with the letter A to stand. Have the group decide how many toes they have all together. If the answer is correct, the students line up. Continue with the other letters of the alphabet until all students are in line.

Review Math Vocabulary

Review with students the meaning of **greater than.** Distribute number cards showing numbers written by tens and ones. For example, one card might read "2 tens and 1 one" for 21.

- Have students compare their card to a partners. Have pairs use their numbers to complete the statement, "________ is greater than ________." Have students exchange cards with another pair and repeat.

Visual Vocabulary Cards

Use Visual Vocabulary Card 24 to reinforce the vocabulary reviewed in this lesson. (The Define/Example/Ask routine is printe d on the back of each card.)

greater than

Differentiated Instruction

Small Group Options

Option 1 LINGUISTIC, VISUAL

Below Level BL

Materials: three-foot lengths of adding machine paper, pencil, scissors, blue crayon

- Invite students to practice writing numbers 1 through 50 on a strip of adding machine tape.
- After they have written the numbers, have students count by tens and point out on their strip each number they say. Then have them circle those numbers in blue.
- Have students exchange number strips and check each other's work.
- For further practice, have students repeat the activity using the back of the strip.

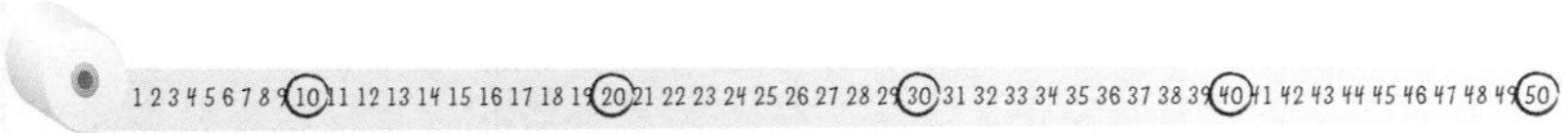

Option 2 LINGUISTIC, INTRAPERSONAL

English Language Learners ELL

Materials: graph paper, pencil
Core Vocabulary: square
Common Use Verb: trace

Write Math This strategy helps students integrate word, number and quantity of amounts to 50.

- Give the student several sheets of graph paper along with sticky notes containing various numbers to 50.
- Have the student trace the number of squares that match the sticky note.
- After tracing the squares, the students will write the number (in words and number format) from the sticky note inside the formation.

Independent Work Options

Option 1 KINESTHETIC/LOGICAL

Early Finishers OL AL

Materials: WorkMat 7: Tens and Ones Chart, base-ten blocks, fifteen number cards with numbers to 50

- Ask students to take turns choosing a number card.
- Have students work together to model the number using base-ten blocks and the place value mat.
- Encourage students to say the values of the numbers in the tens and ones place.
- Ask students to continue the activity until all cards have been used

Option 2

Student Technology

Math Online macmillanmh.com

Math Adventures

Option 3

Learning Station: Social Studies (p. 415H)

Direct students to the Social Studies Learning Station for more opportunities to explore and extend the lesson concept.

Option 4

Problem-Solving Practice

Reinforce problem-solving skills and strategies with the Problem-Solving Practice worksheet.

Problem Solving (p. 24) BL OL AL

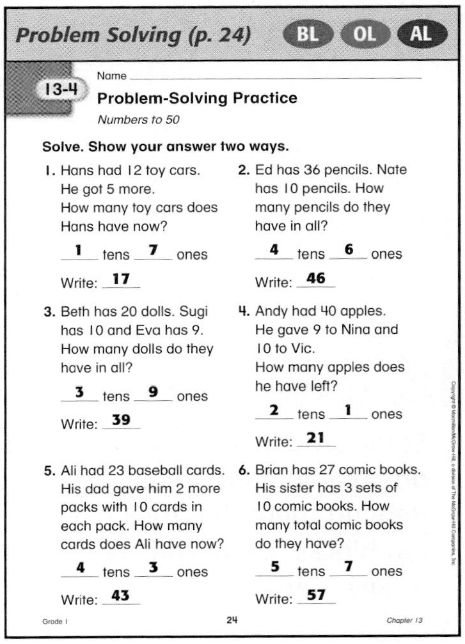
13-4 Name ________

Problem-Solving Practice
Numbers to 50

Solve. Show your answer two ways.

1. Hans had 12 toy cars. He got 5 more. How many toy cars does Hans have now?
   1 tens 7 ones
   Write: 17

2. Ed has 36 pencils. Nate has 10 pencils. How many pencils do they have in all?
   4 tens 6 ones
   Write: 46

3. Beth has 20 dolls. Sugi has 10 and Eva has 9. How many dolls do they have in all?
   3 tens 9 ones
   Write: 39

4. Andy had 40 apples. He gave 9 to Nina and 10 to Vic. How many apples does he have left?
   2 tens 1 ones
   Write: 21

5. Ali had 23 baseball cards. His dad gave him 2 more packs with 10 cards in each pack. How many cards does Ali have now?
   4 tens 3 ones
   Write: 43

6. Brian has 27 comic books. His sister has 3 sets of 10 comic books. How many total comic books do they have?
   5 tens 7 ones
   Write: 57

Grade 1 24 Chapter 13

1 Introduce

Activity Choice 1 • Hands-On

Display a number line and tell students you are thinking of some numbers that are less than 50. Explain that for each set of ten in a number, you will knock on the chalkboard. For each one in a number, you will clap your hands.

- Knock three times. **What is the number?** 30
- Clap five times. **What is the number?** 5
- Next, knock two times and clap three times. **What is the number?** 23
- Repeat with other numbers to 50. Then let volunteers do it.

Activity Choice 2 • Literature

Introduce the lesson with *Zin! Zin! Zin! A Violin* by Lloyd Moss. For additional support, see p. TR61.

Name ______________________

Numbers to 50

Hands-On Activity

Get Ready

Main Idea

I will show numbers to 50 using tens and ones.

Check

Use [ten rod] and [unit cube] and WorkMat 7.
Show groups of tens and ones.
Say and write the numbers.

1.

tens	ones

1 ten 3 ones

Say: thirteen 13

2.

tens	ones

2 tens 4 ones

Say: twenty-four 24

Reteach (p. 21) BL

13-4 Name ______

Reteach

Numbers to 50

tens	ones

4 tens 3 ones
43 forty-three

tens	ones

2 tens 5 ones
25 twenty-five

Write how many tens and ones. Then write the number.

1.

tens	ones

3 tens 4 ones
34 thirty-four

2.

tens	ones

2 tens 7 ones
27 twenty-seven

Grade 1 21 Chapter 13

COMMON ERROR!

Some students may not be as successful with one manipulative or strategy as with another. Remind them that they may use pictures, base-ten blocks, connecting cubes, claps and taps, or any method they like to solve problems.

Use [ten-train] and [cube] and WorkMat 7.
Show groups of tens and ones.
Say and write the numbers.

3.

tens	ones

4 tens
2 ones

Say: forty-two 42

4.

tens	ones

3 tens
7 ones

Say: thirty-seven 37

5.

tens	ones

3 tens
1 one

Say: thirty-one 31

6.

tens	ones

4 tens
8 ones

Say: forty-eight 48

7.

tens	ones

3 tens
9 ones

Say: thirty-nine 39

8.

tens	ones

2 tens
6 ones

Say: twenty-six 26

9. **Talk About It** How are 14 and 41 different? How are they alike?

Sample answer: 14 has 1 ten and 4 ones, 41 has 4 tens and 1 one

GO on

2 Teach

Distribute workmats, connecting cubes, and base-ten blocks.

- **How can we use connecting cubes to build the number 35?** 3 ten-trains and 5 cubes Have students build the number as you model on the overhead projector.
- Line up 10 cubes and 10 base-ten unit blocks. Put a ten-train next to the cubes. Put a rod next to the unit blocks.
- **How are base-ten blocks similar to connecting cubes?** They both can show tens and ones.
- Explain that students will use base-ten blocks today. Have students build the numbers 19, 44, and 50 as you model on the overhead.

Get Ready Use the section at the top of p. 429 to reinforce the lesson concept. Guide students as they show numbers as tens and ones.

Check Observe students as you work through Exercises 1–9 as a class.

Exercise 9 Assess student comprehension before assigning practice exercises.

BL Alternate Teaching Strategy

If students have trouble understanding how to use the base-ten blocks to regroup . . .

Then use one of the following reteach options.

1 CRM **Daily Reteach Worksheet** (p. 21)

2 **Fair or Not Fair?** Give each student between 10 and 30 base-ten blocks.

- Have students count their blocks. Offer each student in turn a combination of rods and units as a trade for their blocks. Make some trades a match and make others a mismatch.
- Have the whole group vote thumbs-up or thumbs-down to show whether or not each offer would be a fair trade.

Skills Practice (p. 22) OL

13-4 Name ______
Skills Practice
Numbers to 50

Write how many tens and ones.
Say and write the number.

1. 2 tens 2 ones — 22 twenty-two
2. 5 tens 0 ones — 50 fifty
3. 4 tens 6 ones — 46 forty-six
4. 3 tens 4 ones — 34 thirty-four
5. 1 tens 7 ones — 17 seventeen
6. 6 tens 9 ones — 69 sixty-nine

Grade 1 22 Chapter 13

3 Practice

Differentiate practice using these leveled assignments for Exercises 10–19.

Level	Assignment
BL Below/ Approaching Level	Guide students through the exercises, using base-ten blocks or connecting cubes.
OL On Level	Complete independently, using manipulatives as needed.
AL Above/Beyond Level	Complete independently. Then ask students to go back and add 6 to each problem. Have them create a new set of answers and pictures.

Name ____________________

Practice

Use [tens] and [ones] and WorkMat 7.
Show groups of tens and ones.
Say and write the numbers.

10. 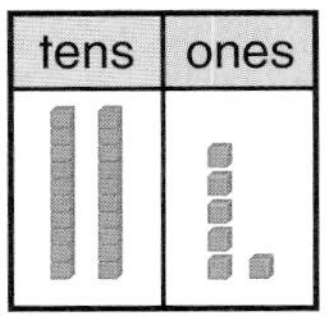

2 tens
6 ones

Say: twenty-six 26

11. 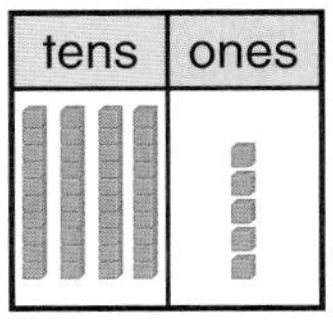

4 tens
5 ones

Say: forty-five 45

12. 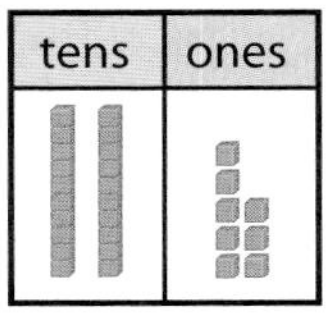

2 tens
8 ones

Say: twenty-eight 28

13. 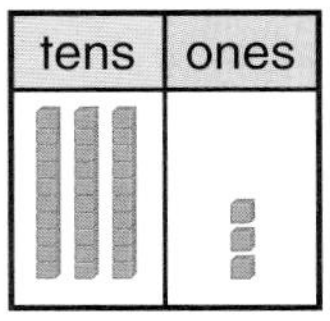

3 tens
3 ones

Say: thirty-three 33

14. 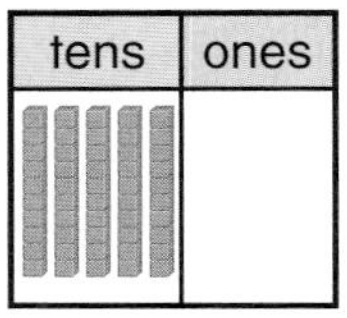

5 tens
0 ones

Say: fifty 50

15. 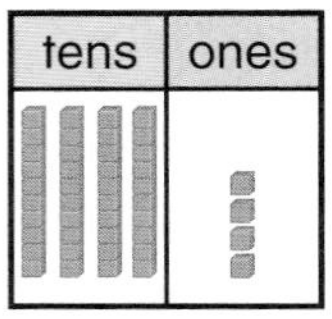

4 tens
4 ones

Say: forty-four 44

Enrich (p. 25) AL

13-4 Name ____________________

Enrich

Oops!

Petey spilled his box of dog bones! He wants to give 10 bones to each of his friends. Color the bones to see if he has enough. Use the key.

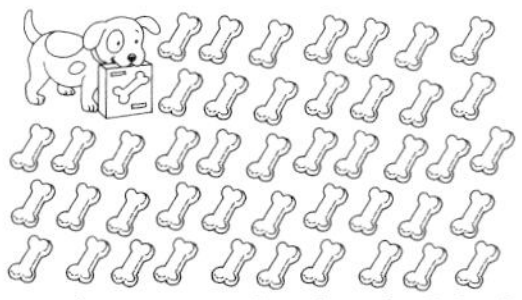

KEY
blue = Spot
red = Daisy
yellow = Sam
green = Lady

10 bones are colored each of the following colors: blue, red, yellow, and green. 5 bones are not colored.

Write how many bones each friend gets.

Spot **10** bones Daisy **10** bones
Sam **10** bones Lady **10** bones

Does Petey have any bones left?

(yes) no

How many? **5** bones

Grade 1 25 Chapter 13

Chapter Resources

Use [tens rod] and [unit cube] and WorkMat 7. Show groups of tens and ones. Say and write the numbers.

16. 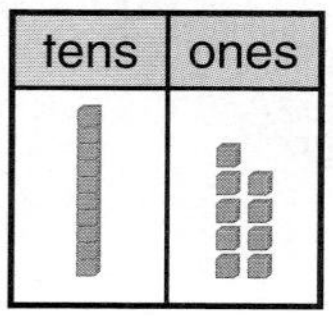

1 tens

9 ones

Say: nineteen 19

17. 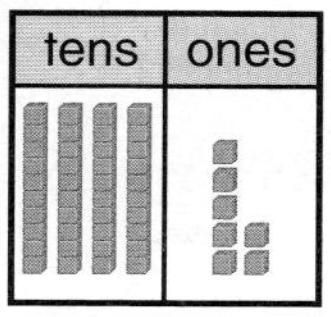

4 tens

7 ones

Say: forty-seven 47

Data File

Many kinds of fruits grow on trees in Maryland. People pick the fruits and eat them.

Fruits Picked

Fruit	Number Picked
Apples	31
Peaches	24
Pears	46
Plums	18

18. How many pears were picked? 46 pears
How many groups of ten? 4
How many ones? 6

19. How many peaches were picked?
24

Math at Home Activity: Put a number of objects (less than 50) out for your child. Have him or her place them in groups of tens and ones and say the number.

4 Assess

Formative Assessment

Display 7 base-ten rods and 4 unit blocks. **How is the number 47 different from the number these blocks show?** Have students name the number the blocks represent. 47 has 4 tens and 7 ones, and the number shown has the opposite; 74

WRITING IN MATH Ask students to write about regrouping with connecting cubes and base-ten blocks. Have them explain how the cubes and base-ten blocks are the same and different.

Homework Practice (p. 23) OL

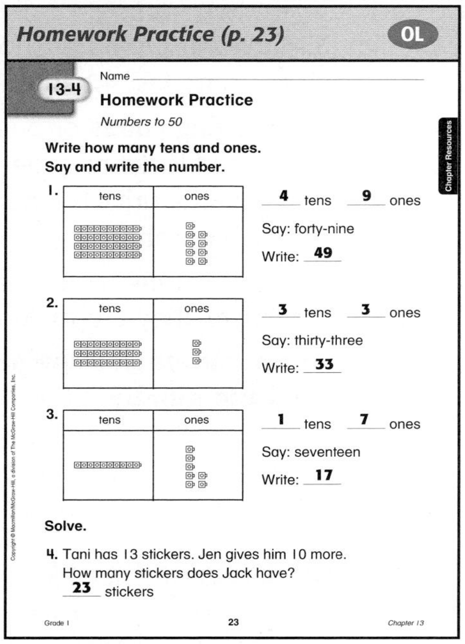
Name

13-4 **Homework Practice**
Numbers to 50

Write how many tens and ones. Say and write the number.

1. 4 tens 9 ones
Say: forty-nine
Write: 49

2. 3 tens 3 ones
Say: thirty-three
Write: 33

3. 1 tens 7 ones
Say: seventeen
Write: 17

Solve.

4. Tani has 13 stickers. Jen gives him 10 more. How many stickers does Jack have?
23 stickers

Grade 1 23 Chapter 13

Quick Check

Are students continuing to struggle with showing numbers up to 50 using tens and ones?

If Yes → Small Group Options (p. 429B)
Strategic Intervention Guide (p. 98)

If No → Independent Work Options (p. 429B)
CRM Skills Practice Worksheet (p. 22)
CRM Enrich Worksheet (p. 25)

LESSON 13-5

Numbers to 100

Lesson Planner

Objective

Learn different ways to show a number.

Review Vocabulary

ones

Resources

Materials: WorkMat 7: Tens and Ones Chart

Manipulatives: connecting cubes, base-ten blocks

Literature Connection: *100 Days of School* by Trudy Harris

Alternate Lesson: Adapt "Estimating and Checking" on pages 308 and 309 of *Math Their Way* for practice in counting numbers to 100.
Use *IMPACT Mathematics:* Unit H to provide practice with modeling numbers to 100.

Teacher Technology

TeacherWorks • Concepts in Motion • Math Tool Chest • Math Songs Track 13 Lesson Plan

Focus on Math Background

Using place value to quantify numbers to 100 is the focus of this lesson. Students will see and use tens and ones unit models to represent these numbers. Being able to visualize 95 as nine sets of ten and five leftovers requires that first graders be able to conserve large numbers. A student who can conserve a large number knows that the quantity remains the same regardless of how it is counted or arranged.

Daily Routine

Use these suggestions before beginning the lesson on p. 433.

5-Minute Check

(Reviews Lesson 13-4)

Use base-ten blocks and WorkMat 7. Say and write the numbers.

1. 31 = ______ tens and ______ ones 3; 1
2. 27 = ______ tens and ______ ones 2; 7
3. 44 = ______ tens and ______ ones 4; 4
4. 18 = ______ tens and ______ ones 1; 8

Problem of the Day

I am thinking of two numbers. Their sum is 13. Their difference is 1. What are the numbers? 6, 7

LINE UP When students line up for recess, lunch, or dismissal, ask a student to give a number under 100. Ask the class to tap the tens and clap the ones.

Review Math Vocabulary

Give each student two number cards, one showing a two-digit number and the other showing the digits in reverse order. (Examples: 42 and 24; 35 and 53)

- Distribute connecting cubes or base-ten blocks. Have students use blocks or cubes to build each of their numbers and write the number of tens and **ones** in each number.
- Monitor students as they work and have them explain the choices they are making.
- **Both of your numbers had the same digits. Did you build the numbers the same way? Explain.** No; the digits were reversed in the second number, so the number of tens and ones shown for the second number is reversed.

Visual Vocabulary Cards

Use Visual Vocabulary Card 32 to reinforce the vocabulary reviewed in this lesson. (The Define/Example/Ask routine is printed on the back of each card.)

Differentiated Instruction

Small Group Options

Option 1 SPATIAL, LOGICAL

Gifted and Talented AL

Materials: hundred chart, crayons

- Give each group member a hundred chart and a crayon.
- Have students color in the following numbers on their charts as you read them aloud: 22, 24, 25, 26, 28, 29, 30, 32, 34, 36, 38, 40, 42, 44, 46, 48, 50, 52, 54, 56, 58, 60, 62, 64, 65, 66, 68, 69, and 70.
- When students have finished coloring the squares, they should see the outline of the number 100.
- Challenge students to color different sets of squares to create other number outlines. Invite them to call out the squares to color while a partner tries to duplicate their pattern.

	22		24	25	26		28	29	30
	32		34		36		38		40
	42		44		46		48		50
	52		54		56		58		60
	62		64	65	66		68	69	70

Option 2 LINGUISTIC, INTRAPERSONAL

English Language Learners ELL

Materials: number lines
Core Vocabulary: begin on, practice, help
Common Use Verb: count backwards

Talk Math This strategy helps students integrate saying numbers to 100.

- Give pairs of students number lines from 0 to 100.
- Have one student start on 100 and read the numbers backwards to 0 while the partner points to the number, listens and assists with pronunciation as necessary.
- Switch roles and repeat.
- As time permits, chorally count back from 100, then by 2's, 5's and/or 10's.
- Extend the strategy by repeating counting backwards without looking at the number line.

Independent Work Options

Option 1 KINESTHETIC, LINGUISTIC

Early Finishers OL AL

Materials: construction paper, crayons, WorkMat 7: Tens and Ones Chart, base-ten blocks, connecting cubes, two-colored counters

- Have students show the following numbers in as many ways as possible: 25, 39, 61, and 94.
- Ask students to use drawings or manipulatives to show each number.
- Encourage groups to share the many ways they showed one of the numbers.

Option 2 Tech Link

Student Technology

Math Online macmillanmh.com

Math Songs, "98 Pink Elephants" Track 13 • Math Tool Chest
Math Adventures

Option 3

Learning Station: Social Studies (p. 415H)

Direct students to the Social Studies Learning Station for more opportunities to explore and extend the lesson concept.

Option 4

Problem-Solving Practice

Reinforce problem-solving skills and strategies with the Problem-Solving Practice worksheet.

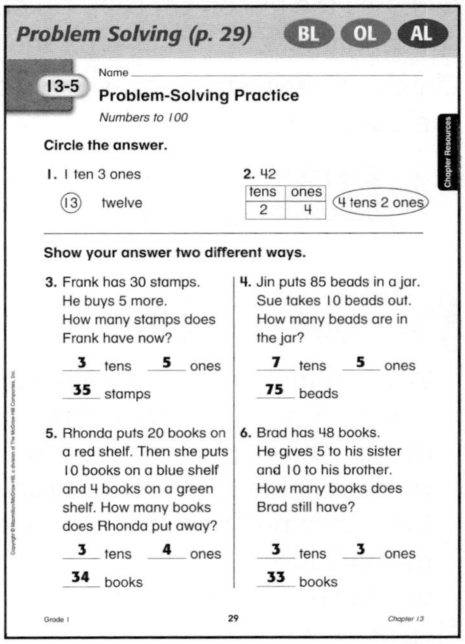

Problem Solving (p. 29) BL OL AL

13-5 Name ____
Problem-Solving Practice
Numbers to 100

Circle the answer.

1. 1 ten 3 ones — (13) twelve

2. 42

tens	ones
2	4

(4 tens 2 ones)

Show your answer two different ways.

3. Frank has 30 stamps. He buys 5 more. How many stamps does Frank have now?
3 tens 5 ones
35 stamps

4. Jin puts 85 beads in a jar. Sue takes 10 beads out. How many beads are in the jar?
7 tens 5 ones
75 beads

5. Rhonda puts 20 books on a red shelf. Then she puts 10 books on a blue shelf and 4 books on a green shelf. How many books does Rhonda put away?
3 tens 4 ones
34 books

6. Brad has 48 books. He gives 5 to his sister and 10 to his brother. How many books does Brad still have?
3 tens 3 ones
33 books

Grade 1 29 Chapter 13

13-5

1 Introduce

Activity Choice 1 • Hands-On

- Give each student a different two-digit number between 11 and 49.
- Have students create a number web showing at least three ways to write the number. Responses will vary and might include showing numbers as sets of tens and ones; using tallies, cube trains, or counters; or writing a number sentence.

Activity Choice 2 • Literature

Introduce the lesson with *100 Days of School* by Trudy Harris. For additional support, see p. TR61.

2 Teach

Distribute connecting cubes and WorkMat 7: Tens and Ones Chart.

- **If Tiffany has 46 seashells, how can you use cubes to model the number of seashells that Tiffany has?** 4 ten-trains and 6 single cubes
- Have students try some other ways to model 46. Assign groups of students different ways to model the number (pictures, tally marks, coins, base-ten blocks, stacks of counters, finger tracing, and so on).
- Have each group display their work. Discuss ways that the displays are similar and different.

Get Ready Use the section at the top of p. 433 to reinforce the lesson concept. Guide students as they show numbers to 100 as tens and ones.

Check Observe students as you work through Exercises 1–3 as a class.

Exercise 3 Assess student comprehension before assigning practice exercises.

COMMON ERROR!

When students first grasp the concept of tens and ones, they may think they no longer need manipulatives. This can lead to errors and confusion. Praise students' progress, but have them continue to check their answers with manipulatives until they build a deeper understanding of place value.

Name ____________________

Hands-On Activity

Numbers to 100

Get Ready

Main Idea
I will write numbers in different ways.

You can write numbers in different ways.

tens	ones	tens	ones
[4 ten-trains]	[2 cubes]	4	2

4 tens 2 ones

42 Say: forty-two

Check

Use [ten-train] and [cube] and WorkMat 7.
Show groups of tens and ones.
Write the number in different ways.

1.

tens	ones	tens	ones
[3 ten-trains]	[1 cube]	3	1

3 tens 1 one

31 Say: thirty-one

2.

tens	ones	tens	ones
[2 ten-trains]	[4 cubes]	2	4

2 tens 4 ones

24 Say: twenty-four

3. Talk About It How can you write 72 in more than one way? 7 tens and 2 ones, seventy-two

---

Reteach (p. 26) BL

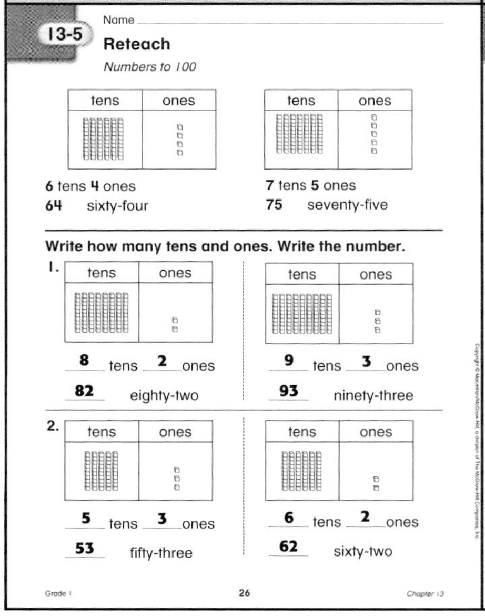

13-5 Name
Reteach
Numbers to 100

tens	ones
[6 tens]	[4 ones]

6 tens 4 ones
64 sixty-four

tens	ones
[7 tens]	[5 ones]

7 tens 5 ones
75 seventy-five

Write how many tens and ones. Write the number.

1. 8 tens 2 ones — 82 eighty-two; 9 tens 3 ones — 93 ninety-three

2. 5 tens 3 ones — 53 fifty-three; 6 tens 2 ones — 62 sixty-two

Grade 1 26 Chapter 13

Skills Practice (p. 27) OL

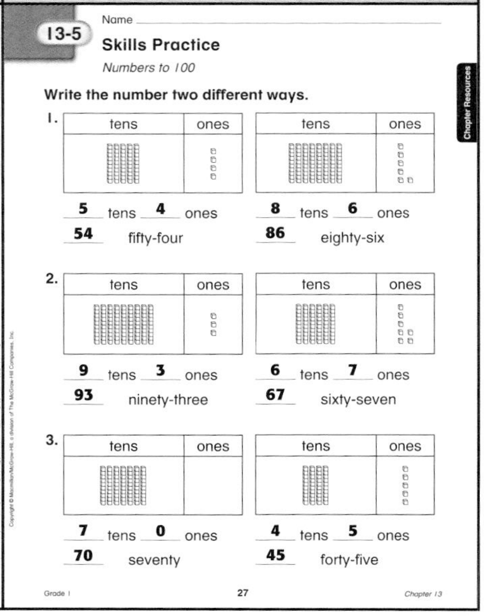

13-5 Name
Skills Practice
Numbers to 100

Write the number two different ways.

1. 5 tens 4 ones — 54 fifty-four; 8 tens 6 ones — 86 eighty-six

2. 9 tens 3 ones — 93 ninety-three; 6 tens 7 ones — 67 sixty-seven

3. 7 tens 0 ones — 70 seventy; 4 tens 5 ones — 45 forty-five

Grade 1 27 Chapter 13

Practice

Use [ten-train] and [cube] and WorkMat 7.
Show groups of tens and ones.
Write the number in different ways.

4. 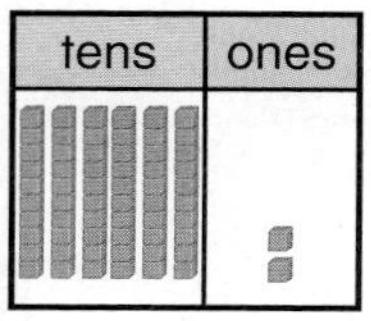

tens	ones
6	2

6 tens 2 ones — 62 Say: sixty-two

5. 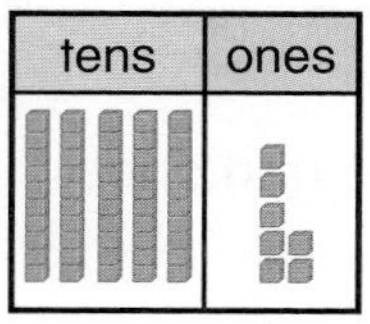

tens	ones
5	7

5 tens 7 ones — 57 Say: fifty-seven

6. 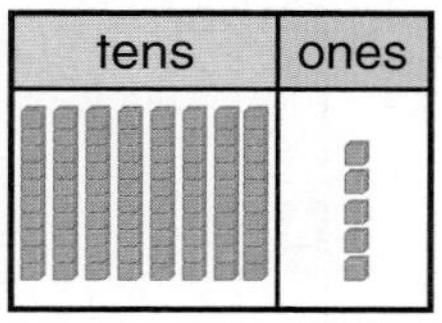

tens	ones
8	5

8 tens 5 ones — 85 Say: eighty-five

7. 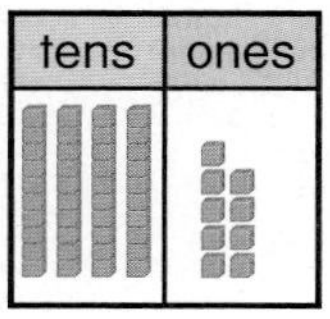

tens	ones
4	9

4 tens 9 ones — 49 Say: forty-nine

Enrich (p. 30) AL

13-5 Name ______
Enrich
Handfuls of Tens and Ones

Work in groups of 4. Your group needs 100 cubes.

- Take a big handful of cubes.
- Count how many in all.
- Make groups of ten.
- Count how many ones are left over.
- Draw your tens and ones in the chart.
- Repeat four times.
- Decide which number is the greatest. Circle it.

___ = ___ tens ___ ones ___ = ___ tens ___ ones

___ = ___ tens ___ ones ___ = ___ tens ___ ones

Answers will vary.

Grade 1 30 Chapter 13

Homework Practice (p. 28) OL

13-5 Name ______
Homework Practice
Numbers to 100

Show groups of tens and ones.
Write the number in different ways.

1. 7 tens 7 ones; 77; Say: seventy-seven
2. 8 tens 3 ones; 83; Say: eighty-three
3. 6 tens 5 ones; 65; Say: sixty-five
4. 2 tens 8 ones; 28; Say: twenty-eight

Grade 1 28 Chapter 13

Alternate Teaching Strategy

If students have trouble representing numbers in a variety of ways . . .

Then use one of the following reteach options.

1 CRM **Daily Reteach Worksheet** (p. 26)

2 **Make a Number Gallery** Have students draw 56 balls and circle sets of ten.

- On another sheet of paper, have them trace 1 ten-train for each group they circled and 1 cube for each ball they did not circle.
- On a third sheet, have students create tally marks to show the same number and circle sets of 10 tally marks.
- On a hundred chart, have students color one row for each set of ten they circled and one box for each tally they did not circle.

3 Practice

Differentiate practice for Exercises 4–7.

Level	Assignment
BL Below/ Approaching Level	Have students work in pairs and model for each other how to build a number with tens and ones
OL On Level	Complete exercises independently.
AL Above/Beyond Level	Complete exercises independently and then find a way to show each number using more than 10 ones. For example, group 43 as 3 tens and 13 ones.

4 Assess

Formative Assessment

Ask students to build the number 58 using connecting cubes and then base-ten blocks. Have them explain how they are similar and different.

Quick Check **Are students continuing to struggle with using tens and ones to show numbers to 100?**

If Yes → Strategic Intervention Guide (p. 98)

If No → Independent Work Options (p. 433B)

CRM Skills Practice Worksheet (p. 27)

CRM Enrich Worksheet (p. 30)

Math Objective

Use technology to model place value.

Resources

Math Tool Chest *(accessible in three ways)*

- **Math Online** macmillanmh.com
- StudentWorks Plus
- Math Tool Chest

Getting Started

- The activities and exercises on pp. 429–430 use the Place Value Tool in Math Tool Chest. They may be completed as a class, in pairs, or individually.
- As a class, read and then work through the information and instructions on the top of p. 435.
- Guide students as they work through the exercise.

Using Math Tool Chest

Place Value Students can use the place-value tool to model numbers quickly and neatly.

- Students should first stamp out tens and then ones. Point out that the stamps should match the model shown at the top of each section.
- Remind students that the boxes at the bottom of the screen keep count as they stamp.
- They can click on the question mark and enter the number. They can then click on the star to check the answer.

Tech Link

Name ______________________

Practice with Technology

Model Place Value • Computer

Use place value mat to make numbers.
Choose a mat to show place value.

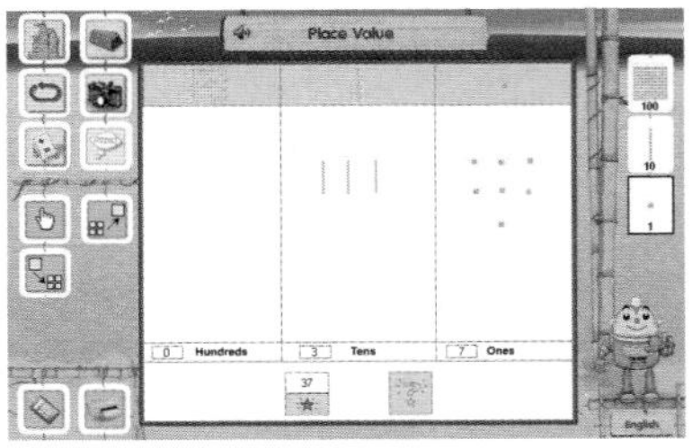

Stamp out 3

Stamp out 7

What is the number? 37

8. You can use the computer to stamp out tens and ones. Then write the number.

Stamp Out		Write the number.
9	3	93
7	8	78
8	0	80
5	3	53
4	4	44
6	6	66

Stamping Place-Value Buttons

The Place-Value mat type offers five buttons that perform functions specific to the Place-Value tool.

Move To move place-value blocks on the mat, students click . The cursor changes to a pointing finger. A red line highlights each block then the cursor can drag or move the blocks.

Trade Up Students use to regroup selected place-value blocks to larger blocks.

Trade Down Students use to regroup selected place-value blocks to smaller blocks.

Sum Students click to automatically add all of the block in part A and B.

Subtract To remove blocks from the total on the mat, students first click .

9. Stamp out [tens rod] and [ones cube] to make each number. Complete the chart.

Write the number.	Stamp Out (tens)	Stamp Out (ones)
89	8	9
71	7	1
43	4	3
59	5	9
11	1	1
62	6	2
58	5	8

Problem Solving

10. **Number Sense** Explain how to show 84 with only 7 tens.

Sample answer: I could use 7 tens and 14 ones.

Math at Home Activity: Ask your child to show 64 in at least two different ways.

Tech Link

Practice

Alone or in pairs, have students complete the charts on pp. 435 and 436 as you observe their work.

Problem Solving

Exercise 10 Assess student comprehension using the Problem Solving question.

Extending the Link

- Give students an opportunity to practice stamping out tens and ones.
- **How do you show 50 on the screen? 4 ones?** I stamp out 50 by clicking on the tens symbol 5 times. I click on the ones cube 4 times.
- **How does the computer help you solve these problems?** Possible answer: It organizes the model so I can find the number.
- **How many tens would you stamp out to model 67? How many ones?** 6; 7
- Write 92 on the board. Have students use the computer to stamp out tens and ones. Then write the number.

Mid-Chapter Check

Lessons 13-1 to 13-5

Formative Assessment

Use the Mid-Chapter Check to assess students' progress in the first half of the chapter.

ExamView Assessment Suite Customize and create multiple versions of your Mid-Chapter Check and the test answer keys.

FOLDABLES Dinah Zike's Foldables

Use these lesson suggestions to incorporate the Foldable during the chapter.

Lesson 13-1 Use the "ones" and "tens" flashcard holders and two sets of flashcards to read and write tens from 10–90 while working with this lesson.

Lesson 13-2 Use the "ones" and "tens" flashcard holders and two sets of flashcards to read and write numbers from 1–25 while working with this lesson.

Lesson 13-4 Use the "ones" and "tens" flashcard holders and two sets of flashcards to read and write numbers from 1–50 while working with this lesson.

Lesson 13-5 Use the "ones," and "tens," flashcard holders and two sets of flashcards to read and write numbers from 1–99.

Name ______________________

Count groups of ten. Write the number.

1. 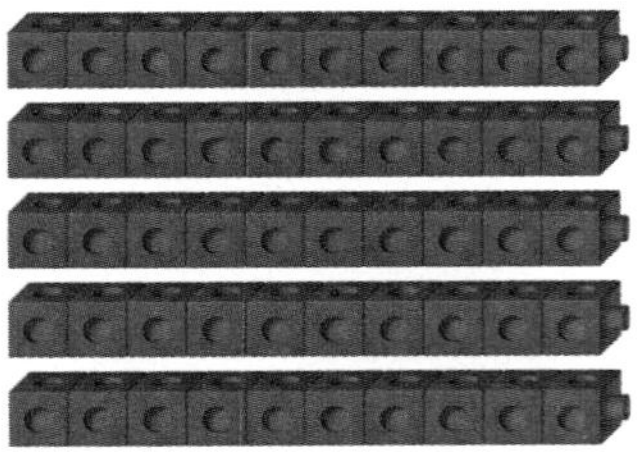

5 tens 50
fifty

2. 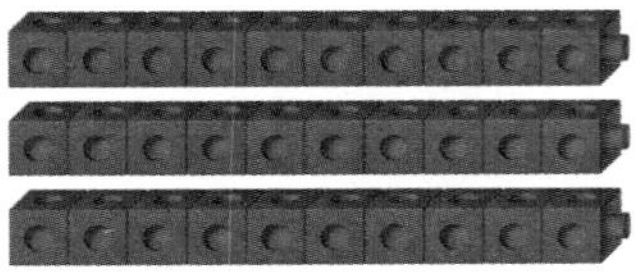

3 tens 30
thirty

Write the number.

3. 56 ones = 5 tens and 6 ones 56

4. 23 ones = 2 tens and 3 ones 23

Write the number in different ways.

5. 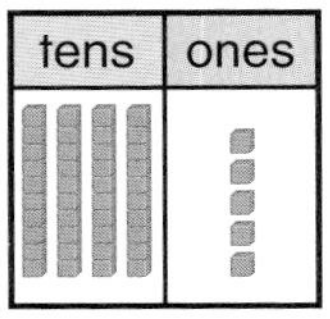

4 tens 5 ones

tens	ones
4	5

45

6. 4 boys each have 4 toy trains.
How many trains do they have in all? 16

Data-Driven Decision Making

Based on the results of the Mid-Chapter Check, use the following resources to review concepts that continue to give students problems.

Exercises	State/Local Standards	What's the Math?	Error Analysis	Resources for Review
1–2 Lesson 13-1		Count, read, and write whole numbers to 100.	Student gets the tens and ones mixed up.	Strategic Intervention Guide (p. 98) CRM Chapter 13 Resource Masters (Reteach Worksheets) Math Online Concepts in Motion Math Adventures
3–4 Lesson 13-2		Group objects in tens and ones.	Student reverses tens and ones.	
5 Lesson 13-4		Group objects in various ways to make numbers less than 100.	Does not write numbers that total forty-five. Reverses ones and tens when writing.	

Spiral Review Chapters 1–13

7. Libby wanted to measure her math book.

First she used  to measure.

Then she used  to measure.

Did she use fewer  or ?

crayons

Write number sentences to show fact families.

8. 7 + 6 = 13

6 + 7 = 13

13 − 7 = 6

13 − 6 = 7

9. 3 + 9 = 12

9 + 3 = 12

12 − 3 = 9

12 − 9 = 3

Look at the two-dimensional figure.
Circle the objects that have a face that shape.

10.
11.
12.

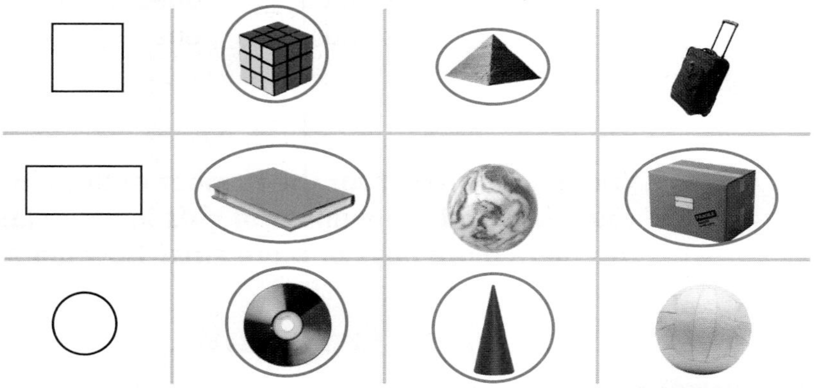

Spiral Review

Reviews Chapters 1 to 13

Objective: Review and assess mastery of skills and concepts from previous chapters.

Resources for Review

Based on student results, refer to these lessons for remediation.

- **Exercise 7: Lesson 9-2** (p. 279)
- **Exercises 8–9: Lesson 6-7** (p. 199)
- **Exercises 10–12: Lesson 12-4** (p. 391)

LESSON 13-6

Estimate Numbers

Lesson Planner

Objective

Learn to estimate numbers.

Review Vocabulary

round

Resources

Materials: coins, rocks, buttons, or other small items

Literature Connection: *Get Up and Go* by Stuart J. Murphy

Alternate Lesson: Use *IMPACT Mathematics:* Unit H to practice estimating numbers.

Teacher Technology

TeacherWorks

Focus on Math Background

In this lesson, students use place value to estimate numbers. When students estimate, they focus on a number's magnitude. For example, when estimating a large amount over 50, children can try to visualize how many sets of ten they can make. In other words, being able to estimate successfully requires that students be able to unitize numbers into sets of tens and ones.

Daily Routine

Use these suggestions before beginning the lesson on p. 439.

5-Minute Check

(Reviews Lesson 13-5)

Use base-ten blocks and WorkMat 7. Say and write the numbers.

1. 82 = ______ tens and ______ ones 8; 2
2. 98 = ______ tens and ______ ones 9; 8
3. 25 = ______ tens and ______ ones 2; 5
4. 63 = ______ tens and ______ ones 6; 3

Problem of the Day

Create a tally chart for the number of boys in your class and the number of girls in your class. Are there more boys or more girls? How many more? See students' work.

LINE UP Ask students to count your steps as you walk across the room. Then have them estimate the number of steps they will take from your classroom to a landmark along the route they are about to take. Have students line up from lowest estimate to highest. Invite them to count the actual steps to the landmark.

Review Math Vocabulary

- **What numbers do you say when you count by tens to 50?** As students count, write 10, 20, 30, 40, and 50 on the board.
- Tell students that one way to estimate an amount is to round it to the nearest ten. Point out that the zero in each ten is round, like a circle. Explain that when you round a number to the nearest ten, you tell which number with a "round" zero at the end is closest to that number.
- Have students find the number 19 on the number line. **Is 19 closer to 10 or 20?** 20
- Explain that a good estimate for 19 is 20, so you say "19 rounds to 20."

Differentiated Instruction

Small Group Options

Option 1 LOGICAL/SPATIAL

Below Level BL

Materials: drawing paper, markers

- On the board, write 10 + 10. Have students draw dots in groups of ten to model the problem. **How many dots are there in all?** 20 dots **How many tens are there?** 2 tens
- Write the problem 10 + 6 on the board. Have students draw dots to represent the numbers. **How many tens are there?** 1 tens **How many ones are there?** 6 ones **How many ones are needed to make another ten?** 4 more
- **Which number is greater, 20 or 16?** 20 **How can you tell?** Twenty has more dots.

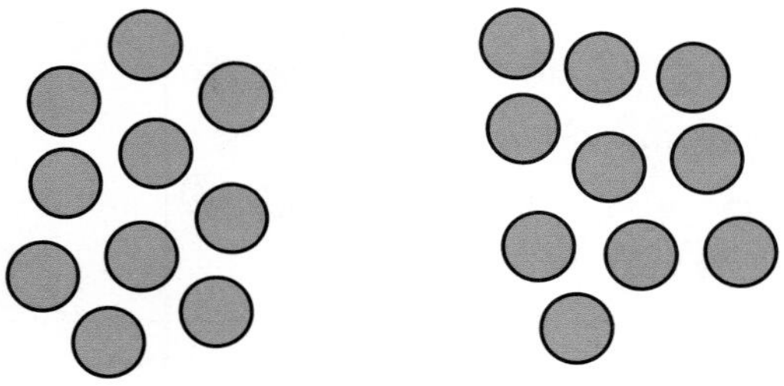

Option 2 VISUAL/SPATIAL, LOGICAL

English Language Learners ELL

Materials: pictures of a bus, bike, car.
Core Vocabulary: best, first graders, family
Common Use Verb: ride

See Math This strategy helps activate background knowledge of estimating numbers

- Show the bike. Ask "About how many people can ***ride*** on this?" 2 people
- Repeat for car and bus pictures.
- Say, "Our class wants to go on a trip. Which would be best, the **bike, car** or the **bus**?"
- Repeat for multiple classes, all the first graders, their family, etc.
- Discuss their answers and have students write number sentences that prove or disprove their estimations.

Independent Work Options

Option 1 KINESTHETIC, LOGICAL

Early Finishers OL AL

Materials: containers filled with various amounts of like items (container of 25 beans)

- Have students take ten items out of their container and look at those left over. Ask students to record their estimate.
- Have students work together to count the items in the container and record the actual number.
- Encourage students to discuss how their estimate compared to the actual number of items.

Option 2

Student Technology

Math Online macmillanmh.com

Option 3

Learning Station: Science (p. 415H)

Direct students to the Science Learning Station for more opportunities to explore and extend the lesson concept.

Option 4

Problem-Solving Practice

Reinforce problem-solving skills and strategies with the Problem-Solving Practice worksheet.

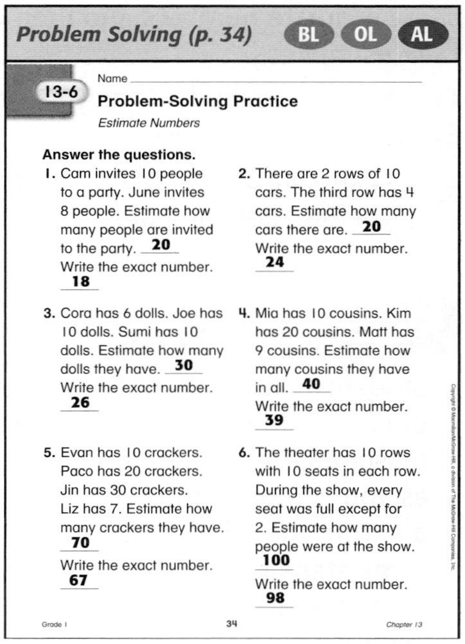

Problem Solving (p. 34) BL OL AL

Name ____

13-6 **Problem-Solving Practice**
Estimate Numbers

Answer the questions.

1. Cam invites 10 people to a party. June invites 8 people. Estimate how many people are invited to the party. 20
   Write the exact number. 18
2. There are 2 rows of 10 cars. The third row has 4 cars. Estimate how many cars there are. 20
   Write the exact number. 24
3. Cora has 6 dolls. Joe has 10 dolls. Sumi has 10 dolls. Estimate how many dolls they have. 30
   Write the exact number. 26
4. Mia has 10 cousins. Kim has 20 cousins. Matt has 9 cousins. Estimate how many cousins they have in all. 40
   Write the exact number. 39
5. Evan has 10 crackers. Paco has 20 crackers. Jin has 30 crackers. Liz has 7. Estimate how many crackers they have. 70
   Write the exact number. 67
6. The theater has 10 rows with 10 seats in each row. During the show, every seat was full except for 2. Estimate how many people were at the show. 100
   Write the exact number. 98

Grade 1 34 Chapter 13

13-6

1 Introduce

Activity Choice 1 • Hands-On

Have students put their feet out in front of them as they sit in a circle on the floor.

- **About how many tennis shoes do you estimate are in the circle?** See students' work. Remind students not to count but to make reasonable estimates.
- Invite a few students to explain how they made their estimates. Then have students count the tennis shoes to check their estimates.

Activity Choice 2 • Literature

Introduce the lesson with *Get Up and Go!* by Stuart J. Murphy. For additional support, see p. TR61.

2 Teach

Give each student a set of coins, rocks, buttons, or other small objects.

- Have students push ten of the objects to one side. Have them look at the rest. **What do you estimate, or guess, is the total number on your desk? Why?** See students' work.
- Have students record their estimate and then count and record the actual number of items.
- **How close was your estimate? Why do you think it was so close/far off?** See students' work.

Get Ready Use the section at the top of p. 439 to reinforce the lesson concept. Guide students as they show estimate numbers and then count to check their estimates.

Check Observe students as you work through Exercises 1–3 as a class.

Exercise 3 Assess student comprehension before assigning practice exercises.

! COMMON ERROR!

Students who make wild guesses may not understand how to use comparisons to make reasonable guesses. Model by thinking aloud as you compare numbers on a number line or a part to the whole. Have students restate the same steps in their own words as they follow your model.

Name ______________________

Estimate Numbers

Get Ready

Main Idea

I will estimate numbers.

Review Vocabulary

estimate

You can estimate to find out *about* how many.

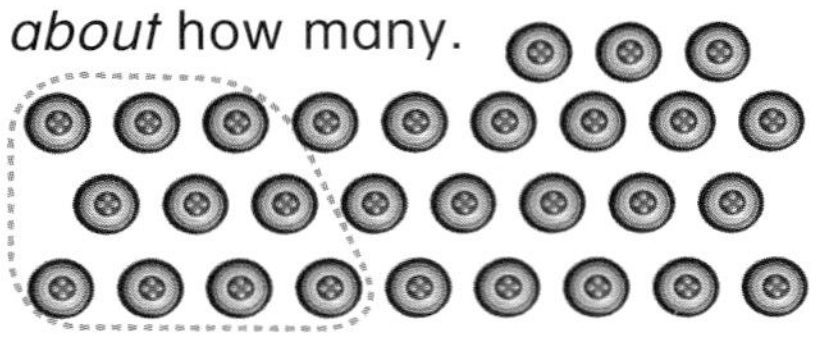

About how many buttons are there?

Estimate: **30** Count: **29**

Check

Circle 10. Estimate about how many. Then count.

1.

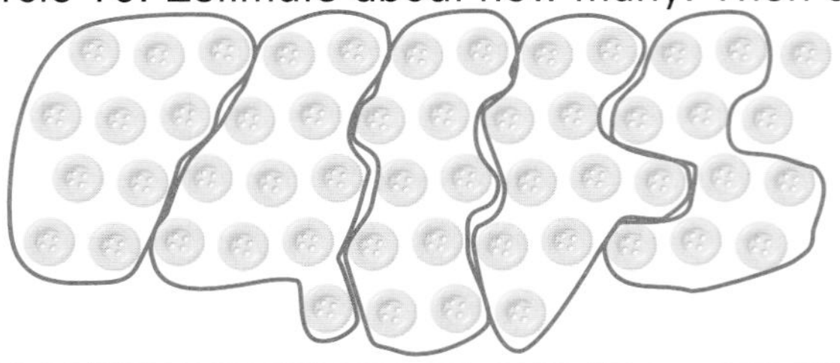

Sample answer:

Estimate: **50**

Count: **52**

2.

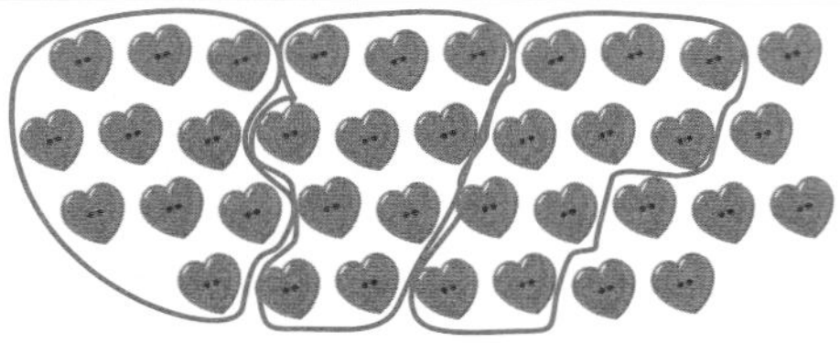

Sample answer:

Estimate: 40

Count: 37

3. Talk About It How does circling 10 help you estimate?

Sample answer: it makes it easier to see how many groups of ten there are.

Reteach (p. 31) BL

13-6 Name ______________________

Reteach

Estimate Numbers

You can count groups of tens to help estimate.

4 tens

Estimate: 40

Count: 41

Count groups of tens. Estimate. Then count.

Estimates will vary.

1. Estimate: **30** Count: **34**

2. Estimate: **70** Count: **79**

3. Estimate: **20** Count: **22**

Chapter Resources

Skills Practice (p. 32) OL

13-6 Name ______________________

Skills Practice

Estimate Numbers

Count groups of ten. Estimate. Then count.

Estimates will vary.

1. Estimate: **40** Count: **42**

2. Estimate: **50** Count: **58**

3. Estimate: **60** Count: **63**

Solve.

4. Chet has 10 baseball cards. Marisa has 10 baseball cards. Max has 8 baseball cards.
Estimate how many baseball cards they have. **30 cards**
Write the exact number. **28 cards**

Differentiated Instruction

Small Group Options

Option 1 Below/Approaching Level BL

KINESTHETIC/LOGICAL

Materials: number cards 0–12; red, yellow, and green connecting cubes

- Have a student draw a number card and build that number with red cubes. Have the student stand the cube train up and compare to other students' trains to make sure they are the same.
- Have another student draw a number and build that number using yellow cubes.
- Have a third student draw a number and build that number with green cubes.
- **Line your trains up together. Which one is the longest? the shortest?**
- Help students use the trains, two at a time, to make "greater than" and "less than" statements.

Option 2 English Language Learners ELL

VISUAL, KINESTHETIC

Materials: picture or puppet of an alligator
Core Vocabulary: even if he has to turn around, open mouth, he's hungry!
Common Use Verb: will pick

Write Math This strategy helps students visualize what the greater than and less than symbols mean.

- Place a large picture on the wall of an alligator with an open mouth.
- Say: "**He's hungry!** He ***will pick*** the most to eat, **even if he has to turn around.** His **open mouth** faces the greatest number."
- Give pairs number cards.
- Have one student write two numbers on the far right and left of the paper. Have the other student use his or her hands (or a puppet) to "eat" the greatest number.
- Repeat as time permits, reminding students that a hungry mouth opens to the greater number.

Independent Work Options

Option 1 Early Finishers OL AL

LINGUISTIC, KINESTHETIC

Materials: base ten blocks

- Ask students to order the following numbers from least to greatest: 82, 27, 97.
- Have students use base ten blocks to justify their thinking. **How many tens does the greatest number have?** 9 tens

Option 2 Student Technology

Math Online macmillanmh.com

Math Adventures

Option 3 Learning Station: Language Arts (p. 415G)

Direct students to the Language Arts Learning Station for more opportunities to explore and extend the lesson concept.

Option 4 Problem-Solving Practice

Reinforce problem-solving skills and strategies with the Problem-Solving Practice worksheet.

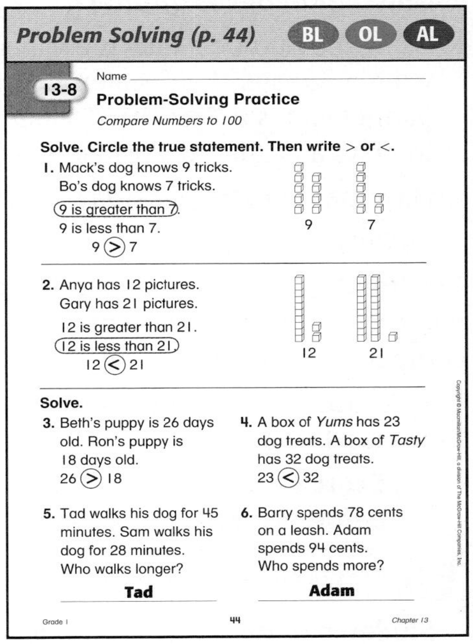

Problem Solving (p. 44) BL OL AL

Name ______

13-8 **Problem-Solving Practice**
Compare Numbers to 100

Solve. Circle the true statement. Then write > or <.

1. Mack's dog knows 9 tricks.
   Bo's dog knows 7 tricks.
   (9 is greater than 7.)
   9 is less than 7.
   9 (>) 7

2. Anya has 12 pictures.
   Gary has 21 pictures.
   12 is greater than 21.
   (12 is less than 21.)
   12 (<) 21

Solve.

3. Beth's puppy is 26 days old. Ron's puppy is 18 days old.
   26 (>) 18

4. A box of *Yums* has 23 dog treats. A box of *Tasty* has 32 dog treats.
   23 (<) 32

5. Tad walks his dog for 45 minutes. Sam walks his dog for 28 minutes. Who walks longer?
   Tad

6. Barry spends 78 cents on a leash. Adam spends 94 cents. Who spends more?
   Adam

Grade 1 44 Chapter 13

1 Introduce

Activity Choice 1 • Hands-On

Give each student a hundred chart and two translucent counters.

- **How do we read numbers in order on the hundred chart?** Start with 1. Read from left to right. When you finish a row, begin again with the next row.
- Have students place one counter on the number 12. Then place the other counter on the number 18 and compare them. **Which is less, 12 or 18?** 12 **How do you know?** It appears first on the chart as you count.
- Repeat with other number pairs.
- **How can you decide which number is less?** See which number you read first when counting on the hundred chart.

Activity Choice 2 • Literature

Introduce the lesson with *Out for the Count: A Counting Adventure* by Kathryn Cave. For additional support, see p. TR61.

2 Teach

Provide number cards for 20–50. Have partners each draw a card and **compare** their numbers.

- **Which number is greater?** See students' work.
- Using the numbers they drew, have one partner write a "greater than" statement while the other partner writes a "less than" statement. Ask students to draw a picture to illustrate their sentence.
- Have partners trade cards with another pair and repeat.

Get Ready Use the section at the top of p. 443 to reinforce the lesson concept. Guide students as they compare pairs of numbers.

Check Observe students as you work through Exercises 1–9 as a class.

Exercise 9 Assess student comprehension before assigning practice exercises.

COMMON ERROR!

Students often reverse the greater than and less than symbols. Remind students to think of each symbol as an alligator with an open mouth that is positioned to "eat" the bigger number.

Name ______________________

Hands-On Activity

Compare Numbers to 100

Get Ready

Main Idea

I will compare two numbers.

2 tens are more than 1 ten.

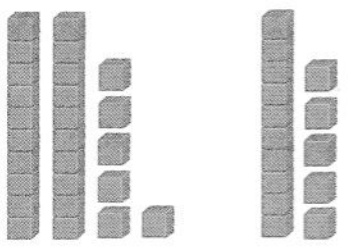

26 > 15
is greater than

5 ones are more than 4 ones.

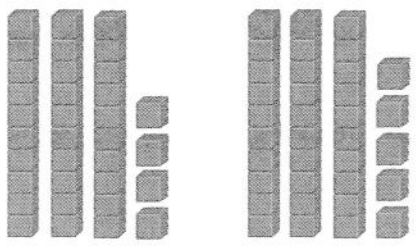

34 < 35
is less than

The tens are the same. The ones are the same.

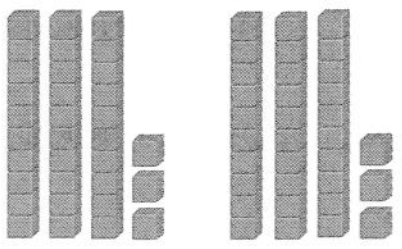

33 = 33
is equal to

Check

Use [ten rod] and [unit cube]. Circle **is greater than**, **is less than**, or **is equal to**.

1. 17 (<) 31
   17 is greater than 31
   (17 is less than 31)
   17 is equal to 31

2. 36 (=) 36
   36 is greater than 36
   36 is less than 36
   (36 is equal to 36)

Use [ten rod] and [unit cube].
Write >, <, or =.

3. 27 (>) 15
4. 99 (=) 99
5. 47 (<) 74
6. 60 (>) 59
7. 63 (>) 36
8. 51 (>) 48

9. Talk About It How do you know 48 is greater than 38?
   Sample answer: There are 4 tens in 48 but only 3 tens in 38.

Reteach (p. 41) BL

13-8 Name ______________

Reteach

Compare Numbers to 100

Compare 25 and 22.
The tens are the same.

	Tens	Ones
25	(2)	5
22	(2)	2

> means *is greater than*
< means *is less than*
= means *is equal to*

Compare the ones.
5 is greater than 2.
So, 25 *is greater than* 22.
25 > 22

You can also use a number line to compare numbers.

20 21 22 23 24 25 26 27 28 29 30

22 is less than 25.
22 < 25

Compare the numbers. Circle *is greater than* or *is less than*. Then write > or <.

1. 40 41 42 43 44 45 46 47 48 49 50
   49 (is greater than) / is less than 47
   49 (>) 47

2. 50 51 52 53 54 55 56 57 58 59 60
   53 is greater than / (is less than) 55
   53 (<) 55

Chapter Resources

Grade 1 41 Chapter 13

Skills Practice (p. 42) OL

13-8 Name ______________

Skills Practice

Compare Numbers to 100

Write >, <, or =.

1. 72 (=) 72
2. 63 (<) 76
3. 39 (<) 40
4. 43 (>) 34
5. 86 (<) 88
6. 17 (<) 18
7. 54 (>) 45
8. 82 (=) 82
9. 100 (>) 98
10. 74 (<) 94

Circle your answer.

11. Which is true about 6 tens and 5 ones?
    The amount is greater than 68.
    The amount is equal to 56.
    (The amount is less than 66.)

12. Which is true about 3 tens and 7 ones?
    (The amount is greater than 35.)
    The amount is equal to 39.
    The amount is less than 28.

Grade 1 42 Chapter 13

Practice

Use [tens] and [ones]. Circle **is greater than, is less than,** or **is equal to.**

10. 64 (>) 23
(64 is greater than 23)
64 is less than 23
64 is equal to 23

11. 19 (=) 19
19 is greater than 19
19 is less than 19
(19 is equal to 19)

Use [tens] and [ones].
Write >, <, or =.

12. 41 (<) 91 **13.** 53 (=) 53 **14.** 87 (>) 78

15. 37 (<) 50 **16.** 56 (<) 63 **17.** 99 (>) 90

18. 82 (<) 86 **19.** 45 (>) 33 **20.** 92 (>) 29

21. 49 (=) 49 **22.** 70 (>) 69 **23.** 68 (<) 71

24. 84 (>) 48 **25.** 63 (>) 28 **26.** 10 (<) 90

Problem Solving

27. Critical Thinking I have fewer than 25 acorns. I have more than 21 acorns. Draw how many acorns I could have.

drawing of 22, 23, or 24 acorns

Math at Home Activity: Write a number. Have your child name two numbers that are less than the number and two numbers that are greater. Ask your child what number is equal to the number.

Enrich (p. 45) AL

13-8 Name ____
Enrich
Compare Football Scores

The team with the greater score wins. Circle the greater score for each game. Then circle the winning team name.

Bears	Rabbits	Winners
(28)	17	(Bears) Rabbits
(35)	24	(Bears) Rabbits
21	(27)	Bears (Rabbits)
(42)	36	(Bears) Rabbits
31	(35)	Bears (Rabbits)
(51)	15	(Bears) Rabbits
24	(28)	Bears (Rabbits)

1. How many games did the Bears win? **4 games**
2. How many games did the Rabbits win? **3 games**
3. Which team won more games? **Bears**

Grade 1 45 Chapter 13

Homework Practice (p. 43) OL

13-8 Name ____
Homework Practice
Compare Numbers to 100

Circle *is greater than, is less than,* or *is equal to.* Write >, <, or =.

1. 14 (<) 29
14 is greater than 29.
(14 is less than 29.)
14 is equal to 29.

2. 22 (<) 25
22 is greater than 25.
(22 is less than 25.)
22 is equal to 25.

3. 15 (=) 15
15 is greater than 15.
15 is less than 15.
(15 is equal to 15.)

4. 72 (>) 44
(72 is greater than 44.)
72 is less than 44.
72 is equal to 44.

Write >, <, or =.

5. 36 (<) 38 6. 77 (>) 25
7. 54 (>) 45 8. 36 (<) 63

Solve.

9. Scott has some pencils. The number he has is greater than 11 and less than 14. How many might he have? **12 or 13**

10. Todd and Monica have some blocks. They count 2 tens and 3 ones. Todd says this is greater than 19. Monica says this is less than 22. Who is right? **Todd**

Grade 1 43 Chapter 13

BL Alternate Teaching Strategy

If students have trouble understanding how to tell which of two numbers is greater . . .

Then use one of the following reteach options.

1 CRM **Daily Reteach Worksheet** (p. 41)

2 **Build and Compare** Choose two numbers between 10 and 100 and write them on the chalkboard. Have pairs of students use connecting cubes to model each number. Remind students to start by building ten-trains. Have partners use their models to decide which number is greater and to explain how they know their decision is correct.

3 Practice

Differentiate practice using these leveled assignments for Exercises 10–27.

Level	Assignment
BL **Below/ Approaching Level**	Guide students through the exercises, using base-ten blocks or connecting cubes.
OL **On Level**	Complete exercises independently, using manipulatives as needed.
AL **Above/Beyond Level**	Complete exercises independently and then write a similar problem, using 3-digit numbers.

4 Assess

Formative Assessment

Have students use base-ten blocks to model which is greater: 35 or 19.

WRITING IN MATH Have students write a greater than/less than problem. Ask them to answer and illustrate their problem.

Quick Check

Are students continuing to struggle with comparing numbers?

If Yes → Small Group Options (p. 443B)
Strategic Intervention Guide (p. 106)

If No → Independent Work Options (p. 443B)
CRM Skills Practice Worksheet (p. 42)
CRM Enrich Worksheet (p. 45)

LESSON 13-9

Order Numbers to 100

Lesson Planner

Objective

Order whole numbers using concrete objects and pictorial models.

Review Vocabulary

before, after, between

Resources

Materials: number cards 1–20, WorkMats 4–5: Number Lines

Manipulatives: two-colored counters

Literature Connection: *Elevator Magic* by Stuart J. Murphy

Alternate Lessons: Adapt "Number Sequence" on page 248 of *Math Their Way* for practice in ordering numbers to 100.
Use *IMPACT Mathematics:* Unit H to provide practice with ordering numbers to 100.

Teacher Technology
TeacherWorks

Focus on Math Background

In this lesson, students will apply their understanding of place value to order numbers to 100. For example, when ordering 63, 57 and 64, students must look at the digits in the tens place to determine that 57 comes before 63 and 64. For 63 and 64, however, students must refer to the digits in the ones place to figure out that 64 comes after 63.

Daily Routine

Use these suggestions before beginning the lesson on p. 445.

5-Minute Check

(Reviews Lesson 13-8)

Write *less than, equal to,* and *greater than* to compare the numbers.

1. 17 _____ 21 less than
2. 26 _____ 29 less than
3. 53 _____ 53 equal to
4. 43 _____ 34 greater than

Problem of the Day

Which choice completes the pattern?

45, 48, 51, _____, 57, 60

4 tens 5 ones
5 tens 4 ones (circled)
5 tens 1 one

LINE UP Give each student a number card. One by one, describe numbers from the cards by telling how many tens and ones they have. When students hear the description of the number they are holding, have them show their card and line up.

Review Math Vocabulary

Introduce the vocabulary terms **before, after,** and **between.**

- Have ten students line up by the classroom door. Use students' names and positions in line to help them understand the vocabulary terms.
- **Who comes just before (student's name)? Who comes just after (student's name)? Who is between (student's name) and (student's name)?**

When water gets cold, it turns to ice. Ice is water as a solid.

This water is about 0 degrees.

C

Steam is water as a gas. This water is about 100 degrees.

	Ice	Waterfall	Gas
Temperature (degrees)	0	60	100

Compare the temperatures. Use > and <.

0 degrees __<__ 60 degrees

100 degrees __>__ 0 degrees

D

FOLD DOWN

Create the Book

Guide students to create their book.

- Have them fold the page in half.
- Ask them to write their name on page A.
- Explain that page A is the front cover and page D is the back cover. If necessary, have them practice flipping through the book in order.
- Guide them in reading the information and word problems on each of the pages.

Use the Student Pages

Have students work individually or in pairs to solve the word problems on page D.

Page D Review with students the concepts of greater than and less than. Make sure they understand how to read the table.

WRITING IN ▶MATH **Would you rather drink water that has been in the refrigerator or sitting out in the classroom? Why?**

Extend the Activity

Have students brainstorm and compare items they have seen that are frozen, liquid, and gas.

FOLDABLES® Dinah Zike's Foldables

If students have not completed their Foldables, guide them to create and fill in the appropriate information using the instructions on pp. 415 and 437.

You may choose to use the Foldable to help students review the concepts presented in this chapter and as a tool for studying for the Chapter Test.

Vocabulary Review

Review the chapter vocabulary using one of the following options:

- **Visual Vocabulary Cards** (24 and 32)
- **eGlossary** at macmillanmh.com

Vocabulary Test

CRM **Chapter 13 Resource Masters** (p. 55)
Assess students comprehension of the chapter vocabulary with the Vocabulary Test.

Math Online **Chapter Test**
Alternative summative assessment options are available online at macmillanmh.com.

Name ______________________

Vocabulary

Draw lines to match.

1. **regroup** — a. a group of 10 ones
2. **tens** — b. to group numbers into tens and ones

Concepts

Count groups of ten. Write the number.

3.
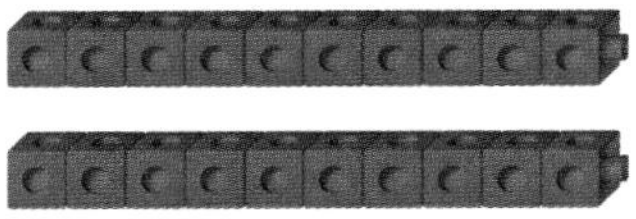

2 tens 0 ones 20 Say: twenty

Write the number.

4. 75 ones = 7 tens and 5 ones 75

5. 92 ones = 9 tens and 2 ones 92

Write the number in different ways.

6.

tens	ones
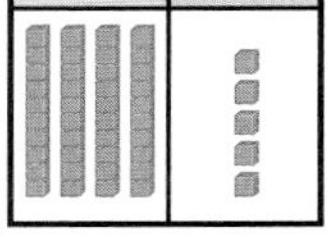	

4 tens 5 ones

tens	ones
4	5

45

Chapter 13 Project

Guess and Check

Have students discuss the results of their completed chapter project as a class. Assess their work using the Chapter Project rubric found in Chapter 13 Resource Masters on p. 60.

Circle groups of ten. Write the number. Sample answers.

7.

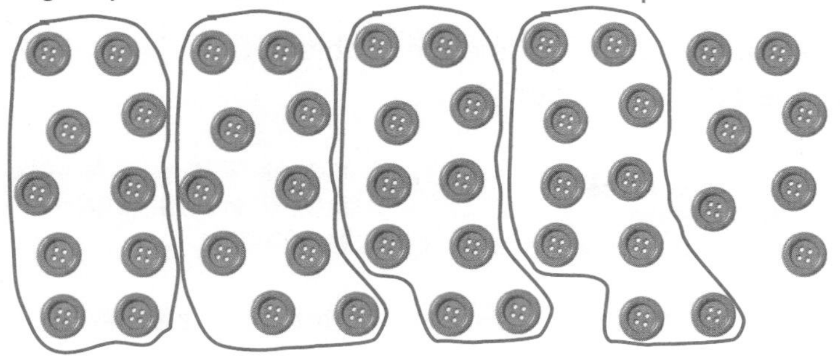

4 tens 7 ones 47

Write the sign. Use > or <.

8. 41 (<) 91 9. 37 (<) 50 10. 86 (>) 82

Write the number that is just **after**.

35 36 37 38 39 40 41 42 43 44 45 46 47 48 49 50

11. 37, 38 12. 39, 40 13. 41, 42

14. 35, 36 15. 49, 50 16. 45, 46

Problem Solving

17. Sue had 25 beads. She ties 5 beads on every piece of string. How many pieces of string does she need? 5 pieces

Summative Assessment

Use these alternate leveled chapter tests to differentiate assessment for the specific needs of your students.

Leveled Chapter 13 Tests

Form	Type	Level	CRM Pages
1	Multiple Choice	BL	62–63
2A	Multiple Choice	OL	64–65
2B	Multiple Choice	OL	66–67
2C	Free Response	AL	68–69
2D	Free Response	AL	70–71

BL = below/approaching grade level
OL = on grade level
AL = above/beyond grade level

ExamView Assessment Suite Customize and create multiple versions of your Chapter Test and their test answer keys.

Data-Driven Decision Making

Based on the results of the Chapter Review/Test, use the following to review concepts that continue to present students with problems.

Exercises	State/Local Standards	What's the Math?	Error Analysis	Resources for Review
1–2		Use vocabulary for creating sets of tens.	Confuses definitions.	Strategic Intervention Guide (p. 98) CRM Chapter 13 Resource Masters (Reteach Worksheets) Math Online Concepts in Motion Math Adventures
3–7		Create sets of tens and ones to describe whole numbers.	Confuses ones and tens.	
8–16		Compare and order whole numbers.	Confuses the greater than and less than symbols. Writes the number just before, instead of after.	
17		Understands the problem, makes a plan, and solves the problem.	Incorrectly answers problem. Confuses parts of problem.	

Test Practice

Formative Assessment

- Use Student Edition pp. 451–452 as practice and cumulative review. The questions are written in the same style as many state tests.
- You can use these two pages to benchmark student progress, or as an alternative homework assignment.

Additional practice pages can be found in the Chapter 13 Resource Masters.

CRM Chapter 13 Resource Masters
Cumulative Test Practice

- Multiple Choice format (pp. 62–67, 72)
- Free Response format (pp. 68–71, 73)

ExamView Assessment Suite Create practice worksheets or tests that align to your state standards.

Math Online
For additional practice, visit macmillanmh.com.

Name ____________________________________

Listen as your teacher reads each problem. Choose the correct answer.

1.

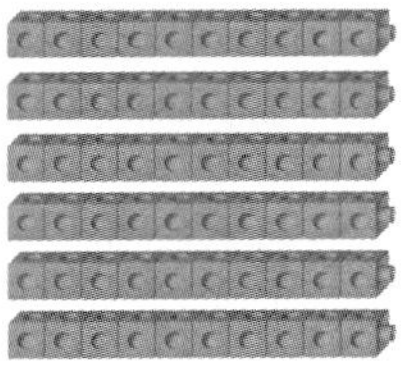

16 ○ 20 ○ 60 ● 100 ○

2. 56

5 tens 6 ones ● 4 tens 8 ones ○

6 tens 5 ones ○ 5 tens 3 ones ○

3.

tens	ones
7	2

27 ○ 62 ○ 67 ○ 72 ●

4.

1 ten 3 ones ○ 2 tens 2 ones ○

2 tens 3 ones ● 3 tens 2 ones ○

5.

10 ○ 20 ○ 30 ● 40 ○

6.

○ ○ ○ ●

Test-Taking Tips

For the Teacher

- It may be helpful to review the vocabulary words and provide examples.
- Repeat instruction often as some students need to hear information multiple times.

For the Student

- Tell students that different types of test questions will take different amounts of time to complete.
- Encourage students to make a good guess for an answer if time is running out and they are stuck on a question.

7.

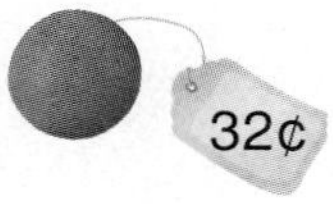

◯ ⬬

◯ ◯

10. 10 − 3 ◯ 7

− ◯ + ◯

> ◯ = ⬬

8.

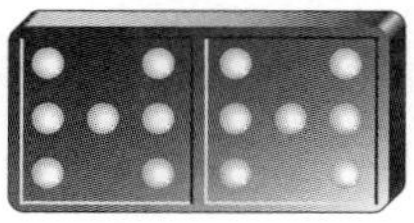

4 + 3 = 7 ◯ 6 + 6 = 12 ◯

7 + 7 = 14 ⬬ 8 + 8 = 16 ◯

11. The puppet show starts at 3:30. If it is an hour long, what time is it over?

4:30

9. 5, 10, 15, 20, 25, 30

35 ⬬ 55 ◯

50 ◯ 40 ◯

12. The hour hand points to 7. The minute hand points to 12. What time is it?

7:00

STOP

Test Directions for Teachers

Read the following directions to students before they begin. Then read each question followed by a pause to allow students time to work and choose an answer. The first test item can be worked as a class example.

- **Write your name at the top of the page.**
- **I am going to read each question to you. Listen carefully to the entire question before you choose an answer.**

Multiple Choice

1. Look at the cubes. Count by tens. Mark the number that shows the number of cubes.
2. Look at the number 56. What is another way to show 56?
3. Look at the tens and ones chart. Mark the number that shows the number of tens and ones.
4. Listen to the story. Carmen drew a picture of flowers. Look at the flowers shown. Which shows the number of tens and ones in Carmen's picture?
5. Look at the hearts. Estimate the number of hearts. About how many hearts are there?
6. Look at the picture. Find the object that is next to the dog.

- **Turn the page over.**

7. Listen to the story. Joe has 3 dimes and 1 nickel. Which toy can Joe buy?
8. Look at the domino. Which addition sentence matches the domino?
9. Listen to the story. Mrs. Smith wrote the numbers 5, 10, 15, 20, 25, 30 on the board counting in a pattern of 5. What number will be next?
10. What is missing?

Short Response

11. The puppet show starts at 3:30. If it is an hour long, what time is it over?
12. The hour hand points to 7. The minute hand points to 12. What time is it?

CHAPTER 14

Chapter Overview

Chapter-at-a-Glance

Identify and describe simple fractions and parts of a set.

Lesson	Math Objective	State/Local Standards
14-1 Equal Parts (pp. 457–458)	Identify equal parts.	
14-2 Problem-Solving Strategy: Draw a Picture (pp. 459–460)	Use the *draw a picture* strategy to solve problems.	
14-3 One Half (pp. 461–462)	Separate a whole into two equal parts.	
14-4 One Third and One Fourth (pp. 463–464)	Identify one third and one fourth of whole.	
14-5 Non-Unit Fractions (pp. 469–470)	Describe whole objects or sets using non-unit fractions.	
14-6 Fractions of a Set (pp. 471–472)	Use appropriate language to describe parts of a set.	
14-7 Problem-Solving Investigation: Choose a Strategy (pp. 473–474)	Choose the best strategy to solve a problem.	

Describe Fractional Parts

BIG Idea Students learned to identify geometric figures in Chapter 12. They can now build on that work by learning to divide shapes into equal parts, such as halves, thirds, and fourths. Students will learn to describe parts using appropriate language.

Focal Points and Connections

G1-FP3 *Geometry:* **Composing and decomposing geometric shapes**

Children compose and decompose plane and solid figures (e.g., by putting two congruent isosceles triangles together to make a rhombus), thus building an understanding of part-whole relationships as well as the properties of the original and composite shapes. As they combine figures, they recognize them from different perspectives and orientations, describe their geometric attributes and properties, and determine how they are alike and different, in the process developing a background for measurement and initial understandings of such properties as congruence and symmetry.

Skills Trace
Vertical Alignment

Kindergarten

In kindergarten, students learned to:

- Share a whole by a separating it into two equal parts.
- Explain why a given part is half of the whole.

First Grade

During this chapter, students will learn to:

- Separate a whole into two, three, or four equal parts and use appropriate language to describe the parts such as three out of four equal parts.
- Use appropriate language to describe part of a set such as three out of the eight crayons are red.

Second Grade

In second grade, students will learn to:

- Use concrete models to represent and name fractional parts of a whole object (with denominators of 12 or less).
- Use concrete models to represent and name fractional parts of a set of objects (with denominators of 12 or less).
- Use concrete models to determine if a fractional part of a whole is closer to 0, $\frac{1}{2}$, or 1.

Backmapping and Vertical Alignment

McGraw-Hill's *Math Connects* program was conceived and developed with the final results in mind: student success in Algebra 1 and beyond. The authors, using the **NCTM Focal Points and Focal Connections** as their guide, developed this brand-new series by backmapping from Algebra 1 concepts, and vertically aligning the topics so that they build upon prior skills and concepts and serve as a foundation for future topics.

Math Vocabulary

The following math vocabulary words for Chapter 14 are listed in the glossary of the ***Student Edition.*** You can find interactive definitions in 13 languages in the **eGlossary** at macmillanmh.com.

equal parts each part is the same size (p. 457)

fraction a number that represents part of a whole or part of a set (p. 461)

one half a fraction that shows one part out of two equal parts (p. 461)

one third a fraction that shows one part out of three equal parts (p. 463)

one fourth a fraction that shows one part out of four equal parts (p. 463)

Visual Vocabulary Cards

Use Visual Vocabulary Cards to reinforce math vocabulary. (The Define/Example/Ask routine is printed on the back of each card.)

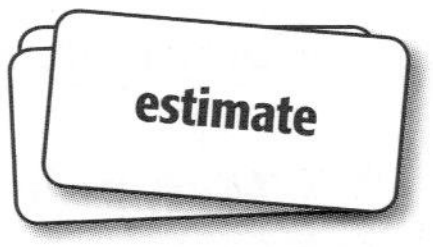

Chapter 14 Chapter Planner

Suggested Pacing		
Instruction	Review and Assessment	TOTAL
7 days	2 days	**9 days**

Diagnostic Assessment
Are You Ready? (p. 454)

	Lesson 14-1 (Pacing: 1 day)	Lesson 14-2 (Pacing: 1 day)	Lesson 14-3 (Pacing: 1 day)
Lesson/ Objective	**Equal Parts** (pp. 457–458) **Objective:** Identify equal parts.	**Problem-Solving Strategy** **Draw a Picture** (pp. 459–460) **Objective:** Use the *draw a picture strategy* to solve problems.	**One Half** (pp. 461–462) **Objective:** Separate a whole into two equal parts.
State/Local Standards			
Math Vocabulary	**equal parts**		**fraction**, **one half**
Lesson Resources	**Materials** brown paper **Manipulatives** fraction circles, pattern blocks **Other Resources** CRM Leveled Worksheets (pp. 6–10) Daily Reteach • 5-Minute Check Problem of the Day	**Materials** pencils, crayons, drawing paper **Manipulatives** connecting cubes **Other Resources** CRM Leveled Worksheets (pp. 11–15) Daily Reteach • 5-Minute Check Problem of the Day *A Lemonade Stand*	**Materials** index cards, yarn **Manipulatives** pattern blocks **Other Resources** CRM Leveled Worksheets (pp. 16–20) Daily Reteach • 5-Minute Check Problem of the Day
Technology Math Online			Math Adventures
Reaching All Learners	Gifted and Talented, p. 457B AL English Learners, p. 457B ELL Early Finishers, p. 457B OL AL	Gifted and Talented, p. 459B AL English Learners, p. 459B ELL Early Finishers, p. 459B OL AL	Gifted and Talented, p. 461B AL English Learners, p. 461B ELL Early Finishers, p. 461B OL AL
Alternate Lesson	*Math Their Way*, pp. 349–350		

KEY

BL Below/Approaching Level — OL On Level — AL Above/Beyond Level — ELL English Learners

SE Student Edition — TE Teacher Edition — CRM Chapter 14 Resource Masters — CD-Rom

Transparency — Flip Chart — Real-World Problem Solving Library

	Lesson 14-4 (Pacing: 1 day)	Lesson 14-5 (Pacing: 1 day)	Lesson 14-6 (Pacing: 1 day)
Lesson/ Objective	**One Third and One Fourth** (pp. 463–464) **Objective:** Identify one third and one fourth of a whole.	**Non-Unit Fractions** (pp. 469–470) **Objective:** Describe whole objects or sets using non-unit fractions.	**Fractions of a Set** (pp. 471–472) **Objective:** Use appropriate language to describe parts of a set.
State/Local Standards			
Math Vocabulary	**one third, one fourth**		
Lesson Resources	**Materials** transparencies showing models for thirds and fourths, fraction flash cards **Manipulatives** pattern blocks **Other Resources** CRM Leveled Worksheets (pp. 21–25) Daily Reteach • 5-Minute Check Problem of the Day	**Materials** pencils, paper **Other Resources** CRM Leveled Worksheets (pp. 26–30) Daily Reteach • 5-Minute Check Problem of the Day	**Materials** overhead markers in several colors **Manipulatives** red and yellow connecting cubes **Other Resources** CRM Leveled Worksheets (pp. 31–35) Daily Reteach • 5-Minute Check Problem of the Day
Technology (Math Online)	Math Adventures Concepts in Motion	Concepts in Motion	
Reaching All Learners	Below Level, p. 463B AL English Learners, p. 463B ELL Early Finishers, p. 463B OL AL	Below Level, p. 469B BL English Learners, p. 469B ELL Early Finishers, p. 469B OL AL	Below Level, p. 471B BL English Learners, p. 471B ELL Early Finishers, p. 471B OL AL
Alternate Lesson			

Extra Practice (p. 465)
Game Time: Fractions (p. 466)

Formative Assessment
- Mid-Chapter Check (p. 467)
- Spiral Review (p. 468)

CHAPTER 14

Chapter Planner

	Lesson 14-7 — Pacing: 1 day
Lesson/ Objective	Problem-Solving Investigation **Choose a Strategy** (pp. 473–474) **Objective:** Choose the best strategy to solve a problem.
State/Local Standards	
Math Vocabulary	
Lesson Resources	**Other Resources** CRM Leveled Worksheets (pp. 36–40) Daily Reteach • 5-Minute Check Problem of the Day *A Lemonade Stand*
Technology	
	Below Level, p. 473B BL English Learners, p. 473B ELL Early Finishers, p. 473B OL AL

Problem Solving in Science (p. 475)

Summative Assessment
- Chapter Review/Test (p. 477)
- Test Practice (p. 479)

Assessment Options

Diagnostic Assessment

- SE *Option 1:* Are You Ready? (p. 454)
- *Option 2:* Online Quiz (macmillanmh.com)
- CRM *Option 3:* Diagnostic Test (p. 42)
- CRM *Option 4:* Chapter Pretest (p. 43)

Formative Assessment

- TE Alternate Teaching Strategies (every lesson)
- SE Talk About It (every lesson)
- SE Writing in Math (every lesson)
- SE Check (every lesson)
- TE Line Up (every lesson)
- SE Mid-Chapter Check (p. 467)
- CRM Mid-Chapter Test (p. 44)

Summative Assessment

- SE Chapter/Review Test (p. 477)
- SE Test Practice (p. 479)
- CRM Vocabulary Test (p. 45)
- CRM Leveled Chapter Tests (pp. 52–61)
- CRM Cumulative Test Practice (p. 62–63)
- CRM Listening Assessment (p. 48–49)
- CRM Oral Assessment (p. 46–47)
- ExamView® Assessment Suite
- Advance Tracker

Professional Development

Targeted professional development has been articulated throughout **McGraw-Hill's *Math Connects*** program. The **McGraw-Hill Professional Development Video Library** provides short videos that support the **NCTM Focal Points and Focal Connections**. For more information, visit macmillanmh.com.

Model Lessons

Instructional Strategies

Teacher Notes

CHAPTER 14

Learning Stations

Cross-Curricular Links

Reading

individual | LINGUISTIC

Read and Share

- Read one of the books at this learning station.
- Choose several shapes from the book and draw them.
- Then divide the shape into two, three, or four equal parts.
- Share the book and your illustration, with a classmate or your teacher.

Teacher Note: Leave several of the books recommended for this chapter at the Learning Station.

Materials:

- construction paper
- markers or crayons
- *The Greedy Triangle* by Marilyn Burns
- *Circus Shapes* by Stuart J. Murphy
- *Pattern Block City* by Planet Dexter

Art

individual | VISUAL/SPATIAL

Painting Fractions

- Fold your paper in half like a hot dog. Open the folded paper.
- Now fold your paper in half like a hamburger. Open the folded paper.
- Your paper should have 4 equal parts.
- Paint $\frac{1}{4}$ of your paper.

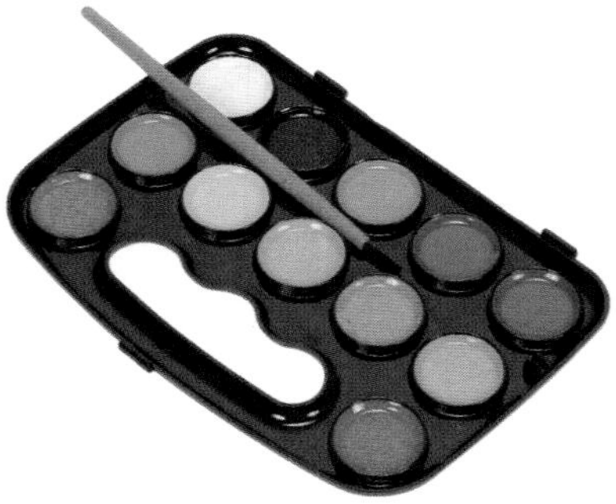

Materials:

- tempera paint
- construction paper
- paper plates to hold paint
- paintbrushes

Language Arts

individual | LINGUISTIC

Fraction Book

- Create a four-page book out of construction paper.
- Title your book "Fractions" and write your name.
- On the first page, draw your favorite shape.
- On the second page, draw one half of the shape.
- On the third page, draw one third of the shape.
- On the fourth page, draw one fourth of the shape.

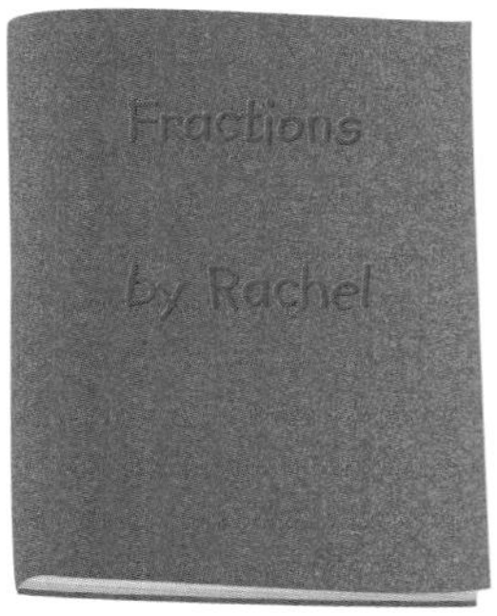

Materials:

- construction paper
- markers or crayons

Science

individual/ pair | AUDITORY

Animal Number Stories

- Draw a picture with objects from nature.
- Your picture should show fractions of a set.
- Describe your fraction to a friend.
- For example, "1 out of 3 shells is yellow."

Teacher Note: Help guide students to draw pictures that can be used to model fractions of a set.

Materials:
- magazines
- construction paper
- scissors
- glue

Health

small groups | KINESTHETIC

A Healthy Meal

- Draw a healthy meal.
- Draw a fruit cut in half.
- Draw a sandwich cut in three equal parts.
- Draw a granola bar cut in four equal parts.

Materials:
- paper plate
- crayons and pencils

Calendar Time

- Highlight the current week on the calendar and the week following it.
- Ask a student to circle today's date.
- Ask students if today's date is in the first or second half of the two weeks.
- Choose other dates and repeat.

Introduce the Chapter

Real World: Equal Parts

Share with the students that in this chapter they are going to learn about equal parts and fractions.

- Have the students draw a circle. **How can you divide your circle into two equal parts?** Sample answer: Draw a line down the middle.
- Ask students to separate their circle into four equal parts. **How did you make four equal parts?** Sample answer: I drew one line down the middle and a second line across the middle.
- Have students shade one out of four parts. Explain that they have shaded $\frac{1}{4}$ of the circle. Write $\frac{1}{4}$ on the board.

Have students turn to p. 453.

- **How many equal parts will there be if Hillary also cuts the pizza across the middle?** 4 equal parts

Key Vocabulary

Introduce the key vocabulary in the chapter using the routine below.

Define: A **fraction** is a number that represents part of a whole or part of a set.

Example: One half is a fraction that shows one part out of two equal parts.

Ask: If I eat one half of an apple, what fraction describes what is left of the apple?

CHAPTER 14

Describe Fractional Parts

Key Vocabulary
equal parts
fraction
one half
one third
one fourth

Explore

Hillary cut the pizza into equal parts. How many equal parts are there? 2

FOLDABLES® Study Organizer — Dinah Zike's Foldables

Guide students to create four Pocket Foldables for describing fractional parts.

1. Fold an 8 1/2 x 11 sheet of paper in half like a hamburger.

2. Open the folded paper and fold one of the long sides up two inches to form a pocket. Refold along the hamburger fold so that the newly formed pockets are on the inside.

3. Glue the outer edges of the two-inch fold with a small amount of glue.

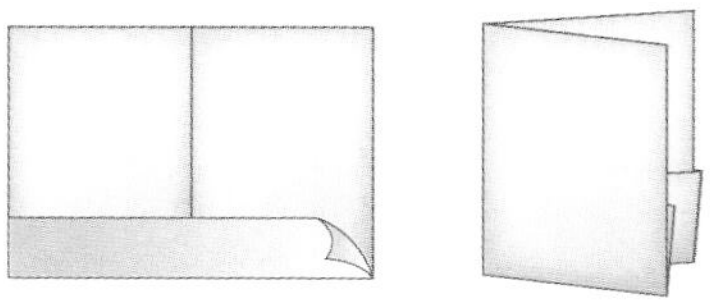

4. Make three sets of Pocket Foldables (enough for each lesson). Glue pockets together to form a Pocket Book.

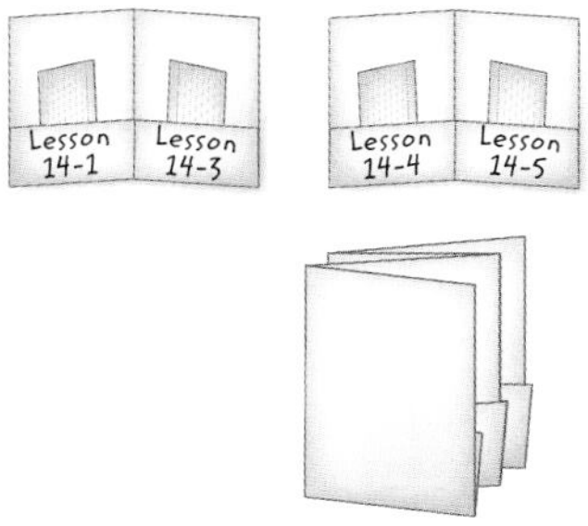

When to Use It *Lessons 14-1, 14-3, 14-4, 14-5, and 14-6. (Additional instructions for using the Foldable with these lessons are found on pp. 467 and 477.)*

Name ______________________

Math Online
Take the Chapter Readiness Quiz at macmillanmh.com.

Are You Ready for Chapter 14?

1. Circle the shape that is divided into 2 equal parts.

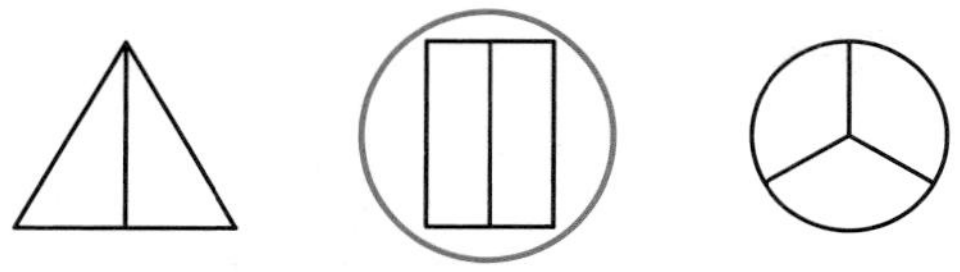

2. Circle the shape that is divided into 4 equal parts.

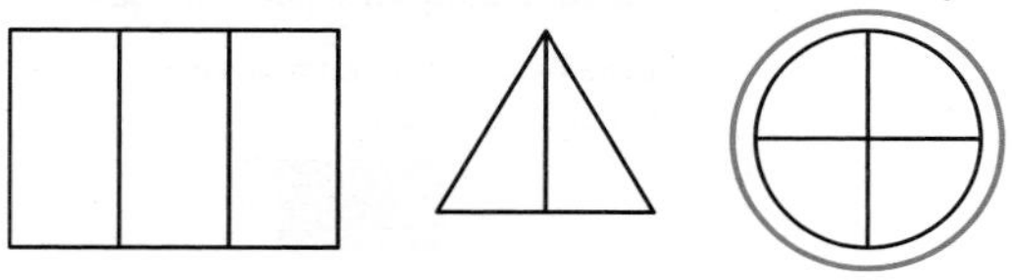

3. Color 1 out of 4 shamrocks green.
Check student's answers.

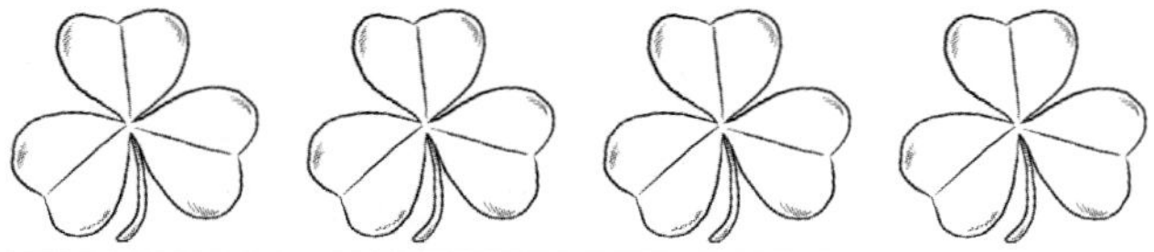

4. Marcia has these crayons. How many out of the 8 crayons are blue?

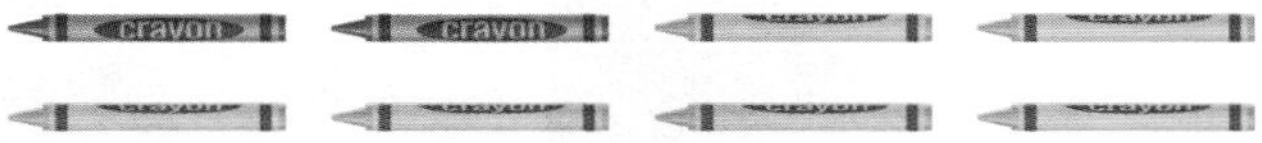

2 crayons

This page checks skills needed for Chapter 14.

Diagnostic Assessment

Check for students' prerequisite skills before beginning the chapter.

- **Option 1:** ***Are You Ready for Chapter 14?***
  SE Student Edition, p. 454
- **Option 2:** ***Online Assessment***
  Math Online macmillanmh.com
- **Option 3:** ***Diagnostic Test***
  CRM Chapter 14 Resource Masters, p. 42

RTI (Response to Intervention)

Apply the Results Based on the results of the diagnostic assessment on p. 454, use the chart below to address individual needs before beginning the chapter.

TIER 3 Intensive Intervention

If students miss three or more of the exercises:

Then use Chapters 5 and 7 of *Math Triumphs*, an intensive math intervention program from McGraw-Hill

TIER 2 Strategic Intervention below/approaching grade level	TIER 1 On-Level	Above/Beyond Level
If students miss two in: **Exercises 1–4**	**If** students miss one in: **Exercises 1–4**	**If** students miss none in: **Exercises 1–4**
Then choose a resource:	**Then** choose a resource:	**Then** choose a resource:
Strategic Intervention Guide (p. 52) CRM Chapter 12 Resource Masters (Reteach Worksheets) Math Online Concepts in Motion	TE Learning Stations (pp. 453G–453H) TE Chapter Project (p. 455) CRM Game: *Matching Shapes* Math Adventures My Math Zone Chapter 13 Math Online Fact Dash	TE Learning Stations (pp. 453G–453H) TE Chapter Project (p. 455) Real-World Problem Solving: *A Lemonade Stand* My Math Zone Chapters 13 and 14 Math Online Games

MATH at HOME

Before you begin Chapter 14:

- Read the Math at Home letter found on p. 455, with the class and have each student sign it.
- Send home copies of the Math at Home letter with each student.
- Use the Spanish letter on student p. 456 for students with Spanish-speaking parents or guardians.

WRITING IN MATH

Starting the Chapter

Ask students to write definitions for *one half, one third* and *one fourth* and provide several examples. Have students use pattern blocks to model the different ways to separate a whole into equal parts.

Read-Aloud Anthology

For an optional reading activity to introduce this chapter's math concepts, see the Read-Aloud Anthology on p. TR39.

MATH at HOME

Dear Family,

Today my class started Chapter 14, **Describe Fractional Parts**. In this chapter, I will learn how to name equal parts of a whole. Here is an activity we can do and a list of books we can read together.

Love, ______________________

Activity

Have your child practice naming equal parts of a whole in everyday situations. For example, show your child how to cut a sandwich in halves and then in fourths.

Key Vocabulary

equal parts each part is the same size

one half a fraction that shows 1 part out of 2 equal parts

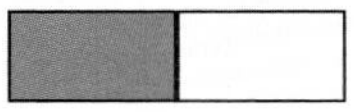

Math Online Click on the eGlossary link at macmillanmh.com to find out more about these words. There are 13 languages.

Books to Read

Fraction Action
by Loreen Leedy
Holiday House, 1996.

Apple Fractions
by Jerry Pallotta
Cartwheel,
2003.

Fraction Fun
by David A. Adler
Holiday House,
1997.

Chapter 14 Project

Create Fractional Parts

- Have students create a poster with a four column chart. Have them draw the geometric figures they have learned down the first column.
- In the second column, have students shade one half of the figure.
- In the third column, have students shade one third of the shape.
- In the fourth column, have students shade one fourth of the figure.

CRM *Refer to Chapter 14 Resource Masters, p. 50 for a rubric to assess students' progress on this project.*

MATEMÁTICAS en CASA

Estimada familia,

Hoy mi clase comenzó el Capítulo 14, **Describe partes fraccionarias.** En este capítulo, aprenderé a nombrar partes iguales de un todo. A continuación, hay una actividad que podemos hacer y una lista de libros que podemos leer juntos.

Cariños, ______________________

Actividad

Pídanle a su hijo(a) que practique nombrando partes iguales de un todo en situaciones cotidianas. Por ejemplo, muéstrenle a su hijo(a) cómo cortar un sándwich en mitades y luego en cuartos.

Vocabulario clave

partes iguales cada parte tiene el mismo tamaño

una mitad una fracción que muestra 1 parte de 2 partes iguales

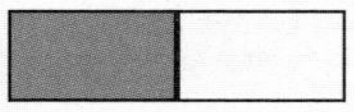

Math Online Visiten el enlace eGlossary en macmillanmh.com para averiguar más sobre estas palabras, las cuales se muestran en 13 idiomas.

Libros recomendados

Sumar y restar
de DK
Estrella Gsp, 2006.

Uno, dos, tres el año se fue
de Gregory Tang
Everest Publishing, 2004.

ELL National ESL Standards Alignment for Chapter 14

Lesson, Page	ESL Standard	Modality	Level
14-1, p 457B	Goal 2, Standard 1, c	Linguistic, Social	Intermediate
14-2, p 459B	Goal 2, Standard 2, c	Visual, Logical	Advanced
14-3, p 461B	Goal 1, Standard 3, k	Social	Intermediate
14-4, p 463B	Goal 1, Standard 3, c	Kinesthetic, Social	Intermediate
14-5, p 469B	Goal 1, Standard 3, c	Logical, Kinesthetic	Intermediate
14-6, p 471B	Goal 1, Standard 3, g	Social, Visual/Spatial	Intermediate
14-7, p 473B	Goal 2, Standard 2, f	Logical, Linguistic	Advanced

The National ESL Standards can be found in the Teacher Reference Handbook.

Chapter 14 Literature List

Lesson	Book Title
14-1	**Piece = Part = Portion** Scott Gifford
14-2	**Five Little Kittens** Nancy Jewell
14-3	**Jump Kangaroo, Jump** Stuart J. Murphy
14-4	**Jump Kangaroo, Jump** Stuart J. Murphy
14-5	**Jump Kangaroo, Jump** Stuart J. Murphy
14-6	**Jump Kangaroo, Jump** Stuart J. Murphy
Any	**Arctic Fives Arrive** Elinor J. Pinczes
Any	**The Cats of Mrs. Calamari** John Stadler
Any	**17 Kings and 42 Elephants** Margaret Mahy

LESSON 14-1

Equal Parts

Lesson Planner

Objective
Identify and count equal parts.

Vocabulary
equal parts

Resources
Materials: brown paper

Manipulatives: fraction circles, pattern blocks

Literature Connection: *Piece = Part = Portions* by Scott Gifford

Alternate Lesson: Adapt "Pattern Block Puzzles" on pages 349 and 350 of *Math Their Way* for practice with fractions and equal parts.

Teacher Technology
TeacherWorks

Focus on Math Background
In this lesson students will use geometrical models to represent fractional equivalencies, including halves, thirds, and fourths. Pattern blocks are symmetrically designed to show proportional relationships. As the students use the pattern blocks to create other shapes, they begin to make sense of how many equal parts are needed to make a whole—e.g. three triangles will make one trapezoid.

Daily Routine

Use these suggestions before beginning the lesson on p. 457.

5-Minute Check
(Reviews Lesson 13-8)

75 76 77 78 79 80 81 82 83 84 85 86 87 88 89 90

Write the number that is just **after:**

1. 79 _____ 80 **2.** 86 _____ 87

Write the number that is just **before**:

3. _____ 90 89 **4.** _____ 83 82

Write the number that is just **between**:

5. 71 _____ 73 72 **6.** 84 _____ 86 85

Problem of the Day
On Monday, Jenny has 10 flowers in her garden. The next morning 2 new flowers have grown. She then cuts 3 for her mother. How many remain in the garden? 9 flowers

LINE UP When it is time to line up, display a variety of shapes—some with equal parts and some with unequal parts. Have students point to one of the shapes, tell whether the parts are equal or unequal, and then get in line.

Building Math Vocabulary
Review the term **equal parts** and write it on the board.

- Draw a pizza on the board. **If we want to cut this pizza into equal parts, what must we do?** Make each piece or part the same size.
- **Why would you want to cut something into equal parts?** So everyone sharing it has the same amount.
- Draw another pizza on the board that has unequal parts. Explain that parts of a whole that are not the same size are unequal parts.

Differentiated Instruction

Small Group Options

Option 1 VISUAL/SPATIAL

Gifted and Talented AL

Materials: index cards, pencils, scissors

- Demonstrate how to fold an index card and draw a figure with the fold as one straight side.
- Cut through both thicknesses of the card to separate out the figure. Point out that you did not cut on the fold. Display the open figure.
- **Does this figure have two equal parts?** yes **How do you know the parts are equal?** They were cut at the same time so they are the same size and shape.
- Let students experiment with creating their own symmetrical shapes from index cards.
- Have students color in one part of their shape and label it one half.

Option 2 SOCIAL

English Language Learners ELL

Materials: index cards, paper circles and other shapes
Core Vocabulary: shade/shaded, flip/flipping, of a
Common Use Verb: show

Do Math This strategy gives students visual representations of one half.

- Model folding circle in half. Say: "Please fold the circles; then **shade** one half of your circle."
- Post one circle card. Say: "This is how we show one half of a circle."
- Repeat for an index card, a square, and a right triangle (each time describing the shaded half as "half of a square", and so on).

Independent Work Options

Option 1 LOGICAL, KINESTHETIC

Early Finishers OL AL

Materials: connecting cubes

- One student makes a train of connecting cubes.
- The other students in the group work together to determine how many cubes make up one half the train.
- Students continue making cube trains and finding the number of cubes that make up one half of each one.

Option 2

Student Technology

Math Online macmillanmh.com

Math Adventures

Option 3

Learning Station: Health (p. 453H)

Direct students to the Health Learning Station for more opportunities to explore and extend the lesson concept.

Option 4

Problem-Solving Practice

Reinforce problem-solving skills and strategies with the Problem-Solving Practice worksheet.

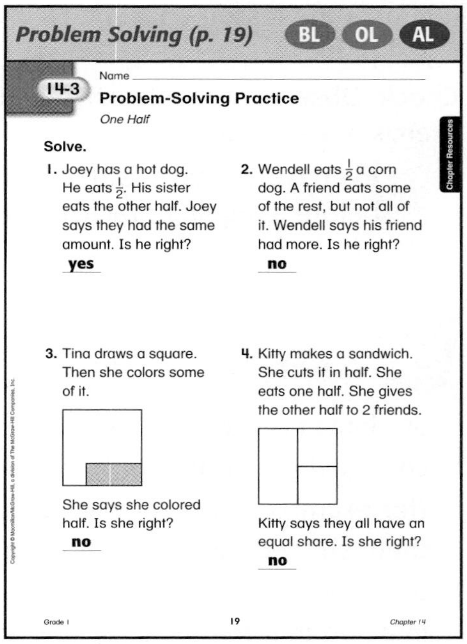

Problem Solving (p. 19) BL OL AL

14-3 Name ______

Problem-Solving Practice

One Half

Chapter Resources

Solve.

1. Joey has a hot dog. He eats $\frac{1}{2}$. His sister eats the other half. Joey says they had the same amount. Is he right?
yes

2. Wendell eats $\frac{1}{2}$ a corn dog. A friend eats some of the rest, but not all of it. Wendell says his friend had more. Is he right?
no

3. Tina draws a square. Then she colors some of it.
She says she colored half. Is she right?
no

4. Kitty makes a sandwich. She cuts it in half. She eats one half. She gives the other half to 2 friends.
Kitty says they all have an equal share. Is she right?
no

Grade 1 19 Chapter 14

1 Introduce

Activity Hands-On

Give the students several of each type of pattern block.

- Display a hexagon on the overhead, and tell the students that it is a hexagon.
- Cover the hexagon with two trapezoids. Explain that these two trapezoids are equal to one hexagon. Remove one trapezoid. Explain that one trapezoid is equal to half a hexagon.
- Ask the students to place two equal pattern blocks side by side to create a new shape. Have them trace the pattern blocks and color half of the new shape.

Activity Choice 2 • Literature Connection

Introduce the lesson with *Jump Kangaroo, Jump* by Stuart J. Murphy. For additional support, see p. TR62.

2 Teach

- Show students a granola bar. **How could you share the snack with your friend equally?** We could cut it in half.
- **How many halves can there be of one thing?** two
- **Are the two halves always equal?** yes

Get Ready Use the section at the top of p. 461 to reinforce the lesson concept. Help students identify equal parts.

Check Observe students as you work through Exercises 1–7 as a class.

Exercise 7 Assess student comprehension before assigning practice exercises.

COMMON ERROR!

Students new to the concept of $\frac{1}{2}$ may be confused by models with more than 2 parts (for example, a model with 6 equal parts, 3 of them shaded). Have students manipulate the parts to look like halves. Then ask them to imagine that the parts making each half are stuck together like one part, or $\frac{1}{2}$.

Name ____________________

One Half

Get Ready

Main Idea

I will name equal parts of a whole.

Vocabulary

fraction

one half

You can use a **fraction** to tell about equal parts.

1 out of 2 total parts is $\frac{1}{2}$ of the pie.

Check

7. Cut it into 2 equal parts; each gets 1 equal part or $\frac{1}{2}$ of the sandwich

Choose a crayon. Color one half.

1. 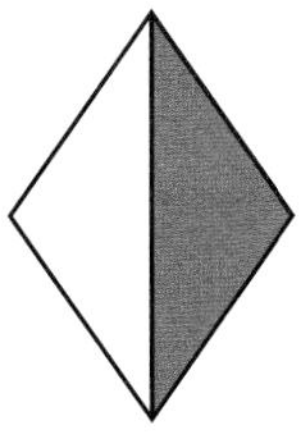

2. 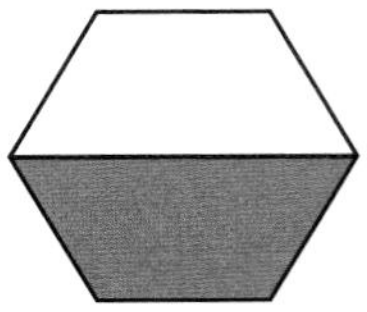

3. 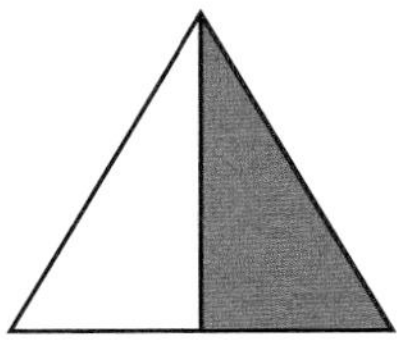

4. 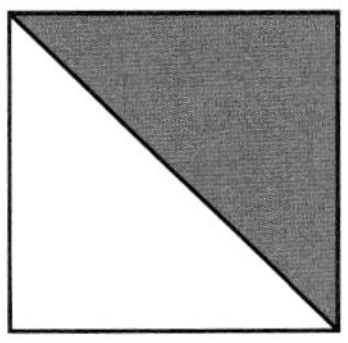

5. 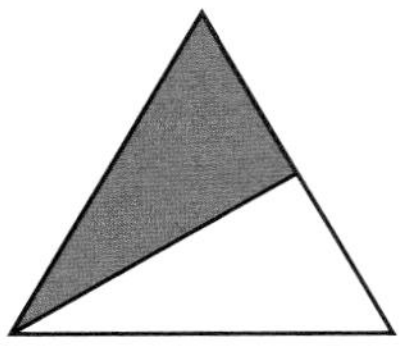

6. 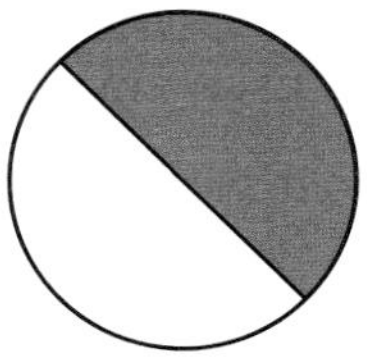

7. Talk About It How could you share a sandwich with your friend?

Reteach (p. 16) BL

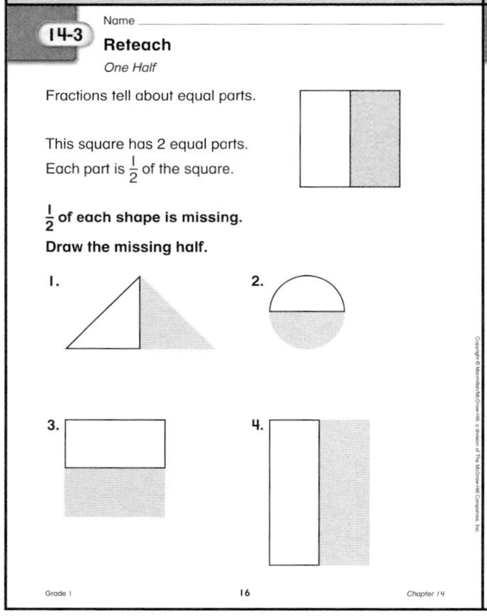

Name

14-3 Reteach

One Half

Fractions tell about equal parts.

This square has 2 equal parts.
Each part is $\frac{1}{2}$ of the square.

$\frac{1}{2}$ of each shape is missing.
Draw the missing half.

1. 2. 3. 4.

Grade 1 16 Chapter 14

Skills Practice (p. 17) OL

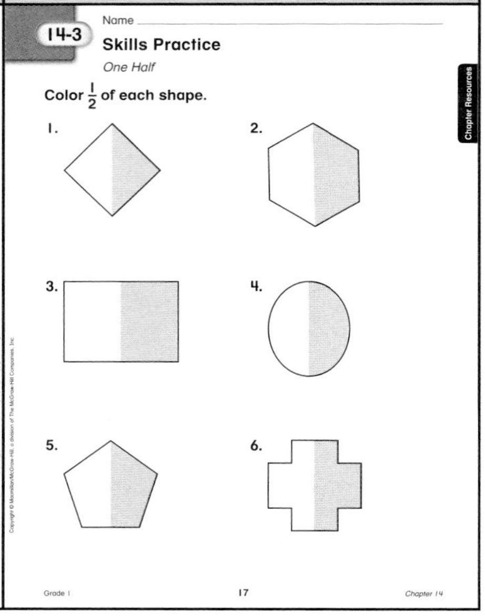

Name

14-3 Skills Practice

One Half

Color $\frac{1}{2}$ of each shape.

1. 2. 3. 4. 5. 6.

Grade 1 17 Chapter 14

Practice

Choose a crayon. Color one half.

8.

9.
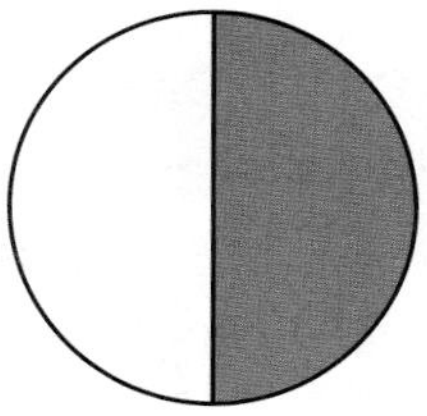

10.

11.
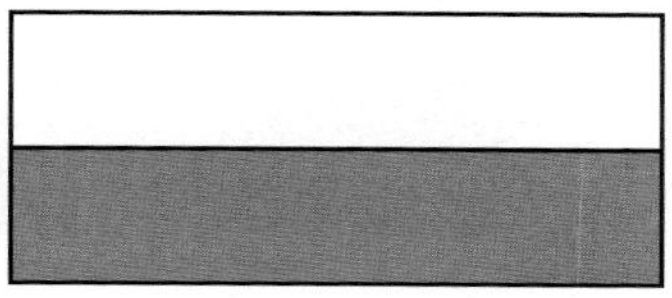

12.
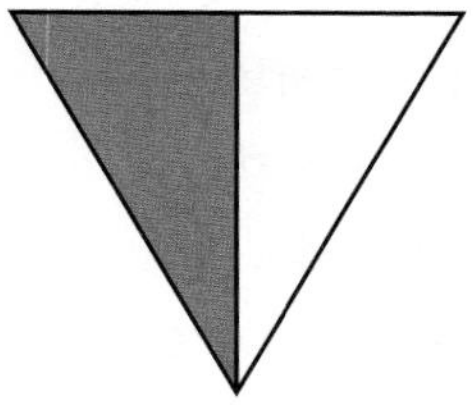

13.
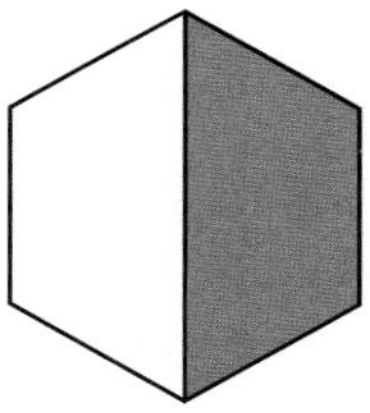

Problem Solving

14. **Critical Thinking** Jenny is eating $\frac{1}{2}$ of an orange. Trish is eating $\frac{1}{2}$ of the same orange. Jenny says she has less than Trish. Can she be right?

Sample answer: No; not if the orange was cut in half and both parts are the same shape and size.

Enrich (p. 20) AL

14-3 Name

Enrich

One Half

Draw the missing half.

What did you draw? teddy bear

Grade 1 20 Chapter 14

Homework Practice (p. 18) OL

14-3 Name

Homework Practice

One Half

Color $\frac{1}{2}$ of each shape.

1.

2.
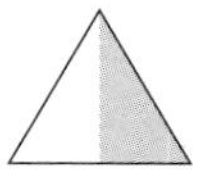

3.
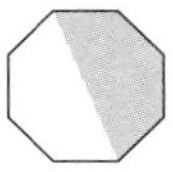

4.
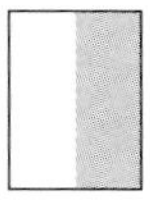

5.

6.
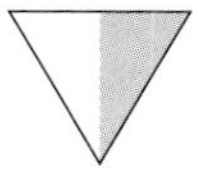

Grade 1 18 Chapter 14

BL Alternate Teaching Strategy

If students have difficulty determining the number of parts that make up one half of a shape . . .

Then use one of these reteach options.

1 CRM **Daily Reteach Worksheet** (p. 16)

2 **Show One Half** Give students a set of eight index cards. Ask them to make a large rectangle with the eight cards and place a length of yarn down the middle separating them.

- **How many cards make up one half of the rectangle?** 4 cards

3 Practice

Differentiate practice using these leveled assignments for Exercises 8–14.

Level	Assignment
BL Below/Approaching Level	Guide students through the exercises. Discuss the number of parts that make up $\frac{1}{2}$ of each shape.
OL On Level	Complete the exercises following the directions given.
AL Above/Beyond Level	Complete the exercises independently.

4 Assess

Formative Assessment

Have students choose three different shapes. Ask students to shade one half of each shape.

WRITING IN MATH Ask students to write about why it is useful to know how to divide something in half.

Quick Check **Are students continuing to struggle with equal parts?**

If Yes → CRM Reteach Worksheet (p. 16)
Small Group Options (p. 461B)

If No → Independent Work Options (p. 461B)
CRM Skills Practice Worksheet (p. 17)
CRM Enrich Worksheet (p. 20)

14-4 One Third and One Fourth

Lesson Planner

Objective

Identify one third and one fourth of a whole.

Vocabulary

one third, **one fourth**

Resources

Materials: transparencies showing models for thirds and fourths, fraction flash cards

Manipulatives: pattern blocks

Literature Connection: *Jump Kangaroo, Jump* by Stuart J. Murphy

Teacher Technology

TeacherWorks • Concepts In Motion

Focus on Math Background

This lesson continues the work students began in the previous lesson using symbols to represent fractional quantities. In this lesson, however, students will learn how to read and write the correct symbolic notation for expressing one-third and one-fourth. Once again, students will learn that the numeral on the top—the numerator—represents the actual part, whereas the digit on the bottom—the denominator—indicates the number of parts needed to construct the whole.

Daily Routine

Use these suggestions before beginning the lesson on p. 463.

5-Minute Check

(Reviews 14–3)

1. Draw a square with 2 equal parts.
2. Draw a triangle with 2 equal parts.
3. Draw a circle with 2 equal parts.
4. Draw a rectangle with 2 equal parts.

Problem of the Day

Continue the following pattern: 4, 7, 10, 13, ___, ___, ___, ___. 16, 19, 22, 25

LINE UP When students line up for recess, lunch, or dismissal, hold up index cards with shapes divided into equal parts and shapes divided into unequal parts. Ask students to say "equal" or "unequal" to describe each card.

Building Math Vocabulary

Write the terms **one third** and **one fourth** on the board.

- Draw two circles on the board. Divide one into three equal parts and the other into four.
- Point to the first circle. **How many parts?** 3 parts
- Color in one part and write $\frac{1}{3}$ next to it. **One third means 1 part out of 3 equal parts.**
- Point to the circle divided into fourths. **How many parts?** 4 parts
- Color in 1 part and write $\frac{1}{4}$ next to it. **One fourth means 1 part out of 4 equal parts.**

Differentiated Instruction

Small Group Options

Option 1 Below Level BL

KINESTHETIC, VISUAL/SPATIAL

Materials: paper shapes, scissors

- Use construction paper to make a variety of shapes in different colors.
- Draw lines to separate the shapes into halves, thirds, or fourths. Have students write the number of parts for each of the shapes.
- Have students cut apart the shapes and mix up the pieces. Ask students to match equal parts to put the shapes back together again.

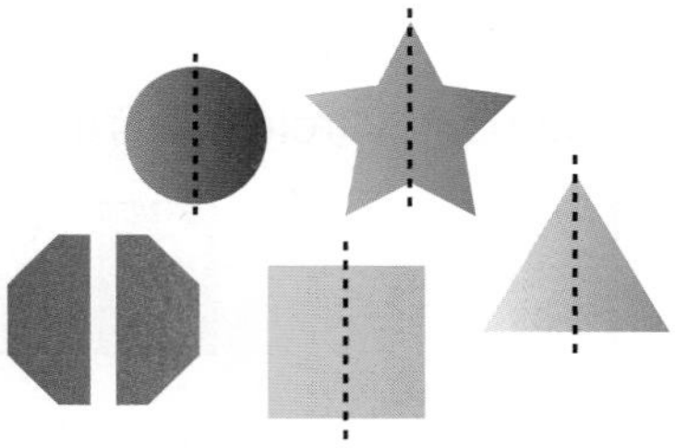

Option 2 English Language Learners ELL

KINESTHETIC, VISUAL/SPATIAL, SOCIAL

Core Vocabulary: total, eyes, hair

Common Use Verb: repeat

Talk Math This lesson helps students see how separating a whole into three or four equal parts works. It also gives them practice using appropriate language to describe fractional parts.

- Have three girls and one boy stand. "How many **total** students are standing?" Write 4. "How many are boys?" Say, "One out of four equal parts."; students repeat.
- Have two students in brown shirts and one student in a different colored shirt stand. "How many **total**?" Write 3. Say "One color out of three equal parts."; students repeat.
- Allow small groups to model thirds and state how many ______ are in 3 equal parts, as time permits.

Independent Work Options

Option 1 Early Finishers OL AL

LOGICAL, KINESTHETIC

Materials: fraction cards with a variety of models

- Players take turns picking up a card and describing the fractional parts of a whole.
- If another student has already collected a model showing that fractional part of a whole, he or she can show it and claim the new card. If no one has the fractional part of a whole, the player who named it claims it.

Option 2 Student Technology

Math Online macmillanmh.com

Math Adventures

Option 3 Learning Station: Art (p. 453G)

Direct students to the Art Learning Station for more opportunities to explore and extend the lesson concept.

Option 4 Problem-Solving Practice

Reinforce problem-solving skills and strategies with the Problem-Solving Practice worksheet.

Problem Solving (p. 24) BL OL AL

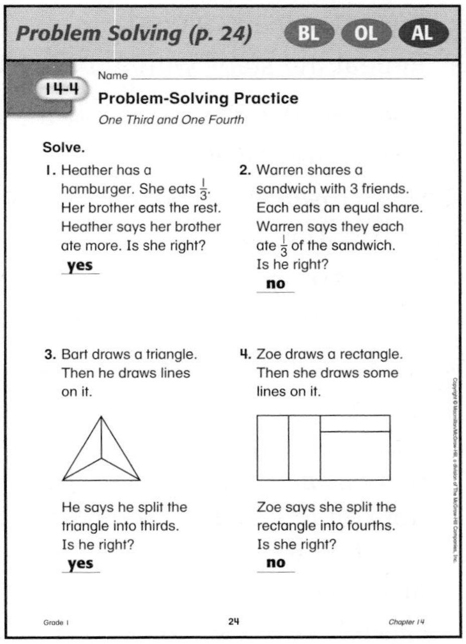

Name ______

14-4 **Problem-Solving Practice**

One Third and One Fourth

Solve.

1. Heather has a hamburger. She eats $\frac{1}{3}$. Her brother eats the rest. Heather says her brother ate more. Is she right? **yes**
2. Warren shares a sandwich with 3 friends. Each eats an equal share. Warren says they each ate $\frac{1}{3}$ of the sandwich. Is he right? **no**
3. Bart draws a triangle. Then he draws lines on it. He says he split the triangle into thirds. Is he right? **yes**
4. Zoe draws a rectangle. Then she draws some lines on it. Zoe says she split the rectangle into fourths. Is she right? **no**

Grade 1 24 Chapter 14

1 Introduce

Activity • Hands-On

Give the students several of each type of pattern block.

- Display a hexagon on the overhead. **How can you show 3 equal parts of a hexagon?** Demonstrate how 3 rhombi cover the hexagon.
- Explain that 1 rhombus is one of 3 equal parts that make up the whole hexagon, so each rhombus is one of three equal parts of the hexagon.
- **What pattern blocks can we divide into 4 equal parts?** Have students experiment to show 4 equal parts of other pattern blocks. Explain that each part is one fourth of the whole shape.

Activity Choice 2 • Literature Connection

Introduce the lesson with *Jump Kangaroo, Jump* by Stuart J. Murphy. For additional support, see p. TR63.

2 Teach

- Display on the overhead a pie chart model showing thirds. **How many equal parts?** 3
- Color one part. How many parts did I color? 1
- Write 1 on the board above 3, and draw a line to show $\frac{1}{3}$.
- Explain that the bottom number tells the total number of equal parts and the top number tells how many are colored.
- Repeat the steps with a model showing fourths.

Get Ready Use the section at the top of p. 463 to reinforce the lesson concept.

Check Observe students as you work through Exercises 1–6 as a class.

Exercise 6 Assess student comprehension before assigning practice exercises.

COMMON ERROR!

Students may write the number of colored parts as a numerator and the number of parts not colored as a denominator. Have them count all the parts and write the denominator first, before thinking about the colored parts.

Name ______________________

One Third and One Fourth

Get Ready

Main Idea

I will name parts of a whole.

Vocabulary

one third

one fourth

One third and **one fourth** are fractions that name parts of a whole.

Thirds

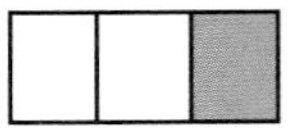

1 out of 3 total parts is blue. $\frac{1}{3}$ is blue.

Fourths

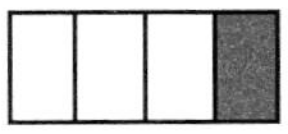

1 out of 4 total parts is red. $\frac{1}{4}$ is red.

Check

Write the fraction.

1. 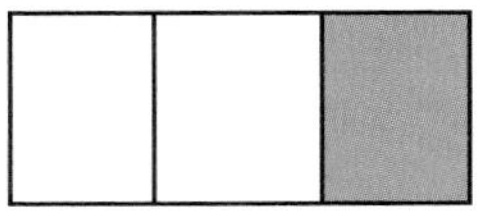 $\frac{1}{3}$

2. 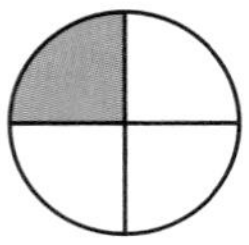 $\frac{1}{4}$

Color 1 equal part. Circle the fraction. Fill in the numbers.

3. 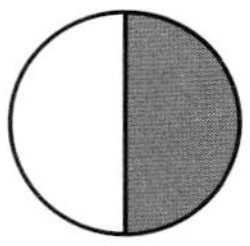

(circled) $\frac{1}{2}$ $\frac{1}{3}$ $\frac{1}{4}$

1 out of 2 parts

4. 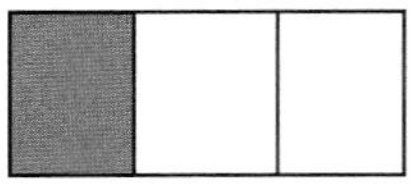

$\frac{1}{2}$ (circled) $\frac{1}{3}$ $\frac{1}{4}$

1 out of 3 parts

5. 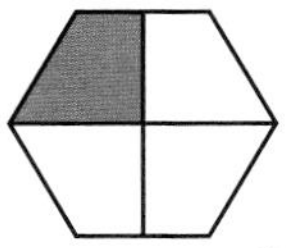

$\frac{1}{2}$ $\frac{1}{3}$ (circled) $\frac{1}{4}$

1 out of 4 parts

6. **Talk About It** How are $\frac{1}{3}$ and $\frac{1}{4}$ different?

Sample Answer: $\frac{1}{3}$ is 1 out of 3 equal parts; $\frac{1}{4}$ is 1 out of 4 equal parts.

Reteach (p. 21) BL

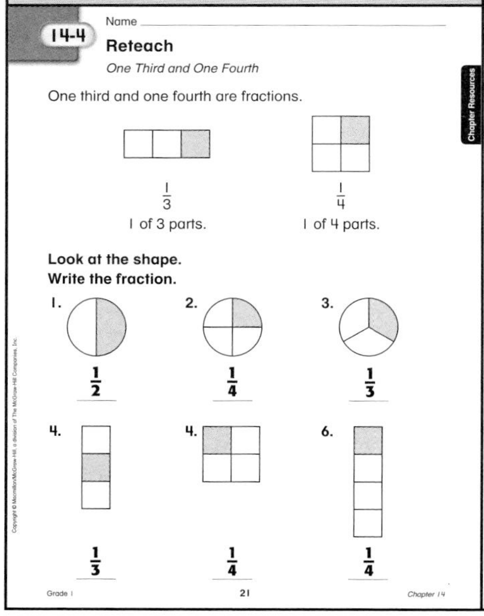

14-4 Name

Reteach

One Third and One Fourth

One third and one fourth are fractions.

$\frac{1}{3}$ 1 of 3 parts. $\frac{1}{4}$ 1 of 4 parts.

Look at the shape. Write the fraction.

1. $\frac{1}{2}$ 2. $\frac{1}{4}$ 3. $\frac{1}{3}$

4. $\frac{1}{3}$ 4. $\frac{1}{4}$ 6. $\frac{1}{4}$

Grade 1 21 Chapter 14

Skills Practice (p. 22) OL

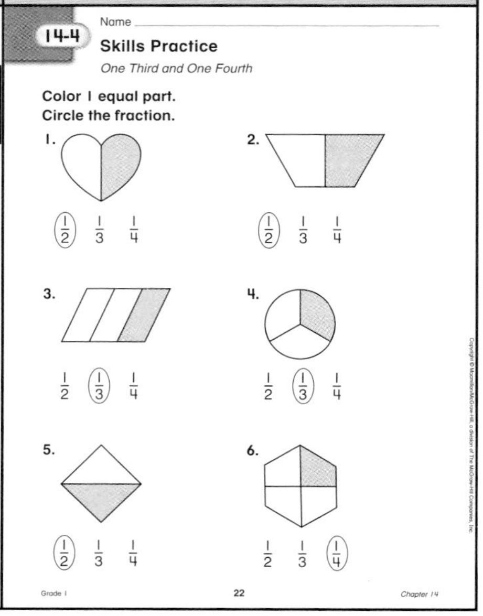

14-4 Name

Skills Practice

One Third and One Fourth

Color 1 equal part. Circle the fraction.

1. (circled) $\frac{1}{2}$ $\frac{1}{3}$ $\frac{1}{4}$
2. (circled) $\frac{1}{2}$ $\frac{1}{3}$ $\frac{1}{4}$
3. $\frac{1}{2}$ (circled) $\frac{1}{3}$ $\frac{1}{4}$
4. $\frac{1}{2}$ (circled) $\frac{1}{3}$ $\frac{1}{4}$
5. (circled) $\frac{1}{2}$ $\frac{1}{3}$ $\frac{1}{4}$
6. $\frac{1}{2}$ $\frac{1}{3}$ (circled) $\frac{1}{4}$

Grade 1 22 Chapter 14

Practice

Write the fraction for the piece that was eaten.

7.

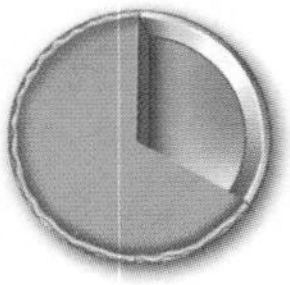

$\frac{1}{3}$

8.

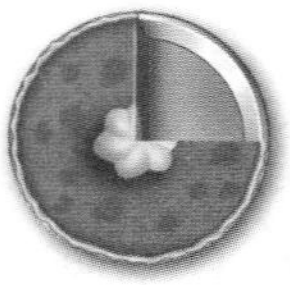

$\frac{1}{4}$

Color 1 equal part. Circle the fraction. Fill in the numbers.

9.

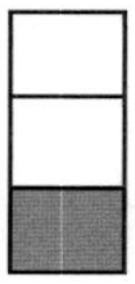

$\frac{1}{2}$ ($\frac{1}{3}$) $\frac{1}{4}$

1 out of 3 parts

10.

($\frac{1}{2}$) $\frac{1}{3}$ $\frac{1}{4}$

1 out of 2 parts

11.

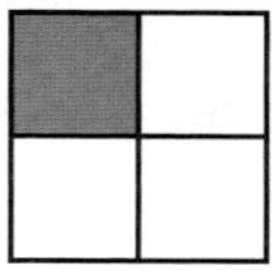

$\frac{1}{2}$ $\frac{1}{3}$ ($\frac{1}{4}$)

1 out of 4 parts

H.O.T. Problem

12. **Make It Right**

Sam says $\frac{1}{3}$ of the pizza has pepperoni.
Tell why Sam is wrong.
Make it right.

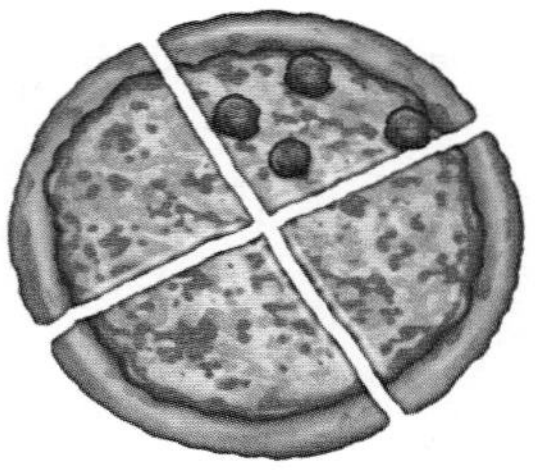

Sample answer: The pizza is cut into 4 equal parts. One part has pepperoni. $\frac{1}{4}$ of the pizza has pepperoni.

Enrich (p. 25) AL

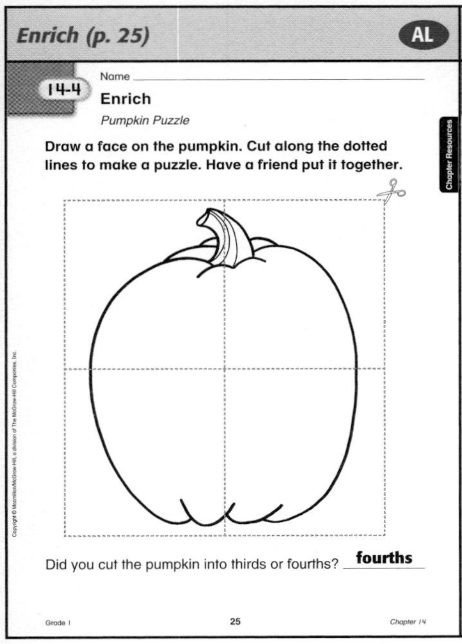

14-4 Enrich
Pumpkin Puzzle

Draw a face on the pumpkin. Cut along the dotted lines to make a puzzle. Have a friend put it together.

Did you cut the pumpkin into thirds or fourths? **fourths**

Grade 1 25 Chapter 14

Homework Practice (p. 23) OL

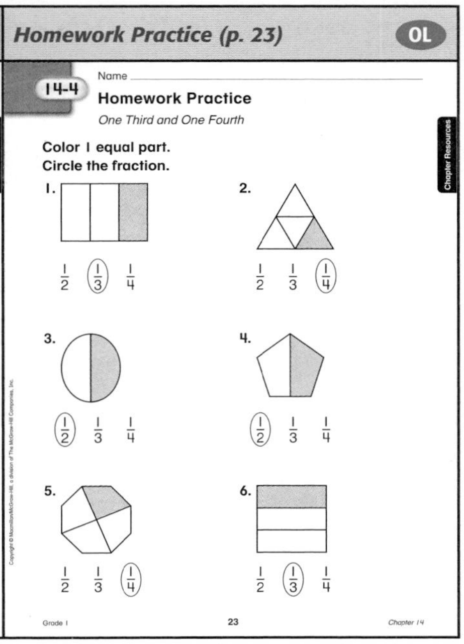

14-4 Homework Practice
One Third and One Fourth

Color 1 equal part.
Circle the fraction.

1. $\frac{1}{2}$ ($\frac{1}{3}$) $\frac{1}{4}$
2. $\frac{1}{2}$ $\frac{1}{3}$ ($\frac{1}{4}$)
3. ($\frac{1}{2}$) $\frac{1}{3}$ $\frac{1}{4}$
4. ($\frac{1}{2}$) $\frac{1}{3}$ $\frac{1}{4}$
5. $\frac{1}{2}$ $\frac{1}{3}$ ($\frac{1}{4}$)
6. $\frac{1}{2}$ ($\frac{1}{3}$) $\frac{1}{4}$

Grade 1 23 Chapter 14

BL Alternate Teaching Strategy

If students have difficulty understanding one third and one fourth . . .

Then use one of these reteach options.

1. CRM **Daily Reteach Worksheet** (p. 21)
2. **Thumbs-Up for Fractions** Hold up, one at a time, flash cards showing models for one half, one third, and one fourth.
   - Have students vote thumbs-up when they see a model showing one half and thumbs-down for all others. When students correctly vote thumbs-up, say, **This card shows** _____ and have students respond "one half."
   - Continue with other models.

3 Practice

Differentiate practice using these leveled assignments for Exercises 7–12.

Level	Assignment
BL Below/Approaching Level	Guide students through the exercises, using fraction models with labels as references.
OL On Level	Complete the exercises independently, checking reference models as needed.
AL Above/Beyond Level	Complete the exercises independently.

4 Assess

Formative Assessment

Have students explain what 1 and 4 each mean in the fraction $\frac{1}{4}$. Then have them draw a model showing $\frac{1}{4}$. The 4 means that there are four equal parts of a whole. The 1 means that there is one part set apart.

WRITING IN MATH Have students write a fraction number story to explain having $\frac{1}{3}$ or $\frac{1}{4}$ of something.

Quick Check Are students continuing to struggle with one third and one fourth?

If Yes → Small Group Options (p. 463B)

If No → Independent Work Options (p. 463B)

CRM Skills Practice Worksheet (p. 22)

CRM Enrich Worksheet (p. 25)

Reviews Lessons 14-1 to 14-4

Objective: Review and assess mastery of previous lessons' skills and concepts.

- Review with students one half.
- Review with students one third.
- Review with students one fourth.

Practice with Technology

Math Online Have students visit macmillanmh.com for additional practice with online activities, games, and quizzes.

Name ______________________

Use . Shade $\frac{1}{2}$ or 1 of the 2 parts.

1. 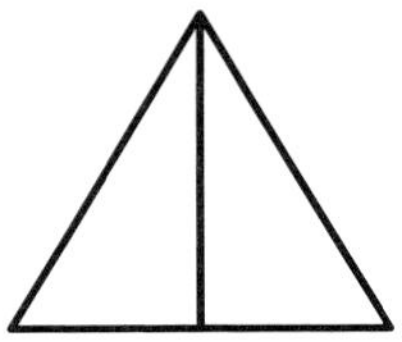

2. 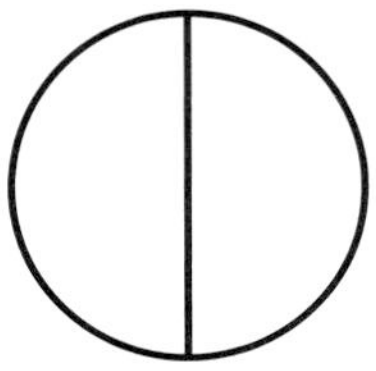

1.–2. One part will be shaded red

Use . Shade $\frac{1}{3}$ or 1 of the 3 parts.

3. 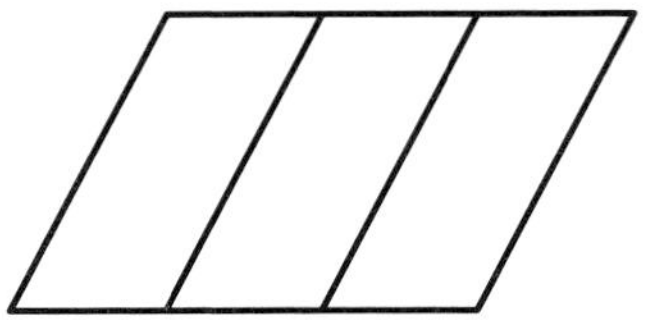

4. 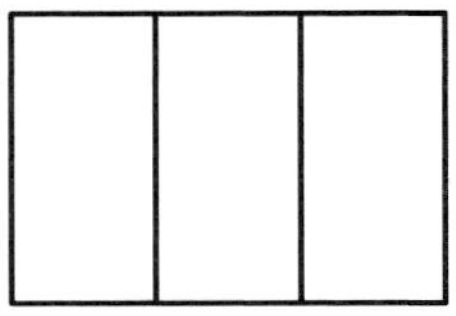

3.–4. One part will be shaded yellow

Use . Shade $\frac{1}{4}$ or 1 of the 4 parts.

5. 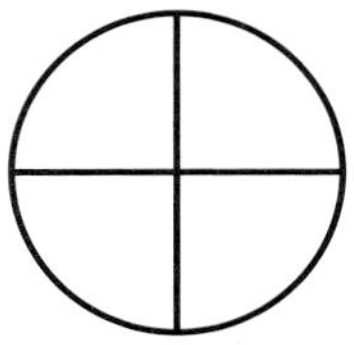

6. 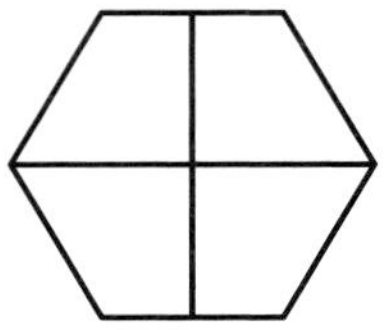

5.–6. One part will be shaded green

Game Time

The Equalizer

Fractions

You Will Need

Play with a partner. Take turns.

- One player uses (dark counter) and the other uses (light counter).
- Pick any figure on the board.
- Find another figure with the same number of equal parts shaded.
- If you are right, place your counters on both spaces.
- The person with the most counters on the board wins.

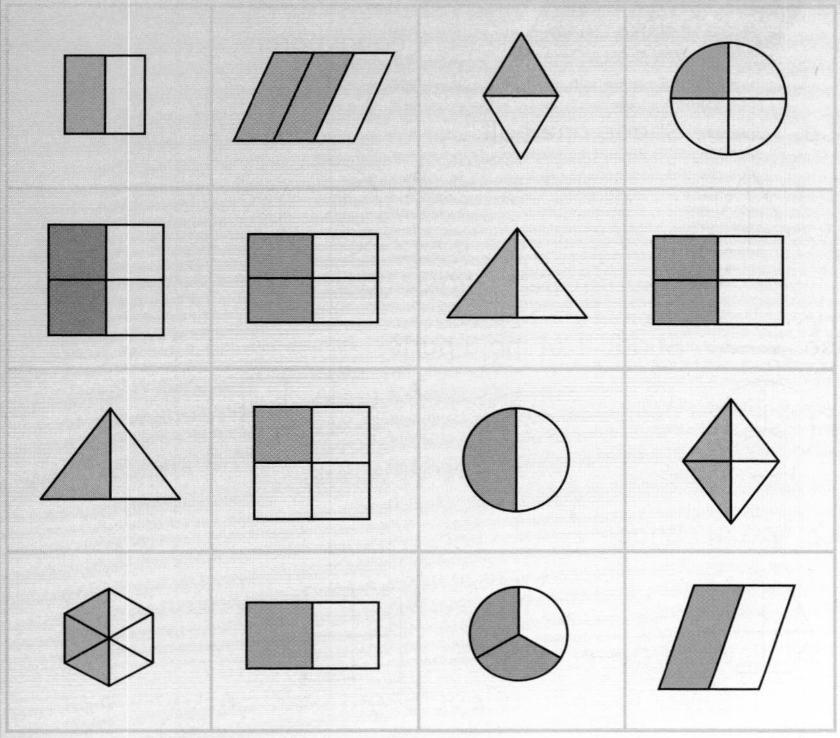

Game Time

The Equalizer

Math Concept: Fractions

Manipulatives: two-colored counters

Introduce the game on p. 466 to students to play as a class, in small groups, or at a learning workstation to review concepts introduced in this chapter.

Instructions

- Put students in pairs.
- Give each student a handful of two-colored counters.
- One player will use the red side. The other player will use the yellow side.
- One partner picks any figure on the board.
- Then, he or she must find another figure with the same number of equal parts shaded.
- If the student is correct, he or she places a counter on both places.
- Then it is the other player's turn to match the figures.
- Students play until the board is covered.
- The player with the most counters on the board wins.

Extending the Game

Have students continue playing, but remove the counters as they find matches. Ask students to name each fraction as they remove the counters from the board.

Differentiated Practice

Use these leveling suggestions to differentiate the game for all learners.

Level	Assignment
BL **Below/Approaching Level**	Have students draw the figures as they make a match.
OL **On Level**	Have students play the game with the rules as written.
AL **Above/Beyond Level**	Have students find figures of the same shape and order them (one half, one third, one fourth).

Mid-Chapter Check

Lessons 14-1 to 14-4

Formative Assessment

Use the Mid-Chapter Check to assess students' progress in the first half of the chapter.

ExamView Assessment Suite Customize and create multiple versions of your Mid-Chapter Check and the test answer keys.

FOLDABLES® Dinah Zike's Foldables

Use these lesson suggestions to incorporate the Foldables during the chapter.

Lesson 14-1 Give students three index cards. On the first card, have students draw a figure divided into two equal parts. On the second card, have students draw a figure divided into three equal parts. On the third card, have students draw a figure divided into four equal parts. Ask students to label each card appropriately.

Lesson 14-3 Give students one index card. Have students write *one half* and $\frac{1}{2}$ on one side of the card. On the other side, have students draw a figure to show one half.

Lesson 14-4 Give students two index cards. On the first card, have students write *one third* and $\frac{1}{3}$ on one side of the card. On the other side, have students draw a figure to show one third. On the second card, have students write *one fourth* and $\frac{1}{4}$ on one side of the card. On the other side, have students draw a figure to show one fourth.

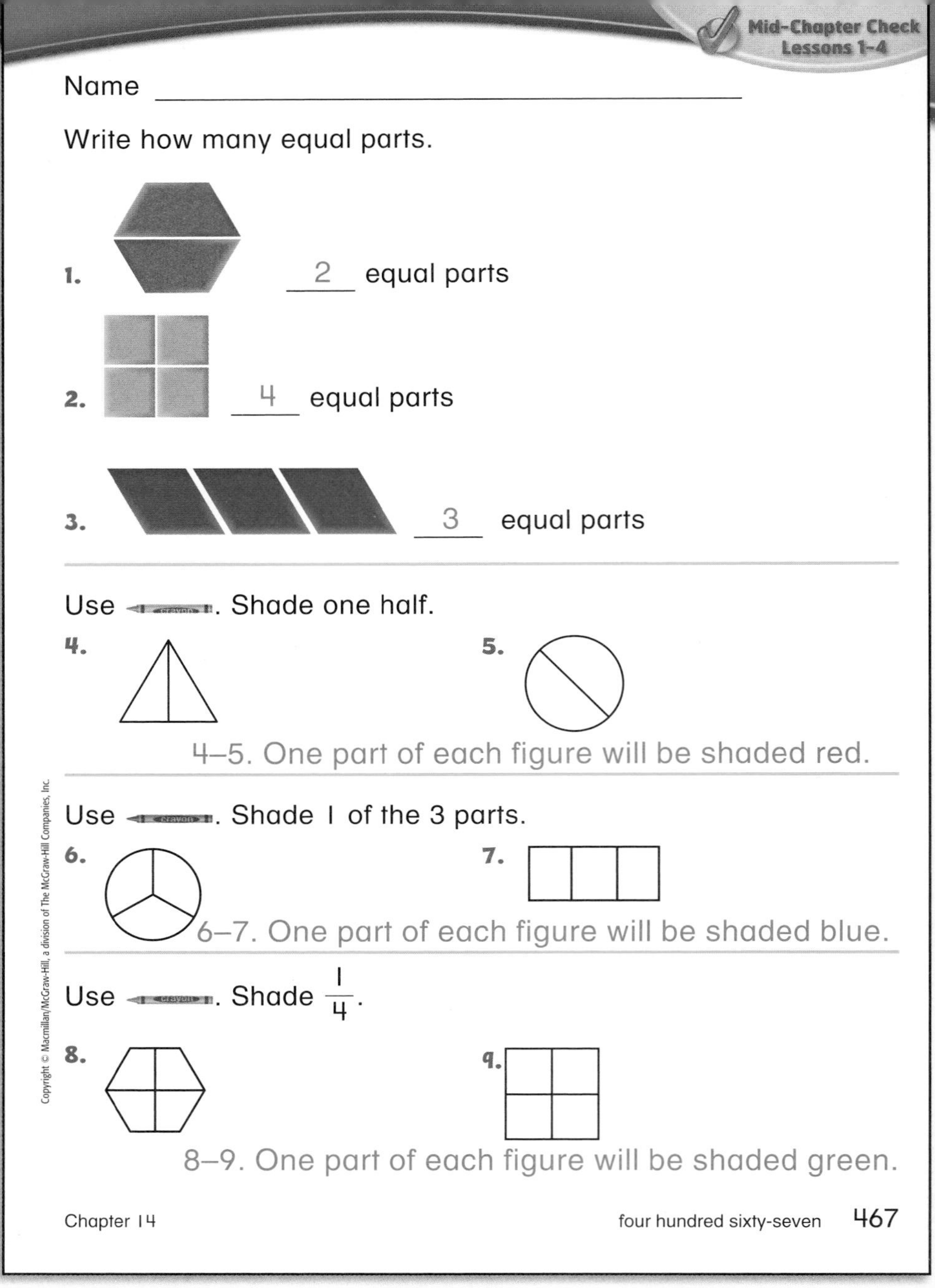
Mid-Chapter Check Lessons 1-4

Name ______

Write how many equal parts.

1. 2 equal parts

2. 4 equal parts

3. 3 equal parts

Use crayon. Shade one half.

4. 5.

4–5. One part of each figure will be shaded red.

Use crayon. Shade 1 of the 3 parts.

6. 7.

6–7. One part of each figure will be shaded blue.

Use crayon. Shade $\frac{1}{4}$.

8. 9.

8–9. One part of each figure will be shaded green.

Chapter 14 four hundred sixty-seven 467

Data-Driven Decision Making

Based on the results of the Mid-Chapter Check, use the following resources to review concepts that continue to give students problems.

Exercises	State/Local Standards	What's the Math?	Error Analysis	Resources for Review
1–3 Lesson 14-1		Identify and describe equal parts.	Does not count parts correctly.	Strategic Intervention Guide (p. 86) CRM Chapter 14 Resource Masters (Reteach Worksheets) Math Online Concepts in Motion Math Adventures
4–8 Lesson 14-3 Lesson 14-4		Shows $\frac{1}{2}$. Shows $\frac{1}{3}$. Shows $\frac{1}{4}$.	Does not shade the parts correctly.	

Spiral Review Chapters 1–14

Write the numbers.

10. 99 ones = 9 tens 9 ones 99

11. 12 ones = 1 ten 2 ones 12

12. 53 ones = 5 tens 3 ones 53

13. Circle the event that takes the most time.

1 hour

half hour

2 hours

14. Rosa has 4 pencils. She bought 9 more. How many pencils does she have now?

4 + 9 = 13

15. Darin has 11 shirts. He gave 5 to his brother. How many shirts does he have now?

11 − 5 = 6

16. Solve the riddle. Draw the hands on the clock. My minute hand is on the 12. My hour hand is on the 8.

What time am I? 8 o'clock

Spiral Review

Review Chapters 1 to 14

Objective: Review and assess mastery of skills and concepts from previous chapters.

Resources for Review

Based on student results, refer to these lessons for remediation:

- **Exercises 10–12: Lesson 13-2** (p. 423)
- **Exercise 13: Lesson 7-6** (p. 227)
- **Exercises 14–15: Lesson 10-6** (p. 329)
- **Exercise 16: Lesson 7-5** (p. 223)

LESSON 14-5

Non-Unit Fractions

Lesson Planner

Objective

Separate a whole into parts using non-unit fractions.

Review Vocabulary

part, whole

Resources

Materials: pencils, paper
Literature Connection: *Jump Kangaroo, Jump* by Stuart J. Murphy
Teacher Technology
TeacherWorks • Concepts in Motion

Focus on Math Background

Students have learned to identify and describe the following fractions: $\frac{1}{2}$, $\frac{1}{3}$, and $\frac{1}{4}$. Since non-unit fractions will have a number other than 1 in the numerator, students will need to develop a strong understanding of what the numerator and denominator represent in a fraction. The numerator "counts" the number of parts. The denominator "names" the number of parts in all. The fact that fractions are numbers is as important as the ability to construct and interpret models that represent them.

Daily Routine

Use these suggestions before beginning the lesson on p. 469.

5-Minute Check

(Reviews Lesson 14–4)

1. Draw a square that shows one out of four parts is blue.
2. Draw a circle that shows one out of two parts is red.

1, 2. See students' work

Problem of the Day

Write the fact family for 6, 8, and 14. 6 + 8 = 14, 8 + 6 = 14, 14 − 6 = 8, 14 − 8 = 6

LINE UP As you prepare for recess, lunch, or dismissal, have each student describe shaded parts of a whole on fraction cards before lining up.

Review Math Vocabulary

- Review the distinction between **part** and **whole** with students.
- Ask students to list foods that are usually shared, such as a pizza or a cake.
- **You would not eat a whole cake, would you?** No.
- **How would you share the cake?** Divide it into parts.
- Draw a circle on the board to represent the cake. Divide it into four parts.
- **How many parts are there in this whole?** 4 parts
- Remind students that a whole is always made up of parts.

Solve Two-Digit Addition and Subtraction Problems

Skills Trace
Vertical Alignment

Kindergarten
In kindergarten, students learned to:
- Understand and describe simple addition and subtraction problems.
- Use concrete objects to determine the answers to addition and subtraction problems with numbers less than 10.

First Grade
During this chapter, students learn to:
- Solve addition and subtraction problems with one- and two-digit numbers.
- Estimate the sum and difference of 2 two-digit numbers.

Second Grade
In second grade, students learn to:
- Count, read, and write numbers to 1,000.
- Understand place value through 1,000.
- Add and subtract three-digit numbers with regrouping.
- Estimate numbers through thousands.

Backmapping and Vertical Alignment
McGraw-Hill's *Math Connects* program was conceived and developed with the final results in mind: student success in Algebra 1 and beyond. The authors, using the **NCTM Focal Points and Focal Connections** as their guide, developed this brand-new series by backmapping from Algebra 1 concepts, and vertically aligning the topics so that they build upon prior skills and concepts and serve as a foundation for future topics.

Math Vocabulary
The following math vocabulary words for Chapter 15 are listed in the glossary of the ***Student Edition.*** You can find interactive definitions in 13 languages in the **eGlossary** at macmillanmh.com.

add to join together sets to find the total sum (p. 485)

addend any numbers or quantities being added together (p. 485)

difference the answer to a subtraction problem (p. 485)

estimate to find a number close to the exact amount (p. 495)

round to change the *value* of a number to one that is easier to work with (p. 495)

subtract to take away, take apart, separate, or find the difference (p. 485)

sum the answer to an addition problem (p. 485)

Visual Vocabulary Cards
Use Visual Vocabulary Cards 1, 2, 13, 15, 17, 46, and 47 to reinforce the vocabulary in this chapter. (The Define/Example/Ask routine is printed on the back of each card.)

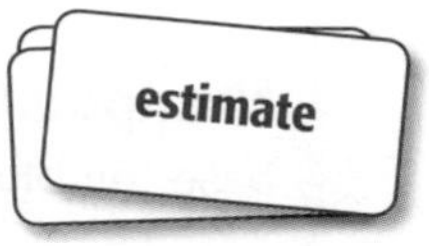

CHAPTER 15

Chapter Planner

Suggested Pacing		
Instruction	Review and Assessment	TOTAL
9 days	2 days	**11 days**

Diagnostic Assessment
Are You Ready? (p. 482)

	Lesson 15-1 (Pacing: 1 day)	Lesson 15-2 (Pacing: 1 day)	Lesson 15-3 (Pacing: 1 day)
Lesson/ Objective	**Add and Subtract Tens** (pp. 485–486) **Objective:** Use base-ten blocks to add and subtract tens.	**Add with Two-Digit Numbers** (pp. 487–488) **Objective:** Add one- and two-digit numbers without regrouping.	Problem-Solving Strategy **Guess and Check** (pp. 489–490) **Objective:** Use the *guess-and-check* strategy to solve problems.
State/Local Standards			
Math Vocabulary			
Lesson Resources	**Materials** hundred chart **Manipulatives** base-ten blocks **Other Resources** CRM Leveled Worksheets (pp. 6–10); Daily Reteach • 5-Minute Check; Problem of the Day	**Materials** hundred chart, WorkMat 4: Number Lines, WorkMat 7: Tens and Ones Chart **Manipulatives** base-ten blocks **Other Resources** CRM Leveled Worksheets (pp. 11–15); Daily Reteach • 5-Minute Check; Problem of the Day	**Manipulatives** base-ten blocks, two-colored counters or connecting cubes **Other Resources** CRM Leveled Worksheets (pp. 16–20); Daily Reteach • 5-Minute Check; Problem of the Day; *A Lemonade Stand*
Technology Math Online	Math Song Track 8	Math Song Track 11; Math Tool Chest, Place Value; Math Adventures	
Reaching All Learners	Gifted and Talented, p. 485B AL; English Learners, p. 485B ELL; Early Finishers, p. 485B OL AL	Gifted and Talented, p. 487B AL; English Learners, p. 487B ELL; Early Finishers, p. 487B OL AL	Gifted and Talented, p. 489B AL; English Learners, p. 489B ELL; Early Finishers, p. 489B OL AL
Alternate Lessons	*Math Their Way*, pp. 294–298	*Math Their Way*, pp. 197–199	

KEY

BL Below/Approaching Level; OL On Level; AL Above/Beyond Level; ELL English Learners
SE Student Edition; TE Teacher Edition; CRM Chapter 3 Resource Masters; CD-Rom
Transparency; Flip Chart; Real-World Problem Solving Library

Solve Two-Digit Addition and Subtraction Problems

	Lesson 15-4 (Pacing: 1 day)	Lesson 15-5 (Pacing: 1 day)	Lesson 15-6 (Pacing: 1 day)
Lesson/ Objective	**Add Two-Digit Numbers** (pp. 491–492) **Objective:** Add 2 two-digit numbers without regrouping.	**Estimate Sums** (pp. 495–496) **Objective:** Estimate the sums of two-digit addends by rounding.	**Subtract with Two-Digit Numbers** (pp. 499–500) **Objective:** Subtract a one-digit number from a two-digit number without regrouping.
State/Local Standards			
Math Vocabulary		**round**	
Lesson Resources	**Materials** WorkMat 7: Tens and Ones Chart **Manipulatives** base-ten blocks **Other Resources** CRM Leveled Worksheets (pp. 21–25) Daily Reteach • 5-Minute Check Problem of the Day	**Materials** WorkMat 4: Number Lines, hundred chart **Manipulatives** two-colored counters **Other Resources** CRM Leveled Worksheets (pp. 26–30) Daily Reteach • 5-Minute Check Problem of the Day	**Materials** WorkMat 7: Tens and Ones Chart, clear or masking tape **Manipulatives** base-ten blocks **Other Resources** CRM Leveled Worksheets (pp. 31–35) Daily Reteach • 5-Minute Check Problem of the Day
Technology Math Online	Math Song Track 11 Math Adventures Concepts in Motion		Math Song Track 15 Math Adventures
Reaching All Learners	Gifted and Talented, p. 491B AL English Learners, p. 491B ELL Early Finishers, p. 491B OL AL	Below Level, p. 495B BL English Learners, p. 495B ELL Early Finishers, p. 495B OL AL	Below Level, p. 499B BL English Learners, p. 499B ELL Early Finishers, p. 499B OL AL
Alternate Lessons	*Math Their Way*, p. 190	*Math Their Way*, p. 205	*Math Their Way*, pp. 193–194

Extra Practice (p. 493)
Game Time: Adding Colors (p. 494)

Formative Assessment
- Mid-Chapter Check (p. 497)
- Spiral Review (p. 498)

CHAPTER 15

Chapter Planner

	Lesson 15-7 (Pacing: 1 day)	Lesson 15-8 (Pacing: 1 day)	Lesson 15-9 (Pacing: 1 day)
Lesson/ Objective	**Subtract Two-Digit Numbers** (pp. 501–502) **Objective:** Subtract a two-digit number from a two-digit number without regrouping.	Problem-Solving Investigation **Choose a Strategy** (pp. 503–504) **Objective:** Choose the best strategy to solve a problem.	**Estimate Differences** (pp. 505–506) **Objective:** Estimate the difference of two-digit numbers by rounding.
State/Local Standards			
Math Vocabulary			
Lesson Resources	**Materials** WorkMat 7: Tens and Ones Chart, hundred chart **Manipulatives** base-ten blocks, dimes and pennies **Other Resources** CRM Leveled Worksheets (pp. 36–40) Daily Reteach • 5-Minute Check Problem of the Day	**Other Resources** CRM Leveled Worksheets (pp. 41–45) Daily Reteach • 5-Minute Check Problem of the Day	**Materials** overhead transparency, hundred chart **Other Resources** CRM Leveled Worksheets (pp. 46–50) Daily Reteach • 5-Minute Check Problem of the Day
Technology Math Online	Math Song Track 15 Math Adventures Concepts in Motion		
Reaching All Learners	Gifted and Talented, p. 501B AL English Learners, p. 501B ELL Early Finishers, p. 501B OL AL	Below Level, p. 503B BL English Learners, p. 503B ELL Early Finishers, p. 503B OL AL	Below Level, p. 505B BL English Learners, p. 505B ELL Early Finishers, p. 505B OL AL
Alternate Lessons	*Math Their Way*, pp. 188–189		*Math Their Way*, pp. 248–249

Problem Solving in Social Studies (p. 507)

Summative Assessment
- Chapter Review/Test (p. 509)
- Test Practice (p. 511)

Assessment Options

Diagnostic Assessment

- SE *Option 1:* Are You Ready? (p. 482)
- *Option 2:* Online Quiz macmillanmh.com
- CRM *Option 3:* Diagnostic Test (p. 52)
- CRM *Option 4:* Chapter Pretest (p. 53)

Formative Assessment

- TE Alternate Teaching Strategies (every lesson)
- SE Talk About It (every lesson)
- SE Writing in Math (every lesson)
- SE Check (every lesson)
- TE Line Up (every lesson)
- SE Mid-Chapter Check (p. 497)
- CRM Mid-Chapter Test (p. 54)

Summative Assessment

- SE Chapter/Review Test (p. 509)
- SE Test Practice (p. 511)
- CRM Vocabulary Test (p. 55)
- CRM Leveled Chapter Tests (pp. 62–71)
- CRM Cumulative Test Practice (pp. 72–73)
- CRM Listening Assessment (pp. 58–59)
- CRM Oral Assessment (pp. 56–57)
- ExamView® Assessment Suite
- Advance Tracker

Mc Graw Hill Professional Development

Targeted professional development has been articulated throughout **McGraw-Hill's *Math Connects*** program. The **McGraw-Hill Professional Development Video Library** provides short videos that support the **NCTM Focal Points and Focal Connections**. For more information, visit macmillanmh.com.

Model Lessons

Instructional Strategies

Teacher Notes

CHAPTER 15

Learning Stations

Cross-Curricular Links

Reading

individual | LINGUISTIC

Read and Share

- Read one of the books at this learning station.
- Draw a picture of your favorite part of the book.
- Write a sentence that describes your illustration.
- Share the book, your illustration, and favorite part with a classmate or your teacher.

Teacher Note: Leave several of the books recommended for this chapter at the Learning Station.

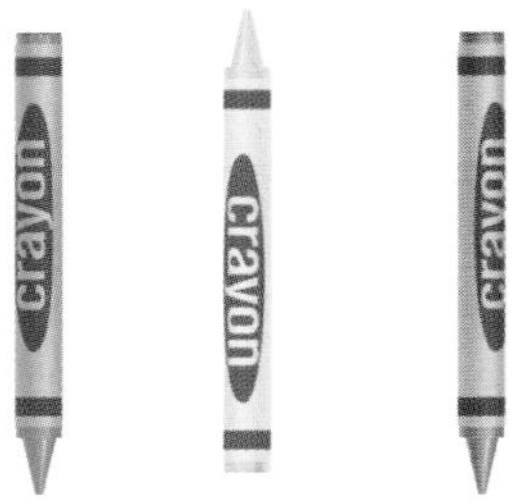

Materials:

- literature (math concepts) books
- paper
- markers or crayons

Art

individual | VISUAL/SPATIAL

Sponge Art

- Use sponge shapes to paint a picture using red, blue, green, and yellow paint.
- Estimate how many sponge prints you made in each color.
- Count the exact number of sponge prints you made in each color and compare with your estimates.
- Write a number sentence for the number of red and blue prints. Write a number sentence for the number of green and yellow prints.

Teacher Note: Provide an example that shows sponge prints in random order, but not overlapping. They will be hard to count if the colors overlap.

Materials:

- red, blue, green, yellow tempera paint
- construction paper
- sponges cut into various shapes for daubing
- paper plates to hold paint

Language Arts

individual | LINGUISTIC

Two-Digit Number Story Book

- Write an addition or a subtraction story problem using two-digit numbers on a sheet of construction paper. Draw an illustration to show your number story and write a number sentence for the story.
- Write other number stories on separate pages. The other pages can continue the first story or make a new story.
- Make a cover and have the teacher staple your book together.
- Share your book with a classmate.

Materials:

- construction paper
- markers or crayons

Solve Two-Digit Addition and Subtraction Problems

Science

individual/pair | AUDITORY

Animal Number Stories

- Cut out a picture of a group of animals from a magazine.
- Glue the picture to a sheet of construction paper.
- Write a number story using the type of animals in the picture and include a number sentence.
- Read your number story to a classmate. Ask your classmate to solve the problem. Check the answer.

Teacher Note: Help guide students to pictures with between ten and fifteen animals. Any more may be too difficult.

Materials:
- magazines
- construction paper
- scissors
- glue

Health

individual | LOGICAL

How Much Water Do You Drink?

- Make a copy of this chart.
- Guess how many glasses of water you drink in 1 school week. Round your estimate to the nearest ten and write your estimate below the chart.
- Every day keep track of how many glasses of water you drink by making a tally mark on the chart for each glass.
- At the end of a school week, total the number of glasses of water you drank and compare it to your estimate. How close was the actual number to your estimate?

Teacher Note: Extend the activity by discussing the importance of drinking plenty of water.

Monday	
Tuesday	
Wednesday	
Thursday	
Friday	

Materials:
- sample recording chart

Calendar Time

- Ask students to tell you the date of their birthday. It does not matter if a student's birthday is in the current month.
- Have students find their birth date on the calendar and tell the class the day of the week and whether that date is before or after today's date.
- Ask students to round their birth date to the nearest ten.
- Find exact and estimated answers for sums and differences of students' birth dates.

Introduce the Chapter

Real World: Add Bigger Numbers

Share with students that in this chapter they are going to learn about adding and subtracting two-digit numbers.

- Divide the class into two groups. Have each student bring one or two pencils.
- Have students find the total number of pencils in their group. **How many pencils are in your group?** Make sure each group has a two-digit number.
- **How can we find the total number of pencils for the whole class?** Sample answers: Add the group totals; count all the pencils.
- Help the class find the total.

Have students turn to p. 481.

- **How many mailboxes can you count?** 10 mailboxes **Do you bring in the mail at home?**

Key Vocabulary

Introduce the key vocabulary in the chapter using the routine below.

Define: When you **round**, you change the *value* of a number to one that is easier to work with.

Example: 47 rounded to the nearest ten is 50.

Ask: What is 57 rounded to the nearest ten?

CHAPTER 15

Solve Two-Digit Addition and Subtraction Problems

Key Vocabulary

round

Explore

What is 10 more than 14? 24

What is 10 more than 18? 28

FOLDABLES Study Organizer — Dinah Zike's Foldables

Guide students to create four Pocket Foldables for adding and subtracting two-digit numbers.

1. Fold an 8 1/2 x 11 sheet of paper in half like hamburger.

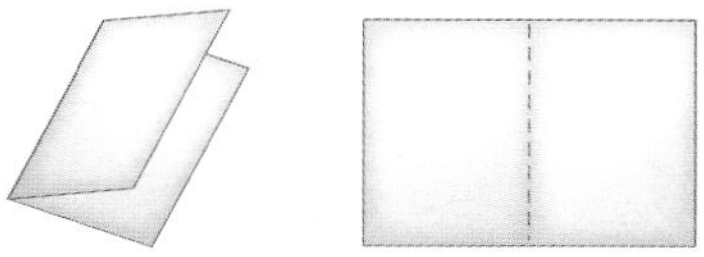

2. Open the folded paper and fold one of the long sides up two inches to form a pocket. Refold along the hamburger fold so that the newly formed pockets are on the inside.

3. Glue the outer edges of the two-inch fold with a small amount of glue.

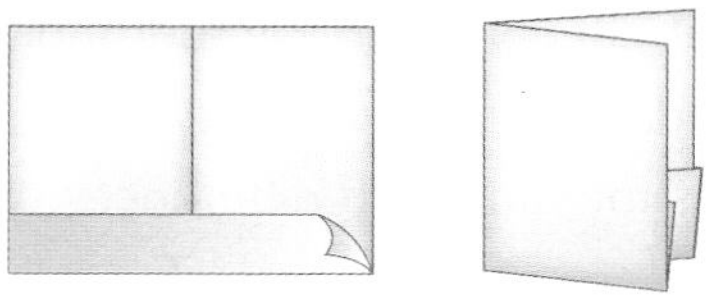

4. Make five sets of Pocket Foldables (enough for each lesson). Glue pockets together to form a Pocket Book.

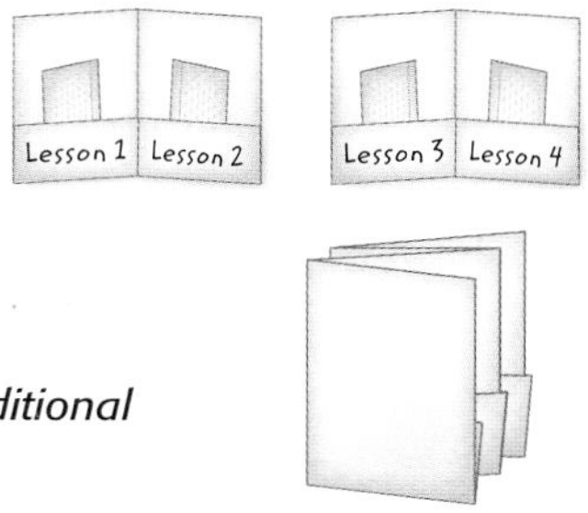

When to Use It *Lessons 15-1, 15-2, 15-3, 15-4, 15-5, 15-6, 15-7, 15-8, and 15-9. (Additional instructions for using the Foldable with these lessons are found on pp. 497 and 509.)*

Name ____________________

Math Online
Take the Chapter Readiness Quiz at macmillanmh.com.

Are You Ready for Chapter 15?

Write how many tens and ones.

1. 

6 tens 4 ones = 64

2. 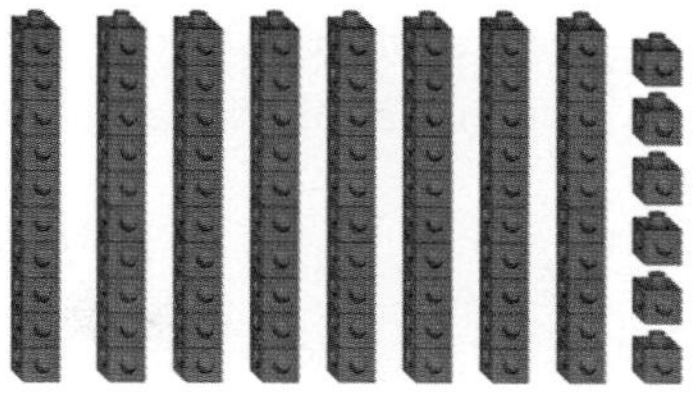

8 tens 6 ones = 86

Add or subtract.

3.	4.	5.	6.	7.
9 + 1 = 10	15 − 7 = 8	4 − 2 = 2	12 − 6 = 6	9 + 3 = 12

8.	9.	10.	11.	12.
4 + 7 = 11	14 − 8 = 6	8 + 3 = 11	7 + 6 = 13	13 − 5 = 8

13. 10 more than 25 35

14. 1 less than 50 49

15. 1 more than 35 36

16. 10 less than 60 50

17. Maya counts 13 tadpoles. 5 of them swim away. How many tadpoles are left? 8 tadpoles

This page checks skills needed for Chapter 15.

Diagnostic Assessment

Check for students' prerequisite skills before beginning the chapter.

- **Option 1:** ***Are You Ready for Chapter 15?***
  SE Student Edition, p. 482
- **Option 2:** ***Online Assessment***
  Math Online macmillanmh.com
- **Option 3:** ***Diagnostic Test***
  CRM Chapter 15 Resource Masters, p. 52

RTI (Response to Intervention)

Apply the Results Based on the results of the diagnostic assessment on p. 482, use the chart below to address individual needs before beginning the chapter.

TIER 3 Intensive Intervention

If students miss eleven or more of the exercises:

Then use Chapters 1, 2, 3, and 5 of *Math Triumphs*, an intensive math intervention program from McGraw-Hill

TIER 2 Strategic Intervention below/approaching grade level	TIER 1 On-Level	Above/Beyond Level
If students miss six to ten in: **Exercises 1–17**	**If** students miss three to five in: **Exercises 1–17**	**If** students miss two or less in: **Exercises 1–17**
Then choose a resource:	**Then** choose a resource:	**Then** choose a resource:
Strategic Intervention Guide (p. 52) CRM Chapter 2 Resource Masters (Reteach Worksheets) Math Online Concepts in Motion	TE Learning Stations (pp. 481G–481H) TE Chapter Project (p. 483) CRM Game: *Adding Tens* Math Adventures My Math Zone Chapter 14 Math Online Fact Dash	TE Learning Stations (pp. 481G–481H) TE Chapter Project (p. 483) Real-World Problem Solving: *A Lemonade Stand* Math Adventures My Math Zone Chapters 14, 15 Math Online Games

MATH at HOME

Before you begin Chapter 15:

- Read the Math at Home letter found on p. 483, with the class and have each student sign it.
- Send home copies of the Math at Home letter with each student.
- Use the Spanish letter on student p. 484 for students with Spanish-speaking parents or guardians.

WRITING IN ▶ MATH

Starting the Chapter
Ask students to write definitions for *one-digit number* and *two-digit number* and provide several examples. Have students explain why adding and subtracting two-digit numbers could be more difficult than adding and subtracting one-digit numbers.

Read-Aloud Anthology
For an optional reading activity to introduce this chapter's math concepts, see the Read-Aloud Anthology on p. TR39.

MATH at HOME

Dear Family,

Today my class started Chapter 15, **Solve Two-Digit Addition and Subtraction Problems**. In this chapter, I will learn to add and subtract two-digit numbers. Here is an activity we can do and a list of books we can read together.

Love, ____________________

Activity

Have your child practice adding and subtracting tens. For example, 4 dimes + 2 dimes = 6 dimes, 40¢ + 20¢ = 60¢.

Key Vocabulary

estimate to find a number close to an exact amount.

round to change the value of a number to one that is easier to work with.

Math Online Click on the eGlossary link at macmillanmh.com to find out more about these words. There are 13 languages.

Books to Read

Arctic Fives Arrive
by Elinor J. Pinczes
Houghton Mifflin Company, 1996.

The Cats of Mrs. Calamari
by John Stadler
Scholastic, Inc., 1997.

17 Kings and 42 Elephants
by Margaret Mahy
Dial, 1987.

Chapter 15 Project

Add and Subtract Two-Digit Numbers

- Have small groups of students create posters to illustrate how to estimate, add, and subtract two-digit numbers.
- Each poster should include a two-digit addition or subtraction problem, steps to estimate the problem and its answer by rounding each number to the nearest ten, steps to solve the problem, and the actual answer.
- Ask groups to share their posters with the class and display them so students can refer to them when solving problems.

CRM *Refer to Chapter 15 Resource Masters, p. 60 for a rubric to assess students' progress on this project.*

MATEMÁTICAS en CASA

Estimada familia:

Hoy mi clase comenzó el Capítulo 15, **Resuelva la adición del dos digito y problemas de sustracción**. En este capítulo, aprenderé a sumar y restar números de dos dígitos. A continuación, hay una actividad que podemos hacer y una lista de libros que podemos leer juntos.

Cariños, ____________________

Actividad

Pídanle a su hijo(a) que practique la suma y la resta de decenas. Por ejemplo, 4 monedas de 10¢ + 2 monedas de 10¢ = 6 monedas de 10¢, 40¢ + 20¢ = 60¢.

Vocabulario clave

estimar hallar un número cercano a la cantidad exacta

redondear cambiar el *valor* de un número a uno con el que es más fácil trabajar

Math Online Visiten el enlace eGlossary en macmillanmh.com para averiguar más sobre estas palabras, las cuales se muestran en 13 idiomas.

Libros recomendados

Sumar y restar
de DK
Estrella Gsp, 2006.

Una, dos, tres el año de fue
de Gregory Tang
Everest Publishing, 2004.

ELL National ESL Standards Alignment for Chapter 15

Lesson, Page	ESL Standard	Modality	Level
15-1, p 485B	Goal 2, Standard 1, c	Spatial, Interpersonal	Intermediate
15-2, p 487B	Goal 1, Standard 3, e	Spatial, Logical	Beginning
15-3, p 489B	Goal 2, Standard 2, h	Spatial, Kinesthetic	Advanced
15-4, p 491B	Goal 1, Standard 3, k	Kinesthetic	Intermediate
15-5, p 495B	Goal 2, Standard 2, j	Visual, Spatial	Intermediate
15-6, p 499B	Goal 1, Standard 1, b	Visual	Beginning
15-7, p 501B	Goal 2, Standard 1, c	Spatial, Linguistic	Intermediate
15-8, p 503B	Goal 1, Standard 3, k	Logical, Linguistic	Intermediate
15-9, p 505B	Goal 2, Standard 1, f	Logical, Social	Advanced

The National ESL Standards can be found in the Teacher Reference Handbook.

Chapter 15 Literature List

Lesson	Book Title
15-1	**Leaping Lizards** Stuart J. Murphy
15-2	**How Many Snails? A Counting Book** Paul Giganti, Jr.
15-3	**Mission: Addition** Loreen Leedy
15-4	**How Many Snails? A Counting Book** Paul Giganti, Jr.
15-5	**Betcha!** Stuart J. Murphy
15-6	**Panda Math: Learning About Subtraction from Hua Mei and Mei Sheng** Ann Whitehead Nagda
15-7	**Shark Swimathon** Stuart J. Murphy
15-9	**Coyotes All Around** Stuart J. Murphy
Any	**Arctic Fives Arrive** Elinor J. Pinczes
Any	**The Cats of Mrs. Calamari** John Stadler
Any	**17 Kings and 42 Elephants** Margaret Mahy

LESSON 15-1

Add and Subtract Tens

Lesson Planner

Objective
Use base-ten blocks to add and subtract tens.

Review Vocabulary
dime

Resources
Materials: hundred chart

Manipulatives: base-ten blocks

Literature Connection: *Leaping Lizards* by Stuart J. Murphy

Alternate Lesson: Adapt "Counting Game: Connecting Symbolization to the Concept" on pages 294–298 of *Math Their Way* for practice in adding and subtracting tens.

Teacher Technology

TeacherWorks • Math Songs Track 8 Lesson Plan

Focus on Math Background

This lesson introduces students to two-digit addition and subtraction. Students will make the connection between the single-digit facts they already know and the addition and subtraction of tens. By demonstrating that multiples of ten can be written as a number of tens, students can use their prior knowledge about basic facts to add or subtract. Explain to students that adding tens is no different than adding stickers or crayons: 3 stickers plus 2 stickers equals 5 stickers, 3 tens plus 2 tens equals 5 tens, or 50.

Daily Routine

Use these suggestions before beginning the lesson on p. 485.

5-Minute Check
(Reviews Lesson 14-7)

Choose a strategy to solve.

1. Eduwa invited 20 friends to her party. Only 16 friends came to the party. How many friends did not come? 4 friends

2. Mark ate a granola bar every morning for 2 weeks. How many granola bars did he eat altogether? 14 granola bars

Problem of the Day
Write a number story to show the following subtraction sentence. 16 − 9 = 7. Sample answer: 16 students were on the playground. Then 9 students went inside. Now 7 students are left on the playground.

LINE UP When students prepare to line up for recess, lunch, or dismissal, hold up addition and subtraction flash cards. Call on students to say the sum or difference of a math fact and then line up.

Review Math Vocabulary
Give each student 8 dime manipulatives.

- **How many dimes do you have?** 8 dimes **How many tens are there in 80?** 8 tens
- Have students take away three dimes. Ask students how much 3 dimes are worth (30¢). **How many tens are there in 30?** 3 tens Explain that they took away or subtracted 3 tens.
- **How much money is left?** 50¢ **How many tens in 50?** 5 tens

Visual Vocabulary Cards
Use Visual Vocabulary Card 15 to reinforce the vocabulary reviewed in this lesson. (The Define/Example/Ask routine is printed on the back of each card.)

Differentiated Instruction

Small Group Options

Option 1 VISUAL/SPATIAL, SOCIAL

Gifted and Talented (AL)

Materials: number cards from 1 to 9, paper or cloth bag, white board, dry-erase marker

Place the number cards in the bag.

- One student pulls two number cards from the bag and writes them as a two-digit number on the white board.
- Another student pulls one card and writes that number below the two-digit number.
- The group works together to add the numbers. Addition with regrouping can occur. Students may need a number line or base-ten blocks for help with these problems.
- Students take turns pulling cards and solving the addition problems.

Option 2 SPATIAL, LOGICAL

English Language Learners (ELL)

Materials: pipe cleaners and round oat cereal

Core Vocabulary: add to it, hold up, slide through the hole

Common Use Verb: string

Do Math This strategy allows students to demonstrate their understanding of the math skill.

- Give each student a number (between 1 and 9) and have them put that number of cheerios on a pipe cleaner.
- Write "23". Have students write a problem that adds their number of cereal pieces to 23.
- Ask all the students who got 24 hold up their pipe cleaner. Visually check to see that they all have only 1 piece. Repeat for other numbers.
- Repeat for other 2 digit numbers as time permits.

Independent Work Options

Option 1 LOGICAL, VISUAL/SPATIAL

Early Finishers (OL) (AL)

Materials: WorkMat 7: Tens and Ones Chart, number cards from 1 to 4, base-ten blocks, red number cube

- One student rolls the red number cube twice to make the digits for a two-digit number.
- Students model the two-digit number with base-ten blocks on WorkMat 7.
- Another student picks a number card at random.
- Students add that number of ones to the workmat to find the sum of the two numbers.

Option 2

Student Technology

Math Online macmillanmh.com

Math Songs, "The Addition Boogie" Track 11 • Math Tool Chest • Math Adventures

Option 3

Learning Station: Reading (p. 481G)

Direct students to the Reading Learning Station for more opportunities to explore and extend the lesson concept.

Option 4

Problem-Solving Practice

Reinforce problem-solving skills and strategies with the Problem-Solving Practice worksheet.

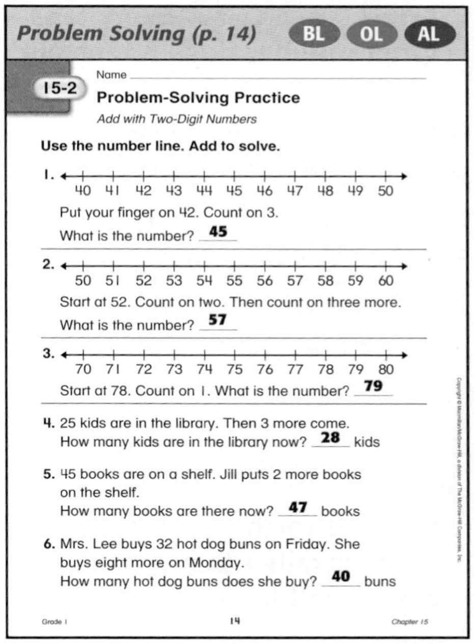

Problem Solving (p. 14) BL OL AL

Name ______

15-2 **Problem-Solving Practice**

Add with Two-Digit Numbers

Use the number line. Add to solve.

1. 40 41 42 43 44 45 46 47 48 49 50

   Put your finger on 42. Count on 3.

   What is the number? **45**

2. 50 51 52 53 54 55 56 57 58 59 60

   Start at 52. Count on two. Then count on three more.

   What is the number? **57**

3. 70 71 72 73 74 75 76 77 78 79 80

   Start at 78. Count on 1. What is the number? **79**

4. 25 kids are in the library. Then 3 more come.

   How many kids are in the library now? **28** kids

5. 45 books are on a shelf. Jill puts 2 more books on the shelf.

   How many books are there now? **47** books

6. Mrs. Lee buys 32 hot dog buns on Friday. She buys eight more on Monday.

   How many hot dog buns does she buy? **40** buns

Grade 1 14 Chapter 15

1 Introduce

Activity Choice 1 • Hands-On

Give pairs of students 5 base-ten rods and 20 units.

- Explain that you will tell a math story, and the students are to use their rods and units to show the following problem:
  Kelly has snacks to take to school. She has 12 apples and 4 bananas.
- **How many snacks does she have altogether?** 16 snacks

Activity Choice 2 • Literature

Introduce the lesson with *How Many Snails?* by Paul Giganti, Jr. For additional support, see p. TR64.

2 Teach

Have students use WorkMat 7: Tens and Ones Chart and base-ten blocks. Write the number 34 on the board and have students read it aloud.

- **What are some ways to show this number?** Sample answers: 3 tens and 4 ones, 30 + 4 Have students use base-ten blocks to model 34 on the workmat.
- Write + 5 on the board to create the addition sentence 34 + 5. **How many ones are in 34?** 4 ones **How many ones are in 5?** 5 ones
- **Do we add the 5 ones to the 3 tens or the 4 ones?** the 4 ones **Why?** Ones add to ones.
- Combine the ones. **How many ones are there total?** 9 ones **How many tens are there?** 3 tens **What number does 3 tens and 9 ones make?** 39

Get Ready Use the section at the top of p. 487 to reinforce the lesson concept.

Check Observe students as you work through Exercises 1–4 as a class.

Exercise 4 Assess student comprehension before assigning practice exercises.

! COMMON ERROR!
Students might add the one-digit number to the tens rather than ones. Emphasize that ones always add to ones.

Name ____________________

Add with Two-Digit Numbers

Get Ready

Main Idea
I will add with two-digit numbers.

Find 25 + 2.

Step 1 Show each number.	Step 2 Add the ones.	Step 3 Add the tens.
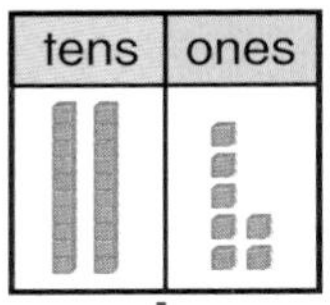	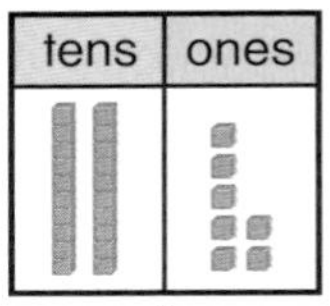	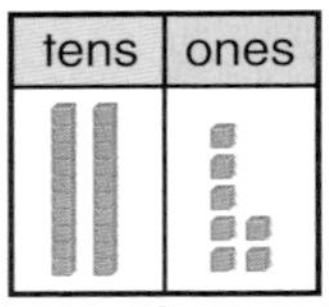

	tens	ones
	2	5
+		2

	tens	ones
	2	5
+		2
		7

	tens	ones
	2	5
+		2
	2	7

Add the ones. 2 ones + 5 ones = 7 ones

The sum is 2 tens and 7 ones or 27.

Check

Use WorkMat 7 and [tens rod] and [unit cube]. Add.

1.

	tens	ones
	1	3
+		4
	1	7

2.

	tens	ones
		6
+	4	1
	4	7

3.

	tens	ones
		6
+	5	3
	5	9

4. **Talk About It** Explain how you add tens and ones? Sample answer: first you add the ones. Then you add the tens.

Reteach (p. 11) BL

15-2 Name ____________________

Reteach

Add with Two-Digit Numbers

You can count on a number line to add with two-digit numbers.

Mary buys 32 eggs.
Jen buys 5 more eggs than Mary.
How many eggs did Jen buy?

32 + 5 = ?

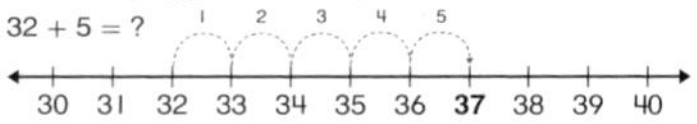

32 + 5 = 37 eggs

Use the number line to add.

1. 10 11 12 13 14 15 16 17 18 19 20
14 + 3 = **17** 18 + 2 = **20**

2. 20 21 22 23 24 25 26 27 28 29 30
21 + 4 = **25** 24 + 3 = **27**

3. 30 31 32 33 34 35 36 37 38 39 40
36 + 3 = **39** 31 + 5 = **36**

4. 60 61 62 63 64 65 66 67 68 69 70
63 + 5 = **68** 65 + 3 = **68**

Grade 1 11 Chapter 15

Skills Practice (p. 12) OL

15-2 Name ____________________

Skills Practice

Add with Two-Digit Numbers

Use WorkMat 7 and [unit cube] and [tens rod]. Add.

1.

	tens	ones
	3	7
+		2
	3	**9**

2.

	tens	ones
	4	4
+		3
	4	**7**

3.

	tens	ones
	6	1
+		5
	6	**6**

4.

	tens	ones
	5	2
+		6
	5	**8**

5.

	tens	ones
	7	6
+		1
	7	**7**

6.

	tens	ones
	2	1
+		7
	2	**8**

Solve.

7. Bob has 33 stamps. He finds 2 more. How many stamps are there? **35** stamps

8. Start at 26. Count on 2. What is the number? **28**

Grade 1 12 Chapter 15

Use WorkMat 7 and [tens rod] and [unit cube]. Add.

Remember start on the right.

5.

	tens	ones
	2	2
+		3
	2	5

6.

	tens	ones
	4	2
+		2
	4	4

7.

	tens	ones
		4
+	4	4
	4	8

8.

	tens	ones
	5	2
+		6
	5	8

9.

	tens	ones
	7	1
+		4
	7	5

10.

	tens	ones
		3
+	9	1
	9	4

11.

	tens	ones
	1	6
+		3
	1	9

12.

	tens	ones
	5	5
+		4
	5	9

13.

	tens	ones
	8	2
+		4
	8	6

H.O.T. Problem

14. Make It Right This is how Helen added 23 + 6. Tell why Helen is wrong. Make it right.

	tens	ones
	2	3
+	6	
	8	3

	tens	ones
	2	3
+		6
	2	9

Sample answer: Helen added 6 as 6 tens instead of 6 ones.

23 + 6 = 29

Math at Home Activity: Your child learned to add a two-digit number and a one-digit number. Ask your child to explain how to add 42 + 5.

Enrich (p. 15) AL

15-2 Name

Enrich

A Sticky Riddle!

Solve the problems.
Then write your answers in order below.

27 + **2** = 29; **56** + 2 = 58; 77 + 2 = **79**; 11 + **8** = 19

5 + 22 = 27; 4 + 44 = **48**; 93 + **4** = 97; **81** + 7 = 88

16 + 3 = **19**; 62 + **7** = 69; 80 + 1 = **81**; **5** + 73 = 78

What did the chewing gum say to the shoe?

KEY	
2 = I	19 = N
4 = K	48 = C
5 = U	56 = M
7 = Y	79 = S
8 = T	81 = O

2 56 | 79 8 5 48 4 | 81 19 | 7 81 5

I'M STUCK ON YOU!

Grade 1 | 15 | Chapter 15

Homework Practice (p. 13) OL

15-2 Name

Homework Practice

Add with Two-Digit Numbers

Use WorkMat 7 and [unit cube] and [tens rod]. Add.

1. 24 + 5 = **29**
2. 42 + 4 = **46**
3. 61 + 1 = **62**
4. 23 + 3 = **26**
5. 77 + 2 = **79**
6. 11 + 3 = **14**

Solve.

7. Ann says that 35 + 2 is 33. Is she right? **no**
8. Start at 44. Count on 5. What is the number? **49**

Grade 1 | 13 | Chapter 15

BL Alternate Teaching Strategy

If students have trouble understanding how to add one- and two-digit numbers . . .

Then use one of the following reteach options.

1 CRM **Daily Reteach Worksheet** (p. 11)

2 **Number Jump** Help students add a one-digit number to a two-digit number by "jumping" on a number line or hundred chart. Have students start with their finger on the two-digit number and count or jump up by the one-digit number.

3 Have students use Math Tool Chest to help complete the problem-solving exercises.

3 Practice

Differentiate practice using these leveled assignments for Exercises 5–14.

Level	Assignment
BL Below/Approaching Level	Assist students in placing base-ten blocks correctly on the workmat.
OL On Level	Complete exercises independently.
AL Above/Beyond Level	Complete the exercises without using the base-ten blocks.

4 Assess

Formative Assessment

- **Show the steps for adding tens and ones in this problem: 64 + 5.** Sample answer: Show each number, add the ones, and then add the tens. The sum is 69.

WRITING IN MATH Have students write a number story for the following addition sentence: 23 + 3 = 26.

Quick Check **Are students continuing to struggle with adding one- and two-digit numbers without regrouping?**

If Yes → Strategic Intervention Guide (p.86)

If No → Independent Work Options (p. 487B)

CRM Skills Practice Worksheet (p. 12)

CRM Enrich Worksheet (p. 15)

Lesson Planner

Objective

Use the *guess-and-check* strategy to solve problems.

Resources

Manipulatives: base-ten blocks, two-colored counters or connecting cubes

Literature Connection: *Mission: Addition* by Loreen Leedy

Teacher Technology
TeacherWorks

Real-World Problem Solving
Math and Social Studies: *A Lemonade Stand*
Use these leveled books to reinforce and extend problem-solving skills and strategies.

Leveled for:
- OL On Level
- ELL Sheltered English
- SP Spanish

For additional support, see the Real-World Problem Solving Teacher Guide.

Daily Routine

Use these suggestions before beginning the lesson on p. 489.

5-Minute Check

(Reviews Lesson 15-2)

Use base-ten blocks to solve.

1. 4 tens + 5 tens = ______ 9 tens
   40 + 50 = ______ 90
2. 2 tens + 1 ten = ______ 3 tens
   20 + 10 = ______ 30
3. 7 tens + 3 tens = ______ 10 tens
   70 + 30 = ______ 100

Problem of the Day

Draw base-ten blocks to model the number 57.
5 rods and 7 units

LINE UP Ask one student to line up. Have the student choose a number between 1 and 9. Ask a second student to line up. Have the student choose a number between 1 and 9. Have a third student make a two-digit number out of the two numbers. Continue this activity until all the students are in line.

Differentiated Instruction

Small Group Options

Option 1 SOCIAL LINGUISTIC

Gifted and Talented AL

Materials: number stories written on index cards, two-colored counters

- Each student in the group picks an index card with a number story.
- Have students take turns reading their story aloud. The group works together, using counters to solve the problem.
- Ask students to reread the problem to make sure they used the correct number of counters to solve.
- Have students write the answer to the problem on the back of the index card.

Option 2 SPATIAL, KINESTHETIC

English Language Learners ELL

Core Vocabulary: hopscotch, closest without going over, hop
Common Use Verb: land on
Materials: chart paper

Do Math This strategy provides practice with the guess and check method.

- Put 2-digit numbers in hopscotch and have 2 teams line up on either side.
- Post a problem. The first player in line hops to the square that is closest to the answer without going over. Allow students to go up and back only once.
- The opposing team must clap if the answer their opponent landed on is the closest to get 1 point, or challenge to try for 2 points.
- When a team challenges an answer, they must hop to the correct answer. Only the first player in line can move.
- The team that lands on the best answer gets 2 points. If a team challenges a best answer, they get 0 points.
- Repeat as time permits. High score wins.

Independent Work Options

Option 1 LOGICAL

Early Finishers OL AL

Materials: construction paper, markers or crayons, coins or base-ten blocks

- Students work in pairs to draw an assortment of items for sale. Students must price each item.
- After the items are priced, have pairs select two of the items and write the total cost of those items above the drawing.

- Ask pairs to exchange pages with another pair and then try to find which items add to the amount written on the page.
- Allow students to use coins or base-ten blocks to model each number.

Option 2

Student Technology

Math Online macmillanmh.com

Option 3

Learning Station: Language Arts (p. 481G)

Direct students to the Language Arts Learning Station for more opportunities to explore and extend the lesson concept.

1 Introduce

Activity Choice 1 • Review

Write the following story on the board:

Beth, Eliot, and Suri measure their heights. Suri is taller than at least one of the other students. Beth is not the shortest student. Who is the shortest student?

- **What problem-solving strategy could you use to answer this problem?** Sample answers: Act it out; draw a picture; use logical reasoning.
- **Guide students to use *logical reasoning*. Can Suri be the shortest student?** no **Why not?** She is taller than one other student.
- **Can Beth be the shortest student?** no **Why not?** The problem says Beth is not the shortest.
- **Who is left?** Eliot

Activity Choice 2 • Literature

Introduce the lesson with *Mission: Addition* by Loreen Leedy. For additional support, see p. TR64.

2 Teach

Have students read the problem on p. 489. Guide them through the problem-solving steps.

Understand Using the questions, review what students know and what they need to find.

Plan Have them discuss their strategy.

Solve Guide students to *guess and check* to solve the problem.

- **How many blue and red birds are there?** 29
- **How many red and yellow birds are there?** 19
- **How many blue and yellow birds are there?** 32

Check Have students look back at the problem to make sure the answer fits the facts given.

- **Is the total of blue and yellow birds 32?** yes

! COMMON ERROR!

Students may lose track of their subtotals before performing the second operation. Have students write the subtotal on their page or use manipulatives to keep track.

Name ____________________

Problem-Solving Strategy

Guess and Check

Main Idea

I will guess and check to solve a problem.

Tara sees 2 colors of birds. She sees a total of 32 birds. Which 2 colors of birds did she see?

21 8 11

Understand

What do I know?

Underline what you know.

What do I need to find?

Circle the question.

Plan

How will I solve the problem?

I can guess and check.

Solve

Try 21 + 8 = 29 This is not correct.

8 + 11 = 19 This is not correct.

21 + 11 = 32 This is correct.

So Tara sees blue and yellow birds.

Check

Look back.

Is my answer reasonable?

Check students' explanations.

Reteach (pp. 16–17) BL

15-3 Name ____________________

Reteach (1)

Problem-Solving Strategy: Guess and Check

Mr. Gil went to the store.
He spent a total of 34 cents.
Which two products did he buy?

Step 1 Understand — **What do I know?**
The bubble bath costs 10 cents.
The hand soap costs 14 cents.
The toothpaste costs 20 cents.
Mr. Gil spent 34 cents.
What do I need to find out?
Which two products did Mr. Gil buy?

Step 2 Plan — **How will I find out what he bought?**
I can guess and check until I find which two products add up to 34 cents.

Step 3 Solve — **Guess and Check**
I will guess that Mr. Gil bought the hand soap and the toothpaste.
Check: 14 cents + 20 cents = 34 cents
The sum is 34. Mr. Gil bought the hand soap and the toothpaste.

Step 4 Check — Is my answer reasonable? **yes**
How do I know? **14 + 20 = 34**

Grade 1 16 Chapter 15

Skills Practice (p. 18) OL

15-3 Name ____________________

Skills Practice

Problem-Solving Strategy: Guess and Check

Guess and check to solve.

1. Mike has 2 toy boxes. He has 29 toys. About how many toys are in each box? Circle your guess. Then check.
   About: 5 10 (15)
   Check: **15 + 15 = 30**. Was your guess close? **yes**
2. Todd sees 2 kinds of things outside. He sees 15 things in all. Which 2 things does he see? Circle your guess. Then check.
   (5) 7 (10)
   Check: **5 + 10 = 15**. Was your guess right? **yes**
3. Ella did 2 chores for her mom. She worked for 35 minutes. Which 2 chores did she do? Circle your guess. Then check.
   (10 minutes) 15 minutes (25 minutes) 30 minutes
   Check: **10 + 25 = 35**. Was your guess right? **yes**
4. Make this number sentence correct. Put in the signs.
   32 (−) 25 (−) 7 = 0

Grade 1 18 Chapter 15

Try It

Remember
Understand
Plan
Solve
Check

Use the guess and check strategy to solve.

1. Joan gets 2 colors of balloons. She gets 27 balloons in all.

What color balloons did she get? green and purple

2. Kim finds 2 colors of leaves. She finds 41 leaves in all.

What color leaves did she find? orange and green

Your Turn

Use the guess and check strategy to solve.

3. Rose bought 2 toys. She spent 17 cents altogether. What toys did she buy?

Rose bought a ball and a doll.

4. Lena bought 2 toys. She spent 28 cents. What did she buy?

Lena bought a fish and a ball.

Math at Home Activity: Give your child an addition or subtraction problem to solve using guess and check.

Enrich (p. 20) AL

15-3 Name ______
Enrich
Add It Up

Use the shapes to add. Write the addition sentence and solve.

1. △△△△△△ △△△△△ ○○○ **11 + 3 = 14**
2. ☆☆☆☆☆☆ ☆☆☆☆☆☆ □□□□□ **12 + 5 = 17**
3. □□□□□□ □□□□□□□ △△△ △△△ **13 + 6 = 19**
4. △△△△△△△ △△△△△△△ ☆ ☆☆ **14 + 3 = 18**
5. ○○○○○○○ ○○○○○○○○ ☆ **15 + 1 = 16**

Grade 1 20 Chapter 15

Homework Practice (p. 19) OL

15-3 Name ______
Homework Practice
Problem-Solving Strategy: Guess and Check

Circle your guess. Then check.

1. Bob sees 2 kinds of flowers in the yard. He sees 38 flowers in all. Which 2 flowers does he see?

Check: **20 + 18 = 38**. Was your guess right? **yes**

2. Marlee sees 2 kinds of birds in the yard. She sees 21 birds in all. Which 2 birds does she see?

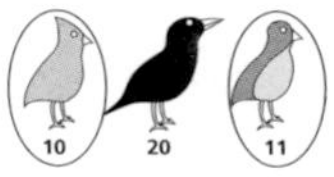

Check: **10 + 11 = 21**.
Was your answer right? **yes**

3. James sees 2 kinds of bugs in the yard. He sees 48 bugs in all. Which 2 bugs does he see?

Check: **20 + 28 = 48**. Was your guess right? **yes**

4. Erika plants 2 packets of seeds. She plants 52 seeds in all. Which packets does she plant?

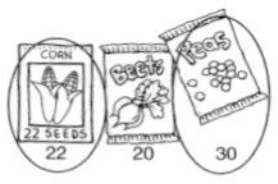

Check: **22 + 30 = 52**.
Was your guess right? **yes**

Grade 1 19 Chapter 15

Chapter Resources

Try It Observe students as you work through Exercises 1–2 as a class.

BL Alternate Teaching Strategy

If students have trouble understanding how to guess and check . . .

Then use one of the following reteach options.

1. CRM **Daily Reteach Worksheet** (pp. 16–17)
2. **Make a List** One of the more difficult aspects of guess and check for students is keeping track of the eliminated guesses so they do not check them again. Help students make a list or table of all the possible guesses. Have them mark out those that have already been checked.

3 Practice

Your Turn

Exercises 3 and 4 Students must be fluent with addition and subtraction facts up to 20 to easily solve these problems. Allow slower students to use two-colored counters, base-ten blocks, or a number line for help.

4 Assess

Formative Assessment

- Have students name all the possible guesses for Exercise 3. plus and plus, plus and minus, minus and plus, minus and minus
- Ask students if a problem had 50 possible guesses, would guess and check be a good strategy? Sample answer: No, it would take a long time to check each possible guess.

WRITING IN MATH Have students describe how to use the guess and check strategy.

Quick Check **Are students continuing to struggle with the *guess-and-check* strategy?**

If Yes → Strategic Intervention Guide (p.86)

If No → Independent Work Options (p. 489B)
CRM Skills Practice Worksheet (p. 18)
CRM Enrich Worksheet (p. 20)

LESSON 15-4

Add Two-Digit Numbers

Lesson Planner

Objective

Add 2 two-digit numbers without regrouping.

Review Vocabulary

addend, sum

Resources

Materials: WorkMat 7: Tens and Ones Chart

Manipulatives: base-ten blocks

Literature Connection: *How Many Snails?* by Paul Giganti, Jr.

Alternate Lesson: Adapt "Listen and Count" on page 190 of *Math Their Way* for practice in addition with two-digit numbers.

Teacher Technology

TeacherWorks • Concepts in Motion • Math Songs Track 11 Lesson Plan

Focus on Math Background

In this lesson, students add two-digit numbers. To accomplish this task, students might need to regroup the sum of the digits in the ones place into a unit of ten. To calculate the final sum, students add the 1 representing the new set of ten with the digits in the tens place. Throughout this procedure of regrouping, students should be careful not to digitize the numbers to the extent of ignoring the quantity's size.

Daily Routine

Use these suggestions before beginning the lesson on p. 491.

5-Minute Check

(Reviews Lesson 15-3)

Use base-ten blocks and WorkMat 7 to add.

1. 25 + 4 = ____ 29

2. 52 + 3 = ____ 55

3. 37 + 2 = ____ 39

4. 14 + 5 = ____ 19

5. 61 + 6 = ____ 67

6. 43 + 1 = ____ 44

Problem of the Day

Write a number story for the following addition sentence. 13 + 5 = 18. Sample answer: Ahmad collected 13 shells on the beach. His brother collected 5. Together they collected 18 shells.

LINE UP When students line up for recess, lunch, or dismissal, call out a two-digit number to each student and ask the student to tell you how many tens and how many ones make up that number.

Review Math Vocabulary

- Write 15 + 22 = 37 on the board.
- **What is the sum in this addition sentence?** 37 **What are the addends in this addition sentence?** 15 and 22
- Ask a volunteer to come to the board. Have the student rewrite this addition sentence, but replace the numbers with the vocabulary words. addend + addend = sum
- **What is a way to remember what addend means?** Sample answer: You add addends.

Visual Vocabulary Cards

Use Visual Vocabulary Cards 2 and 47 to reinforce the vocabulary reviewed in this lesson. (The Define/Example/Ask routine is printed on the back of each card.)

Differentiated Instruction

Small Group Options

Option 1 Gifted and Talented AL

VISUAL/SPATIAL

Materials: red number cubes

- Divide students into pairs.
- Each student rolls two red number cubes and makes a two-digit number from the results. Have students write down their numbers in a vertical addition format.
- Partners work together to add the numbers and find the total. Addition with regrouping can occur. Students may need base-ten blocks for help with these problems.
- Partners take turns rolling the number cube and making other addition problems to solve.

Option 2 English Language Learners ELL

KINESTHETIC

Materials: craft sticks, rubber bands, index cards
Core Vocabulary: rubber band, sticks, tie together/ untie
Common Use Verb: twist

Do Math This strategy shelters the math skill of adding two-digit numbers and adds new vocabulary.

- Give students a random handful of sticks. Allow them to count and bind groups of 10 with a rubber band.
- Have all students write their number of sticks on a card.
- Have pairs work together with sticks to solve and write a problem.
- Have students present their problem and solution to the class. Restate their steps as you write out the standardized forms on the board. If there are mistakes, have students act out the step with the sticks, recount their original number, etc.
- Discuss and repeat as time permits.

Independent Work Options

Option 1 Early Finishers OL AL

VISUAL/SPATIAL

Materials: WorkMat 7, two-digit addition flash cards, base-ten blocks

- Divide students into groups of three. Have students mix up the flash cards and place them facedown.
- Students each pick a card, make the numbers with base-ten blocks on the workmat, and find the sum.
- Students check each other's work. The student with the greatest sum keeps all three cards.
- Continue until all cards have been used.

Option 2 Student Technology

Math Online macmillanmh.com

Math Songs, "The Addition Boogie" Track 11 • Math Adventures

Option 3 Learning Station: Science (p. 481H)

Direct students to the Science Learning Station for more opportunities to explore and extend the lesson concept.

Option 4 Problem-Solving Practice

Reinforce problem-solving skills and strategies with the Problem-Solving Practice worksheet.

Problem Solving (p. 24) BL OL AL

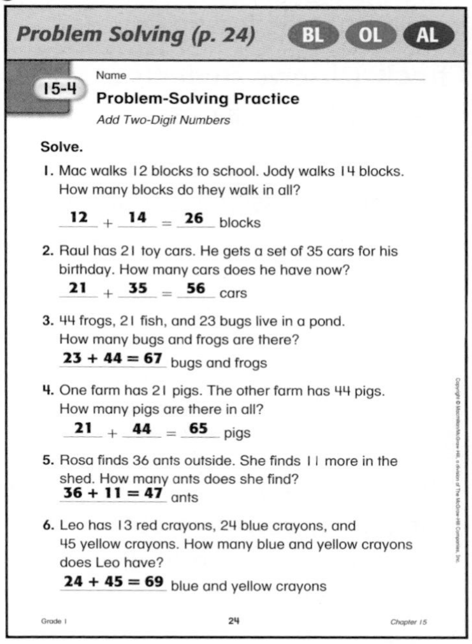

Name ______

15-4 **Problem-Solving Practice**
Add Two-Digit Numbers

Solve.

1. Mac walks 12 blocks to school. Jody walks 14 blocks. How many blocks do they walk in all?
12 + **14** = **26** blocks
2. Raul has 21 toy cars. He gets a set of 35 cars for his birthday. How many cars does he have now?
21 + **35** = **56** cars
3. 44 frogs, 21 fish, and 23 bugs live in a pond. How many bugs and frogs are there?
23 + 44 = 67 bugs and frogs
4. One farm has 21 pigs. The other farm has 44 pigs. How many pigs are there in all?
21 + **44** = **65** pigs
5. Rosa finds 36 ants outside. She finds 11 more in the shed. How many ants does she find?
36 + 11 = 47 ants
6. Leo has 13 red crayons, 24 blue crayons, and 45 yellow crayons. How many blue and yellow crayons does Leo have?
24 + 45 = 69 blue and yellow crayons

Grade 1 24 Chapter 15

15–4

1 Introduce

Activity Choice 1 • Hands-On

Give students 5 base-ten rods and 20 units.

- Explain that you will tell a math story, and the students are to use their rods and units to model the problem.
- *I have 16 red pencils and 11 yellow pencils.*
- **How many pencils do I have altogether?** 27 pencils
- **Did you have to regroup?** no **Why not?** Sample answer: There were fewer than 10 ones.

Activity Choice 2 • Literature

Introduce the lesson with *How Many Snails?* by Paul Giganti, Jr. For additional support, see p. TR64.

2 Teach

Write this problem vertically on the board: 35 + 42.

- Point to each component as you ask:
- **How many ones in the top number?** 5 ones
- **How many ones in the bottom number?** 2 ones
- **How many ones altogether?** 7 ones Write 7 below the ones column.
- Use similar questions about the tens. Write 7 below the tens column.
- **What is the sum of 35 and 42?** 77
- **What numbers did you add first?** the ones

Get Ready Use the section at the top of p. 491 to reinforce the lesson concept.

Check Observe students as you work through Exercises 1–4 as a class.

Exercise 4 Assess student comprehension before assigning practice exercises.

! COMMON ERROR!

If students add ones to tens or tens to ones, help them rewrite problems in a vertical format. You may also wish to draw vertical column lines to link the ones to ones and the tens to tens.

Name ______________________

Add Two-Digit Numbers

Get Ready

Main Idea

I will add two-digit numbers.

Find 15 + 24.

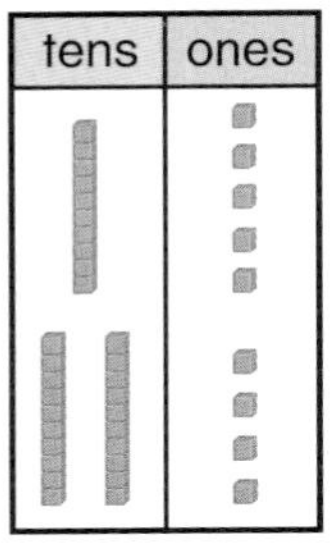

Step 1 Show each number.

	tens	ones
	1	5
+	2	4

Step 2 Add the ones.

	tens	ones
	1	5
+	2	4
		9

Step 3 Add the tens.

	tens	ones
	1	5
+	2	4
	3	9

15 + 24 = **39**

Check

Use WorkMat 7 and [rod] and [unit]. Add.

1.

	tens	ones
	2	3
+	1	4
	3	7

2.

	tens	ones
	1	1
+	3	6
	4	7

3.

	tens	ones
	3	6
+	1	3
	4	9

4. **Talk About It** How did using addition facts help you?
Sample answer: They make adding faster.

Reteach (p. 21) BL

15-4 Name ______

Reteach

Add Two-Digit Numbers

You can use a number line to add ones or tens.

Lu plants 23 flowers. Meg plants 35 flowers.
How many flowers are there now?

23 + 35 = ?

Count on by ones to add one.
Start with the greater number.

0 1 2 3 4 5 6 7 8 9 10 — 5 + 3 = 8 ones

Count on by tens to add ten.
Start with the greater number.

0 10 20 30 40 50 60 70 80 90 100 — 30 + 20 = 50

50 tens and 8 ones = 58 flowers

Use the number lines to add ones and tens.

0 1 2 3 4 5 6 7 8 9 10

0 10 20 30 40 50 60 70 80 90 100

1. 42 + 24 = **66**
2. 78 + 11 = **89**
3. 31 + 52 = **83**
4. 15 + 14 = **29**

Grade 1 21 Chapter 15

Skills Practice (p. 22) OL

15-4 Name ______

Skills Practice

Add Two-Digit Numbers

Use WorkMat 7 and [unit] and [rod]. Add.

1.

	tens	ones
	3	7
+	1	2
	4	**9**

2.

	tens	ones
	5	0
+	3	3
	8	**3**

3.

	tens	ones
	1	7
+	6	2
	7	**9**

4.

	tens	ones
	3	5
+	2	3
	5	**8**

5.

	tens	ones
	7	7
+	2	2
	9	**9**

6.

	tens	ones
	3	4
+	1	5
	4	**9**

Solve.

7. Lu counts 51 cents in her pocket. She finds 26 more. How many cents does she have now?
51 + 26 = 77

8. The letter carrier brings mail to 13 houses each day. How many houses does he visit in 2 days?
13 + 13 = 26

Grade 1 22 Chapter 15

Differentiated Instruction

Small Group Options

Option 1 Gifted and Talented AL

VISUAL/SPATIAL

Materials: two-digit number cards 11–99, WorkMat 7: Tens and Ones Chart, base-ten blocks, pencil, paper

- Divide students into pairs. Each student picks one card from a pile of number cards that are down on a table.
- Have the student with the greater number take both cards and write a subtraction fact.
- Have the other student model the subtraction fact with base-ten blocks and WorkMat 7.
- Ask students to work together to find the difference.
- Have students continue activity as time permits.

Option 2 English Language Learners ELL

LINGUISTIC, SPATIAL

Materials: ½ cup large beans, ½ cup split peas, 2 sheets of paper per pair
Core Vocabulary: remove, collect, type of
Common Use Verb: pair up

Write Math This strategy helps students kinesthetically understand subtraction of larger numbers.

- Give supplies to pairs. Have each collect one type of bean or pea and count them.
- Have students write each number to use to write a subtraction problem of the paper.
- Have them pair beans with peas and remove pairs by putting them back into the bag.
- Have each count the remaining peas to find the answer to the subtraction problem.
- Discuss as time permits.

Independent Work Options

Option 1 Early Finishers OL AL

SOCIAL, LOGICAL

Materials: index cards with money amounts, pennies, dimes

- Create two decks of cards. One deck should be made up of money amounts from 50¢ to 99¢. The other deck will be the take away deck with money amounts from 1¢ to 49¢.
- Have students pick a card from the first deck and use pennies and dimes to model the amount.
- Have students pick a card from the second deck and take away the appropriate amount of pennies and dimes.
- Allow students to check each other's work.

Option 2 Student Technology

Math Online macmillanmh.com

Math Songs, "Take It Away" Track 15 • Math Adventures

Option 3 Learning Station: Science (p. 481H)

Direct students to the Science Learning Station for more opportunities to explore and extend the lesson concept.

Option 4 Problem-Solving Practice

Reinforce problem-solving skills and strategies with the Problem-Solving Practice worksheet

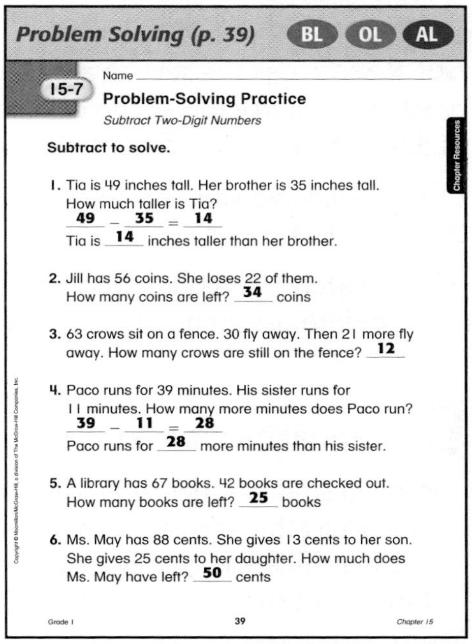

Problem Solving (p. 39) BL OL AL

15-7 Name ____________

Problem-Solving Practice

Subtract Two-Digit Numbers

Subtract to solve.

1. Tia is 49 inches tall. Her brother is 35 inches tall. How much taller is Tia?
   49 – **35** = **14**
   Tia is **14** inches taller than her brother.
2. Jill has 56 coins. She loses 22 of them. How many coins are left? **34** coins
3. 63 crows sit on a fence. 30 fly away. Then 21 more fly away. How many crows are still on the fence? **12**
4. Paco runs for 39 minutes. His sister runs for 11 minutes. How many more minutes does Paco run?
   39 – **11** = **28**
   Paco runs for **28** more minutes than his sister.
5. A library has 67 books. 42 books are checked out. How many books are left? **25** books
6. Ms. May has 88 cents. She gives 13 cents to her son. She gives 25 cents to her daughter. How much does Ms. May have left? **50** cents

Chapter Resources

Grade 1 39 Chapter 15

15-7

1 Introduce

Activity Choice 1 • Hands-On

Draw these items on the board and price them in cents: a pint of milk, 47¢; an apple, 35¢; a granola bar, 72¢; a bottle of water, 99¢. Have students use their dime and penny manipulatives.

- Tell students that they have 99¢ each and to show it with their coins.
- **How many dimes?** 9 dimes **How many pennies?** 9 pennies
- Each of them should decide what they want to buy and choose the coins they need.
- **How much money do you have left? Can you buy anything else?** See students' work.

Activity Choice 2 • Literature

Introduce the lesson with *Shark Swimathon* by Stuart J. Murphy. For additional support, see p. TR65.

2 Teach

Write 65 − 23 in vertical form on the board.

- Have students work in pairs to use base-ten blocks and WorkMat 7 to model the problem.
- **How do you show subtraction using the blocks?** Remove ones and tens from the workmat.
- **What is the first subtraction step?** Subtract ones.
- **What is the difference of the ones?** 2 ones
- **What should we do now?** Remove 2 tens.
- **How many tens remain?** 4 tens **What is the difference of 65 and 23?** 42

Get Ready Use the section at the top of student p. 501 to reinforce the lesson concept. Guide students as they subtract 2 two-digit from two-digit numbers.

Check Observe students as you work through Exercises 1–4 as a class.

Exercise 4 Assess student comprehension before assigning practice exercises.

COMMON ERROR!

Remind students that subtracting the ones and subtracting the tens are each a simple subtraction fact. If a student is getting incorrect answers, have the student check answers by "adding up."

Name ____________________

Subtract Two-Digit Numbers

Get Ready

Main Idea

I will subtract two-digit numbers.

Find 74 − 51.

Step 1 Show the number 74.

tens	ones

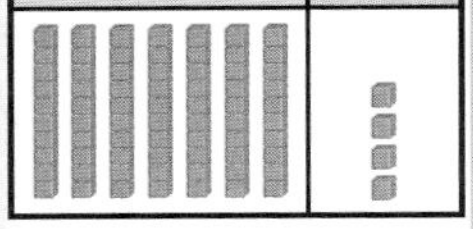

	tens	ones
	7	4
−	5	1

Step 2 Subtract the ones.

tens	ones

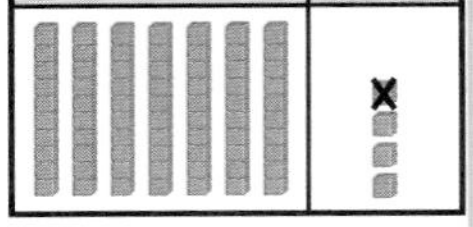

	tens	ones
	7	4
−	5	1
		3

Step 3 Subtract the tens.

tens	ones

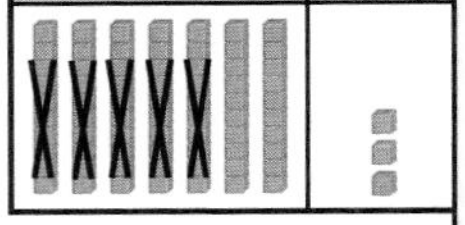

	tens	ones
	7	4
−	5	1
	2	3

Check

Use WorkMat 7 and [ten rod] and [unit cube]. Subtract.

1.

	tens	ones
	2	8
−	1	5
	1	3

2.

	tens	ones
	6	1
−	5	0
	1	1

3.

	tens	ones
	3	4
−	1	4
	2	0

4. **Talk About It** What goes in the tens place of the difference if you subtract all of the tens? For example: 66 − 64.
nothing or zero

Reteach (p. 36) BL

15-7 Name ____________________

Reteach

Subtract Two-Digit Numbers

68 birds are in a tree. 47 fly away.
How many birds stay in the tree?

68 − 47 = ?

Count back by ones to subtract one.

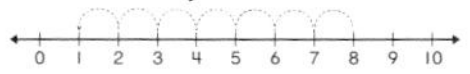

8 − 7 = 1

Count back by tens to subtract ten.

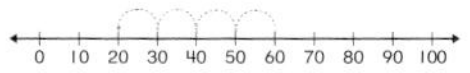

60 − 40 = 20

20 and 1 = 21 birds

Use the number lines to subtract tens and ones.

0 1 2 3 4 5 6 7 8 9 10

0 10 20 30 40 50 60 70 80 90 100

1. 78 − 17 = **61**
2. 38 − 15 = **23**
3. 49 − 19 = **30**
4. 76 − 33 = **43**
5. 57 − 22 = **35**
6. 65 − 21 = **44**

Skills Practice (p. 37) OL

15-7 Name ____________________

Skills Practice

Subtract Two-Digit Numbers

Use WorkMat 7 and [unit cube] and [ten rod]. Subtract.

1.

	tens	ones
	5	7
−	1	5
	4	**2**

2.

	tens	ones
	3	9
−	2	3
	1	**6**

3.

	tens	ones
	4	7
−	3	4
	1	**3**

4.

	tens	ones
	6	4
−	3	1
	3	**3**

5.

	tens	ones
	8	3
−	1	1
	7	**2**

6.

	tens	ones
	9	5
−	1	3
	8	**2**

Solve.

7. Jeff bought 38 cherries. He gave 23 to his dad. How many cherries are left?
15 cherries

8. Marge counted 59 leaves on a tree. She counts 31 the next day. How many leaves fell off the tree?
28 leaves

Chapter Resources

Practice

Use WorkMat 7 and and . Subtract

5.

	tens	ones
	5	8
−	1	3
	4	5

6.

	tens	ones
	4	7
−	2	3
	2	4

7.

	tens	ones
	4	4
−	1	1
	3	3

8.

	tens	ones
	6	9
−	1	5
	5	4

9.

	tens	ones
	9	4
−	2	1
	7	3

10.

	tens	ones
	3	9
−	1	2
	2	7

11.

	tens	ones
	9	4
−	2	1
	7	3

12.

	tens	ones
	5	5
−	1	4
	4	1

13.

	tens	ones
	8	2
−	1	2
	7	0

Problem Solving

14. **Number Sense** Ricardo has 30 cards in one box and 20 cards in another box. He gives 10 cards to Rex.

How many cards does he have now? 40 cards

Math at Home Activity: Have your child explain how to find 93 − 51.

Enrich (p. 40) AL

15-7 Name

Enrich

Domino Subtraction

Play a game of Domino Subtraction.
Put your facedown.
Turn over 1 .
Make a subtraction sentence subtracting the little number from the big number.
Add to check.

6 − 4 = 2   4 + 2 = 6

Answers will vary depending on the dominoes chosen.

1. 2. 3. 4. 5. 6.

Grade 1   40   Chapter 15

Homework Practice (p. 38) OL

15-7 Name

Homework Practice

Subtract Two-Digit Numbers

Use WorkMat 7 and and . Subtract.

1.

	tens	ones
	4	7
−	2	3
	2	**4**

2.

	tens	ones
	2	9
−	1	2
	1	**7**

3.

	tens	ones
	4	2
−	1	1
	3	**1**

4.

	tens	ones
	7	8
−	5	5
	2	**3**

5.

	tens	ones
	6	6
−	5	3
	1	**3**

6.

	tens	ones
	2	7
−	1	6
	1	**1**

Solve.

7. Eva found 57 pennies. She keeps 25. How many pennies does she give away? **32** pennies

8. Rick picked 59 apples. He sells 36. How many apples are left? **23** apples

Grade 1   38   Chapter 15

BL Alternate Teaching Strategy

If students have trouble understanding how to subtract 2 two-digit numbers . . .

Then use one of the following reteach options.

1. CRM **Daily Reteach Worksheet** (p. 36)
2. **Use a Hundred Chart** Have students put their finger on the starting number and count back the number subtracted. When students are proficient at this, have them count back by ones only the ones subtracted and then skip down rows of ten for the tens subtracted.

3 Practice

Differentiate practice using these leveled assignments for Exercises 5–14.

Level	Assignment
BL **Below/ Approaching Level**	Have students work in pairs. One student is in charge of the tens rods; the other is in charge of the unit blocks
OL **On Level**	Complete exercises independently.
AL **Above/Beyond Level**	Complete exercises without using base-ten blocks and WorkMat 7.

4 Assess

Formative Assessment

- **When you subtract using WorkMat 7 and base-ten blocks, what happens to the number of blocks on your workmat** When you subtract, you take blocks off the mat, so you end with fewer blocks than you started with.

WRITING IN MATH Have students write about what they think would happen if more ones are subtracted than are in the starting number.

Quick Check **Are students continuing to struggle to subtract two-digit numbers?**

If Yes → Strategic Intervention Guide (p.86)

If No → Independent Work Options (p. 501B)

CRM Skills Practice Worksheet (p. 37)

CRM Enrich Worksheet (p. 40)

15-8 Problem-Solving Investigation
Choose a Strategy

Lesson Planner

Objective
Choose the best strategy to solve a problem.

Resources
Teacher Technology
TeacherWorks

Real-World Problem Solving
Math and Social Studies: *A Lemonade Stand*
Use these leveled books to reinforce and extend problem-solving skills and strategies.

Leveled for:
- OL On Level
- ELL Sheltered English
- SP Spanish

For additional support, see the Real-World Problem Solving Teacher Guide.

Daily Routine

Use these suggestions before beginning the lesson on p. 503.

5-Minute Check
(Reviews Lesson 15-7)
Use base-ten blocks and WorkMat 7 to subtract.
1. 35 − 14 = _____ 21
2. 67 − 25 = _____ 42
3. 85 − 53 = _____ 32
4. 74 − 32 = _____ 42
5. 59 − 19 = _____ 40
6. 48 − 47 = _____ 1

Problem of the Day
I have 0 faces and 0 corners. What three-dimensional figure am I? sphere

LINE UP When students line up for recess, lunch, or dismissal, give two students a two-digit number. Ask one student to say the number that is ten more than the two-digit number. Ask the other student to say the number that is ten less than two-digit number. Repeat down the line.

Differentiated Instruction

Small Group Options

Option 1 LOGICAL, SOCIAL

Below/Approaching Level BL

Materials: construction paper, markers or crayons, decorating materials

- Present students with a list of problem-solving strategies: *make a table; guess and check; write a number sentence; logical reasoning.*
- Have students choose one strategy from the list and work together to write a story problem that can be solved using this strategy. You may want to allow them to look back at previous chapters' Problem-Solving Strategy lessons for examples.

- Students should also draw and color a picture to show the story.
- When students are finished, have them pose the story problem to the class.

Option 2 LOGICAL, LINGUISTIC

English Language Learners ELL

Core Vocabulary: minus, equals, plus
Common Use Verbs: read

Talk Math This strategy helps students use mental math and their background knowledge to determine whether the problem reflects sums or differences.

- Write equations on cards without putting the subtraction and equals symbols in.
- Show a card. Model reading the numbers as a problem. For example: 38, 10, 28 would be read 38 minus 10 equals 28.
- Repeat for all cards chorally.
- Have students move into a circle and pass cards around, as everyone practices reading the numbers as equations.
- Increase the difficulty by adding cards that call for addition, repeating as time permits.

Independent Work Options

Option 1 LOGICAL, SOCIAL

Early Finishers OL AL

Materials: construction paper, crayons, markers

- Divide students into pairs.
- Students discuss which problem-solving strategies they used or will use to solve each exercise on p. 503.
- Students then try to use each of the problem-solving strategies listed at the top of p. 503 to solve each exercise.
- **Are any of the answers different when you use a different strategy?** No.

Option 2

Student Technology

Math Online macmillanmh.com

Option 3

Learning Station: Health (p. 481H)

Direct students to the Health Learning Station for more opportunities to explore and extend the lesson concept.

1 Introduce

Activity Choice 1 • Review

Write the following problem on the board:

16 ◯ 8 ◯ 3 = 11

- Explain that the plus and minus signs are missing from this number sentence. **What problem-solving strategy can help us find the missing signs?** Sample answers: make a table; guess and check
- Have students *guess and check* to find the answer. Ask students to guess the signs. Let a different student guess each sign. Write the signs on the board and check the answer.

2 Teach

Have students read the problem on p. 503. Guide them through the problem-solving steps.

Understand Using the questions, review what students know and what they need to find.

Plan Have them discuss their strategy.

Solve Guide students to *make a table* to solve the problem.

- **How many marbles does Mariah have?** 14 marbles **How will you write 14 in the table?** Write a 1 in the tens column and a 4 in the ones column.
- **How many marbles does her sister have?** 24 marbles **How will you write 24 in the table?** Write a 2 in the tens column and a 4 in the ones column.
- **Is this an addition or a subtraction problem?** addition **How do you know?** Sample answer: We are joining groups to find the total number of marbles.
- **How many marbles in all?** 38 marbles

Check Have students look back at the problem to make sure the answer fits the facts given. **Estimate this addition by rounding each number. What is the estimated answer?** 30 marbles **Does the exact answer seem reasonable?** Yes; 38 is close to 30.

! COMMON ERROR!

Students will need guidance to see what the chart is for. Explain that the table separates tens and ones.

Name ____________________

Problem-Solving Investigation

Main Idea

I will choose a strategy to solve a problem.

Your Mission:

Find out how many marbles in all.

Understand

What do I know?

Underline what you know.

What do I need to find?

Circle it.

Plan

How will I solve the problem?

One way is to make a table.

Solve

Make a table.

Name	Tens	Ones
Mariah	1	4
Sister	2	4
Total:	3	8

The girls have __38__ marbles in all.

Check

Look back.

Is my answer reasonable?

Check students' explanations.

Reteach (pp. 41–42) BL

15-8 Name ____________________

Reteach (1)

Problem-Solving Investigation: Choose a Strategy

There are 54 dogs and 32 cats at the pet store.
How many more dogs are in the store than cats?

Step 1 Understand

What do I know?
There are 54 dogs.
There are 32 cats.

What do I need to find out?
How many more dogs are there than cats?

Step 2 Plan

How will I find out?
I can guess and check. But I may not guess the answer right away. Making a table might be easier. I will make a table.

Step 3 Solve

Make a table.

Pets	Tens	Ones
Dogs	50	4
Cats	30	2

There are __22__ more dogs than cats.

Step 4 Check

Does my table show how many more dogs there are? __yes__

Did I choose a good strategy? __yes__

Grade 1 41 Chapter 15

Skills Practice (p. 43) OL

15-8 Name ____________________

Skills Practice

Problem-Solving Investigation: Choose a Strategy

Choose a strategy and solve.

Problem Solving Strategies
- Guess and check
- Choose the operation
- Make a table

1. Lin plants 12 seeds. Dee plants 34 seeds. How many seeds do they plant? __46__ seeds
2. Raul has 10 toy cars. He gets a set of 30 cars for his birthday. How many cars does he have now? __40__ cars
3. Lita sees two kinds of objects on her trip. She sees 39 in all. Which two objects does she see? Circle your answer.

4. The letter carrier brings mail to 20 homes on Lee Street. He brings mail to 10 homes on Main Street. How many homes is that? __30__ homes
5. Jen's block has 48 trees. Sam's block has 23 trees. How many more trees are on Jen's block? __25__ trees
6. Lou has 16 shirts. Greg has 11 shirts. About how many shirts do they have? Round to the nearest ten. About __30__ shirts

Grade 1 43 Chapter 15

Mixed Problem Solving

Problem-Solving Strategies
- Make a table
- Draw a picture
- Write a number sentence

Choose a strategy. Solve.

1. 13 children had dogs. 21 children had either a fish or a hamster. How many children had pets in all? 34 children

2. Isaiah started with 12 peas and 5 beans on his plate. Later he had 6 peas left on his plate. How many peas and beans has Isaiah eaten so far?

11 peas and beans

3. 66 children can be seated on the school bus. After Emily got on, there were 42 children on the bus. How many more children can get on the bus?

24 children

4. The library had 38 magazines. 12 students each checked out 2 magazines. How many magazines were left?

14 magazines

Math at Home Activity: Take advantage of problem-solving opportunities during daily routines such as riding in the car, bedtime, doing laundry, putting away groceries, planning schedules, and so on.

Enrich (p. 45) AL

Name

15-8 **Enrich**

Subtraction Stories

Read the story. Draw a picture. Write a subtraction sentence to solve.

1. There are 11 bones and 3 dogs. How many more bones are there than dogs?

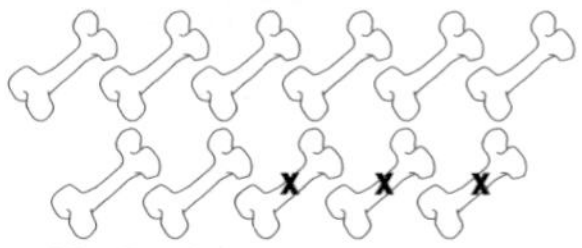

11 − 3 = 8

2. There are 12 balloons. 6 balloons pop. How many balloons are left?

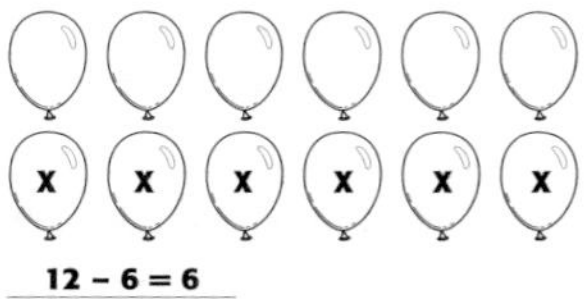

12 − 6 = 6

Grade 1 45 Chapter 15

Homework Practice (p. 44) OL

Name

15-8 **Homework Practice**

Problem-Solving Investigation: Choose a Strategy

Choose a strategy and solve.

Problem Solving Strategies
- Guess and check
- Choose the operation
- Make a table

1. Nick's teddy bear is 22 inches high. Fred's teddy bear is 10 inches high. How many inches taller is Nick's teddy bear? 12 inches

2. The classroom is 35 feet long. A shelf is 3 feet long. How much longer is the classroom than the shelf? 32 feet

3. Lisa has 32 marbles. Tim has 41 marbles. About how many marbles do they have? Round. About 70 marbles

4. Mr. Lin spends 40 cents at the store. He buys 2 objects. What does Mr. Lin buy? Circle your answer.

5. 21 birds are in a field. 18 more fly in. How many birds are there now? 39 birds

6. Jan has 12 red stickers and 31 yellow stickers. About how many stickers does she have? Round. About 40 stickers

Grade 1 44 Chapter 15

BL Alternate Teaching Strategy

If students are having trouble choosing a problem-solving strategy . . .

Then use one of the following reteach options.

1. CRM **Daily Reteach Worksheet** (pp. 41–42)
2. **Talk It Out** Discuss with students each of the problem-solving strategies listed on the page. Have students suggest which strategies will help with which exercises.

3 Practice

Mixed Problem Solving

Exercise 1 This problem contains more information than is necessary to solve the problem. Have students focus on the question asked; they can cross out the unnecessary information.

Exercise 4 This is a multistep problem. Students must add two numbers before subtracting to find the answer. Discuss with students the number of magazines each student picked out; lead students to understand that they will need to use a strategy to find the number to subtract from 38.

4 Assess

Formative Assessment

What problem-solving strategy did you choose to solve Exercise 3? How did it help you? Sample answer: Make a table; the table helped me keep tens with tens and ones with ones.

WRITING IN MATH Have students name their favorite problem-solving strategy and tell why it is their favorite.

Quick Check **Are students continuing to struggle to choose a problem-solving strategy?**

If Yes → Small Group Options (p. 503B)
Strategic Intervention Guide (p. 80)

If No → Independent Work Options (p. 503B)
CRM Skills Practice Worksheet (p. 43)
CRM Enrich Worksheet (p. 45)

LESSON 15-9

Estimate Differences

Lesson Planner

Objective

Estimate the difference of two-digit numbers by rounding.

Review Vocabulary

estimate

Resources

Materials: number line of overhead transparency, hundred chart

Literature Connection: *Coyotes All Around* by Stuart J. Murphy

Alternate Lesson: Adapt *The Magic Box* on pages 248 and 249 of *Math Their Way* for practice in two-digit subtraction.

Teacher Technology

TeacherWorks

Focus on Math Background

In this lesson, students will learn strategies for estimating differences. In a subtraction situation, as in addition, students should concentrate on the magnitude of the whole numbers, versus the individual digits, in order to make a reasonable estimate. When subtracting 12 from 31, for example, a student can think of the former as a 10 and the later as a 30 in order to estimate a difference of about 20.

Daily Routine

Use these suggestions before beginning the lesson on p. 505.

5-Minute Check

(Reviews Lesson 15-8)

Mrs. Rosko had 4 papers on her desk, 12 on the table, and 4 in her bag. She had already graded 5 of the papers. How many papers does Mrs. Rosko have left to grade?
15 papers

Problem of the Day

Round each number to the nearest ten.

1. 46 ____ 50	2. 13 ____ 10
3. 32 ____ 30	4. 79 ____ 80
5. 94 ____ 90	6. 61 ____ 60
7. 87 ____ 90	8. 28 ____ 30

LINE UP When students line up for recess, lunch, or dismissal, give two students a number and ask them each to round to the nearest ten. Have a third student find the difference. Repeat down the line.

Review Math Vocabulary

- Review estimating. Explain to students that estimating is guessing a number as close to the exact amout as you can.
- Fill a plastic jar with connecting cubes and seal it with a lid.
- Have each student write down their **estimate**. Then count the cubes out loud with the class. Give a prize to students who estimated correctly or were the closest to the exact number.

Visual Vocabulary Cards

Use Visual Vocabulary Cards to reinforce the vocabulary reviewed in this lesson. (The Define/Example/Ask routine is printed on the back of each card.)

Differentiated Instruction

Small Group Options

Option 1 Below/Approaching Level (BL)

LOGICAL

Materials: hundred chart, 6-color spinner

Prepare the 6-color spinner with the numbers 2, 3, 4, 6, 7, and 8.

- Students take turns making a two-digit number with the spinner. One student spins to get the tens number, and another student spins to get the ones number. This activity can also be done individually.
- After students have made the two-digit number, have them use the hundred chart to round their number to the nearest ten.
- Have students repeat this activity several times to practice rounding.

Option 2 English Language Learners (ELL)

LOGICAL, SOCIAL

Core Vocabulary: third, fourth, second
Common Use Verb: tag

Do Math This strategy uses teamwork to help students estimate differences.

- Tell students that they are going to have a math relay in teams of 4.
- Write 100 on the board. Model rounding 42 to 40 and subtracting it from 100. Writing 60.
- Say: "Round both numbers before you subtract. Write your answer on the board before you ***tag*** the next person."
- Whisper 23 to all starting players, 57 to the seconds, 96 to thirds and 15 to the fourths so that all teams' answers will be 0 if done correctly.
- Discuss results. Repeat with other numbers as time permits.

Independent Work Options

Option 1 Early Finishers (OL) (AL)

SOCIAL, LOGICAL

Materials: books and magazines

- Have students open the book at random and record the page number.
- Students round the page number to the nearest ten.
- When students have 6 or 8 page numbers, they should write subtraction sentences using the page numbers and find both estimated and exact differences.

Option 2 Student Technology

Math Online macmillanmh.com

Option 3 Learning Station: Art (p. 481G)

Direct students to the Art Learning Station for more opportunities to explore and extend the lesson concept.

Option 4 Problem-Solving Practice

Reinforce problem-solving skills and strategies with the Problem-Solving Practice worksheet.

Problem Solving (p. 49) BL OL AL

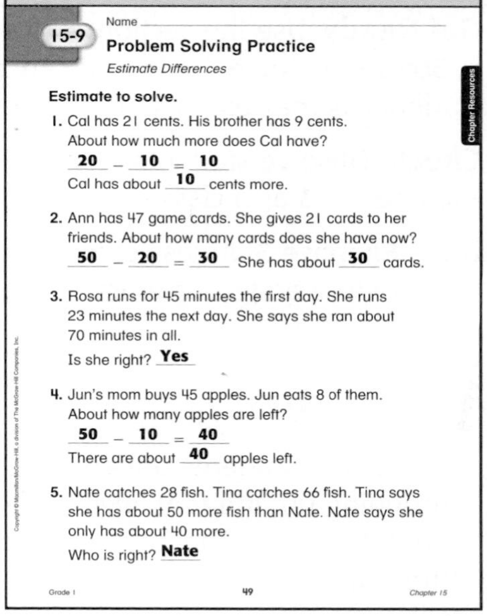

Name ______

15-9 **Problem Solving Practice**
Estimate Differences

Estimate to solve.

1. Cal has 21 cents. His brother has 9 cents. About how much more does Cal have?
   20 − 10 = 10
   Cal has about 10 cents more.
2. Ann has 47 game cards. She gives 21 cards to her friends. About how many cards does she have now?
   50 − 20 = 30 She has about 30 cards.
3. Rosa runs for 45 minutes the first day. She runs 23 minutes the next day. She says she ran about 70 minutes in all.
   Is she right? Yes
4. Jun's mom buys 45 apples. Jun eats 8 of them. About how many apples are left?
   50 − 10 = 40
   There are about 40 apples left.
5. Nate catches 28 fish. Tina catches 66 fish. Tina says she has about 50 more fish than Nate. Nate says she only has about 40 more.
   Who is right? Nate

Grade 1 49 Chapter 15

1 Introduce

Activity Choice 1 • Hands-On

Group students in two to four teams for board races. For each team, write a two-digit subtraction problem vertically on the board.

- Tell the students that they are going to estimate differences by rounding numbers and subtracting.
- The first person will round the first number. The second will round the second number. The third will write the estimated difference.
- The first team finished gets 1 point. The first three players will move to the end of their line.

Activity Choice 2 • Literature

Introduce the lesson with *Coyotes All Around* by Stuart J. Murphy. For additional support, see p. TR65.

2 Teach

Display an overhead number line from 40 to 60. Write this problem vertically on the board: 53 – 41.

- **Is 53 closer to 50 or 60?** 50 **Round up or down?** down **What is the estimated number?** 50
- **Is 41 closer to 40 or 50?** 40 **Round up or down?** down **What is the estimated number?** 40
- **What number sentence will help us find the estimated difference between 53 and 41?** 50 – 40 **What is 50 minus 40?** 10
- **What is the exact difference between 53 and 41?** 12 **Explain why was 10 a good estimate?** 10 is close to 12.

Get Ready Use the section at the top of student p. 505 to reinforce the lesson concept. Guide students as they estimate differences.

Check Observe students as you work through Exercises 1–3 as a class.

Exercise 3 Assess student comprehension before assigning practice exercises.

! COMMON ERROR!

Make sure students understand that when rounding up, the tens digit increases by one, but when rounding down, the tens digit stays the same.

Name ______________________

Estimate Differences

Get Ready

Main Idea

I will estimate differences.

Sometimes when you subtract, you do not need an exact answer. You can estimate to find the difference.

Estimate 32 – 21.

20 21 22 23 24 25 26 27 28 29 30 31 32 33 34 35

Step 1: Round to the nearest 10.

32 is closer to 30 ⟶ 32 rounds to 30.

21 is closer to 20 ⟶ 21 rounds to 20.

Step 2: Subtract.

30 – 20 = 10

3 – 2 = 1, so 30 – 20 = 10

Check

Round each number to the nearest ten. Then subtract.

1. 79 – 41

   79 rounds to 80

   41 rounds to 40

   80 – 40 = 40

2. 64 – 37

   64 rounds to 60

   37 rounds to 40

   60 – 40 = 20

3. Talk About It: Explain how you would estimate 42 – 21.
   42 rounds to 40, 21 rounds to 20. 40 – 20 = 20

Reteach (p. 46) BL

15-9 Name ______

Reteach

Estimate Differences

If you do not need an exact difference, you can estimate.

If a number ends in 5, 6, 7, 8, or 9, you can round up.

If a number ends in 0, 1, 2, 3, or 4, you can round down.

What is 26 – 13?

26 is about the same as 30.

13 is about the same as 10.

30 – 10 = 20, so the exact difference of 26 – 13 will be about 20.

Round each number to the nearest *ten*. Then subtract.

1. 59 rounds to **60**
   12 rounds to **10**
   59 – 12 is about **50**
   60 – **10** = **50**

2. 28 rounds to **30**
   19 rounds to **20**
   28 – 19 is about **10**
   30 – **20** = **10**

3. 42 rounds to **40**
   21 rounds to **20**
   42 – 21 is about **20**
   40 – **20** = **20**

4. 67 rounds to **70**
   33 rounds to **30**
   67 – 33 is about **40**
   70 – **30** = **40**

Grade 1 46 Chapter 15

Skills Practice (p. 47) OL

15-9 Name ______

Skills Practice

Estimate Differences

Round to the nearest *ten*. Then subtract. Use the number lines to help.

10 11 12 13 14 15 16 17 18 19 20 21 22 23 24 25 26 27 28 29 30

30 31 32 33 34 35 36 37 38 39 40 41 42 43 44 45 46 47 48 49 50

1. 39 – 32
   39 rounds to **40**
   32 rounds to **30**
   40 – **30** = **10**

2. 48 – 24
   48 rounds to **50**
   24 rounds to **20**
   50 – **20** = **30**

3. 47 – 28
   50 – **30** = **20**

4. 49 – 17
   50 – **20** = **30**

5. 38 – 21
   40 – **20** = **20**

6. 43 – 14
   40 – **10** = **30**

Solve.

7. Lily has 57 marbles. Her brother has 22 marbles. About how many more marbles does Lily have?
   60 – **20** = **40**
   She has about **40** more marbles.

Grade 1 47 Chapter 15

Chapter Resources

Practice

Round each number to the nearest ten.
Then subtract.

4. 91 − 29

91 rounds to 90

29 rounds to 30

90 − 30 = 60

5. 41 − 12

41 rounds to 40

12 rounds to 10

40 − 10 = 30

6. 54 − 28

54 rounds to 50

28 rounds to 30

50 − 30 = 20

7. 49 − 37

49 rounds to 50

37 rounds to 40

50 − 40 = 10

8. 58 − 26

58 rounds to 60

26 rounds to 30

60 − 30 = 30

9. 42 − 28

42 rounds to 40

28 rounds to 30

40 − 30 = 10

10. WRITING IN ▸MATH Why is 40 a better estimate than 30 for 59 − 21?

Sample answer: 59 is closer to 60, 21 is closer to 20, and 60 − 20 = 40, so the better estimate is 40.

Math at Home Activity: Have your child estimate 82 − 27 and then explain his or her reasoning.

Enrich (p. 50) AL

15-9 Name ____

Enrich

Skating into Estimation

Round to solve the subtraction sentences.
Draw a line from the skater to the skateboard.

Grade 1 | 50 | Chapter 15

Homework Practice (p. 48) OL

15-9 Name ____

Homework Practice

Estimate Differences

Round to the nearest *ten*. Then subtract.
Use the number lines to help.

30 31 32 33 34 35 36 37 38 39 40 41 42 43 44 45 46 47 48 49 50

50 51 52 53 54 55 56 57 58 59 60 61 62 63 64 65 66 67 68 69 70

1. 48 − 31
48 rounds to **50**
31 rounds to **30**
50 − **30** = **20**

2. 67 − 43
67 rounds to **70**
43 rounds to **40**
70 − **40** = **30**

3. 55 − 41
60 − **40** = **20**

4. 68 − 39
70 − **40** = **30**

5. 46 − 32
50 − **30** = **20**

6. 68 − 42
70 − **40** = **30**

Solve.

7. Ms. Green makes 65 cookies for the bake sale. She sells about 25. About how many cookies are left?

about **40** cookies

Grade 1 | 48 | Chapter 15

BL Alternate Teaching Strategy

If students have trouble estimating two-digit differences . . .

Then use one of the following reteach options.

1 CRM **Daily Reteach Worksheet** (p. 46)

2 Use a Hundred Chart Have students shade each multiple of 10. When students need to round a number, have them place a two-colored counter on the number and look to see which ten it is closer to.

3 Practice

Differentiate practice using these leveled assignments for Exercises 4–10.

Level	Assignment
BL Below/ Approaching Level	Allow students to use a number line or hundred chart for help with rounding.
OL On Level	Complete exercises independently.
AL Above/Beyond Level	Also find each exact answer.

4 Assess

Formative Assessment

- **How does estimating a difference help you check the exact answer to a subtraction problem?** Sample answer: If the estimated difference is close to the exact answer, then the answer is probably right. If it is not close, the answer should be reworked.

WRITING IN ▸MATH Ask students to write a story problem that can be answered with an estimate. Students should use the word *about* in their story.

Quick Check **Are students continuing to struggle to estimate differences?**

If Yes → Small Group Options (p. 505B)
Strategic Intervention Guide (p. 86)

If No → Independent Work Options (p. 505B)
CRM Skills Practice Worksheet (p. 47)
CRM Enrich Worksheet (p. 50)

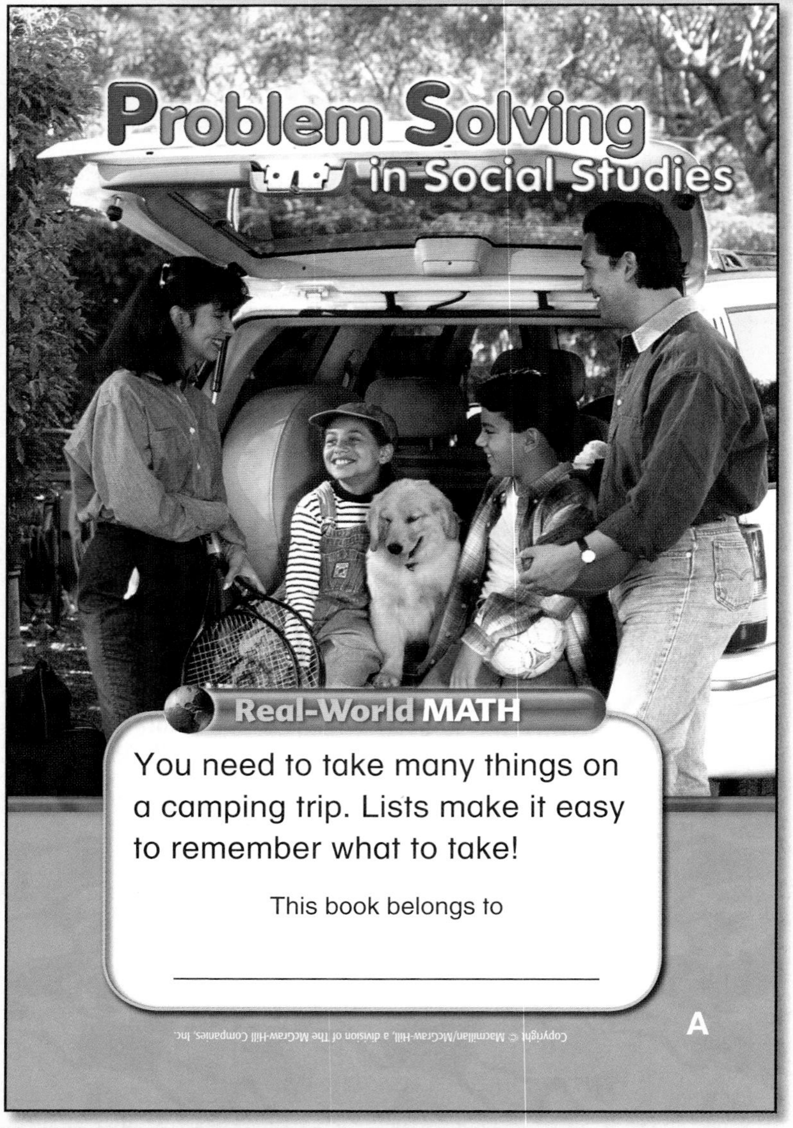

Lesson Planner

Objectives

Add and subtract with two-digit numbers to solve problems in Social Studies.

National Standards

Students should understand how human actions modify physical environments.

Activate Prior Knowledge

Before you turn students' attention to the pages, discuss preparing for camping and going on a camping trip.

- Share any camping stories you may have with the students. Ask students if they have been camping. Have students explain where they went and what they packed.
- **What time of year do most people like to go camping?** Sample answer: in the summer or when it is warm outside
- **Why would you make a list before you went camping?** Sample answer: To go camping, you need to bring lots of things and a list will help you remember them all.

Tabatha took 11 hot dogs. Brad took 7 hot dogs.
How many hot dogs did they take?

18 hot dogs

C

There were 38 marshmallows in the bag. Seth got hungry. He ate 6 marshmallows. How many marshmallows are left?

32 marshmallows

D

FOLD DOWN

Create the Book

Guide students to create their book.

- Have them fold the page in half.
- Ask them to write their name on page A.
- Explain that page A is the front cover and page D is the back cover. If necessary, have them practice flipping through the book in order.
- Guide them in reading the information and word problems on each of the pages.

Use the Student Pages

Have students work individually or in pairs to solve the problems on pages B–D.

Page B Help students count on a number line to solve the problem.

Page C Remind students how to make a ten to add.

Page D Provide connecting cubes to help students solve this problem.

Extend the Activity

As a class, make a list of items to take camping. Write the numbers of individual bottles of water, tents, and so on. Total all the items on your list.

WRITING IN MATH Have students write about a place they would like to go camping.

Chapter Review/Test

FOLDABLES® Dinah Zike's Foldables

If students have not completed their Foldables, guide them to create and fill in the appropriate information using the instructions on pp. 497 and 509.

You may choose to use the Foldable to help students review the concepts presented in this chapter and as a tool for studying for the Chapter Test.

Vocabulary Review

Review chapter vocabulary using one of the following options.

- **Visual Vocabulary Cards (1, 2, 13, 15, 17, 46, and 47)**
- **eGlossary at** macmillanmh.com

Vocabulary Test

CRM **Chapter 15 Resource Masters** (p. 55)
Assess student comprehension of the chapter vocabulary with the Vocabulary Test.

Math Online **Chapter Test**
Alternative summative assessment options are available online at macmillanmh.com.

Name ______________________

Vocabulary

Complete the sentences.

Word Bank
round
estimate

1. When you do not need an exact answer you can estimate.
2. You round to the nearest 10.

Concepts

Add or subtract.

3. 6 tens + 2 tens = 8 tens   60 + 20 = 80
4. 5 tens − 2 tens = 3 tens   50 − 20 = 30

Add.

5.

	tens	ones
	9	3
+		5
	9	8

6.

	tens	ones
	7	6
+	1	3
	8	9

7.

	tens	ones
	1	4
+	2	5
	3	9

Round each number to nearest ten. Then add.

40 41 42 43 44 45 46 47 48 49 50 51 52 53 54 55 56 57 58 59 60

8. 43 + 17
43 rounds to 40
17 rounds to 20
40 + 20 = 60

9. 48 + 21
48 rounds to 50
21 rounds to 20
50 + 20 = 70

Chapter 15 Project

Add and Subtract Two-Digit Numbers

Have students discuss the results of their completed chapter project as a class. Assess their work using the Chapter Project rubric found in Chapter 15 Resource Masters on p. 60.

Subtract.

10.

	tens	ones
	7	9
−		7
	7	2

11.

	tens	ones
	8	6
−		5
	8	1

12.

	tens	ones
	4	7
−	1	5
	3	2

13.

	tens	ones
	6	7
−	1	3
	5	4

Round each number to the nearest ten. Then subtract.

14. 57 − 26

57 rounds to 60

26 rounds to 30

60 − 30 = 30

15. 94 − 36

94 rounds to 90

36 rounds to 40

90 − 40 = 50

16. 88 − 16

88 rounds to 90

16 rounds to 20

90 − 20 = 70

17. 19 − 11

19 rounds to 20

11 rounds to 10

20 − 10 = 10

Problem Solving

18. Matthew wants to buy two books.
Each book costs 23¢.
How much money does Matthew need? 46¢

Summative Assessment

Use these alternate leveled chapter tests to differentiate assessment for the specific needs of your students.

Leveled Chapter 15 Tests

Form	Type	Level	CRM Pages
1	Multiple Choice	BL	62–63
2A	Multiple Choice	OL	64–65
2B	Multiple Choice	OL	66–67
2C	Free Response	AL	68–69
2D	Free Response	AL	70–71

BL = below/approaching grade level
OL = on grade level
AL = above/beyond grade level

ExamView Assessment Suite Customize and create multiple versions of your Chapter Tests and their test answer keys.

Data-Driven Decision Making

Based on the results of the Chapter Test/Review, use the following to review concepts that continue to present students with problems.

Exercises	State/Local Standards	What's the Math?	Error Analysis	Resources for Review
3–4		Add and subtract tens.	Adds incorrectly. Add two zeros to tens addition	Strategic Intervention Guide (p. 86) CRM Chapter 15 Resource Masters (Reteach Worksheets) Math Online Concepts in Motion Math Adventures
5–7 10–13		Add or subtract with one- and two-digit numbers.	Does not regroup when adding ones. Adds or subtracts inaccurately.	
8–9 14–17		Use estimation strategies in computation and problem solving that involve numbers that use ones and tens.	Does not round to correct ten. Rounds up each time. Adds then rounds.	
18		Add two-digit numbers in problem situations.	Misreads and only buys one of the items wanted. Does not add correctly.	

Formative Assessment

- Use Student Edition pp. 511–512 as practice and cumulative review. The questions are written in the same style as many state tests.
- You can use these two pages to benchmark student progress, or as an alternative homework assignment.

Additional practice pages can be found in the Chapter 15 Resource Masters.

CRM Chapter 15 Resource Masters
Cumulative Test Practice
- Multiple Choice format (pp. 62–67, 73)
- Free Response format (pp. 68–72)

End-of-Year Assessment

Use the **End-of-Year Test** to assess student comprehension of the skills and concepts presented in Grade 1.

CRM Chapter 15 Resource Masters
End-of-Year Test (pp. 74–77)

ExamView Assessment Suite Create practice worksheets or tests that align to state standards.

Math Online
For additional practice, visit macmillanmh.com.

Name ____________________

Listen as your teacher reads each problem.
Choose the correct answer.

1.

	tens	ones
	2	4
+	3	0

34 ○ 36 ○ 50 ○ 54 ●

2. 43
+ 33

63 ○ 66 ○ 76 ● 78 ○

3.
40 − 10 = ● 40 + 10 = ○
10 − 40 = ○ 10 + 40 = ○

4. 33 − 23 =

50 ○ 40 ○ 20 ○ 10 ●

5.

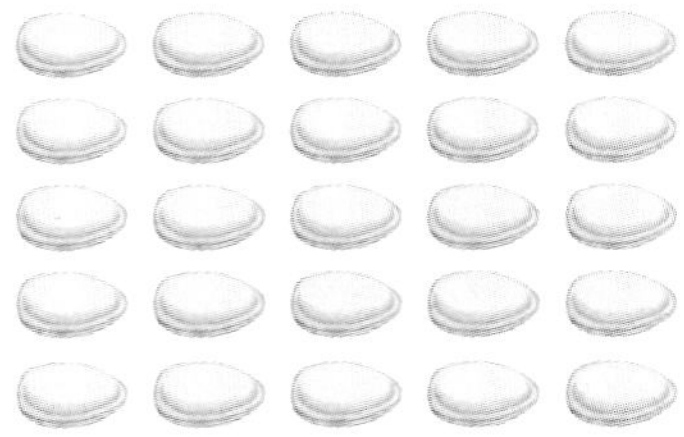

35 ○ 30 ○ 25 ○ 20 ●

6. 3 − 3 = ____

3 ○ 2 ○ 1 ○ 0 ●

Test-Taking Tips

For the Teacher

- Make sure each student undertands the directions before beginning the test.
- Make sure there are no distractions (audio or visual) in the room.

For the Student

- Listen carefully to what the teacher reads.
- Do not mark your answer until the teacher is finished reading.

7. 5, 10, 15, 20

21, 22, 23 ○ 22, 24, 26 ○

25, 30, 35 ● 30, 40, 50 ○

8.

66 ● 65 ○ 55 ○ 46 ○

9. ☐ < 28

82 ○ 58 ○ 34 ○ 23 ●

10. 9 + 9 = ____

0 ○ 9 ○

18 ● 99 ○

11. There were 63 crows sitting on a fence. Then 30 flew away. How many crows are still on the fence?

33 crows

12. Cole has a total of 18 cards in 2 boxes. She put 10 cards in one box. How many cards are in the second box?

8 cards

STOP

Test Directions for Teachers

Read the following directions to students before they begin. Then read each question followed by a pause to allow students time to work and choose an answer. The first test item can be worked as a class example.

- **Write your name at the top of the page.**
- **I am going to read each question to you. Listen carefully to the entire question before you choose an answer.**

Multiple Choice

1. Listen to the story. Pat baked 24 blueberry muffins and 30 chocolate chip muffins for the bake sale. How many muffins did he bake in all?
2. Look at the addition problem. What is the sum?
3. Round 38 and 14 each to the nearest ten.
4. Look at the numbers 33 and 23. Round each number to the nearest ten. Then subtract.
5. Listen to the story. Mrs. Cheng bought 25 pumpkin seeds. She planted 5 of them. How many more pumpkin seeds can she plant?
6. What is the difference of 3 – 3?

- **Turn the page over.**

7. Look at the group of numbers. Skip count by 5s. Which numbers come next?
8. Which number shows 10 more than 56?
9. What number is less than 28?
10. Find the sum.

Short Response

11. There were 63 crows sitting on a fence. Then 30 flew away. How many crows are still on the fence?
12. Cole has a total of 18 cards in 2 boxes. She put 10 cards in one box. How many cards are in the second box?

Looking Ahead

The lessons in **Looking Ahead** can be used to extend concepts and skills present during the current year. Also, some lessons can be used at the end of the year after your state testing is completed. By presenting these important concepts and skills, you can help students be more successful.

Looking Ahead

Let's Look Ahead

1. Missing Addends **LA3**
2. Count on Tens and Ones **LA5**
3. Hundreds, Tens, and Ones **LA7**
4. Place Value to 1,000 . . . . **LA9**
5. Measure to the Nearest Inch **LA11**
6. Measure to the Nearest Centimeter. . . . **LA13**

Missing Addends

Lesson Planner

Objective
Find the missing number in addition and subtraction sentences.

Vocabulary
missing addend

Resources
Materials: construction paper, WorkMat 3: Part-Part-Whole

Manipulatives: connecting cubes

Teacher Technology

TeacherWorks

Focus on Math Background

Missing addends are difficult for students. Believing the answer always comes immediately after an equals sign, students can be confused when they see 3 + ___ = 12. Being able to solve for missing addends depends on one's understanding of balance in an equation and the function of the equals sign. These big ideas are part of the foundation for algebra as well as for later work in arithmetic.

Daily Routine

Use these suggestions before beginning the lesson on p. LA3.

5-Minute Check

(Reviews Lesson 15-9)

Estimate the difference.

1. 62 − 19 = 40
2. 41 − 21 = 20
3. 58 − 33 = 30
4. 25 − 14 = 20

Problem of the Day

How can you use the addition sentence 5 + 3 = 8, to find 8 − 3? The missing number in the subtraction sentence is 5, which is the first number in the addition sentence.

LINE UP When students line up for lunch, make a group of 7 students. Ask how many more students are needed to make 12 students. Write 7 + ______ = 12 on the board. Have students find the missing addend.

Building Math Vocabulary

Write the term **missing addend** on the board. Explain that a missing addend is a number missing from an addition sentence.

- Have half the students in class roll a red number cube. Have the other half roll a blue number cube.
- Have a pair of volunteers, one from each group, make a subtraction sentence out of the numbers they roll. Then help them find the missing addend.

Differentiated Instruction

Small Group Options

Option 1 Below/Approaching Level

LOGICAL, LINGUISTIC

Materials: connecting cubes, blue and red number cubes

- Ask one student to roll the blue number cube. That number is the sum.
- Have each student use cubes to model the sum.
- Ask another student to roll the red number cube. That is one addend.
- Have each student use cubes to model the first addend.
- Then ask the group to use the cubes to find the missing addend. Remind students that the addends need to make the sum.
- Have students repeat the activity as time permits.

Option 2 English Language Learners ELL

VISUAL/SPATIAL, LOGICAL

Materials: cubes
Core Vocabulary: missing, up, back
Common Use Verb: counting

Write Math This strategy continues to use the relationship between addition and subtraction with 10 facts to help students with missing addends.

- Show the class 10 cubes. Students close their eyes while you grab 6 cubes in your left hand.
- Write "10 – ____ = 4." Accept guesses. Have students tally or draw to solve the problem. Model counting up and subtracting back to write an addition and a subtraction problem.
- Repeat. Prompt students to write their solutions. One student solves by counting up; the other by counting back.
- Compare and discuss written equations.

Independent Work Options

Option 1 Gifted and Talented OL AL

KINESTHETIC, VISUAL/SPATIAL

Materials: index cards, markers

- Have students draw a domino.
- On a card, have students write an addition fact and a subtraction fact with missing addends that can be solved using the domino.

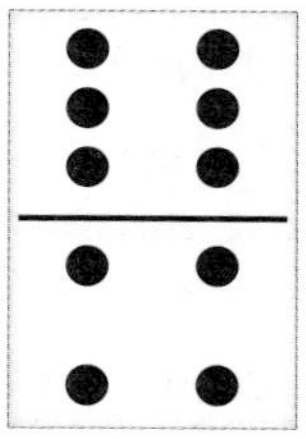

10 – 4 = __
4 + __ = 10

- Students combine cards, place in grid, and take turns matching dominoes with their related facts.

Option 2 Student Technology

Math Online macmillanmh.com

Math Adventures

1 Introduce

Activity Choice 1 • Hands-On

- Draw 10 circles on the board. Have students count the circles to verify that there are 10.
- Ask students to close their eyes while you affix a construction paper mat to the board that covers some of the circles. **How many circles do we still see?** 7 (for example) We know there are 10 circles in all, but we only see 7.
- Write 7 + ___ = 10 on the board. **How can we find the missing addend?** Count the circles still showing, then count on from that number to 10.
- Have students count on from 7 to 10 and predict that there are 3 circles hidden. Remove the construction paper mat so students can verify.

2 Teach

Display an overhead part-part-whole workmat. Place 4 red counters in one part and 4 red and 3 yellow counters in the whole section.

- Point to the whole. Say you need 7 counters. Point to the 4. Say you have 4 counters. **How many more counters do I need to make 7?** 3 Write 4 + ____ = 7
- Say you have to find how many more. **Will I add or subtract?** subtract **How do you know?** "how many more" means subtract
- Write 7 – 4 = ____. **What is the answer?** 3

Get Ready Use the section at the top of p. LA3 to reinforce the lesson concept. Guide students through the example, emphasizing using related facts to find the missing addend.

Check Observe students as you work through Exercises 1-4 as a class.

Talk About It **Exercise 5** Assess student comprehension before assigning practice exercises.

! COMMON ERROR!

Students may make mistakes with number facts. If so, have them work with dominoes to visualize the facts.

Name ______________________________

1 Missing Addends

Get Ready

Main Idea

I will recall subtraction facts to help find missing addends.

Vocabulary

missing addend

You can use a related subtraction fact to help you find a **missing addend**.

9 + ☐ = 13

13 − 9 = 4

So 9 + 4 = 13

4 is the missing addend.

Check

5. Sample answer: 13 − 5 = 8, so 5 + 8 = 13.

Find the missing addend. Draw dots to help.

1. 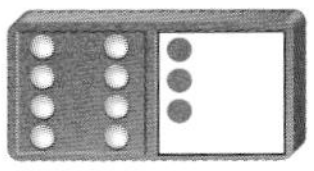

8 + 3 = 11   11 − 8 = 3

2. 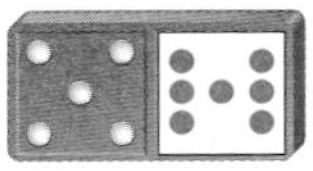

5 + 7 = 12   12 − 5 = 7

3. 

4 + 5 = 9   9 − 4 = 5

4. 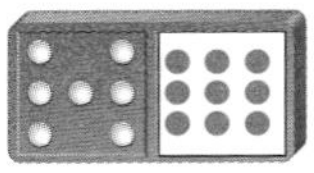

7 + 9 = 16   16 − 7 = 9

5. Talk About It How do you find the missing addend in 6 + 8 = 14? By thinking 14 − 6 = 8.

Practice

Find the missing addend.

> **Remember**
> Addition and subtraction facts with the same three numbers are related facts.

6. 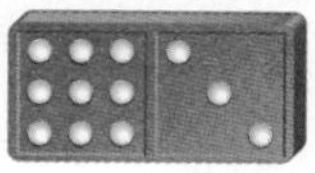
$12 - 9 = \boxed{3}$
$9 + \boxed{3} = 12$

7. $12 - 4 = \boxed{8}$
$\boxed{8} + 4 = 12$

8. $9 - 7 = \boxed{2}$
$7 + \boxed{2} = 9$

9. $12 - 6 = \boxed{6}$
$6 + \boxed{6} = 12$

10. $5 - 2 = \boxed{3}$
$\boxed{3} + 2 = 5$

11. $15 - \boxed{9} = 6$
$6 + \boxed{9} = 15$

12. $\boxed{16} - 8 = 8$
$8 + \boxed{8} = 16$

13. $7 + \boxed{8} = 15$ $\quad 15 - \boxed{8} = 7$

14. $4 + \boxed{9} = 13$ $\quad 13 - \boxed{9} = 4$

Problem Solving

15. **Algebra** There are 13 students with brown hair, red hair, or blonde hair. 7 have brown hair. 4 have red hair. How many have blonde hair?

$7 + 4 + \boxed{2} = 13$ 2 students

Math at Home Activity: Ask your child to tell you the subtraction fact that will help him or her add 7 + ☐ = 15.

BL Alternate Teaching Strategy

If students have trouble finding missing addends …

Then use one of these reteaching options.

Counting to 13 Give students 7 connecting cubes of one color and more than 6 of another color. Hold up a number card for 13. Have students connect the 7 cubes. Then have them connect cubes of another color to make 13.

- **How many of the second color did you use?** 6 Write the addition fact. 7 + 6 = 13 Write a related subtraction fact. 13 − 7 = 6 or 13 − 6 = 7

3 Practice

Differentiate practice using these suggestions.

Level	Assignment
BL Below/ Approaching Level	Guide students through the exercises. Have them use connecting cubes to model the problems.
OL On Level	Complete the exercises independently.
AL Above/Beyond Level	Complete the exercises and then write some problems of their own.

4 Assess

Formative Assessment

- **What makes addition and subtraction inverse operations?** They undo each other.

WRITING IN MATH Have students look at any problem in the first 14 exercises. Have them explain how the subtraction sentence helps them find the missing addend.

Quick Check **Are students continuing to struggle with missing addends?**

If Yes → Small Group Options (p. LA3)
If No → Independent Work Options (p. LA3)

Count On Tens and Ones

Lesson Planner

Objective
Count on by tens and ones to add.

Review Vocabulary
ones, tens

Resources
Manipulatives: base-ten blocks, whiteboards

Alternate Lesson Use "Unifix Stacks" on p. 320 of *Math Their Way* to provide practice with counting on by ones and tens.

Teacher Technology
TeacherWorks

Focus on Math Background
Although learned previously for ones, this lesson applies "counting on" to tens and ones. Critical for number sense is the grounding of any teaching of computation on the base-ten foundation upon which we build elementary arithmetic. Because students know how to add ones, it may be tempting to treat computation in a digit-based way, treating all numbers as ones. However, approached this way, arithmetic becomes a series of digit manipulations and prevents true understanding of numbers.

Daily Routine

Use these suggestions before beginning the lesson on p. LA5.

5-Minute Check
(Reviews Lesson LA-1)

Find the missing addends.

1. 9 + _____ = 14 5
2. 7 + _____ = 12 5
3. 2 + _____ = 9 7
4. 8 + _____ = 15 7

Problem of the Day
Look at the clock. What time is it? Count on to figure out what time it will be in 30 minutes.
See students' work.

LINE UP When students line up, give them addition problems to solve that involve adding 2 two-digit numbers. One number should be a multiple of 10. For example, 20 + 31? 51

Review Math Vocabulary
- Write 52 on the board. Point to the 2. Remind students that 2 is in the ones column, and it represents the number 2.
- Point to the 5. Remind students that 5 is in the tens column. It represents 5 tens or 50. Point out that 5 tens plus 2 ones equals 52.
- Have students identify tens and ones in other numbers.

Differentiated Instruction

Small Group Options

Option 1 — Gifted and Talented (AL)

VISUAL/SPATIAL, LOGICAL

Materials: 0–99 board, 0–9 spinner, 2 game markers

- Have students place their game markers on the 0 space on the board.
- The first student spins to determine the number of spaces to move on the board. The student may choose either to count on from 0 by ones or by tens depending on the best strategy to use.
- The other student repeats the steps. If player 1 lands on the same space as player 2, then player 2 is bumped and sent back to 0.
- The student who lands exactly on 99 first wins.

Option 2 — English Language Learners (ELL)

VISUAL/SPATIAL

Materials: pennies, dimes, number lines, tape
Core Vocabulary: cents, penny, dime
Common Use Verb count on

See Math This strategy activates background knowledge of money to help students count on from ones and tens.

- Tape a penny to the board above 1 on a number line. Write 1 above it. Repeat for a dime. Ask how much students have.
- Write "1 **dime** is 10 **cents**, plus one **penny** is 11 **cents**." Model bouncing the dime from 0 to 10 and then placing the penny next to it.
- Give students 1 dime and 3 pennies and ask them to use the coins and the number line to count on. Say: "For **pennies**, ***count on*** by ones. For **dimes**, ***count on*** by tens. Use your number line."
- Give each student 4 more pennies and have them repeat, as you write 13 + 4 = 17 on the board.
- Give each student 2 dimes. Write 17 + 20 = 37 on the board.
- Continue with different amounts as time permits.

Independent Work Options

Option 1 — Early Finishers (OL) (AL)

KINESTHETIC, SOCIAL

Materials: spinner, base-ten blocks, WorkMat 6

- A player spins twice to get a two-digit number. Another player models the number with rods and units.
- Players take turns showing new ways of naming the number.

tens	ones
0	26
1	16
2	6

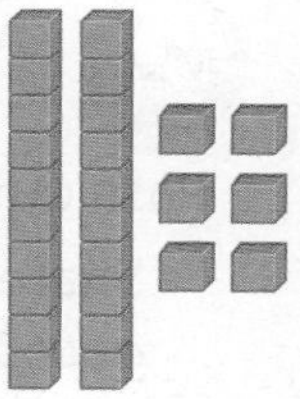

Option 2 — Student Technology

Math Online macmillanmh.com

Math Adventures

Looking 2 Ahead

1 Introduce

Activity Choice 1 • Hands-On

Have students use their whiteboards. Write a number on the board. Have students write the number that is one more. Repeat with a number that is ten more than the number you wrote.

- **What is one more than 22?** 23
- **What is ten more than 22?** 32

2 Teach

Pass out base-ten blocks. Write 26 on the board.

- Share these stories: *Sara has 26 stickers. She gets 3 more. How can Sara count on to find how many in all?* Count on 3 from 26. Students get 3 blocks and count on 3. **How many in all?** 29 **What number sentence tells about Sara's stickers?** 26 + 3 = 29
- *Tom also has 26 stickers. He gets 30 more stickers. How can Tom count on to find how many in all?* Count on by tens from 26. Students count out 3 tens blocks and count on by tens. **How many in all?** 56 **What number sentence tells about Tom's stickers?** 26 + 30 = 56
- **Do Sara and Tom still have the same number of stickers?** no **Why not?** Tom added more.

Get Ready Use the section at the top of p. LA5 to reinforce the lesson concept. Guide students through the example. Use base-ten blocks.

Check Observe students as you work through Exercises 1–6 as a class.

Talk About It **Exercise 7** Assess student comprehension before assigning practice exercises.

! COMMON ERROR!

Some students may confuse counting on by ones and counting on by tens. Tell them to place a counter on the first addend on a hundred chart. Have them move to the right to count on ones and down to count on tens.

Name ______________________

Hands-On Activity

2 Count On Tens and Ones

Get Ready

Main Idea

I will count on by tens and ones to find sums.

Find 26 + 3.
Count on by ones.

26 + 3 = 29

Think
Start at 26.
Count 27, 28, 29.

Find 26 + 30.
Count on by tens.

26 + 30 = 56

Think
Start at 26.
Count 36, 46, 56.

Check

Count on to add. Write the sum. Use [base-ten rod] to help.

1. 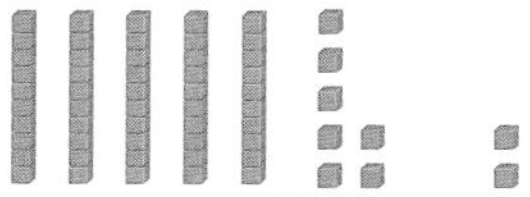

57 + 2 = **59**

2. 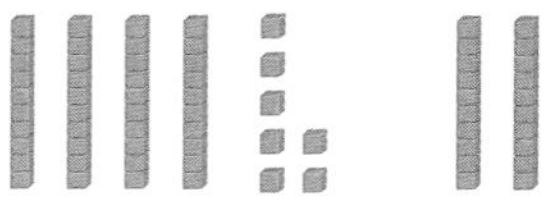

47 + 20 = 67

3. 

13 + 3 = 16

4. 

13 + 50 = 63

5. 3 + 24 = 27

6. 60 + 32 = 92

7. Talk About It How many tens do you count on to add 32 + 50? Explain. Count on 5 tens, because 50 is equal to 5 tens.

Practice

> **Remember**
> To count on by tens, Keep adding 10 to the number.

Count on to add. Write the sum. Use [tens rod] to help.

8. 66 + 3 = 69	**9.** 14 + 70 = 84	**10.** 12 + 2 = 14
11. 25 + 3 = 28	**12.** 51 + 30 = 81	**13.** 45 + 10 = 55
14. 53 + 20 = 73	**15.** 3 + 12 = 15	**16.** 66 + 30 = 96
17. 51 + 5 = 56	**18.** 20 + 76 = 96	**19.** 32 + 1 = 33
20. 30 + 32 = 62	**21.** 3 + 32 = 35	**22.** 20 + 44 = 64

23. 3 + 41 = 44

24. 10 + 88 = 98

25. 1 + 88 = 89

26. 32 + 20 = 52

Problem Solving

27. **Number Sense** Zina and Jack each have 25 points. Zina scores 3 more points. How many points does Zina have now?

Zina has 28 points.

Jack gets 30 more points. How many points does Jack have now?

Jack has 55 points.

Math at Home Activity: Say a number between 10 and 50. Ask your child to count on by 1, 2, or 3 and then by 10, 20, or 30.

BL Alternate Teaching Strategy

If students have trouble understanding how to count on ones and tens …

Then use one of these reteach options.

Domino Addition Give each student a domino. Ask them to count the number of dots on the left side of the domino. Have students start with that number and count on the number of dots on the right side to find the sum.

3 Practice

Differentiate practice using these suggestions.

Level	Assignment
BL Below/ Approaching Level	Guide students through the exercises. Help them use base-ten blocks to add the tens and ones.
OL On Level	Complete the exercises independently.
AL Above/Beyond Level	Complete the exercises without the base-ten blocks.

4 Assess

Formative Assessment

Ask students to explain how they would solve the problem 42 + 31 by writing or drawing pictures.

WRITING IN MATH Ask students to explain why they think it was important to learn how to count by tens in kindergarten.

Quick Check **Are students continuing to struggle with counting on tens and ones?**

If Yes → Independent Work Options (p. LA5B)

If No → Small Group Options (p. LA5B)

Hundreds, Tens, and Ones

Looking Ahead 3

Lesson Planner

Objective
Read, write, and model numbers to 1,000.

Review Vocabulary
skip count

Resources
Materials: WorkMat 7: Place Value Chart

Manipulatives: base ten blocks

Alternate Lessons: Use "Estimating and Checking" on pp. 308–309 of *Math Their Way* to provide practice with counting, reading, and writing numbers to 1,000.

Teacher Technology

TeacherWorks

Focus on Math Background

This apparently simple lesson is a great deal more. How many young students, after they have learned to count to one hundred, think the next counting number is two hundred? For some, the process of righting this and other misconceptions takes all of the primary years. Students' understanding of the relationship between and among hundreds, tens, and ones is critical for all conceptual development in arithmetic.

Daily Routine

Use these suggestions before beginning the lesson on p. LA7.

5-Minute Check
(Reviews Lesson LA-2)

Count on to add. Write the sum.

1. 32 + 30 = 62

2. 27 + 60 = 87

3. 79 + 1 = 80

4. 40 + 22 = 62

Problem of the Day
The school lunchroom can seat 185 students. How many hundreds? _____ 1 How many tens? _____ 8 How many ones? _____ 5

LINE UP When students line up for recess, lunch, or dismissal, play "before and after."

- Give students the hundreds number 400. Ask a volunteer to tell you what hundred comes before and after 400. 300, 500
- Repeat with other hundreds.

Review Math Vocabulary
Discuss the term **skip count** and write it on the board.

- On the board, draw a number line with the hundreds from 0 to 1000 marked. **How can I use a number line to count the hundreds?** skip count Have a volunteer demonstrate how to skip count hundreds on the number line.
- Repeat with skip counting by 10s, 2s, and 5s.

Differentiated Instruction

Small Group Options

Option 1 LOGICAL/SPATIAL

Below Level BL

Materials: base-ten blocks

- Give students varying groups of base-ten materials.
- Tell them to sort by hundreds, tens, and ones. Then have them count each group and record the number.
- Students repeat with different groups of base-ten blocks.

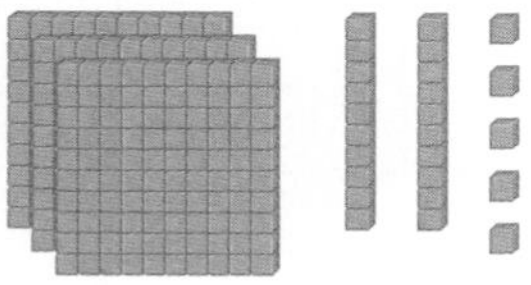

Option 2 VISUAL/SPATIAL, LOGICAL

English Language Learners ELL

Materials: unit block
Core Vocabulary: thousands place, strategy, trade
Common Use Verb: add

See Math This strategy allows students to act out and integrate the math with aquired language.

- Write 999 + 1 on the board. Model and draw 999 in place value blocks.
- Ask students to repeat ***adding*** 1 unit block to 999 and model it. Restate their strategy as necessary as they work.
- In small groups, give a problem between (999 to 990) + (2 −10).
- Ask students to act out or draw their solution and present their strategy.

Independent Work Options

Option 1 SPATIAL, LINGUISTIC

Early Finishers OL AL

Materials: spinner

- Students spin to get 4 numbers. They write the first number in the ones place, second in the tens place, etc.
- Students read the numbers they wrote.
- They trade papers. **How many ones in your partner's number? How many tens? hundreds? thousands?**
- Students write the numbers in expanded form and read them aloud.

Option 2

Student Technology

Math Online macmillanmh.com

Math Adventures

Looking Ahead 4

1 Introduce

Activity Choice 1 • Hands-On

- Write 100 on the board and have students place one hundreds base-ten block in the hundreds section of a place value workmat.
- **What number did you show?** 100
- **If you add one to the workmat, how will the number shown change?** It will be one more.
- Write 100 + 1 = 101 on the board.

2 Teach

- Write 127 on the board and have students model it with base ten blocks. **What is the first number you see when you look at 127?** 100 Write 100 on the board.
- **What is the next number you see when you look at 127?** 20 Write the number 20 below 100.
- **What is the last number you see when you look at 127?** 7 Write 7 below 20 to form a vertical addition problem.
- **What is the sum of these numbers?** 127 Write the sum. Write 100 + 20 + 7 = 127 horizontally. Explain that this is the **expanded form** of 127.

Get Ready Use the section at the top of p. LA9 to teach the lesson concept.

Check Observe students as you work through Exercises 1–6 as a class.

Talk About It **Exercise 7** Assess student comprehension before assigning practice exercises.

! COMMON ERROR!

Students may have difficulty writing numbers in expanded form. Tell them the digit in the hundreds place is always followed by two zeros. The digit in the tens place is always followed by one zero.

Name ______________________

Looking Ahead 4 Place Value to 1,000

Get Ready

Main Idea

I will use expanded form to write numbers up to 1,000.

Vocabulary

expanded form

Place value tells the value of a digit in a number.

Think: You can write a number in **expanded form**.

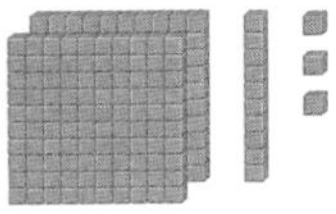

hundreds	tens	ones
2	1	3

2 hundreds 1 ten 3 ones

200 + 10 + 3

213

Check

7. 762 and 267 have the same digits and the same number of tens. They have different values and a different number of hundreds and ones.

Write the number in expanded form. Then write the number.

1. 1 hundred 6 tens 2 ones
 100 + 60 + 2
 162

2. 1 hundred 2 tens 5 ones
 100 + 20 + 5
 125

Write the number.

3. 300 + 70 + 6 = 376

4. 700 + 60 + 1 = 761

Circle the value of the red digit.

5. 931
 300 (30) 3

6. 277
 (200) 20 2

7. Talk About It How are 762 and 267 the same? How are they different?

Practice

Write the number in expanded form.
Then write the number.

8. 6 hundreds 2 tens 5 ones

600 + 20 + 5

625

9. 9 hundreds 9 tens 9 ones

900 + 90 + 9

999

Write the number.

10. 600 + 30 + 8 = 638

11. 100 + 30 + 9 = 139

12 500 + 20 + 4 = 524

13. 200 + 70 + 2 = 272

Circle the value of the red digit.

14. 965

(900) 90 9

15. 673

300 30 (3)

16. 468

600 (60) 6

17. 890

(800) 80 8

H.O.T. Problem

18. Make it Right
Mario wrote 365 in expanded form like this: 300 + 50 + 6.
Tell why Mario is wrong.
Then make it right.

He wrote the 5 as a 50 and the 60 as a 6.

300 + 60 + 5

Math at Home Activity: Have your child tell you a three digit number. Then ask your child to tell you the value of the first digit.

BL Alternate Teaching Strategy

If students have trouble understanding how to identify place value to 1,000 ...

Then use one of these reteach options.

Show a Model Write 1,000 in a place value chart. **What number is in the hundreds place?** 0 **thousands place?** 1 Students write their responses on a whiteboard and hold it up.

- Repeat the procedure with 950.

3 Practice

Differentiate practice using these suggestions.

Level	Assignment
BL Below/ Approaching Level	Guide students through the exercises. Help them use place-value workmats to solve the problems.
OL On Level	Complete independently.
AL Above/Beyond Level	Complete exercises without the place-value workmats.

4 Assess

Formative Assessment

- **What is 800 + 20 + 8 in standard form?** 828 **What is 567 in expanded form?** 500 + 60 + 7

WRITING IN MATH Have students explain how they know the place value of the 6 in 362.

Quick Check **Are students continuing to struggle with place value to 1,000?**

If Yes → Small Group Options (p. LA9B)

If No → Independent Work Options (p. LA9B)

Measure to the Nearest Inch

Looking Ahead 5

Lesson Planner

Objective
Estimate and measure length using inches.

Vocabulary
inch

Resources
Materials: yarn, scissors, classroom objects that can be measured with a ruler

Manipulatives: rulers

Teacher Technology

TeacherWorks • Concepts in Motion

Focus on Math Background

Measuring to the nearest inch is most students' first introduction to rounding. Between two ticks on a measuring stick there is a critical "halfway point." Whether the halfway point is denoted or not, there must be an understanding of its presence to make the judgment of which tick is closer to the edge of the measured object.

Daily Routine

Use these suggestions before beginning the lesson on p. LA11

5-Minute Check

(Reviews Lesson LA-4)

Wtite the number.

1. 100 + 40 + 4 144
2. 200 + 10 + 9 219
3. 800 + 30 + 5 835
4. 600 + 70 + 1 671

Problem of the Day

Fiona is making a necklace with 15 beads. If the pattern unit is yellow, red, blue, how many times can the pattern repeat? 5 times

LINE UP Have students play a game of "What Do I See?"

- Ask volunteers to call out the color and estimated length of an object they see. For example, "I see something yellow and about four inches long."

Building Math Vocabulary

Write **inch** and its definition on the board.

- inch—a customary unit for measuring length and height. 12 inches = 1 foot
- Explain that there are 12 inches in a foot, which is another customary unit for measuring length and height. **What other units of length do you know?** yard, meter, mile Write "12 inches = 1 foot" on the board. Point out and underline the *-es* ending of the word *inches*.

Differentiated Instruction

Small Group Options

Option 1 VISUAL/SPATIAL

Below Level BL

Materials: empty pocket chart, different lengths of string (enough for each student), index cards, tape, rulers

- Have students measure their piece of string to the nearest inch.
- Have them tape the string on the index card and record the length in inches.
- Call on students to place their cards in the pocket chart.
- Have students organize the lengths from the shortest string to the longest string.

Option 2 VISUAL/SPATIAL, AUDITORY

English Language Learners ELL

Materials: rulers
Core Vocabulary: exact measurement, long, wide
Common Use Verb: can use

Do Math This strategy gives students practice with measurement vocabulary and experience measuring.

- Say: "When we measure with nonstandard units, the answers can be different. When we want the **measurement** to be **exact**, we ***can use*** an inch for a unit." Show students a ruler and how it is divided into inches.
- Say: "Use a ruler to measure (an identical book that each student has) to the inch." Discuss how all the answers for length are the same, and that all the answers for width are the same too.
- Play Simon Says. While playing, show students what and how you are asking them to measure. Say: "Simon says, estimate how many inches **long** your shoes are. Simon says, find the **exact measurement** of how **long** your shoes are. Simon says, estimate how many inches wide your chair seat is. Simon says, find the **exact measurement** of how **wide** your seat is." etc.

Independent Work Options

Option 1 VISUAL/SPATIAL, LINGUISTIC

Early Finishers OL AL

Materials: classroom objects, drawing paper, crayons, rulers

- Write these instructions on the board:
  1. Measure 2. Draw 3. Write
- Students find four things to measure that are 12 inches long or less.
- They choose two objects to draw actual size and state the length of each object in a sentence.

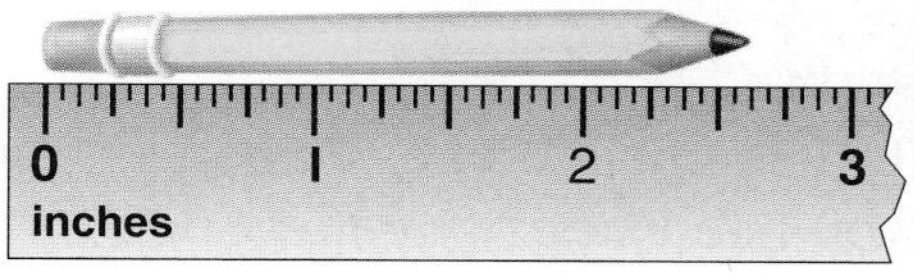

Option 2

Student Technology

Math Online macmillanmh.com

Looking Ahead 5

1 Introduce

Activity Choice 1 • Hands-On

- Model how to measure an object to the nearest inch, using a ruler.
- **What does "nearest inch" mean?** the next inch up or down, whichever is closer to the end tip of the object
- Call on students to measure various classroom objects in front of the class, such as an eraser, a book, or a crayon.

2 Teach

Explain that you need to make a paper chain and you need strips of paper about "this long" (hold your fingers about 6 inches apart).

- **To do this job, can I estimate the length of the strips or do I have to measure them?** estimate
- **If I'm buying new carpet for the bedroom, can I estimate the size of the room or should I measure it?** measure
- Explain that when we measure to the nearest inch and round up or down, we are estimating.
- Review measuring to the nearest inch.

Get Ready Use the section at the top of student p. LA11 to reinforce the lesson concept. Guide students in measuring to the nearest inch.

Check Observe students as you work through Exercises 1–2 as a class.

Talk About It **Exercise 3** Assess student comprehension before assigning practice exercises.

COMMON ERROR!

Students may not align the ruler with the "0" mark, using the "1" mark instead. Remind them to check the alignment every time they measure.

Name ________________________

Hands-On Activity

Measure to the Nearest Inch

Get Ready

Main Idea

I will use an inch ruler to measure.

Vocabulary

inch

Use an **inch** ruler to measure length.

First, line up the object with the end of the ruler starting at zero.

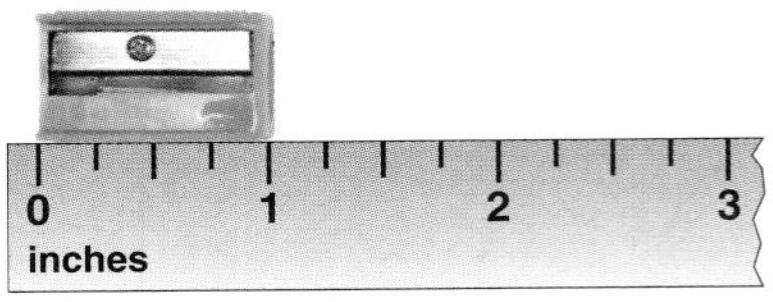

Next, look at the marks on the ruler. Find the measurement that is closest to the end of the object.

This pencil sharpener is about ___ inch long.

Check

3. Line up the object with the 0 mark on the ruler. Then look to see what number is closest to the other end of the object.

Find the object. Estimate. Then use an inch ruler to measure. 1.–2. Answers will vary depending on objects measured.

Find	Estimate	Measure
1. 	about _____ inches	about _____ inches
2. 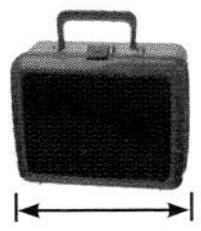	about _____ inches	about _____ inches

3. Talk About It Describe how you use an inch ruler to measure.

Practice

Remember
Line up the object with the end of the ruler.

Find the object. Estimate. Measure to the nearest inch.

Find	Estimate	Measure
4. 	about _____ inches	about _____ inches
5. 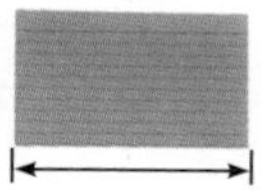	about _____ inches	about _____ inches
6. 	about _____ inches	about _____ inches
7. 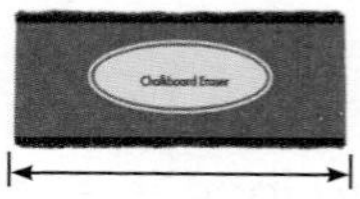	about _____ inches	about _____ inches
8. 	about _____ inches	about _____ inches

4.–8. Answers will vary depending on objects measured.

Problem Solving

9. **Thinking Math** A large paper clip is about 2 inches long. How long is a chain of 4 paper clips?

about 8 inches

Math at Home Activity: Ask your child to show you how to measure the length of a piece of yarn or string with an inch ruler.

BL Alternate Teaching Strategy

If students have trouble correctly measuring with a ruler ...

Then use one of these reteach options.

Match the Measurement Provide five common objects that you have already measured. List the objects in one column on the board. List the measurements in another column, out of order. Have students measure the items and draw lines on the board that connect the object to its measurement.

3 Practice

Differentiate practice using these suggestions.

Level	Assignment
BL Below/ Approaching Level	Guide students through the exercises, modeling how to measure correctly. Make sure they understand what "nearest inch" means.
OL On Level	Complete the exercises independently.
AL Above/Beyond Level	Complete the exercises and measure other objects independently.

4 Assess

Formative Assessment

- **Why is it a good idea to use inches to measure instead of paper clips or other objects?** An inch is an exact, standard unit of measure that nearly everyone knows.

WRITING IN MATH Ask students to explain measuring to the nearest inch to a kindergartener.

Quick Check **Are students continuing to struggle with measuring with a ruler?**

If Yes → Small Group Options (p. LA11B)

If No → Independent Work Options (p. LA11B)

Looking Ahead 6 Measure to the Nearest Centimeter

Lesson Planner

Objective
Estimate and measure length using centimeters.

Vocabulary
centimeter

Resources
Materials: classroom objects that can be measured with a ruler

Manipulatives: centimeter rulers

Teacher Technology

TeacherWorks • Concepts in Motion

Focus on Math Background
To measure to the nearest centimeter is to work with rounding: "It measures between four and five, but it is closer to five." This statement acknowledges an intuitive understanding of some sort of halfway mark. This intuition, possessed by some, needs to be visually represented and discussed for the benefit of all.

Daily Routine

Use these suggestions before beginning the lesson on p. LA13.

5-Minute Check
(Reviews Lesson LA-5)

A stapler is about 7 inches long. How long is a row of 3 staplers? 21 inches

Problem of the Day
Draw a square. Draw 5 + 3 dots inside the square. Draw 9 – 5 stars outside the square.

LINE UP Have students play a game of "What Do I See?" using centimeters.

- Ask volunteers to call out the color, estimated length, and any other clues for an object they see. For example, "I see something blue about two centimeters wide. It is on a coat." button

Building Math Vocabulary
- **What units have we learned to use to measure length and width?** inch, foot, yard
- Display a ruler with inches and **centimeters**.
- Explain that another way to measure length and width is by using centimeters. Tell students that centimeters are smaller than inches. There are 30 centimeters on this ruler.
- Point out that centimeters are a standard unit of measure, just like inches, but that they are part of another system, the metric system.
- Model measuring an object in centimeters.

End-of-Year Projects

1. I Spy Patterns! **P3**
2. Fruit Kabob Factory **P7**
3. Let's Go to the Zoo! **P11**
4. Toys from the Past and Present **P15**

P2

Problem-Solving Projects PROJECT 1

Lesson Planner

Objective

Students create and extend repeating patterns, collect and sort data, separate a whole into equal parts, and communicate grade level mathematics using informal language as they explore and create their own board games.

Review Vocabulary

pattern, bar graph, certain, impossible

Resources

Materials: board games, crayons or markers, scissors, glue, cardboard

Manipulatives: connecting cubes, number cube, spinner, pattern blocks

Day 1

This project involves having students explore board games and the math concepts they use when playing them. Students review concepts in patterning, data collection, and communicating these math concepts to create their own board game.

- Collect board games for students to use throughout this project. You may also ask students to bring in a board game from home to share with the class.
- Patterns can be found on checkerboards, chessboards, and other children's games.
- Allow students time to explore each board game on display.
- Ask students to look for patterns on the board games. Remind students that patterns can come in different shapes and colors.
- Discuss page P3 with students.
- Have students use connecting cubes to model the patterns they find in board games.

Name: ______________________

Projects

You will find patterns in board games. You will also make your own board game.

Day 1: Can you find the pattern?

1. Look for a pattern on the board games. Describe it.

Check students' answers.

2.–6. Check students' answers.

2. Identify the pattern unit on the board. Color the pattern below.

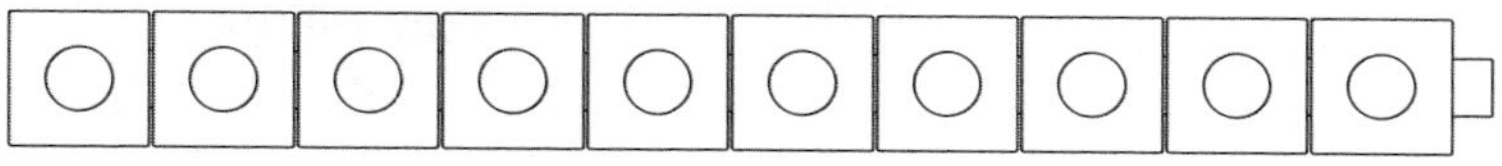

Day 2: Moving Forward

3. Find a partner. Take turns rolling the  15 times.

4. Make a bar graph to show your data.

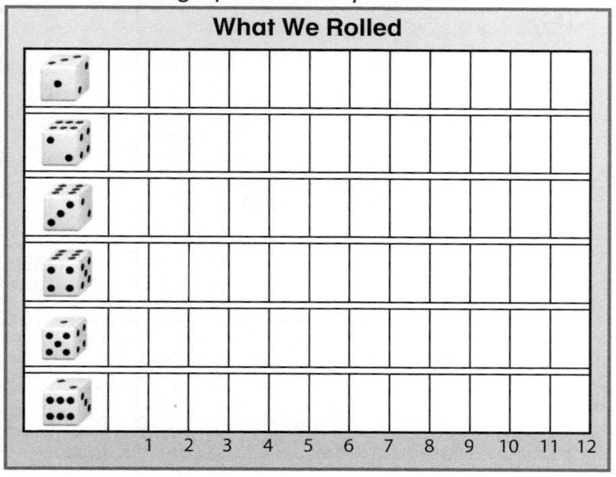

5. What number did you roll the greatest number of times? _____

6. What number did you roll the least number of times? _____

P4 I Spy Patterns!

Day 2

- Divide students into groups of two.
- Review how graphs are used to organize data.
- Discuss page P4 with students. Point out that in many games players use a number cube or spinner to move across the board.
- Ask students to take turns rolling the number cube 15 times. Show students how to record their data in the bar graph.
- Have students use their graphs to complete Exercises 5 and 6.
- **How many more times did you roll _____ than _____?** Insert various numbers. See students' work.
- **Was it certain or impossible that you would roll the number seven?** impossible
- If time permits, extend the activity. Have students use the data from Exercise 4 to create either a line plot or a picture graph.

Day 3

- Discuss page P5 with students.
- Review patterning and different ways players can move across a game board.
- Ask students to follow the directions to create their own board game.
- If time and supplies are available, allow students to transfer their game board onto a piece of cardboard.

Day 3: Design your own board game.

7. Create a pattern on the game board.
8. Cut and paste the game squares onto the board.
9. Use to move forward.

You will need:

Game squares:

Go ahead 2 spaces
Go back 2 spaces
Take an extra turn
Miss 1 turn
Go ahead 1 space
Go back 1 space

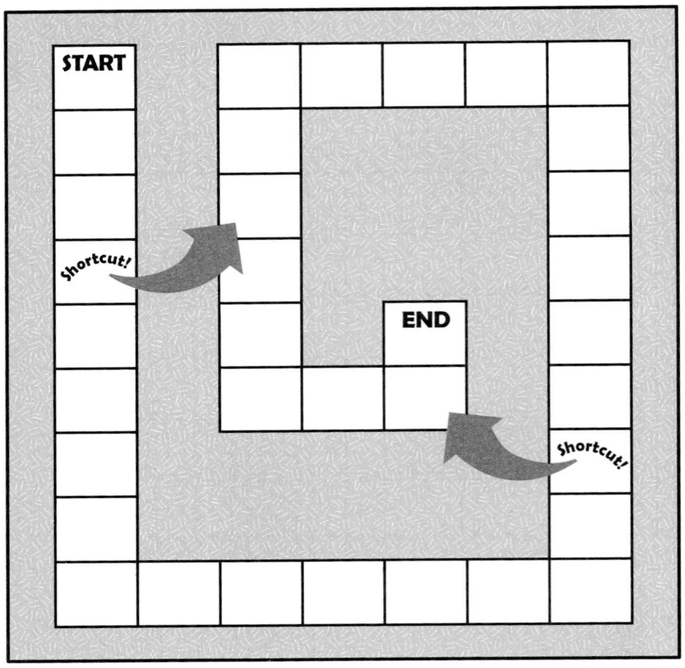

7–9. Check students' work.

Day 4: Game Day!

10. Exchange your board game with a partner.

11. How long does it take to play your game? Draw the hands on the clocks. Check students' work.

Start

Finish

Day 5: Act It Out

12. James moved forward 2 spaces. Sada moved forward 6 spaces. How many more spaces did Sada move forward?

4 spaces

13. It was Héctor's turn. He rolled:

How many spaces did he move forward?

19 spaces

14. Write your own board game problem. Ask your friend to solve.

Check students' work.

P6 I Spy Patterns!

Day 4

- Have students exchange games with a partner or small group.
- Ask students to explain how to play their games.
- Encourage students to identify the patterns on other students' board games.
- Allow time for students to take turns playing the games they created.

Extension: Have students bring their games to another classroom. Ask students to explain the rules and play the game.

Day 5

Ask students to share their repeating pattern and the math concepts they used to create the game. Encourage students to share which math concepts players will use to play the game.

Wrap-Up

- Use these Wrap-Up questions to assess students' work.
- **What math did you use to plan and create your board game?** Sample answers: creating patterns, data collection, problem solving
- **How might you design and create your board game differently if you were to do it again? Why?** Sample answers: I would change the repeating color pattern to match the game pieces. I would use a spinner with more numbers instead of a number cube so a player could move more spaces in one turn.

Lesson Planner

Objective

Students design and create a fruit kabob by taking a survey and drawing conclusions based on the data they gathered, design a repeating pattern for the kabob, determine the total cost of the ingredients, and the sequence of events necessary to produce the kabob. Students will also communicate the use of mathematics as it pertains to this project.

Review Vocabulary

pattern, tally chart, bar graph

Resources

Materials: apples and other types of fruit, kabob sticks, knife, grocery store ads

Manipulatives: plastic coins

Day 1

This project involves having students research, plan, and design a product to build and sell.

- Discuss page P7 with students.
- Tell students that they are going to make fruit kabobs. A fruit kabob is a snack with different pieces of fruit placed on a stick.
- Explain to students that they will make a fruit kabob they can sell. They need to find which fruit is liked best by their customers.
- Have students list three fruits on the tally chart on page P7.
- Have students survey 10 people in order to decide which fruits to use on their fruit kabobs.

Name: ____________________

You will make fruit kabobs in your classroom's factory.

Day 1: Which type of fruit is best to sell?

1. Ask 10 people to choose the fruit they like the best.
2. Organize your data in a tally chart.

Favorite Fruit

Type of Fruit	Tally	Total

3. Make a picture graph to show your data.

Favorite Fruit

4. Circle the fruit you should use to make the fruit kabobs.

1.–4. Check students' answers.

Day 2: Design your kabob

5. Create patterns with different kinds of fruit.

5–8. Check students' drawings.

6. Draw your patterns.

Remember to use the fruits people liked the most.

7. Circle the pattern that your team will make.

8. Make a sign to show your product. Also tell people why they should buy your fruit kabob.

Day 3: It's time to buy supplies and pick a price.

9. Look at the fruit kabob pattern your team will make. Write the supplies your group needs to buy.

10. Look in store ads to find the prices of the ingredients.

11. Draw the coins you used. Write the amount.

_______ ¢

12. How much will you charge for your fruit kabob?

9–12. Check students' work.

_______ ¢

P8 Fruit Kabob Factory

Day 2

- Discuss page P8 with students. Divide the students into small groups to complete the activity.
- The students will need different types of fruit and kabob sticks to make their patterns.
- Have students draw their patterns in Exercise 6.
- Each group will choose a pattern to make as a group.
- For Exercise 8, explain to students that they are making advertisements. Advertisements tell people why they should buy a product. For example, television commericals are advertisements.
- Encourage students to share their advertisements for their fruit kabobs.

Day 3

- Explain to students that *ads* is the short way to write *advertisements*.
- Discuss Exercises 9–12 with the students.
- Have students make a list of the ingredients needed for the fruit kabobs they made on Day 2.
- Set up a store in the classroom. Price the ingredients or make a store ad with the prices.
- Give students plastic coins so they can buy the ingredients they need.

Day 4

- Explain how assembly lines can be helpful.
- Tell students that each of them will have a job. List possible jobs on the board.
- Have each student draw the sequence of steps needed to make the fruit kabob.
- Encourage students to share their drawings with the class and write about each step on a separate sheet of paper.
- If possible, show students photos or video clips of how assembly lines are used to make various products such as a bike or type of food.

Day 4: Get to work!

13. Draw the steps for making your fruit kabobs.

Check students' drawings.

First	Second

Third	Fourth

14. Circle the step that takes the longest amount of time.

Check students' answers.

Day 5: Managers' Meeting

15. Explain how your team chose a price for your fruit kabobs.

Check students' answers.

16. Draw coins to show the price of your fruit kabobs. Students' answers will vary.

One Way	Another Way

17. Each apple is 10¢. How many apples can you buy with 90¢?

9 apples

18. Oranges are 2 for 25¢. How many oranges can you buy with 75¢?

6 oranges

Day 5

Invite students to present their fruit kabobs to the class. Have each student share the following:

1. survey data and conclusions
2. their fruit kabob pattern
3. amount spent on ingredients
4. assembly line drawings.

Wrap-Up

- Use these Wrap-Up questions to assess students' work.
- **How did you use math to design and create your fruit kabob?** Sample answers: I took a survey to determine which apple would be best to use in my kabob. I designed a pattern for the kabob. I determined how much the ingredients would cost. I sequenced the jobs necessary to make the kabobs.
- **If you designed another fruit kabob, how would it be different?** Sample answer: I would use watermelon, strawberries, and pineapple instead of apples and oranges.

Lesson Planner

Objective

To plan a trip to the zoo, students graph favorite zoo animals and draw conclusions to create a schedule based on the data they collected. Students draw pictures and skip count to calculate the costs of transportation and lunch.

Review Vocabulary

bar graph, data, skip count

Resources

Materials: various zoo maps

Manipulatives: two-colored counters

Day 1

This project involves having students prepare and plan for a visit to the zoo. Students create a bar graph of favorite animals, draw conclusions to create a schedule, calculate how much it will cost to get to the zoo, and how many pizzas will need to be ordered for lunch.

- Ask students to help you generate a list of animals that might be seen at the zoo. Record these animals on the board.
- Discuss page P11 with students.
- Divide the class into small groups. Have each group ask 10 classmates the following survey question, *Which is your favorite animal to see at the zoo?* Students record the data in a bar graph.
- As a class, make a list of the students' favorite animals.

Name: ____________________

I will plan a trip to the zoo.

Day 1: What animals will you see?

1. Ask 10 classmates to vote for their favorite animal.
2. Make a bar graph to show your data. Check students' work.

Favorite Animal

Bear									
Lion									
Elephant									
Giraffe									

Let's Go to the Zoo! P11

Projects

Day 2: Let's plan our day. Check students' work.

3. Look at the bar graph you made.

4. List the animals in the order your class will see them.

First	Third
Second	**Fourth**

5. Use the *Zoo Trip Schedule* to complete the chart on the next page.

Zoo Trip Schedule

- You will arrive at the zoo at 9:00.
- You will see the first animal a half hour after you arrive.
- You will leave the zoo at 1:00.
- You will see the fourth animal a half hour before you leave the zoo.
- You will eat lunch 2 hours before you leave the zoo.
- You will see the second animal a half hour after you see the first animal.
- You will see the third animal a half hour before lunch.

Day 2

- Review the bar graphs from Day 1 as a class.
- Ask students to brainstorm things they should think about when planning a zoo trip schedule.
- Provide students with possible scenarios. For example, if time is limited, what animals should we see first? Should we visit the animals that are students' favorites or visit the animals according to their location in the zoo?
- **What animal do you think we should see first, second, third, and fourth?** Sample answer: We should see elephants first because elephants received the most votes for a favorite animal.
- **Use words to justify your thinking.** Sample answer: We should see lions first because it received the greatest number of votes for a favorite animal.
- Ask students to refer back to their list in Exercise 4 and create a *Zoo Trip Schedule* on page P13.

Extension: Bring in maps of the local zoo. Ask students to trace the route of their schedule across the map with their fingers.

Day 3

- Explain that you are ordering pizzas for lunch and each person can have $\frac{1}{4}$ of a small pizza.
- Have students draw a picture to find how many pizzas are needed.
- Review skip counting by fives.
- Discuss with students a more inexpensive way to have lunch on a field trip. For example, each student could bring a bag lunch from home.

6. Use the zoo trip schedule on P12. Draw hands on the clocks to match the times on the schedule. Write the activity.

Zoo Trip Schedule		
9:00		Arrive at the zoo.
9:30		See 1st animal
10:00		See 2nd animal
10:30		See 3rd animal
11:00		Lunch
12:30		See 4th animal
1:00		Leave the zoo.

Day 3: Zoo Lunch Budget

7. Each student can have $\frac{1}{4}$ of a pizza. Draw a picture to solve. How many pizzas will your class need to order?

Answers will vary depending on number of students in the class. _______ pizzas

8. Each pizza costs 5 dollars. Count by 5's to find the total cost of the pizzas. Write the amount.
Answers will vary depending on number of pizza purchased. dollars

9. You received the first grader discount! The pizzas are 2 dollars each. Write the new amount.
Answers will vary depending on number of pizzas purchased. dollars

Day 4: How will you get to the zoo?

Don't forget your teacher!

10. If each van can hold 6 people, how many vans will you need to take? ______ vans
Use counters and the boxes below to solve the problem.

Answers will vary depending on number of people going to the zoo.

Day 5: Design your own zoo.

11. On a separate piece of paper, draw a map of a zoo.

12. Draw hands on the clock to show when your zoo will open and close.
11–12. Check students' work.

Zoo Hours

Open

Close

Day 4

- Ask students to brainstorm a list of different types of transportation. List their responses on the board.
- Discuss page P14 with students. Explain that you will be taking vans to the zoo and each van can hold six people.
- Give each student 36 counters.
- Ask students to use the counters and "vans" on page P14 to find how many vans you will need to take to the zoo.
- **If each van cost ten dollars to rent for the day, how much money will the class spend?** See students' work.
- Remind students to skip count by tens in order to figure out how much it will cost to rent the vans.

Day 5

- Have students create another zoo schedule according to their zoo hours.
- Ask students to draw the route of the schedule on their zoo maps.

Wrap-Up

- Use these Wrap-Up questions to assess students' work.
- **What math did you use to plan a trip to the zoo?** Sample answers: data collection, drawing conclusions, creating a schedule, calculating cost for transportation and lunch, and deciding how many vans and pizzas were needed
- **How could you use what you learned about planning a trip to the zoo to plan a trip to an amusement park?** Sample answer: I would plan my route through the park depending on what our favorite rides were and figure out how much money the trip would cost if my whole family wanted to visit. I would look for coupons for admission and lunch and subtract that from the total cost.

Lesson Planner

Objective

Students research and draw conclusions about various games that were played in the past, use coins to show the cost of different games, solve problems by creating and putting together a puzzle, and organize and lead outdoor games.

Resources

Materials: chart paper, necessary materials needed to play outdoor games chosen by students, masking tape, paper clips, chalk, glue

Manipulatives: plastic coins

Day 1

This project involves having students research and discuss how games from the past are different from those played today. Students will learn about puzzles and other games as they prepare to lead their own games during a game day.

- Before this lesson, have each student interview an adult about the games and toys he/she played with as a child.
- Ask students to help you generate a list of games and toys the adults they interviewed played with when they were a child. Record their responses on chart paper.
- Share with students that the prices of games and toys have changed over time. Some toys cost more now than when they were first made.
- Discuss page P15 with students. Point out the various toys.

Name: ______________________________

Toys From the Past and Present

You will compare toys and games from the past and present.

Day 1: Compare prices

1. Use coins to show each amount.
   Draw the coins you used.

Past	Present
 Check students' drawing.	

Check students' drawing.

2. Use coins to show each amount. Draw the coins you used.

Past	Present
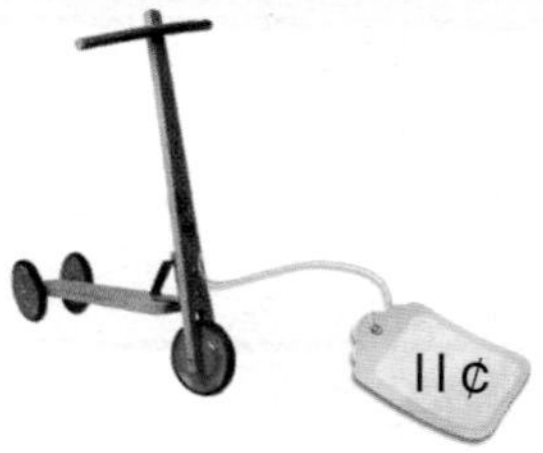	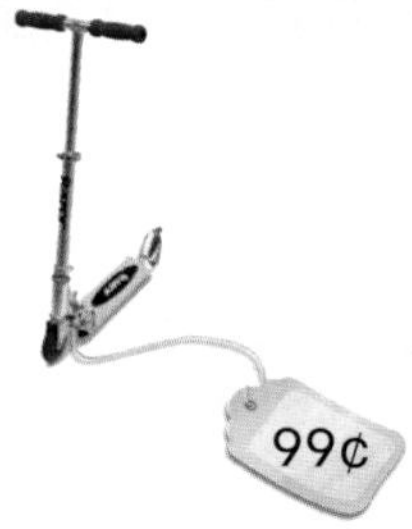
	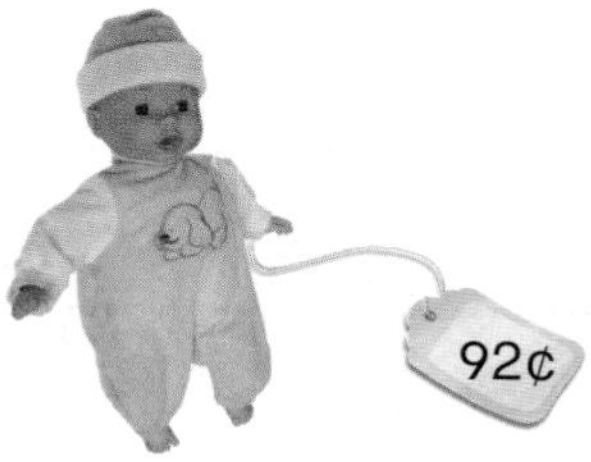

- Discuss the toys on page P16.
- Ask students which scooter and which doll looks like it was made more recently. Have students explain their thoughts.
- Draw students attention to the differences in prices between the newer toys and the older toys.

Day 2

- Share examples of different puzzles and sizes of puzzle pieces. Tell students that puzzles have been around for a long time.
- Discuss page P17 with students. Help them draw a pattern in each row.
- Explain that puzzles are easier to complete when there is color or a part of a design on each puzzle piece.
- Give students a plastic bag in which to store their puzzle pieces. Be sure students put their name on the bags.
- Have students exchange puzzles with a classmate.

Day 2: Make your own puzzle

Puzzles have been around for a long time. Did you know you can make your own?

3. Look at the puzzle. Draw a pattern in each row.

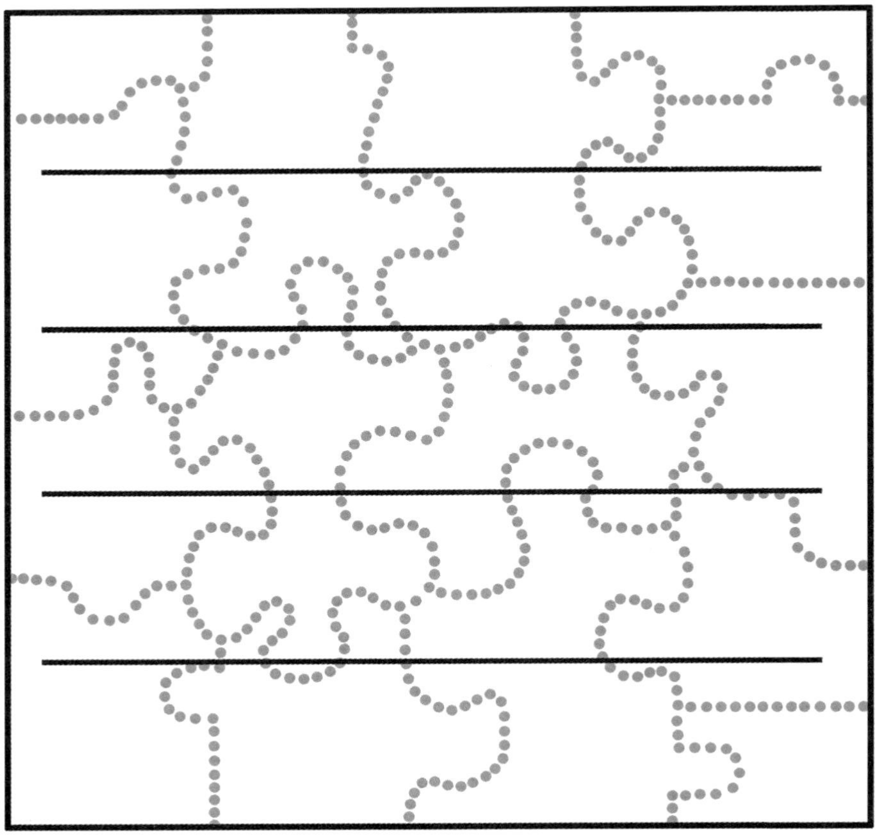

4. Describe your patterns to a friend. Check students' work.

5. Cut along the dotted lines to make puzzle pieces. Put them in a plastic bag.

6. Give your puzzle to a friend to put together.

Toys From the Past and Present P17

7–10. Check students' work.

Day 3: Make your own outdoor game.

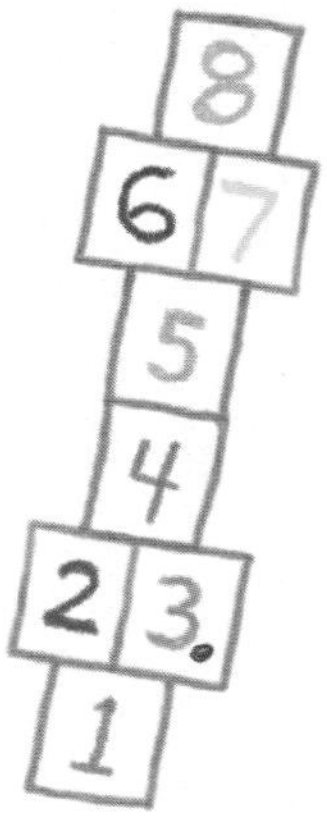

7. Design a hopscotch game. Draw squares on a separate sheet of paper.

8. Your hopscotch should have 8 squares, 10 squares, or 12 squares.

9. Each square should be 2 paper clips long and 2 paperclips wide. Number the squares.

10. Go outside. Use chalk to draw your hopscotch squares on the ground.

Day 4: Turn your classroom into a toy store.

11–12. Check students' work.

11. Use toys from the past and present to set up a toy store in your classroom.

12. As a class, choose a price for each toy. Then, pretend to shop or work at the toy store.

Day 5: Games from the past.

Check students' work.

13. Ask an adult to describe a game they played when they were your age. Explain the game to a friend.

Day 3

- Ask students if they have played hopscotch. Invite students to explain the object and rules of the game.
- Help students create a hopscotch game on paper and use different colored chalk to make a larger hopscotch game outside on the cement. Remind students to look at their designs when drawing their games.
- When drawing the game outside, have students make each square 13 paper clips wide and 13 paper clips long.
- If students are unable to go outside, have them use masking tape to create the hopcotch game on the floor of the classroom.

Day 4

- Gather games and toys played in the past and present. Price each toy to be used in a classroom store.
- Allow one group of students to be "workers" at the store. The other students will be "shoppers".
- Give each group plastic coins to use. Guide the "workers", so they can give each student the correct change.

Day 5

Invite students to present a game the adult they interviewed played as a child. Have each group share the following:

1. the name and an explanation of the game the adult played
2. materials needed to play the game
3. game rules
4. math concepts that were used to set up or play the game.

Wrap-Up

- Use these Wrap-Up questions to assess students' work.
- **What did you use to measure the squares for your hopscotch game?** paperclips
- **How are the games you play today different from those that were played long ago?** Sample answers: The games we play today require less interaction with other people. The games played long ago cost much less. None of the games in the past were video games.

Student Handbook

Student Handbook

Built-In Workbook

Concepts and Skills Bank **CS1**

Preparing for Standardized Tests **TP1**

Facts Practice **FP5**

WorkMats 1–8

Reference

English-Spanish Picture Glossary **G1**

Photo Credits

Hundred Chart, Number
Words, and Measurement . . . **Inside Back Cover**

How to Use the Student Handbook

Use the Student Handbook

You, or your teacher, may decide that working through some additional problems would be helpful. The **Facts Practice** section is useful:

- when you need more practice with addition facts and subtraction facts
- when you need to show different ways to make numbers, show the order of numbers, count on to add, count back to subtract, or write numbers as hundreds, tens, and ones
- when you need to know the meaning of a math word
- when you need to find number patterns, to order numbers, or to skip count
- when you need help writing the number names

Teacher Notes

Concepts and Skills Bank

Name ______________________________

1 True and False Statements

In math, statements can be true or false.

A true statement is correct.

5 + 1 = 6 is **true**

A false statement is incorrect.

5 + 1 = 5 is **false**

Concepts and Skills

Practice

Circle true or false.

1. This is a triangle.

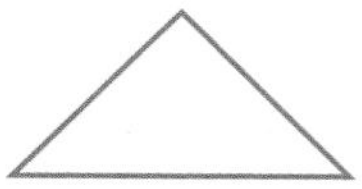

(true) false

2. 8 is greater than 2

(true) false

Concepts and Skills Bank

1 True and False Statements

Lesson Planner

Objective

Identify mathematical statements as true or false.

Vocabulary

true, false

Materials: index cards, construction paper, markers

Activate Prior Knowledge

Lead a discussion about true and false statements.

- Explain to students that when a statement is **true** it is real or correct. If a statement is incorrect or not true, then it is **false.**
- On the board, write 4 + 5 = 9. **Is this true or false?** true
- Write 7 + 7 = 12. **Is this true or false?** false **How could we change 7 + 7 = 12 to make a true math statement?** Sample answers: 7 + 7 = 14; 6 + 6 = 12

Using student page CS1.

- **Why is 5 + 1 = 6 a true math statement?** the number sentence is correct **Can you name another true math statement?** Sample answers: 5 + 8 = 13; 7 > 2
- **Why is 5 + 1 = 5 a false math statement?** 5 + 1 does not equal 1, so it is incorrect or false. **Can you name another false math statement?** Sample answers: 8 – 7 = 0; 3 > 9
- **How can you correct your math statement to make it true?** Sample answers: 8 – 7 = 1; 3 < 9

Using student page CS2.

- Give each student two index cards. Have students write *true* on one card and *false* on the other card.
- Say aloud or write math statements similar to the ones on p. CS2. After each math statement, ask students to hold up the correct index card.

Using the Exercises

Exercises 3–6 If the statement is false, ask students how they can make the statement true.

Exercises 7–8 Encourage students to share their true and false statements with a partner. Ask students to correct their partner's false statement.

Assess and Close

True or False Statements Give students markers to write a true or false statement on a piece of construction paper. On a classroom wall, display their statements either under a "True" or "False" label. Allow students to decide which label is appropriate for their statement.

Practice

Circle true or false.

3. 13 + 3 = 43

true (false)

4. 23 − 10 = 13

(true) false

5. This clock shows 2:00.

(true) false

6. This clock shows 9:00.

true (false)

7. Write your own true math statement.

See students' work.

8. Write your own false math statement.

See students' work.

Concepts and Skills

CS2 Concepts and Skills Bank

Name ______________________

2 Half Dollars and Dollars

A dollar has a value of 100 cents. A half dollar has a value of 50 cents.

When you write one dollar, use a dollar sign and a decimal point.

dollar sign → $1.00 ← decimal point

100 pennies = $1.00	20 nickels = $1.00	10 dimes = $1.00	4 quarters = $1.00	2 half dollars = $1.00

Concepts and Skills

Concepts and Skills Bank

2 Half Dollar and Dollar

Lesson Planner

Objective

Identify by name and value half dollars and dollars.

Vocabulary

half dollar, dollar

Materials: manipulative coins

Activate Prior Knowledge

Have students recall Chapter 11, Identify Coins. Remind students that they counted coins up to a quarter.

- **How did we start counting the coins?** Sample answer: We started with the greatest valued coin.
- Explain to students that today they will be counting up to half dollars and dollars. Show students a half dollar and a dollar.

Using student page CS3.

- Give students a handful of pennies, nickels, dimes, and quarters. **How can we use these coins to show 50¢?** Sample answers: 2 quarters; 50 pennies; 1 quarter, 2 dimes, and 1 nickel
- Show students a half dollar. Explain that a half dollar equals 50¢.
- **Hold up the coin that is worth 1¢. What is the name of that coin?** penny **If one penny makes 1¢, how many pennies do you think we need to make 100¢?** 100 pennies
- Direct students to the chart on p. CS3. Explain to students that a dollar is the same as 100¢.
- Challenge students to use their coins including a half dollar to find other ways to make 100¢.

Using student page CS4.

Exercises 1–3 If students are having trouble counting dollars and cents use money from the manipulative kit. Give groups of students' dollars and cents to manipulate and recreate the amount on the student page.

Assess and Close

Ask students to write a story problem using money amounts with coins and dollars. Have students trade papers and ask a classmate to solve.

Concepts and Skills

1. Mika needs $1.00 to buy some erasers.
Here are the coins Mika has.

How much money does Mika have? $1.29

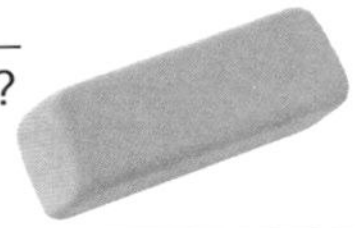

Does she have enough money for the erasers?
(yes) no

2. Emilio needs $1.00 to buy a pencil.
Here are the coins Emilio has.

How much money does Emilio have? ________

Does he have enough money for the pencil?
yes (no) 96¢

3. Tessa needs $1.00 to buy a yo-yo.
Here are the coins Tessa has.

How much money does Tessa have? ________

Does she have enough money for the yo-yo?
(yes) no $1.25

Concepts and Skills Bank

Name ______________________________

3 Symmetry and Congruence

Figures that are the same size and shape are congruent.

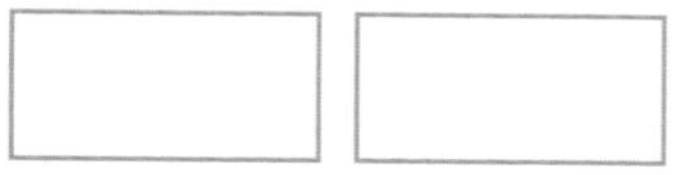

A figure has a line of symmetry if it can be folded in half and the two halves are congruent.

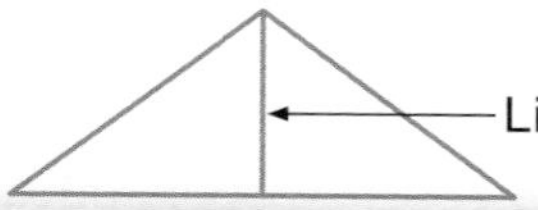

Concepts and Skills

Practice

Circle the shape that is congruent.

1.

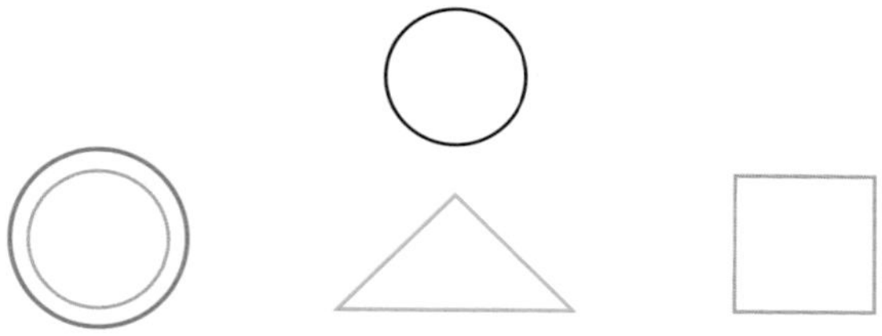

Draw a line of symmetry.

2.

See students' work.

Concepts and Skills Bank

3 Symmetry and Congruence

Lesson Planner

Objective

Identify congruent figures and draw a line of symmetry on two-dimensional figures.

Vocabulary

congruent, line of symmetry

Materials: paper cut-outs of a rectangle for each student; construction paper, markers

Activate Prior Knowledge

- Give each student a paper cut-out of a rectangle. Have the students identify and describe the two-dimensional figure.
- Ask students to fold their rectangle in half. Have students unfold their rectangle and draw a line on the fold.
- **What figures do you see on each side of the line you drew?** rectangle or square **Are those figures the same size?** yes **Are those figures the same shape?** yes **How do you know?** Sample answer: I can fold my rectangle in half and side matches exactly.
- **The figures on each side of the line you drew are congruent. Figures are congruent if they are the same size and shape.**
- Explain to students that the line they drew is called a **line of symmetry.**

Using student page CS5.

Continue to explain the concept of symmetry to the students.

- Have students look at the triangle on p. CS5. Explain how the line is directly in the center of the triangle.
- **What is the name of the line that divides the triangle into two figures that are the same size and shape?** line of symmetry

Using student page CS6.

Exercises 3–4 If students have trouble deciding whether each figure is congruent or not, encourage students to draw a line of symmetry. Then ask students to compare the figures on each side of the line. Tell students to ask themselves if both figures are the same size and shape.

Exercises 5–6 After students draw a line of symmetry, ask them if the figures on both sides of the line are congruent. If they are not, have students erase and redraw their line of symmetry.

Assess and Close

Have students use markers to draw a two-dimensional figure on a piece of construction paper. Ask students to exchange their drawing with a partner. Have each pair draw a figure congruent to the one given to them.

Practice

Concepts and Skills

Circle the shape that is congruent.

3.

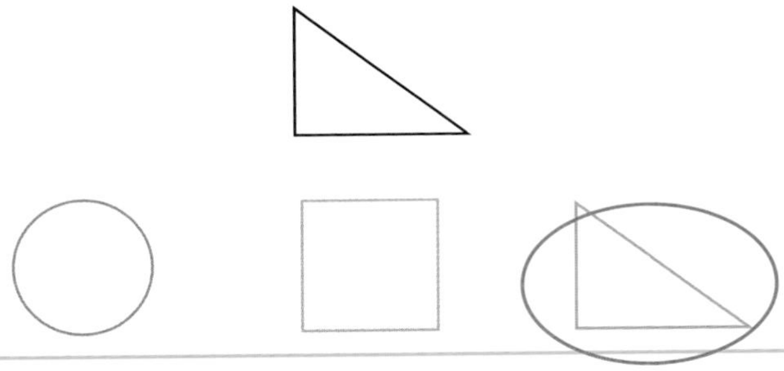

4.

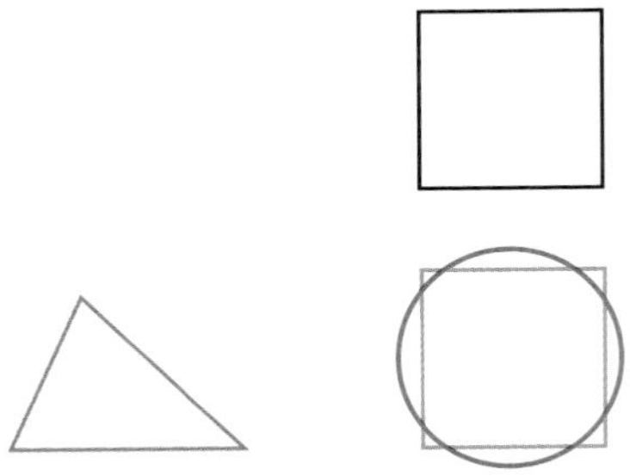

Draw a line of symmetry.

5.

See students' work.

6.

See students' work.

Name ______________________

4 Perimeter

Perimeter is the sum of all the sides.

4 + 4 + 4 + 4 = 16

The perimeter is 16.

Perimeter can be used to find the distance around an object.

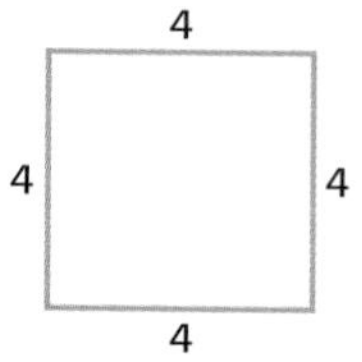

Practice

Find the perimeter.

1.

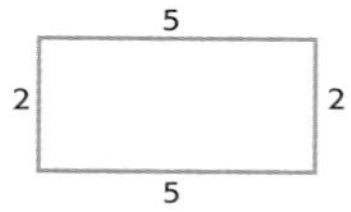

5 + 2 + 5 + 2 = 14

Perimeter: 14

2.

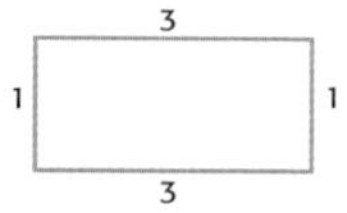

3 + 1 + 3 + 1 = 8

Perimeter: 8

Concepts and Skills Bank

4 Perimeter

Lesson Planner

Objective

Determine the perimeter of two-dimensional figures.

Vocabulary

perimeter

Materials: 1-inch grid paper, masking tape

Activate Prior Knowledge

Give students a piece of one-inch grid paper.

- Explain to students that they are going to draw a square on the grid paper. **How many sides does a square have?** 4 sides **How is a square different from a rectangle?** The fours sides of a square are equal, and all four sides of a rectangle are not equal.
- Explain to students that they will all draw a square that is the exact same size. To do this, they will need to use the squares of the paper as nonstandard units of measurement.
- Ask students to draw a square with sides that are five squares in both length and height. Have students write a 5 next to each side of the square.
- Tell students that they are going to find the **perimeter** of their square. Explain that the perimeter is the sum of a figure's sides.

Using student page CS7.

- Direct students to the square on p. CS7. Ask students to trace their finger around the perimeter of the square.
- **How do you know that this is a square?** Each side is the same length.
- **How can you find the perimeter of the square?** add the four sides **What number sentence can you write to find the perimeter?** 4 + 4 + 4 + 4 = 16

Using student page CS8.

Exercises 3–6 Allow students to draw each figure on grid paper. For example, students can model the figure in Exercise 4 by drawing a rectangle that is 4 grid squares by 3 grid squares. Then students can count how many squares on the grid paper make up the perimeter.

Assess and Close

Give small groups masking tape and directions to create a rectangle on the floor. For example: *Use tape to make a rectangle with two sides that are 7 footsteps long and two sides that are 3 footsteps tall.* Ask students to find the perimeter or the sum of the sides. Then have students walk on the perimeter of their rectangle.

Practice

3.

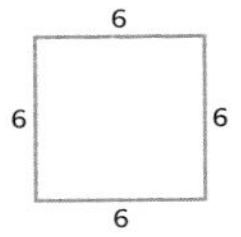

6 + 6 + 6 + 6 = 24

Perimeter: 24

4.

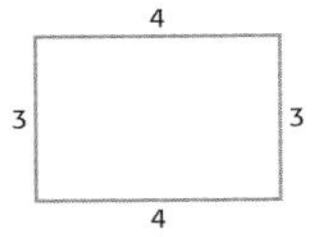

4 + 3 + 4 + 3 = 14

Perimeter: 14

5.

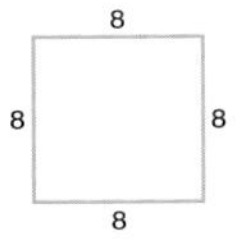

8 + 8 + 8 + 8 = 32

Perimeter: 32

6.

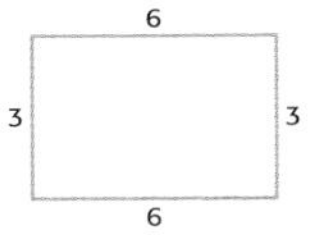

6 + 3 + 6 + 3 = 18

Perimeter: 18

Concepts and Skills

Name ___________________________

5 Temperature

A thermometer is used to measure temperature.

The red shows the temperature.

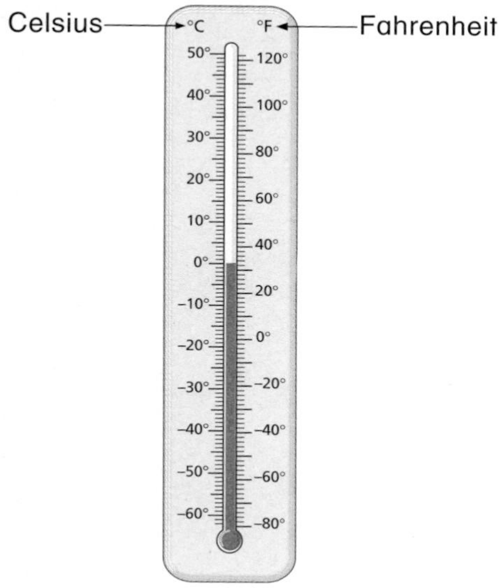

This thermometer shows 32°F and 0°C.

Concepts and Skills Bank

5 Temperature

Lesson Planner

Objective

Read temperatures to the nearest degree from Celsius and Fahrenheit thermometers.

Vocabulary

temperature, thermometer, Celsius, Fahrenheit

Materials: thermometer, number line

Activate Prior Knowledge

Have students recall Lesson 9-6, Compare and Order Temperatures.

- Show students a **thermometer.** Explain that a thermometer tells the exact **temperature.**
- Explain to students how to read a thermometer. Write **Celsius** and **Fahrenheit** on the board. Challenge students to find those words on the thermometer.
- Ask them whether the greater numbers are on the top or bottom of the thermometer. If students are having difficulty understanding the order of the numbers, hold a number line vertically for them to observe.

Using student page CS9.

- Have students point to the thermometer on p. CS9.
- Ask students to explain what they see on the thermometer. Make a list of the students' observations on the board.
- Show students how the numbers under Celsius are different from the numbers under Fahrenheit.
- Give a basic explanation of the difference between Celsius degrees and Fahrenheit degrees. Show students the weather page of the newspaper. Explain how the temperature is usually written in Fahrenheit degrees.

Using student page CS10.

Exercises 1–4 Give students two different colors of highlighters so they can highlight or circle Celsius or Fahrenheit.

Assess and Close

Place a thermometer on the outside of the window for students to observe. Ask students to record the temperature of at least three days throughout the week. Have students graph their data.

Practice

Write the temperature.

1. 70° Fahrenheit

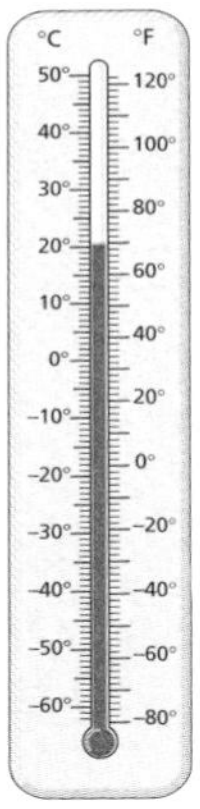

2. 10° Celsius

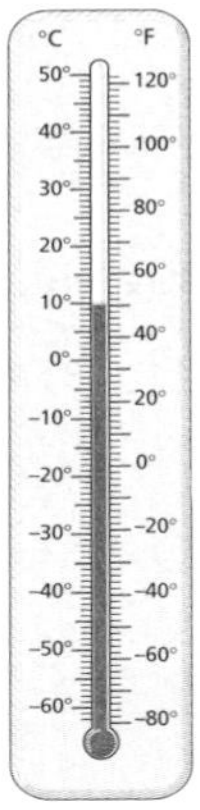

3. −10° Celsius

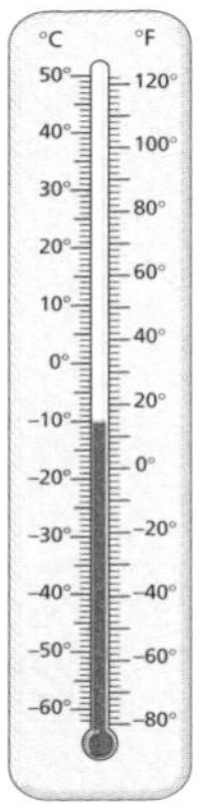

4. 40° Fahrenheit

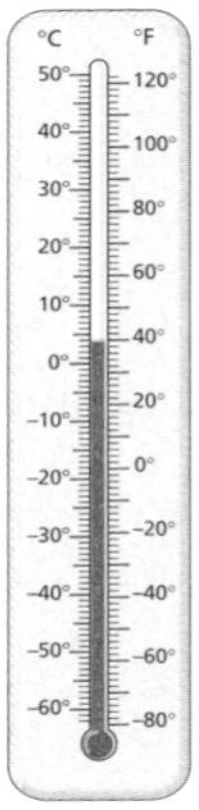

Teacher Notes

Preparing for Standardized Tests

It's time to review how to take a standardized test. You have been building your math skills in class. Soon you will have a chance to put them to work.

Tips for Success!

Before a Test

- Go to bed early the night before.
- Eat a good breakfast the next morning.

During a Test

- Listen carefully as your teacher reads each question.
- Work carefully.

Whatever you do...

- Do not rush.
- Do not give up.

English	Español
doubles (and doubles plus 1) Two addends that are the same number. (pages 169 and 171)	**dobles (y dobles más 1)** Dos sumandos que son el mismo número.
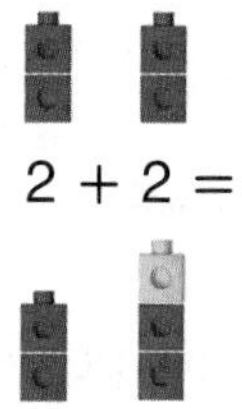 $2 + 2 = 4$; $2 + 3 = 5$	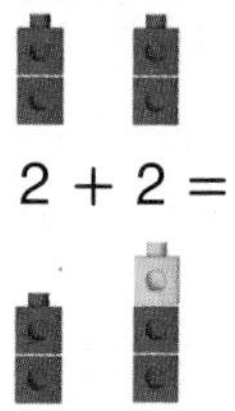 $2 + 2 = 4$; $2 + 3 = 5$
equal parts Each part is the same size. (page 457) A muffin cut in equal parts. 	**partes iguales** Cada parte es del mismo tamaño. Un panecillo cortado en partes iguales. 
equals (=) Having the same value as or is the same as. (page 55) $2 + 4 = 6$ (equal sign)	**igual (=)** Que tienen el mismo valor o son iguales a. $2 + 4 = 6$ (signo de igual)
estimate To find a number close to an exact amount. (page 255)	**estimar** Hallar un número cercano a la cantidad exacta.

English	Español
even Numbers that end with 0, 2, 4, 6, 8. (page 263)	**par** Números que terminan en 0, 2, 4, 6, 8.
evening The time after school when it is dark. (page 213)  evening	**anochecer** Hora después de la escuela cuando está oscuro.  anochecer
face The flat part of a 3-dimensional figure. (page 387) 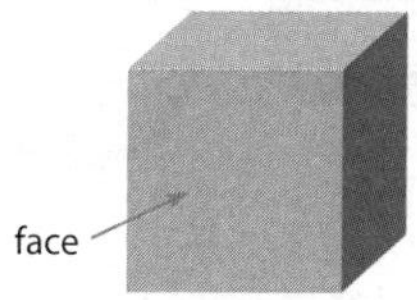	**cara** Parte plana de una figura de 3 dimensiones. 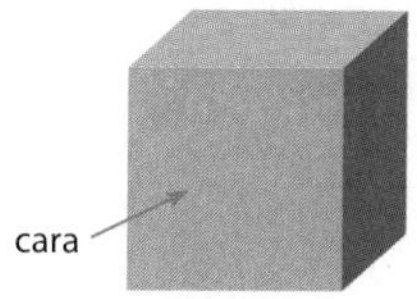

Glossary/Glosario

English	Español

F

fact family Addition and subtraction sentences that use the same numbers. Sometimes called *related facts.* (page 199)

$6 + 7 = 13 \quad 13 - 7 = 6$
$7 + 6 = 13 \quad 13 - 6 = 7$

familia de datos Expresiones de suma y resta que utilizan los mismos números. Algunas veces se llaman *datos relacionados.*

$6 + 7 = 13 \quad 13 - 7 = 6$
$7 + 6 = 13 \quad 13 - 6 = 7$

fraction A number that represents part of a whole or part of a set. (page 461)

$\frac{1}{2}, \frac{1}{3}, \frac{1}{4}, \frac{3}{4}$

fracción Número que representa la parte de un todo o la parte de un conjunto.

$\frac{1}{2}, \frac{1}{3}, \frac{1}{4}, \frac{3}{4}$

G

graph A way to present data collected. Also a type of chart. (page 125)

bar graph

gráfica Forma de presentar datos recogidos. También tipo de tabla.

una gráfica de barras

Glossary/Glosario

English	Español

H

half hour (or half past) One half of an hour is 30 minutes. Sometimes called *half past* or *half past the hour.* (page 217)

media hora (o y media) Media hora son 30 minutos. Algunas veces se llama 'y media'.

heavy (heavier, heaviest) Weighs more. (page 285) An elephant is heavier than a mouse.

heavier

pesado (más pesado, el más pesado) Pesa más. Un elefante es más pesado (pesa más) que un ratón.

más pesado

holds less/least (page 291)

The glass holds less than the pitcher.

contener menos

El vaso contiene menos que la jarra.

Glossary/Glosario

English	Español

H

holds more/most (page 291)

The pitcher holds more than the glass.

contener más

El vaso contiene más que la jarra.

hot/hotter/hottest (page 295)

hot

caliente/más caliente/ el más caliente

caliente

hour A unit of time
I hour = 60 minutes (page 215)

hora Unidad de tiempo.
I hora = 60 minutos

hour hand The hand on a clock that tells the hour. It is the shorter hand. (page 215)

manecilla horaria Manecilla del reloj que dice la hora. Es la manecilla más corta.

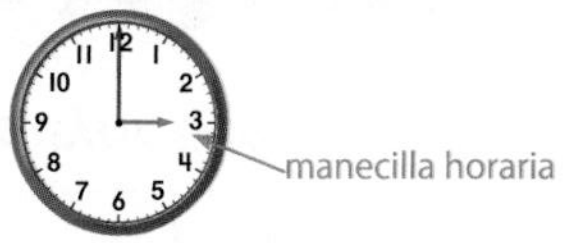

Glossary/Glosario

English	Español

H

hundred chart A chart that shows numbers 1–100. (page 249)

1	2	3	4	5	6	7	8	9	10
11	12	13	14	15	16	17	18	19	20
21	22	23	24	25	26	27	28	29	30
31	32	33	34	35	36	37	38	39	40
41	42	43	44	45	46	47	48	49	50
51	52	53	54	55	56	57	58	59	60
61	62	63	64	65	66	67	68	69	70
71	72	73	74	75	76	77	78	79	80
81	82	83	84	85	86	87	88	89	90
91	92	93	94	95	96	97	98	99	100

tabla de cien Tabla que muestra los números. 1–100.

1	2	3	4	5	6	7	8	9	10
11	12	13	14	15	16	17	18	19	20
21	22	23	24	25	26	27	28	29	30
31	32	33	34	35	36	37	38	39	40
41	42	43	44	45	46	47	48	49	50
51	52	53	54	55	56	57	58	59	60
61	62	63	64	65	66	67	68	69	70
71	72	73	74	75	76	77	78	79	80
81	82	83	84	85	86	87	88	89	90
91	92	93	94	95	96	97	98	99	100

I

impossible An event that cannot happen. (page 143)

You cannot pick a blue cube.

imposible Un evento que no puede ocurrir.

No puedes elegir un cubo azul.

is equal to = (page 35)

6 = 6
6 is equal to 6

igual a =

6 = 6
6 es igual a 6

Glossary/Glosario

English	Español

I

is greater than > (page 35)

$7 > 2$

7 is greater than 2

mayor que >

$7 > 2$

7 es mayor que 2

is less than < (page 35)

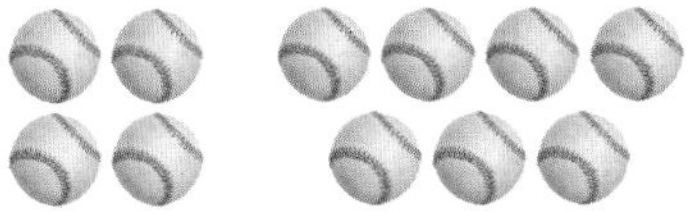

$4 < 7$

4 is less than 7

menor que <

$4 < 7$

4 es menor que 7

L

length (page 277)

longitud

Glossary/Glosario

English	Español

L

light (lighter, lightest) Weighs less. (page 285)
The mouse is lighter than the elephant.

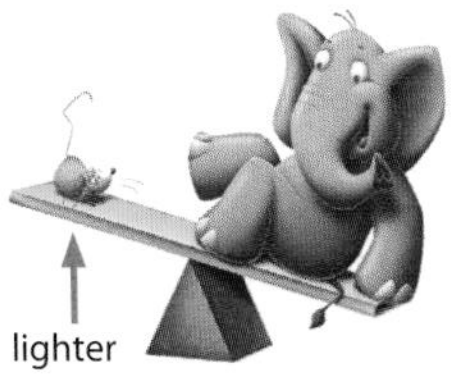

liviano (más liviano, el más liviano) Pesa menos.
El ratón es más liviano (pesa menos) que el elefante.

long (longer, longest) A way to compare the lengths of two objects. (page 277)

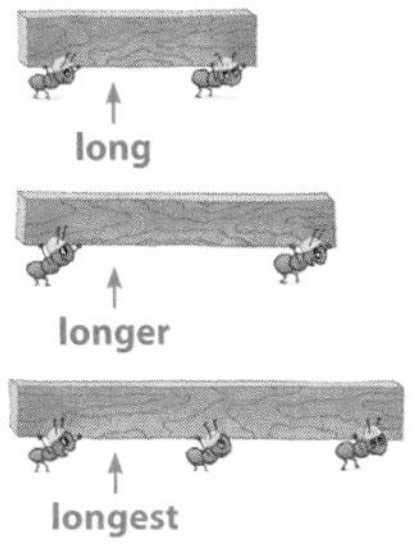

largo (más largo, el más largo) Forma de comparar la longitud de dos objetos.

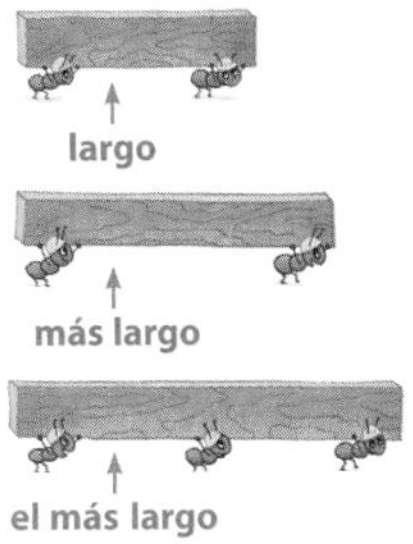

M

measure To find the length, height, or weight using standard or nonstandard units. (page 279)

medir Hallar la longitud, estatura o peso mediante unidades estándar o no estándar.

Glossary/Glosario

English	Español
minus (–) The sign used to show subtraction. (page 91)	**resta (–)** Signo que se usa en la resta.

$5 - 2 = 3$ (minus sign)

$5 - 2 = 3$ (signo de resta)

minute hand The longer hand on a clock that tells the minutes. (page 215)

minutero La manecilla más larga de un reloj que indica los minutos.

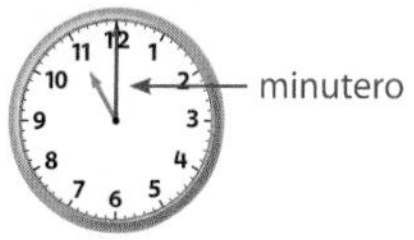

missing addend

9 + ____ = 16

The missing addend is 7. (page 211)

sumando desconocido

9 + ____ = 16

El sumando desconocido es 7.

morning The period of time from sunrise to noon. (page 213)

morning

mañana Período de tiempo que va del amanecer al mediodía.

mañana

Glossary/Glosario

English / **Español**

N

nickel 5¢ or 5 cents (page 351)

moneda de cinco centavos 5¢ ó 5 centavos

number Tells how many. 1, 2, 3, 4, 5, 6, 7, 8, 9, 10, ... (page 23)

There are 3 chicks.

números Decir cuántos. 1, 2, 3, 4, 5, 6, 7, 8, 9, 10, ...

Hay 3 pollito.

number line A line with number labels. (page 39)

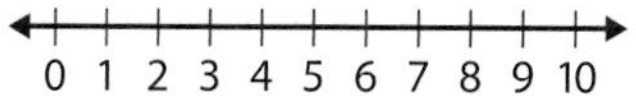

línea de números Línea con rótulos de números.

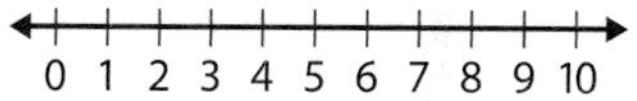

O

o'clock At the beginning of the hour. (page 215)

It is 3 o'clock.

en punto Al comienzo de la hora.

Son las 3 en punto.

odd Numbers that end with 1, 3, 5, 7, 9. (page 263)

impar Números que terminan en 1, 3, 5, 7, 9.

Glossary/Glosario

Glossary/Glosario

English	Español

O

one fourth A fraction that shows 1 piece out of 4 equal pieces. (page 463)

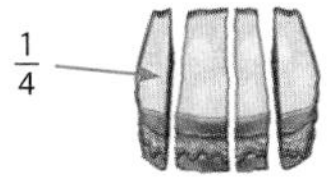

un cuarto Fracción que muestra 1 de 4 partes iguales.

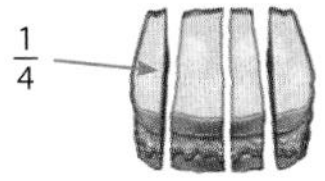

one half A fraction that shows 1 piece out of 2 equal pieces. (page 461)

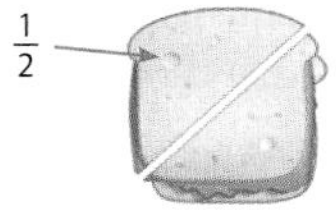

un medio Fracción que muestra 1 de 2 partes iguales.

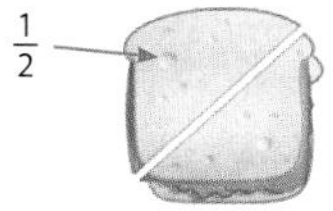

one third A fraction that shows 1 piece out of the 3 equal pieces. (page 463)

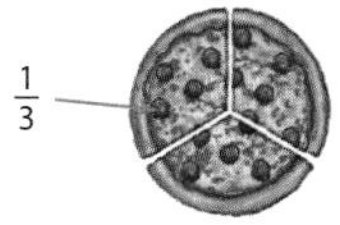

un tercio Fracción que muestra 1 de 3 partes iguales.

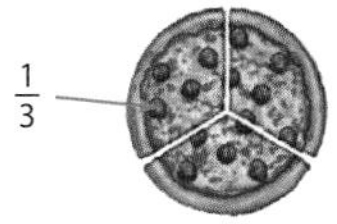

ones
This number has 3 ones. (page 243)

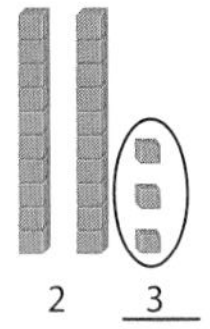

unidades
Este número tiene 3 unidades.

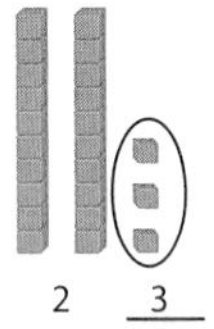

Glossary/Glosario

English	Español

O

order
1, 3, 6, 7, 9 (page 39)
These numbers are in order from least to greatest.

orden
1, 3, 6, 7, 9
Estos números están en orden del menor al mayor.

P

pattern An order that a set of objects or numbers follows over and over. (page 17)
A, A, B, A, A, B, A, A, B

patrón Orden que sigue continuamente un conjunto de objetos o números.
A, A, B, A, A, B, A, A, B

penny 1¢ or 1 cent (page 351)

moneda de un centavo
1¢ ó 1 centavo

picture graph A graph that has different pictures to show information collected. (page 125)

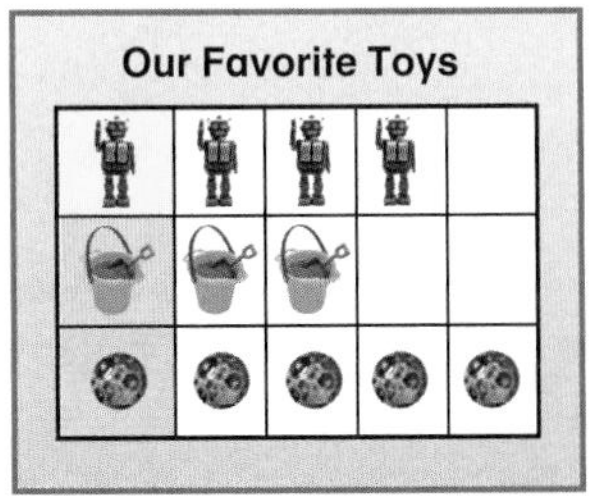

gráfica con imágenes Gráfica que tiene diferentes imágenes para mostrar la información recogida.

Glossary/Glosario

English	Español

P

plane figure See 2-dimensional figure. (page 375)

figura plana Ver figuras de 2 dimensiones.

plus (+) A symbol to show addition. (page 55)

$4 + 5 = 9$

↑ plus sign

suma (+) Símbolo para mostrar la suma.

$4 + 5 = 9$

↑ signo de suma

position Tell where an object is. (page 401)

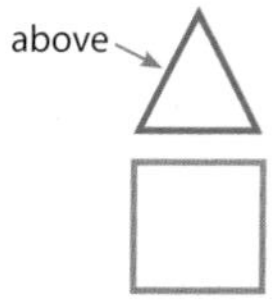

posición Dice dónde está un objeto.

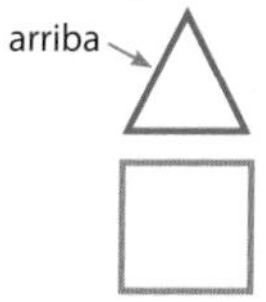

pyramid A solid figure with a polygon as a base and triangular shaped faces. (page 385)

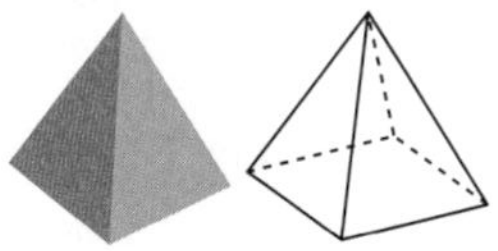

pirámide Figura sólida con un polígono como base y caras de forma triangular.

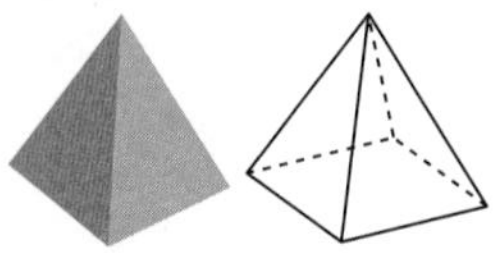

Q

quarter 25¢ or 25 cents (page 365)

head tail

moneda de 25 centavos 25¢ ó 25 centavos

cara escudo

Glossary/Glosario

English	Español

R

rectangle A shape with four sides and four corners. (page 395)

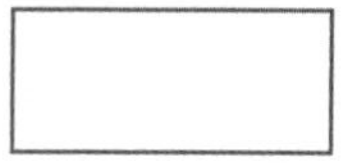

rectángulo Figura con cuatro lados y cuatro esquinas.

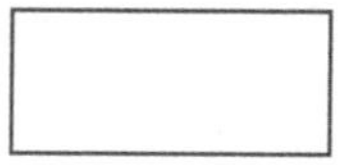

rectangular prism A 3-dimensional shape. (page 385)

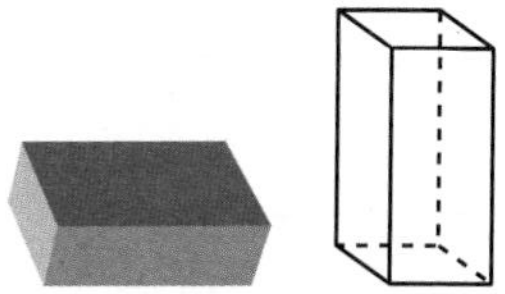
rectangular prism

prisma rectangular Figura de 3 dimensiones.

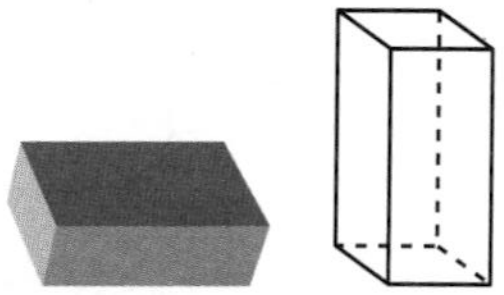
Prisma rectangular

regroup To take apart a number to write it in a new way. (page 423)

1 ten + 2 ones becomes 12 ones

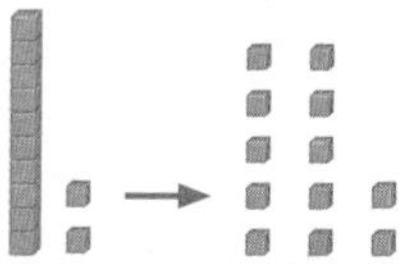

reagrupar Separar un número para escribirlo en una nueva forma.

1 decena + 2 unidades se convierten en 12 unidades.

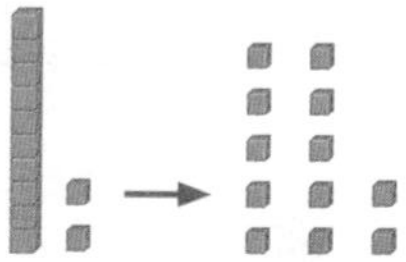

round To change the *value* of a number to one that is easier to work with. (page 495)

24 rounded to the nearest 10 is 20.

redondear Cambiar el *valor* de un número a uno con el que es más fácil trabajar.

24 redondeado a la decena más cercana es 20.

Glossary/Glosario

Glossary/Glosario

English	Español
short (shorter, shortest) To compare length or height of two (or more) objects. (page 277) 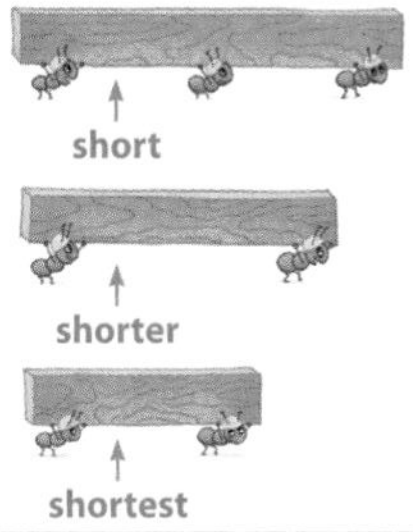	**corto (más corto, el más corto)** Comparar la longitud o la altura de dos (o más) objetos. 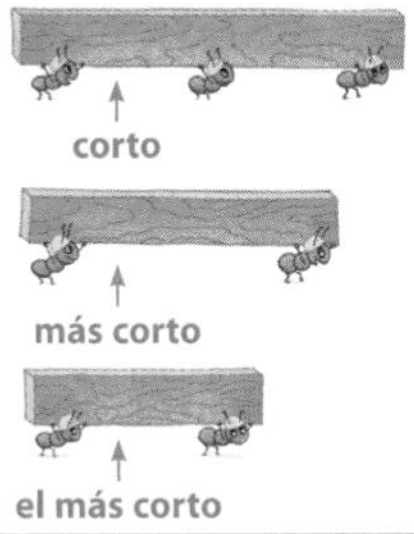
side (page 395) 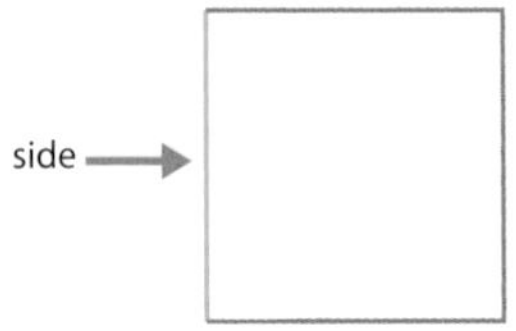	**lado** 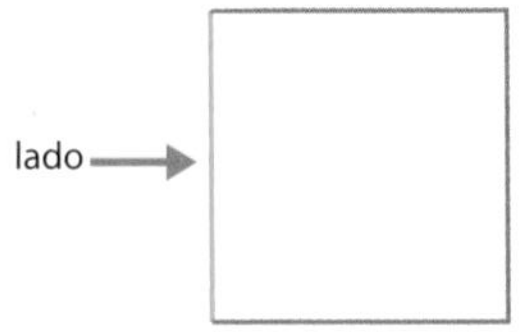
skip count To count objects in equal groups of two or more. (page 259) 2,4,6,8,10 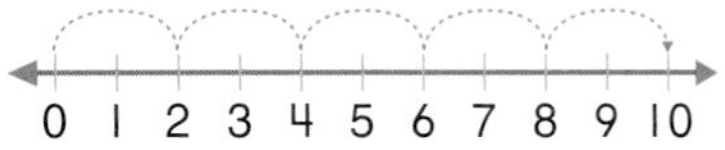	**conteo en grupos** Contar objetos en grupos iguales de dos o más. 2,4,6,8,10 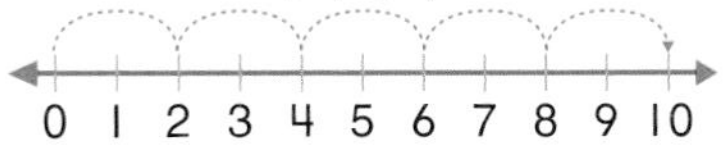
solid figure See 3-dimensional figure. (page 385)	**figura sólida** Ver figura de 3 dimensiones.

Glossary/Glosario

English	Español
sort To group together like items. (page 123) 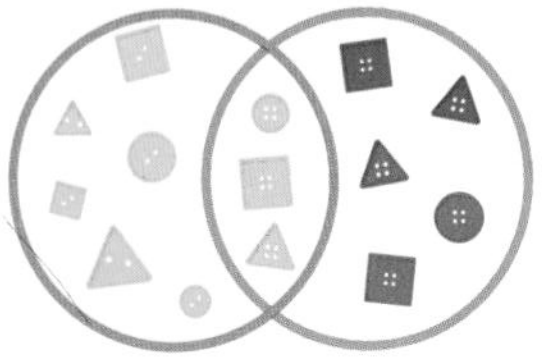	**ordenar** Agrupar elementos iguales. 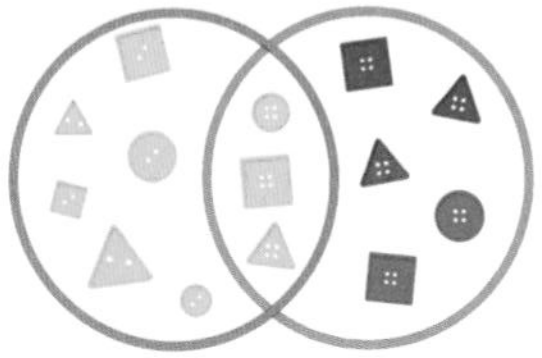
sphere A solid figure that has the shape of a round ball. (page 367) 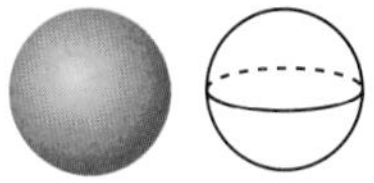	**esfera** Figura sólida con la forma de una pelota redonda. 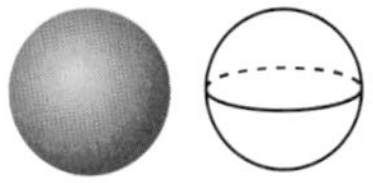
square A rectangle that has four equal sides. (page 395) 	**cuadrado** Rectángulo que tiene cuatro lados iguales. 
subtract (subtracting, subtraction) To take away, take apart, separate, or find the difference between two sets. The opposite of addition. (page 89) 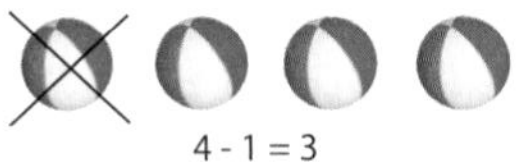	**restar (resta, sustracción)** Eliminar, quitar, separar o hallar la diferencia entre dos conjuntos. Lo opuesto de la suma. 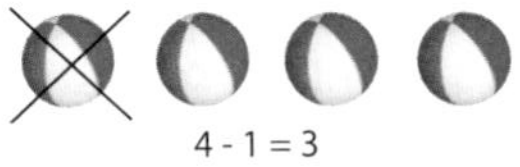

Glossary/Glosario

English	Español

S

subtraction sentence An expression using numbers and the – and = signs. (page 91)

$9 - 5 = 4$

expresión de resta Expresión que contiene números y los signos de – y =.

$9 - 5 = 4$

sum The answer to an addition problem. (page 55)

$2 + 4 = 6$ ↑ sum

suma Respuesta a un problema de suma.

$2 + 4 = 6$ ↑ suma

survey To collect data by asking people the same question. (page 129)

Favorite Foods	
Food	Votes
	𝍸
	|||
	𝍸 |||

This survey shows favorite foods.

encuesta Recoger datos haciendo las mismas preguntas a las personas.

Comidas Favoritas	
Comida	Votos
	𝍸
	|||
	𝍸 |||

Esta encuesta muestra las comidas favoritas.

T

tally chart A way to show data collected using tally marks. (page 129)

Favorite Foods	
Food	Votes
	𝍸
	|||
	𝍸 |||

tabla de conteo Forma de mostrar los datos recogidos utilizando marcas de contar.

Comidas Favoritas	
Comida	Votos
	𝍸
	|||
	𝍸 |||

Glossary/Glosario

English	Español

T

tens (page 419)
This number has 2 tens.

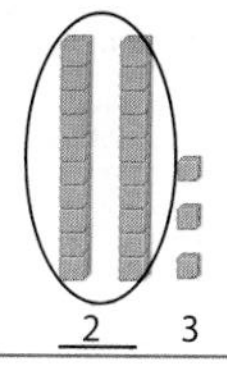

decenas
Este número tiene 2 decenas.

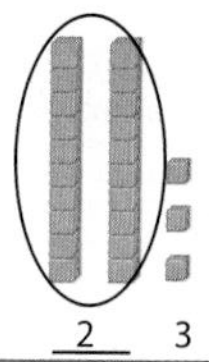

three-dimensional figure
A solid figure. (page 385)

figura de 3 dimensiones
Figura solida.

triangle A shape with three sides. (page 395)

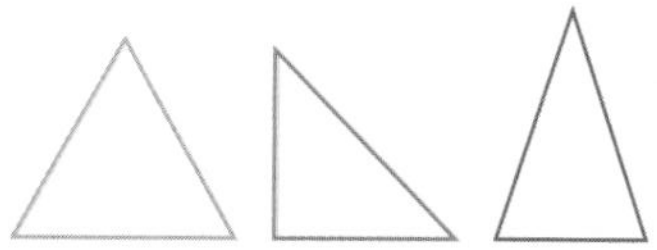

triángulo Figura con tres lados.

two-dimensional figure
The outline of a figure such as a triangle, square, or rectangle. (page 395)

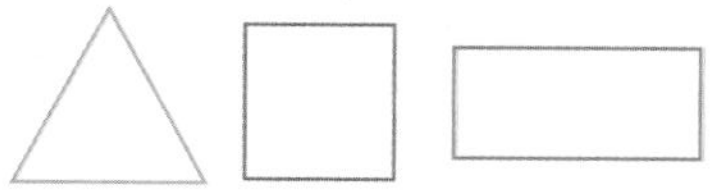

figura de 2 dimensiones
Esquema de una figura como un triángulo, cuadrado o rectángulo.

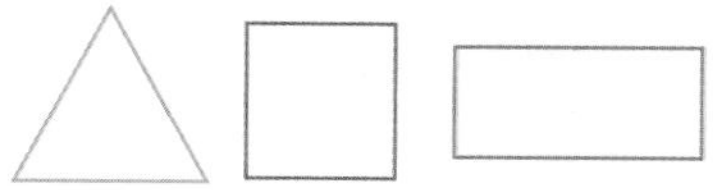

Glossary/Glosario

English		Español
unit An object used to measure. (page 279)	U	**unidad** Objeto que se usa para medir.

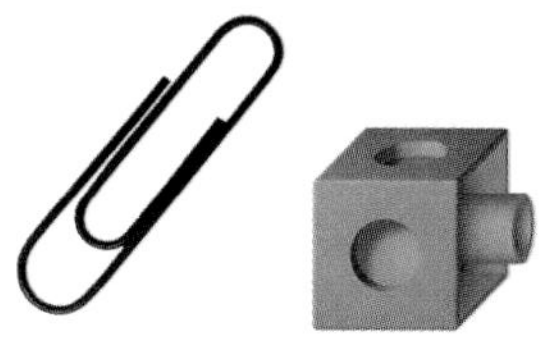

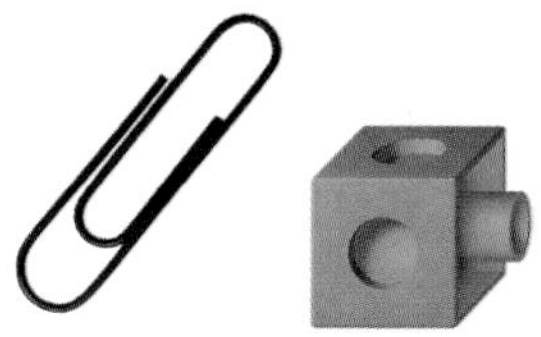

venn diagram A drawing that uses circles to sort and show data. (page 123)	V	**diagrama de Venn** Dibujo que utiliza círculos para ordenar y mostrar datos.

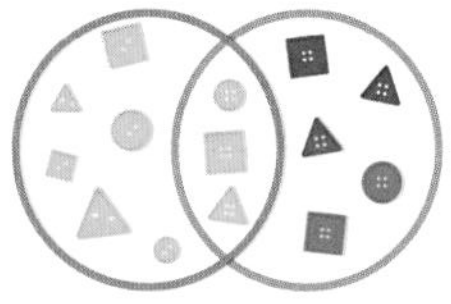

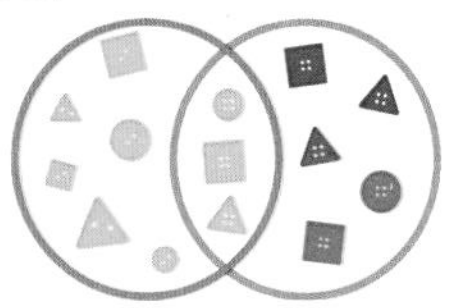

weight (page 285)	W	**peso**

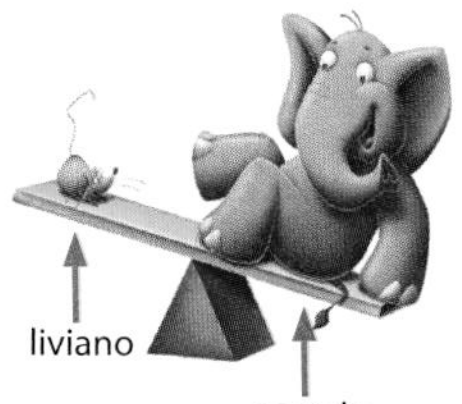

zero 0 The number zero equals none or nothing. (page 59)	Z	**cero 0** El número cero es igual a nada o ninguno.

U V W Z

Photo Credits

Unless otherwise credited, all currency courtesy of the US Mint.
vi Doug Martin; **vii** (others) Doug Martin, (br)File Photo; **1** Sami Suni/iStockphoto; **2** Masterfile; **3** (tc)Buffalo Zoo, (cl)R. Usher/Peter Arnold, Inc., (bl)S. Muller/Peter Arnold, Inc., (bcl)Paul J. Fusco/Photo Researchers, (bc)age fotostock/SuperStock; **4** (tc)DLILLC/CORBIS, (cl)imagebroker/Alamy Images, (c)R. Wittek/Peter Arnold, Inc.; **5** (tc)Arco Images/Alamy Images, (bl)Foodfolio/Imagestate; **6** (c)iStockphoto, (bcl)Jupiterimages; **7** David Muench/CORBIS; **9** Scott Barrow, Inc./SuperStock; **11** altrendo travel/Getty Images; **12** David Madison/Getty Images; **13** José Fuste Raga/CORBIS; **15** (green apple) Getty Images, (red apple) Stockdisc/PunchStock, (girl bookcovers) Eclipse Studios; **16** (green apple)Getty Images, (red apple)Stockdisc/PunchStock, (girl)Eclipse Studios; **19** Richard Hutchings/Digital Light Source; **23** (t)Getty Images, (tc c)photos.com, (cr)Stockdisc/PunchStock; **24** (l)photos.com, (cl)Getty Images, (r)Stockdisc/PunchStock; **25** (l tl tcl)Stockdisc/PunchStock, (cl bl)Getty Images, (c)Punchstock, (r bcl)Ryan McVay/Getty Images, (bc)Punchstock; **26** Danny Lehman/CORBIS; **28** (tl b)2006 Photos To Go, (cl)The McGraw-Hill Companies; **30** (tl)2006 Photos To Go, (tcl cl)Getty Images, (b)Georgette Douwma/Imagestate; **31** (cl bcl)G. K. & Vikki Hart/Getty Images, (r bcr)Stockbyte, (bl)C Squared Studios/Getty Images; **32** (cl)Getty Images, (bl)Stockdisc/PunchStock, (bcl bc)C Squared Studios/Getty Images; **33** Veer; **41** (cr)Richard Du Toit/naturepl.com, (b)Barry Mansel/naturepl.com; **42** (tr)Stockbyte/Getty Images, (b)Michael & Patricia Fogden/CORBIS; **44** (birdhouse)Brand X Pictures/PunchStock, (button)The McGraw-Hill Companies; **46** Richard Du Toit/naturepl.com; **47** Getty Images; **48** (tl tcl)Stockdisc/PunchStock, (tcr tr)Getty Images; **49 50** (t)The McGraw-Hill Companies, (b)Eclipse Studios; **51** ed-imaging; **55** (balloons blue wagon)Getty Images, (kites red wagon)C Squared Studios/Getty Images, (yoyos)Siede Preis/Getty Images, (toy cars)The McGraw-Hill Companies; **56** (cw from t)CORBIS, Getty Images, Ryan McVay/Getty Images, Stockdisc/Punchstock, C Squared Studios/Getty Images, Getty Images, Ryan McVay/Getty Images, Getty Images, Getty Images, Getty Images, Norber Schaefer/CORBIS, Norbert Schaefer/CORBIS, C Squared Studios/Getty Images, C Squared Studios/Getty Images ; **63** (tcr c cr)Stockdisc/PunchStock, (cl)Getty Images; **65** ed-imaging; **67** (c)Richard Hutchings/Digital Light Source, (r)BananaStock/Alamy Images; **72** (l)Noel Hendrickson/Masterfile, (r)Fedor Patrakov/iStockphoto; **73** Richard Hutchings/Digital Light Source; **77** (t)Richard Hutchings/PhotoEdit, (b)Robert W. Ginn/PhotoEdit; **78** (tc)Karl Weatherly/Getty Images, (cl)David Young-Wolff/PhotoEdit, (bc)Steven Sutton/CORBIS; **79** Stockdisc/PunchStock; **83** Jeremy Woodhouse/Masterfile; **85 86** Eclipse Studios; **87** Richard Hutchings/Digital Light Source; **88** Gerry Ellis/Getty Images; **91** (t br)CORBIS, (cl)Dave King/Dorling Kindersley, (cr)photos.com, (bl)Getty Images; **92** (cl)CORBIS, (l)ImageState, (tl)Getty Images, (tcl cr)C Squared Studios/Getty Images, (tr)Peter Sebastian/Getty Images, (bcl)Andy Crawford/Dorling Kindersley (bcr)Steve Gorton/Dorling Kindersley, (tcr)Thomas Northcut/Getty Images; **93** (l cl bcl)Getty Images, (tl c)Ryan McVay/Getty Images, (bl)CORBIS; **95** (t cl)2006 Photos To Go, (cr)IndexOpen, (tc)Getty Images, (bcl)C Squared Studios/Getty Images, (bcr)photos.com; **96** (tcr cr)2006 Photos To Go, (tr)Getty Images, (cl)CORBIS; **97** Richard Hutchings/Digital Light Source; **98** (tr br)Stockdisc/PunchStock, (tcr) D. Hurst/Alamy, (cr)photos.com ; **99** (l bc)Geoff Dann/Getty Images, (tc cl)John Foxx/Getty Images, (c)Dave King/Getty Images; **100** (t tl)The McGraw-Hill Companies, (tc tr tcr)Getty images; **101 103** Richard Hutchings/Digital Light Source; **105** Getty Images; **110** (cl bl bcl)Getty Images, (cr)Jeff Greenberg/Alamy Images, (bcr)europhotos/Alamy Images; **113 114 115** Getty Images; **119** Katherine Fawssett/Getty Images; **121 122** Eclipse Studios; **134** (l to r, t to b) Steve Bloom Images, Gerry Ellis/Minden Pictures, Frans Lanting/Minden Pictures, Tui De Roy/Minden Pictures, Jose B. Ruiz/naturepl.com, Jurgen Freund/Minden Pictures, Dale Sanders/Masterfile; **139** (tr)The McGraw-Hill Companies, (b)Getty Images, (bcr)Stockdisc/PunchStock, (br)C Squared Studios/Getty Images; **141** Getty Images; **143** Richard Hutchings/Digital Light Source; **145** (t)Getty Images, (b)Larry Hirshowitz/CORBIS; **146** (t)Chris George/Alamy Images, (b)Getty Images; **147** (grapes)C Squared Studios/Getty Images, (strawberry)Getty Images, (apple orange)Stockdisc/PunchStock; **151** Frank Parker/Bruce Coleman, Inc.; **153** (cl)Getty Images, (others)Eclipse Studios; **154** Eclipse Studios; **157** Richard Hutchings/Digital Light Source; **160** Chuck Eckert/Alamy Images; **161** CORBIS; **163** Photodisc/Getty Images; **173** Richard Hutchings/Digital Light Source; **175** (inset)Jeff Foott/Getty Images, (br)Charles Krebs/Jupiterimages, (t)Konrad Wothe/Getty Images; **176** Art Montes De Oca/Getty Images; **181** Gandee Vasan/Getty Images; **183 184** Eclipse Studios; **186** Véronique Le Velly/iStockphoto; **188** (tcr br)Getty Images (tr cr)G.K. Vikki Hart/Getty Images; **190** Daniel Dempster Photography/Alamy Images; **193** Ellen B. Senisi/The Image Works; **194** The McGraw-Hill Companies; **197** Kraig Scarbinsk/Getty Images; **203** Getty Images; **203** Sharon Lowe/Alamy Images; **204** (t)Papilio/Alamy Images, (b)Photodisc/Alamy Images; **209** Kwame Zikomo/SuperStock; **210** (bc)Eclipse Studios, (others)Richard Hutchings/Digital Light Source; **211 212** Eclipse Studios; **217** Richard Hutchings/Digital Light Source; **222** (tl)photos.com, (tc)Getty Images, (cl)Stockdisc/PunchStock; **223** Richard Hutchings/Digital Light Source; **228** Getty Images; **231** Richard Hutchings/Digital Light Source; **233** (c)Spencer Grant/PhotoEdit, (inset)CORBIS; **237** Kai Chiang/SuperStock; **239** SuperStock; **241 242** Eclipse Studios; **255** (tcr)Richard Hutchings/Digital Light Source, (cl bl)Getty Images, (bcl)photos.com; **256** photos.com; **257** Richard Hutchings/Digital Light Source; **262** David R. Frazier Photolibrary; **267** (b)Ariel Skelley/Alamy Images, (t)Kevin Horan/Getty Images; **268** The McGraw-Hill Companies; **270** Stockdisc/PunchStock; **273** SuperStock; **275 276** Eclipse Studios; **277** Richard Hutchings/Digital Light Source; **279** (tc)Richard Hutchings/Digital Light Source, (others)Dorling Kindersley; **282** (t)Don Farrall/Getty Images, (cl)C Squared Studios/Getty Images, (c)Stockdisc/PunchStock, (bl)Getty Images; **283** (book)Nikreates/Alamy Images, (door)Burazin/Getty Images, (cube)StudiOhio, (glue scissors)The McGraw-Hill Companies, (paperclips)Getty Images, (pencil)PhotoLink/Getty Images; **285** (tr)Richard Hutchings/Digital Light Source, (cl)Getty Images, (cr)Dorling Kindersley, (bl)PhotoLink/Getty Images, (bcl)The McGraw-Hill Companies, (bc)Michael Newman/PhotoEdit, (br)Siede Preis/Getty Images; **286** (l to r, t to b) Getty Images, photos.com, Comstock Images/Alamy, The McGraw Hill Companies, The McGraw Hill Companies, Getty Images, The McGraw Hill Companies, 2006 Photos To Go, CORBIS, 2006 Photos To Go, 2006 Photos To Go, 2006 Photos To Go, Jupiterimages, Getty Images, The McGraw Hill Companies; **287** (tl)PictureQuest, (tcl)Ryan McVay/Getty Images, (tr)Spike Mafford/Getty Images, (cl)Dorling Kindersley/Getty Images, (c b)Alamy Images, (cr r bc)The McGraw-Hill Companies, (bcl br)2006 Photos To Go, (bcr)Comstock Images/Alamy; **288** (t)Getty Images, (tl cl)2006 Photos To Go, (tc)The McGraw-Hill Companies, (tr)C Squared Studios/Getty Images, (bl)Fabrice Bettex/Alamy Images; **291** (tc)Richard Hutchings/Digital Light Source, (cl)Alamy Images, (c)Ian O'Leary/Dorling Kindersley, (cr)Jupiterimages, (bl)Dorling Kindersley, (bcl)Getty Images, (bcr)Ryan McVay/Getty Images, (br)Jules Frazier/Getty Images; **292** (basket pot pitcher teacup)photos.com, (ship wheelbarrow)CORBIS, (raft)Kristi J. Black/CORBIS, (sailboat)Randy Lincks/CORBIS, (pot)Andy Crawford/Getty Images, (watering can)Peter Anderson/Getty Images, (backpack lunchbox)2006 Photos To Go; **293** (mug)Jupiterimages, (teapot)photos.com, (bowl)Jupiterimages, (plastic cup)Jupiterimages, (rounded basket)Jupiterimages, (fishing basket)Jupiterimages, (glass)Jupiterimages, (suitcase)Ryan McVay/Getty Images, (purse)Jules Frazier/Getty Images, (juice)Andy Crawford/Getty Images, (wheelbarrow)CORBIS, (plastic bag)B. Pepone/CORBIS, (fish bowl)Jupiterimages, (aquarium)Steve Gorton/Dorling Kindersley, (milk jug)The McGraw-Hill Companies, (metal pot)photos.com, (pitcher)photos.com; **294** (l bl)Kristi J. Black/CORBIS, (tl tc c)photos.com, (cl)Jupiterimages, (cr)Jules Frazier/Getty Images, (bc)C Squared Studios/Getty Images, (br)CORBIS; **299** Jupiterimages; **305** Richard Hutchings/Digital Light Source; **307** John Cullen/Masterfile; **308** (tl)Getty Images, (others)Alamy Images; **309** (bl)Dorling Kindersley/Getty Images, (b)Edward R. Degginger/Bruce Coleman Inc., (bcl)2006 Photos To Go (bc)CORBIS, (bcr)Ingram Publishing/SuperStock, (br)A. Huber/CORBIS, (r)Peter Fakler/Alamy Images, (cr)Spike Mafford/Getty Images; **310** (tl)The McGraw-Hill Companies, (tcl)Stephen Oliver/Dorling Kindersley, (tcr)Getty Images, (tr cr)C Squared Studios/Getty Images, (cl)Jupiterimages, (c)2006 Photos To Go, (b)Siede Preis/Getty Images; **313** Frans Lanting/Minden Pictures; **315** Eclipse Studios; **317** Richard Hutchings/Digital Light Source; **326** (tr)Lee Karney/U.S. Fish and Wildlife Service, (tcr)Stockdisc/PunchStock, (bcr br)Getty Images; **333** Ariel Skelley/Getty Images; **334** (br)Meul/naturepl.com, (others)Getty Images;

Photo Credits

337 The McGraw-Hill Companies; **340** M Stock/Alamy Images; **341** (t)Comstock/PunchStock, (b)David Young-Wolff/PhotoEdit; **342** (t)Image Source/Age fotostock, (b)Dean Muz/Age fotostock; **347** Mitch Diamond/Index Stock Imagery; **349 350** Eclipse Studios; **351 353 357 363** Richard Hutchings/Digital Light Source; **365** (bl)2006 Photos To Go, (bcr)Jupiterimages; **366** (tr)Stockdisc/PunchStock, (bcl)Ingram Publishing/SuperStock, (bl cl)Getty Images; **367** The McGraw-Hill Companies; **368** LMR Group/Alamy Images; **369** Veer; **370** Getty Images; **371** Richard Hutchings/Digital Light Source; **373** (kite)C Squared Studio/Getty Images, (plane)Getty Images, (yoyo)Siede Preis/Getty Images; **377** Getty Images; **378** 2006 Photos To Go; **381** StudiOhio; **383 384** Eclipse Studios; **385** (baseball gift football)Getty Images, (red ball)CORBIS, (frozen juice can)Michael Newman/PhotoEdit, (boxes partyhat)Dorling Kindersley, (trash can)Matthew Ward/Dorling Kindersley, (glass blueberries funnel)Jupiterimages, (Egyptian pyramid)SuperStock, (blocks)Ken Cavanagh/The McGraw-Hill Companies, (briefcase) Siede Preis/Getty Images, (wooden shapes) The McGraw-Hill Companies SuperStock; **386** (c r)The McGraw-Hill Companies, (l)Ryan McVay/Getty Images; **390** Dave King/Dorling Kindersley; **391** Richard Hutchings/Digital Light Source; **392** (t cl)SuperStock, (tc)Stefano Bianchetti/CORBIS, (tr)Dave King/Dorling Kindersley, (tcr cr)Getty Images, (c)Alamy Images, (r)Stephen Oliver/Getty Images, (b)Don Farrall/Getty Images, (bc)Dorling Kindersley, (bcl)Tim Ridley/Getty Images, (bcr)photos.com; **397** (b)Stefano Bianchetti/CORBIS, (bc)SuperStock, (br)Dave King/Dorling Kindersley; **402** Photodisc/SuperStock; **408** L. Clarke/CORBIS; **409** Alamy Images; **410** (tc)Andersen-Ross/Alamy Images, (bkgd)Jacky Chapman/Alamy Images; **411** (br)Getty Images, (others)Jupiterimages; **415** Walter Bibikow/Index Stock Imagery; **417 418** Eclipse Studios; **419 423** Richard Hutchings/Digital Light Source; **428** Stockdisc/PunchStock; **429** Richard Hutchings/Digital Light Source; **432** Stone+/Getty Images; **433** Richard Hutchings/Digital Light Source; **435** The McGraw-Hill Companies; **438** (l to r, t to b)C Squared Studios/Getty Images, Stefano Bianchetti/CORBIS, SuperStock, Ryan McVay/Getty Images, The McGraw-Hill Companies, The McGraw-Hill Companies,Getty Images, Getty Images, Dorling Kindersley, Getty Images; **439 440** The McGraw-Hill Companies; **441** Barbara Peacock/Getty Images; **447** (t)Ron Chapple/Jupiterimages, (b)Don Farrall/Getty Images; **448** (t)Bryan Mullennix/Getty Images, (b)Daniel Barillot/Masterfile; **450** The McGraw-Hill Companies; **452** (l tcl)C Squared Studios/Getty Images, (t)Siede Preis/Getty Images, (tl)CORBIS; **453** Digital Light Source; **455 456** Eclipse Studios; **457** Richard Hutchings/Digital Light Source; **459** Renee Comet/Getty Images; **460** (tcr)Paul Bradforth/Alamy Images, (c)David Page/Alamy Images, (cr)C Squared Studios/Getty Images, (bcr)Stockdisc/PunchStock; **473** Eclipse Studios; **475** (b)John Anderson/Alamy Images, (t)TH Foto/Alamy Images; **476** (t)Andrea Jones/Alamy Images, (b)FoodCollection/SuperStock; **481** Charles O'Rear/CORBIS; **483 484** Eclipse Studios; **486** Tim Fitzharris/Minden Pictures; **498** (l)2006 Photos To Go, (t tcr)Getty Images, (tl tc)CORBIS, (tr)Ryan McVay/Getty Images; **503** Masterfile; **507** David W. Hamilton/Getty Images; **508** (t)Thinkstock/Jupiterimages, (b)CORBIS; LA1 Mark Steinmetz/Amanita Pictures; **LA2** Tim Fuller; **LA6** Bill Aron/PhotoEdit; **LA11** (r)Richard Hutchings/Digital Light Source, (l)2006 Photos To Go; **LA12** (t to b, l to r)Burke/Triolo/Brand X Pictures/Jupiterimages, StudiOhio, The McGraw-Hill Companies, The McGraw-Hill Companies, PhotoLink/Getty Images, Getty Images, Getty Images, Getty Images, Getty Images; **LA14** (tl cl)The McGraw-Hill Companies, (tcl)Getty Images, (bl)C Squared Studios/Getty Images, (bcl)PhotoLink/Getty Images; **P1** (bcl)Jeff Greenberg/PhotoEdit, (others)PunchStock; **P2** Tim Fuller; **P3** Jack Hollingsworth/CORBIS; **P7** SuperStock; **P10** Stockdisc/PunchStock; **P11** Dennis MacDonald/PhotoEdit; **P12** (tr)Getty Images, (b)Creatas/PunchStock; **P15** (t)William McKellar /Alamy Images, (bl)Alamy Images, (br)Imagestate; **P16** (tl)D. Hurst/Alamy Images, (tr)David Young-Wolff/PhotoEdit, (bl)Robert Llewellyn/Imagestate, (br)D. Hurst/Alamy Images; **P18** CORBIS; **CS3** (cl)Michael Houghton/StudiOhio, (b bc bcl)StudiOhio, (bl)The McGraw-Hill Companies; **CS4** (tr)Getty Images, (cr)PhotoLink/Getty Images, (br)Siede Preis/Getty Images; **GL8** Alamy Images; **GL13 GL14 GL17** Getty Images; **GL26** C Squared Studios/Getty Images.

McGraw-Hill would like to acknowledge the artists and agencies who contributed to illustrating this program: Cover Ron Berg represented by Mendola Ltd.; Anthology, Inc.; Argosy Publishing; Fian Arroyo; Articulate Graphics; Terri Chicko represented by Cornell & McCarthy, LLC; Gary Colby represented by American Artists Rep., Inc.; Bob Depew; Jon Horn; Hurix; Monotype; Precision Graphics; Peter Lacalamita; Teresa Smolinski.

Unless otherwise credited, all currency courtesy of the US Mint. **13G 13H** Richard Hutchings/Digital Light Source; **16** Eclipse Studios; **17A** G.K. Vikki Hart/Getty Images; **17** Eclipse Studios; **19 through 29** Eclipse Studios; **33B** Richard Hutchings/Digital Light Source; **35** Eclipse Studios; **39B** Richard Hutchings/Digital Light Source; **39** Eclipse Studios; **47G 47H** Richard Hutchings/Digital Light Source; **50** Eclipse Studios; **51B** Richard Hutchings/Digital Light Source; **51 through 75** Eclipse Studios; **83H** Richard Hutchings/Digital Light Source; **86 through 91** Eclipse Studios; **95A** (b)2006 Jupiterimages, and its licensors. All rights reserved, (t)Tim Ridley/Getty Images; **95** Eclipse Studios; **97B** Richard Hutchings/Digital Light Source; **97** Eclipse Studios; **101B** Richard Hutchings/Digital Light Source; **101** Eclipse Studios; **103B** Richard Hutchings/Digital Light Source; **103** Eclipse Studios; **105B** Richard Hutchings/Digital Light Source; **107** Eclipse Studios; **111B** Richard Hutchings/Digital Light Source; **111** Eclipse Studios; **119B** Siede Preis/Getty Images; **119G** C Squared Studios/Getty Images; **119H** (b)The McGraw-Hill Companies, (others)Stockdisc/PunchStock; **122 123 125** Eclipse Studios; **127B** Richard Hutchings/Digital Light Source; **127** Eclipse Studios; **129** Eclipse Studios; **133B** The McGraw-Hill Companies; **133** Eclipse Studios; **137B** Richard Hutchings/Digital Light Source; **137** Eclipse Studios; **143** Eclipse Studios; **151H 153B** Richard Hutchings/Digital Light Source; **154 through 169** Eclipse Studios; **171B** Richard Hutchings/Digital Light Source; **171** Eclipse Studios; **181H** Richard Hutchings/Digital Light Source; **184** Eclipse Studios; **185** Eclipse Studios; **187** Eclipse Studios; **189B** Richard Hutchings/Digital Light Source; **193B** Richard Hutchings/Digital Light Source; **195B** Richard Hutchings/Digital Light Source; **195** Eclipse Studios; **197** Eclipse Studios; **199B** Richard Hutchings/Digital Light Source; **199** Eclipse Studios; **209H** Richard Hutchings/Digital Light Source; **212** Eclipse Studios; **213B** Richard Hutchings/Digital Light Source; **213** Eclipse Studios; **215B** Richard Hutchings/Digital Light Source; **215** Eclipse Studios; **217 219** Eclipse Studios; **223B** Richard Hutchings/Digital Light Source; **223** Eclipse Studios; **227** Eclipse Studios; **239H** (t)Getty Images, (others)Richard Hutchings/Digital Light Source; **242** Eclipse Studios; **243B** Richard Hutchings/Digital Light Source; **243 through 255** Eclipse Studios; **257B** Richard Hutchings/Digital Light Source; **259 through 266** Eclipse Studios; **273G 273H 275H 277B** Richard Hutchings/Digital Light Source; **277 281** Eclipse Studios; **285B** Richard Hutchings/Digital Light Source; **285** Eclipse Studios; **291B** Richard Hutchings/Digital Light Source; **291 through 305** Eclipse Studios; **313G** 2006 Photos To Go; **313H** Richard Hutchings/Digital Light Source; **316 through 323** Eclipse Studios; **325B** Richard Hutchings/Digital Light Source; **325 through 339** Eclipse Studios; **347H** Richard Hutchings/Digital Light Source; **350 through 371** Eclipse Studios; **381G** 2006 Photos To Go; **381H** Richard Hutchings/Digital Light Source; **384** Eclipse Studios; **385B** Richard Hutchings/Digital Light Source; **385 387 390** Eclipse Studios; **391B** Richard Hutchings/Digital Light Source; **391 395** Eclipse Studios; **401B** Richard Hutchings/Digital Light Source; **401 405 407** Eclipse Studios; **415H** Richard Hutchings/Digital Light Source; **418** Eclipse Studios; **419B** Richard Hutchings/Digital Light Source; **419 through 439** Eclipse Studios; **441B** Richard Hutchings/Digital Light Source; **443 445** Eclipse Studios; **453G** 2006 Jupiterimages, and its licensors. All rights reserved.; **453H** (t)Getty Images, (b)Richard Hutchings/Digital Light Source; **456 through 469** Eclipse Studios; **481H** Richard Hutchings/Digital Light Source; **484 485** Eclipse Studios; **487B** Richard Hutchings/Digital Light Source; **487** through **503A** Eclipse Studios; **505B** Siede Preis/Getty Images; **505** Eclipse Studios; **LA13B** Richard Hutchings/Digital Light Source; **T3** Stockbyte/Getty Images; **T8** Bloom Works Inc./Alamy; **T12** Royalty-free/Corbis; **T13** Bananastock/PunchStock; **T14** Creasource/Corbis.

McGraw-Hill would like to acknowledge the artists and agencies who contributed to illustrating this program: Cover Ron Berg represented by Mendola Ltd.; Anthology, Inc.; Argosy Publishing; Fian Arroyo; Articulate Graphics; Terri Chicko represented by Cornell & McCarthy, LLC; Gary Colby represented by American Artists Rep., Inc.; Bob Depew; Jon Horn; Hurix; Monotype; Precision Graphics; Peter Lacalamita; Teresa Smolinski.

Name ____________________

Count On 1, 2, and 3 (Use with Chapter 5)

1. $1 + 7 = 8$ $3 + 3 = 6$ $8 + 1 = 9$ $7 + 1 = 8$ $5 + 1 = 6$ $9 + 1 = 10$

2. $2 + 3 = 5$ $1 + 6 = 7$ $2 + 5 = 7$ $6 + 3 = 9$ $3 + 5 = 8$ $1 + 5 = 6$

3. $2 + 2 = 4$ $2 + 7 = 9$ $3 + 1 = 4$ $4 + 2 = 6$ $2 + 4 = 6$ $7 + 3 = 10$

Name ____________________

Count Back 1, 2, and 3 (Use with Chapter 6)

1. $9 - 3 = 6$ $4 - 1 = 3$ $7 - 2 = 5$ $3 - 3 = 0$ $5 - 3 = 2$ $7 - 3 = 4$

2. $10 - 2 = 8$ $3 - 1 = 2$ $9 - 2 = 7$ $2 - 1 = 1$ $6 - 2 = 4$ $3 - 2 = 1$

3. $4 - 2 = 2$ $10 - 3 = 7$ $5 - 1 = 4$ $5 - 2 = 3$ $8 - 3 = 5$ $4 - 3 = 1$

Name ______________________

Count On 1, 2, and 3 (Use with Chapter 5)

4. $1+9=10$ | $3+6=9$ | $6+2=8$ | $1+4=5$ | $3+7=10$ | $4+3=7$

5. $3+2=5$ | $1+8=9$ | $2+1=3$ | $7+2=9$ | $5+2=7$ | $1+3=4$

6. $5+3=8$ | $3+4=7$ | $4+1=5$ | $6+1=7$ | $2+8=10$ | $2+6=8$

Name ______________________

Count Back 1, 2, and 3 (Use with Chapter 6)

4. $6-3=3$ | $8-3=5$ | $10-2=8$ | $3-2=1$ | $5-3=2$ | $2-1=1$

5. $5-2=3$ | $4-2=2$ | $9-2=7$ | $10-1=9$ | $2-2=0$ | $7-3=4$

6. $9-3=6$ | $10-3=7$ | $4-3=1$ | $6-1=5$ | $6-2=4$ | $8-2=6$

Name ______________________

Doubles and Doubles Plus 1 (Use with Chapter 7)

1. $6+6=12$ | $4+5=9$ | $5+5=10$ | $3+2=5$ | $2+1=3$ | $3+4=7$

2. $6+5=11$ | $3+2=5$ | $2+2=4$ | $4+3=7$ | $5+4=9$ | $4+4=8$

3. $2+3=5$ | $3+3=6$ | $1+1=2$ | $0+0=0$ | $1+2=3$ | $5+6=11$

Name ______________________

Use Doubles or Count Back (Use with Chapter 8)

1. $4-2=2$ | $11-3=8$ | $3-2=1$ | $7-3=4$ | $3-3=0$ | $10-5=5$

2. $8-3=5$ | $7-2=5$ | $8-4=4$ | $12-3=9$ | $9-1=8$ | $6-2=4$

3. $12-6=6$ | $2-2=0$ | $6-3=3$ | $11-2=9$ | $5-2=3$ | $8-3=5$

Name ______________________

Doubles and Doubles Plus 1 (Use with Chapter 7)

4.	0	1	3	2	3	5
	+ 0	+ 2	+ 2	+ 2	+ 4	+ 5
	0	3	5	4	7	10
5.	4	5	2	6	3	4
	+ 3	+ 4	+ 3	+ 5	+ 3	+ 4
	7	9	5	11	6	8
6.	6	5	2	3	4	1
	+ 6	+ 6	+ 1	+ 4	+ 5	+ 1
	12	11	3	7	9	2

Name ______________________

Use Doubles or Count Back (Use with Chapter 8)

4.	12	11	6	5	6	3
	− 6	− 3	− 2	− 3	− 1	− 2
	6	8	4	2	5	1
5.	8	7	11	4	8	10
	− 3	− 3	− 2	− 2	− 2	− 5
	5	4	9	2	6	5
6.	12	8	9	2	9	6
	− 3	− 4	− 2	− 2	− 3	− 3
	9	4	7	0	6	3

Name ______________________

Make a Ten (Use with Chapter 9)

1.	4	6	5	8	4	8
	+ 6	+ 7	+ 8	+ 6	+ 6	+ 5
	10	13	13	14	10	13
2.	2	5	9	1	3	7
	+ 8	+ 9	+ 7	+ 9	+ 7	+ 9
	10	14	16	10	10	16
3.	7	5	6	7	9	4
	+ 8	+ 5	+ 4	+ 3	+ 8	+ 9
	15	10	10	10	17	13

Name ______________________

Subtract Zero and All (Use with Chapter 10)

1.	1	5	3	2	6	8
	− 0	− 0	− 3	− 0	− 0	− 8
	1	5	0	2	6	0
2.	2	7	8	6	7	5
	− 2	− 7	− 0	− 6	− 0	− 5
	0	0	8	0	7	0
3.	4	3	9	9	1	4
	− 4	− 0	− 9	− 0	− 1	− 0
	0	3	0	9	0	4

Name ______________________

Make a Ten (Use with Chapter 9)

4. $6 + 8 = 14$ | $9 + 4 = 13$ | $2 + 9 = 11$ | $5 + 7 = 12$ | $8 + 9 = 17$ | $9 + 1 = 10$

5. $7 + 7 = 14$ | $8 + 2 = 10$ | $3 + 8 = 11$ | $8 + 4 = 12$ | $9 + 6 = 15$ | $7 + 3 = 10$

6. $9 + 5 = 14$ | $6 + 9 = 15$ | $4 + 7 = 11$ | $7 + 5 = 12$ | $8 + 8 = 16$ | $3 + 9 = 12$

Name ______________________

Subtract Zero and All (Use with Chapter 10)

4. $6 - 0 = 6$ | $2 - 0 = 2$ | $8 - 0 = 8$ | $6 - 6 = 0$ | $7 - 7 = 0$ | $9 - 0 = 9$

5. $8 - 8 = 0$ | $1 - 1 = 0$ | $9 - 9 = 0$ | $4 - 0 = 4$ | $4 - 4 = 0$ | $2 - 2 = 0$

6. $3 - 3 = 0$ | $5 - 0 = 5$ | $7 - 0 = 7$ | $1 - 0 = 1$ | $3 - 0 = 3$ | $5 - 5 = 0$

Name ______________________

Facts to 10 (Use with Chapter 10)

1. $4 + 6 = 10$ | $4 + 5 = 9$ | $3 + 2 = 5$ | $2 + 6 = 8$ | $2 + 5 = 7$ | $1 + 3 = 4$

2. $1 + 7 = 8$ | $1 + 1 = 2$ | $3 + 7 = 10$ | $5 + 1 = 6$ | $7 + 3 = 10$ | $7 + 2 = 9$

3. $4 + 3 = 7$ | $0 + 5 = 5$ | $8 + 2 = 10$ | $5 + 3 = 8$ | $9 + 1 = 10$ | $5 + 4 = 9$

Name ______________________

Subtract from 10 or Less (Use with Chapter 11)

1. $10 - 2 = 8$ | $9 - 4 = 5$ | $10 - 7 = 3$ | $10 - 8 = 2$ | $9 - 6 = 3$ | $10 - 7 = 3$

2. $10 - 4 = 6$ | $8 - 6 = 2$ | $10 - 1 = 9$ | $9 - 7 = 2$ | $10 - 9 = 1$ | $8 - 5 = 3$

3. $9 - 8 = 1$ | $10 - 5 = 5$ | $8 - 7 = 1$ | $10 - 3 = 7$ | $10 - 4 = 6$ | $10 - 6 = 4$

Name ______________________

Facts to 10 (Use with Chapter 10)

4.	5	3	6	9	3	7
	+ 5	+ 6	+ 4	+ 1	+ 3	+ 1
	10	9	10	10	6	8
5.	1	0	4	5	5	0
	+ 6	+ 9	+ 1	+ 3	+ 2	+ 9
	7	9	5	8	7	9
6.	3	3	6	7	1	0
	+ 4	+ 1	+ 3	+ 0	+ 8	+ 7
	7	4	9	7	9	7

Name ______________________

Subtract from 10 or Less (Use with Chapter 11)

4.	10	8	10	10	10	10
	− 7	− 4	− 9	− 5	− 7	− 3
	3	4	1	5	3	7
5.	10	10	10	9	9	10
	− 8	− 6	− 4	− 2	− 8	− 8
	2	4	6	7	1	2
6.	10	10	10	9	10	9
	− 2	− 1	− 6	− 3	− 3	− 6
	8	9	4	6	7	3

Name ______________________

Facts to 12 (Use with Chapter 11)

1.	3	4	8	0	5	3
	+ 5	+ 8	+ 4	+ 8	+ 2	+ 4
	8	12	12	8	7	7
2.	6	2	4	9	5	7
	+ 5	+ 5	+ 2	+ 1	+ 6	+ 4
	11	7	6	10	11	11
3.	5	4	7	0	4	8
	+ 4	+ 4	+ 1	+ 6	+ 7	+ 1
	9	8	8	6	11	9

Name ______________________

Subtract from 12 or Less (Use with Chapter 12)

1.	12	10	12	12	11	12
	− 9	− 7	− 4	− 7	− 5	− 6
	3	3	8	5	6	6
2.	12	11	11	11	12	12
	− 3	− 3	− 6	− 2	− 5	− 7
	9	8	5	9	7	5
3.	12	11	12	11	12	12
	− 6	− 7	− 8	− 8	− 9	− 4
	6	4	4	3	3	8

Name ______________________

Facts to 12 (Use with Chapter 11)

4.	7	4	3	8	2	5
	+ 5	+ 3	+ 6	+ 3	+ 4	+ 7
	12	7	9	11	6	12
5.	2	2	1	3	6	8
	+ 6	+ 2	+ 5	+ 6	+ 6	+ 2
	8	4	6	9	12	10
6.	5	6	2	1	9	3
	+ 3	+ 4	+ 7	+ 7	+ 2	+ 3
	8	10	9	8	11	6

Name ______________________

Subtract from 12 or Less (Use with Chapter 12)

4.	12	12	10	12	12	12
	− 8	− 9	− 4	− 3	− 4	− 5
	4	3	6	9	8	7
5.	12	10	12	10	12	12
	− 5	− 8	− 7	− 6	− 8	− 9
	7	2	5	4	4	3
6.	11	11	12	12	12	10
	− 4	− 9	− 3	− 7	− 6	− 9
	7	2	9	5	6	1

Name ______________________

Facts to 14 (Use with Chapter 12)

1.	9	5	7	6	5	4
	+ 4	+ 3	+ 2	+ 8	+ 8	+ 4
	13	8	9	14	13	8
2.	1	0	6	9	7	6
	+ 6	+ 6	+ 3	+ 0	+ 6	+ 2
	7	6	9	9	13	8
3.	7	4	9	1	1	8
	+ 7	+ 9	+ 5	+ 4	+ 8	+ 5
	14	13	14	5	9	13

Name ______________________

Subtract from 14 or Less (Use with Chapter 12)

1.	14	11	14	11	14	14
	− 8	− 5	− 6	− 2	− 9	− 7
	6	6	8	9	5	7
2.	14	13	14	12	12	12
	− 5	− 6	− 8	− 8	− 7	− 5
	9	7	6	4	5	7
3.	13	14	13	14	13	12
	− 9	− 7	− 8	− 6	− 8	− 9
	4	7	5	8	5	3

Name ____________________

Facts to 14 (Use with Chapter 12)

4.	6 + 4 10	2 + 9 11	0 + 4 4	5 + 9 14	9 + 3 12	0 + 9 9
5.	0 + 7 7	3 + 8 11	2 + 3 5	6 + 7 13	3 + 7 10	7 + 0 7
6.	4 + 3 7	8 + 0 8	3 + 2 5	8 + 6 14	4 + 6 10	5 + 1 6

Name ____________________

Subtract from 14 or Less (Use with Chapter 12)

4.	14 − 9 5	13 − 4 9	14 − 8 6	12 − 8 4	13 − 5 8	14 − 5 9
5.	11 − 5 6	11 − 9 2	13 − 7 6	14 − 6 8	11 − 3 8	14 − 7 7
6.	12 − 8 4	14 − 7 7	14 − 6 8	11 − 7 4	14 − 9 5	12 − 4 8

Name ____________________

Facts to 16 (Use with Chapter 13)

1.	8 + 8 16	3 + 8 11	5 + 2 7	8 + 4 12	3 + 9 12	2 + 5 7
2.	7 + 5 12	9 + 7 16	8 + 6 14	6 + 6 12	8 + 7 15	9 + 6 15
3.	9 + 4 13	6 + 4 10	5 + 8 13	2 + 9 11	5 + 9 14	7 + 8 15

Name ____________________

Subtract from 16 or Less (Use with Chapter 13)

1.	15 − 9 6	13 − 8 5	14 − 9 5	14 − 6 8	15 − 6 9	16 − 9 7
2.	14 − 7 7	16 − 7 9	16 − 8 8	14 − 8 6	13 − 9 4	14 − 5 9
3.	16 − 9 7	15 − 7 8	14 − 7 7	16 − 7 9	16 − 8 8	15 − 8 7

Name ______________________

Facts to 16 (Use with Chapter 13)

4.	1 + 8 9	3 + 8 11	5 + 7 12	8 + 5 13	7 + 4 11	3 + 5 8
5.	7 + 9 16	7 + 7 14	7 + 6 13	6 + 7 13	5 + 9 14	9 + 7 16
6.	6 + 5 11	8 + 4 12	4 + 8 12	6 + 8 14	7 + 8 15	4 + 4 8

Name ______________________

Subtract from 16 or Less (Use with Chapter 13)

4.	16 − 9 7	15 − 9 6	14 − 7 7	13 − 5 8	13 − 7 6	16 − 9 7
5.	15 − 7 8	12 − 9 3	13 − 9 4	16 − 8 8	13 − 8 5	13 − 6 7
6.	14 − 9 5	16 − 7 9	13 − 4 9	15 − 6 9	14 − 6 8	15 − 8 7

Name ______________________

Facts to 18 (Use with Chapter 15)

1.	8 + 9 17	3 + 8 11	8 + 7 15	9 + 8 17	6 + 6 12	9 + 7 16
2.	0 + 8 8	9 + 6 15	6 + 9 15	6 + 3 9	1 + 8 9	3 + 6 9
3.	3 + 9 12	8 + 5 13	5 + 5 10	2 + 7 9	8 + 2 10	9 + 9 18

Name ______________________

Subtract from 18 or Less (Use with Chapter 14)

1.	18 − 9 9	13 − 8 5	15 − 9 6	14 − 5 9	16 − 8 8	14 − 9 5
2.	16 − 7 9	17 − 9 8	14 − 8 6	16 − 9 7	13 − 9 4	18 − 9 9
3.	17 − 8 9	14 − 7 7	14 − 6 8	15 − 6 9	15 − 8 7	13 − 7 6

Name ______________________

Facts to 18 (Use with Chapter 15)

4.	9	1	2	4	7	4
	+ 8	+ 6	+ 9	+ 9	+ 6	+ 2
	17	7	11	13	13	6
5.	3	8	8	4	6	5
	+ 4	+ 4	+ 9	+ 5	+ 4	+ 8
	7	12	17	9	10	13
6.	9	9	5	6	7	5
	+ 2	+ 9	+ 7	+ 8	+ 9	+ 9
	11	18	12	14	16	14

Name ______________________

Subtract from 18 or Less (Use with Chapter 15)

4.	13	12	12	18	13	12
	− 6	− 4	− 9	− 9	− 4	− 7
	7	8	3	9	9	5
5.	13	16	16	15	16	17
	− 5	− 9	− 8	− 8	− 7	− 8
	8	7	8	7	9	9
6.	12	12	18	17	15	12
	− 8	− 5	− 9	− 9	− 9	− 6
	4	7	9	8	6	6

Facts Practice

WorkMat 1

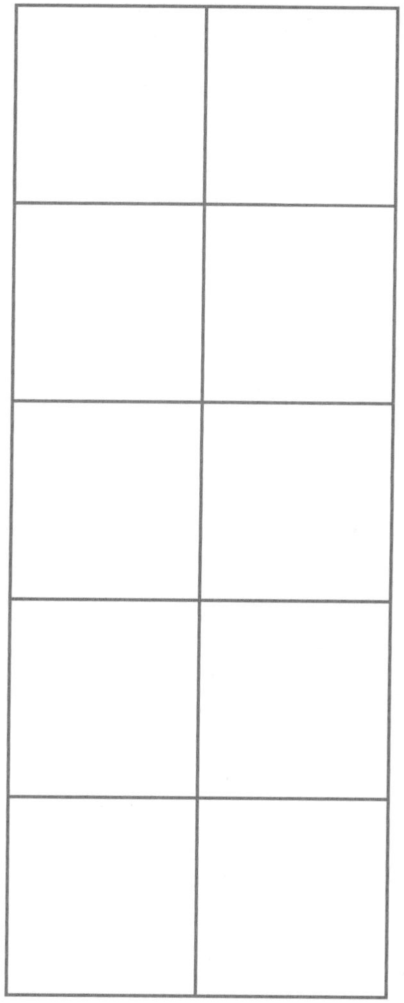

Facts Practice

WorkMat 3: Part-Part-Whole

Whole

Part

Part

WorkMat 3

WorkMat 2

WorkMat 2: Ten-Frames

WorkMat 5

61 62 63 64 65 66 67 68 69 70 71 72 73 74 75 76 77 78 79 80

81 82 83 84 85 86 87 88 89 90 91 92 93 94 95 96 97 98 99 100

WorkMat 5: Number Lines

WorkMat 4

0 1 2 3 4 5 6 7 8 9 10 11 12 13 14 15 16 17 18 19 20

21 22 23 24 25 26 27 28 29 30 31 32 33 34 35 36 37 38 39 40

41 42 43 44 45 46 47 48 49 50 51 52 53 54 55 56 57 58 59 60

WorkMat 4: Number Lines

WorkMat 6

WorkMat 6: Grid

WorkMat 7

Tens	Ones

WorkMat 7: Tens and Ones Chart

WorkMat 8

Hundreds	Tens	Ones

WorkMat 8: Hundreds, Tens, and Ones Chart

WorkMats

Index

A

Above-Level Suggestions. *See also* Early Finishers.
- diagnostic assessment options, 14, 48, 84, 120, 152, 182, 210, 240, 274, 314, 348, 382, 416, 454, 482
- Game Time, 38, 58, 94, 136, 160, 202, 230, 266, 284, 322, 374, 394, 426, 466, 494
- leveled assignments, 18, 20, 25, 28, 30, 36, 38, 40, 52, 54, 56, 58, 60, 66, 68, 71, 76, 88, 90, 92, 94, 96, 102, 104, 109, 112, 124, 126, 130, 134, 136, 138, 144, 156, 158, 160, 164, 166, 170, 172, 186, 190, 196, 198, 200, 202, 214, 216, 218, 225, 228, 230, 244, 246, 251, 256, 260, 262, 264, 266, 278, 280, 282, 284, 287, 293, 297, 302, 306, 318, 320, 322, 324, 330, 332, 336, 340, 352, 354, 356, 358, 364, 366, 372, 374, 386, 388, 392, 394, 396, 403, 406, 408, 421, 424, 426, 431, 434, 440, 444, 446, 458, 462, 464, 466, 470, 472, 486, 488, 492, 494, 496, 500, 502, 506
- leveled tests, 44, 80, 116, 148, 179, 206, 236, 270, 310, 344, 378, 412, 450, 478, 510

Addends, 151B, 155

Addition, 47A–82, 151A–180, 313A–346, 481A–512
- of 1, 2, or 3, 163–164
- in any order, 155–156
- count on 1, 2, or 3, 157–158
- doubles, 169–170, 317–318
- doubles plus 1, 171–172, 319–320
- estimate sums, 495–496
- making ten, 323–324
- modeling, 53–54
- number line for, 165–166
- subtraction related to, 197–198, 331–332
- of tens, 485–486
- two-digit, 487–488, 491–492
- vertical, 75–76
- of zero, 59–60

Addition sentences, 47B, 55–56

Addition stories, 51–52, 51A, 73

Addressing Individual Needs. *See* Differentiated Instruction

After, 13B, 39, 209B, 213, 415B, 445

Afternoon, 209B, 213

Algebra Concepts of algebra develop informally with the awareness of patterns, sorting/classifying, use of symbols and variables in expressions and equations, and initial exposure to functions.

Algebra Readiness
- commutative property of addition, 313A
- comparing coins, 347A
- comparing data, 119A
- equation concepts, 47A, 151A, 239A
- estimating sums and differences, 481A
- extending and creating patterns, 13A
- guess and check strategy, 415A
- objects on a coordinate plane, 381A
- operation symbols, 181A
- ordering events, 209A
- ordering objects, 273A
- using number sentences, 83A

Analog clocks, 209B, 223

Area
- comparing, 301–304
- ordering, 305–306

Are You Ready for Chapter, 14, 48, 84, 120, 152, 182, 210, 240, 274, 314, 348, 382, 416, 454, 482

Art. *See* Learning Stations; Problem-Solving

Assessment, *See also* Data-Driven Decision Making; Mid-Chapter Check.
- Chapter Projects, 15, 43, 49, 79, 85, 115, 121, 147, 153, 177, 183, 205, 211, 235, 241, 269, 275, 309, 315, 343, 349, 377, 383, 411, 417, 449, 455, 477, 483, 509
- Chapter Review/Test, 43–44, 79–80, 115–116, 147–148, 177–179, 205–206, 235–236, 269–270, 309–310, 343–344, 377–378, 411–412, 449–450, 477–478, 509–510
- Diagnostic Assessment, 13C, 13F, 14, 47C, 47F, 48, 83C, 83F, 84, 119C, 119F, 120, 151C, 151F, 152, 181C, 181E, 182, 209C, 209E, 210, 239C, 239F, 240, 273C, 273F, 274, 313C, 313F, 314, 347C, 347F, 348, 381C, 381F, 382, 415C, 415F, 416, 453C, 453E, 454, 481C, 481F, 482
- Formative Assessment, 13F, 18, 20, 22, 26, 28, 30, 31, 32, 33, 36, 40, 45, 47F, 52, 54, 56, 60, 62, 63, 64, 66, 68, 72, 74, 76, 81, 83F, 88, 90, 92, 96, 98, 99, 100, 102, 104, 106, 110, 112, 117, 119F, 124, 126, 128, 130, 131, 132, 134, 138, 142, 144, 148, 151F, 156, 158, 162, 164, 166, 167, 168, 170, 172, 174, 179, 181E, 186, 188, 190, 191, 192, 194, 196, 198, 200, 207, 209E, 214, 216, 218, 220, 221, 222, 226, 228, 232, 237, 239F, 244, 246, 248, 252, 253, 254, 256, 260, 262, 264, 271, 273F, 278, 280, 282, 288, 289, 290, 294, 298, 300, 306, 311, 313F, 318, 320, 324, 326, 327, 328, 330, 332, 334, 336, 340, 345, 347F, 352, 354, 356, 358, 360, 361, 362, 364, 366, 370, 372, 379, 378, 381F, 386, 388, 390, 392, 396, 397, 398, 400, 404, 406, 408, 413, 415F, 422, 424, 428, 432, 434, 437, 438, 440, 442, 444, 446, 451, 453E, 458, 460, 462, 464, 467, 468, 470, 472, 474, 479, 481F, 486, 488, 490, 492, 496, 497, 498, 500, 502, 504, 506, 511
- Spiral Review, 32, 64, 100, 132, 168, 192, 222, 254, 290, 328, 362, 398, 438, 468, 498
- Summative Assessment, 13F, 43, 45, 47F, 79, 81, 83F, 115, 117, 119F, 148, 149, 151F, 177, 179, 181E, 205, 207, 209E, 235, 237, 239F, 269, 271, 273F, 309, 311, 313F, 343, 345, 347F, 377, 379, 381F, 411, 413, 415F, 449, 451, 453E, 477, 479, 481F, 509, 511
- Test Practice, 45–46, 81–82, 117–118, 149–150, 180–181, 207–208, 237–238, 271–272, 311–312, 345–346, 379–380, 413–414, 451–452, 479–480, 511–512
- Vocabulary Review and Test, 43, 79, 115, 147, 177, 205, 235, 269, 309, 343, 377, 411, 449, 477, 509
- Auditory Learners. *See* Learning Styles

B

Balance scale, 285B, 287

Bar graphs
- making, 137–140
- reading, 133–134

Before, 13B, 39, 209B, 213, 415B, 445

Below-Level Suggestions
- Game Time, 38, 58, 94, 136, 160, 202, 230, 266, 284, 322, 374, 394, 426, 466, 494
- leveled assignments, 18, 20, 25, 28, 30, 36, 38, 40, 52, 54, 56, 58, 60, 66, 68, 71, 76, 88, 90, 92, 94, 96, 102, 104, 109, 112, 124, 126, 130, 134, 136, 138, 144, 156, 158, 160, 164, 166, 170, 172, 186, 190, 196, 198, 200, 202, 214, 216, 218, 225, 228, 230, 244, 246, 251, 256, 260, 262, 264, 266, 278, 280, 282, 284, 287, 293, 297, 302, 306, 318, 320, 322, 324, 330, 332, 336, 340, 352, 354, 356, 358, 364, 366, 372, 374, 386, 388, 392, 394, 396, 403, 406, 408, 421, 424, 426, 431, 434, 440, 444, 446, 458, 462, 464, 466, 470, 472, 486, 488, 492, 494, 496, 500, 502, 506
- leveled tests, 44, 80, 116, 148, 179, 206, 234, 270, 310, 344, 378, 412, 450, 478, 510
- Small Group Options, 17B, 27B, 29B, 33B, 39B, 59B, 65B, 69B, 73B, 75B, 89B, 95B, 97B, 107B, 129B, 133B, 137B, 163B, 169B, 171B, 173B, 187B, 189B, 193B, 215B, 223B, 227B, 231B, 249B, 255B, 261B, 263B, 277B, 279B, 301B, 305B, 317B, 319B, 331B, 333B, 335B, 339B, 355B, 363B, 365B, 385B, 387B, 389A, 391B, 399B, 401B, 405B, 407B, 419B, 429B, 439B, 441B, 443B, 445B, 463B, 469B, 473B, 495B, 499B, 503B, 505B
- Strategic Intervention, 14, 48, 84, 120, 152, 182, 210, 240, 274, 314, 348, 382, 416, 454, 482

Benchmark Students. *See* On-Level Suggestions

Index

Between, 13B, 39, 415B, 445

Big Idea
addition and subtraction problems, 313A
addition concepts, 47A
addition strategies, 151A
coins, 347A
data, organizing and using, 119A
describing and comparing numbers, 13A
fractions, 453A
geometric figures, 381A
measurement, 273A
number patterns, 239A
place value, 415A
subtraction concepts, 83A
subtraction strategies, 181A
time, 209A
two-digit addition and subtraction, 481A

C

Calendar Time, 13H, 47H, 83H, 119H, 151H, 181H, 209H, 239H, 273H, 313H, 347H, 381H, 415H, 453H, 481H

Capacity, 291–294

Cents, 347B, 351

Certain, 119B, 143

Chapter Projects, 15, 43, 49, 79, 85, 115, 121, 147, 153, 177, 183, 205, 211, 235, 241, 269, 275, 309, 315, 343, 349, 377, 383, 411, 417, 449, 455, 477, 483, 509

Chapter Review/Test, 43–44, 79–80, 115–116, 147–148, 177–179, 205–206, 235–236, 269–270, 309–310, 343–344, 377–378, 411–412, 449–450, 477–478, 509–510

Charts
tally charts, 129–130

Circles, 381B, 395

Clocks, 209B, 223

Coins, 347A–380
counting, 357–358, 371–372
equal amounts, 363–364
pennies and dimes, 353–354
pennies and nickels, 351–352
pennies, nickels, and dimes, 355–356
quarters, 365–368

Communication Opportunities to develop mathematical fluency and vocabulary are provided in the *Talk About It* and the *Writing In Math* features. Students talk, listen, and write mathematically.

Communication, *See* Talk about it, Writing in math

Comparing
area, 301–304
capacity, 291–294
lengths, 277–278
measurement, 273A–312
numbers to 100, 443–444
temperature, 295–298
weight, 285–288

Concepts and Skills Bank
Half Dollars and Dollars, CS3–CS4
Perimeter, CS7–CS8
Symmetry and Congruence, CS5–CS6
Temperature, CS9–CS10
True and False Statements, CS1–CS2

Concepts in Motion, 17A, 39A, 53A, 69A, 89A, 107A, 123A, 137A, 165A, 171A, 185A, 189A, 227A, 233A, 245A, 255A, 279A, 323A, 329A, 331A, 339A, 357A, 363A, 391A, 407A, 423A, 433A, 463A, 469A, 471A, 491A, 501A

Cones, 381B, 385

Cooperative Groups. *See* Above-Level Suggestions; Below-Level Suggestions; English Language Learners (ELL); Gifted and Talented; On-Level Suggestions

Corners, of shapes, 387–388

Counting, 357–358
on 1, 2, or 3 to add, 157–158
to 20, 243–244
back 1, 2, or 3, 185–186
coins, 357–358, 371–372
hundred chart, 249–252
money, 357–358, 371–372
skip, by 2's, 5's and 10's, 259–260
skip on a hundred chart, 261–262
by tens, 245–246

Critical thinking. *See* Problem-Solving

Cross-Curricular Links. *See* Learning Stations

Cubes, 381B, 385

Cylinders, 381B, 385

D

Daily Routine, 17A, 19A, 21A, 23A, 27A, 29A, 33A, 35A, 39A, 51A, 53A, 55A, 59A, 61A, 65A, 67A, 69A, 73A, 75A, 87A, 89A, 91A, 95A, 97A, 101A, 103A, 105A, 107A, 111A, 123A, 125A, 127A, 129A, 133A, 137A, 141A, 143A, 155A, 157A, 161A, 163A, 165A, 169A, 171A, 173A, 185A, 187A, 189A, 193A, 195A, 197A, 199A, 213A, 215A, 217A, 219A, 223A, 227A, 231A, 243A, 245A, 247A, 249A, 255A, 257A, 259A, 261A, 263A, 277A, 279A, 281A, 285A, 291A, 295A, 299A, 301A, 305A, 317A, 319A, 323A, 325A, 329A, 331A, 333A, 335A, 339A, 351A, 353A, 355A, 357A, 359A, 363A, 365A, 369A, 371A, 385A, 387A, 389A, 391A, 395A, 399A, 401A, 405A, 407A, 419A, 423A, 427A, 429A, 433A, 439A, 441A, 443A, 445A, 457A, 459A, 461A, 463A, 469A, 471A, 473A, 485A, 487A, 489A, 491A, 495A, 499A, 501A, 503A, 505A

Data Collection Real-world situations encourage students to gather, organize, and analyze data.

Data, 119A–150. *See also* Graphs.
bar graphs, 133–134, 137–140
certain or impossible, 143–144
picture graphs, 125–126
sort and classify, 123–124
tally charts, 129–130

Data-Driven Decision Making, 31, 44, 63, 80, 99, 116, 131, 148, 167, 178, 191, 206, 221, 236, 253, 270, 289, 310, 327, 344, 361, 378, 397, 412, 437, 450, 467, 478, 497, 510

Data File, 26, 72, 110, 134, 164, 190, 228, 262, 288, 340, 368, 408, 432, 472, 486

Diagnostic Check A quick assessment of prerequisite skills required for each chapter is provided.

Diagnostic Assessment, 13C, 13F, 14, 47C, 47F, 48, 83C, 83F, 84, 119C, 119F, 120, 151C, 151F, 152, 181C, 181E, 182, 209C, 209E, 210, 239C, 239F, 240, 273C, 273F, 274, 313C, 313F, 314, 347C, 347F, 348, 381C, 381F, 382, 415C, 415F, 416, 453C, 453E, 454, 481C, 481F, 482

Differences, 83B, 91, 481B, 485
estimating, 505–506

Differentiated Instruction
adding zero, 59B
addition, 53B, 155B, 163B
addition of two-digit numbers, 487B, 491B
addition related to subtraction, 197B, 331B
addition sentences, 55B
addition stories, 51B
area, 301B, 305B
bar graphs, 133B, 137B
capacity, 291B
certain or impossible, 143B
coins, 351B, 353B, 355B, 365B
comparing numbers, 35B, 443B
counting back, 185B
counting by tens, 245B
counting money, 357B, 371B
counting on, 157B
counting to 20, 243B
directions, 407B
doubles, 169B, 195B, 317B, 329B
doubles plus 1, 171B, 319B
equal amounts, 363B
equal parts, 457B
estimating, 255B
estimating differences, 505B
estimating numbers, 439B
estimating sums, 495B
even and odd, 263B
faces and corners, 387B
fact families, 199B, 335B
fractions of a set, 471B
hundred chart, 249B, 261B
length, 273B, 279B
leveled assignments, 18, 20, 25, 28, 30, 36, 38, 40, 52, 54, 56, 58, 60, 66, 68, 71, 76, 88, 90, 92, 94, 96, 102, 104, 109, 112, 124, 126, 130, 134, 136, 138, 144, 156, 158, 160, 164, 166, 170, 172, 186, 190, 196, 198, 200, 202, 214, 216, 218, 225, 228, 230, 244, 246, 251, 256, 260, 262, 264, 266, 278, 280, 282, 284, 287, 293, 297, 302, 306, 318, 320, 322, 324, 330, 332, 336, 340, 352, 354, 356, 358, 364, 366, 372, 374, 386, 388, 392, 394, 396, 403, 406, 408, 421, 424, 426, 431, 434, 440, 444, 446, 458, 462, 464, 466, 470,

472, 486, 488, 492, 494, 496, 500, 502, 506
making new figures, 405B
making ten, 323B
modeling numbers, 339B
non-unit fractions, 469B
number line, 165B, 189B
numbers 11 to 15, 27B
numbers 16 to 20, 29B
numbers to 10, 23B
numbers to 100, 433B
numbers to 50, 429B
one half, 461B
ones, 423B
one third and one fourth, 463B
ordering events, 213B
ordering numbers, 39B, 445B
patterns, 17B, 19B
picture graphs, 125B
position, 401B
problem-solving investigations, 33B, 73B, 105B, 141B, 173B, 193B, 231B, 257B, 299B, 333B, 369B, 399B, 441B, 473B, 503B
problem-solving strategies, 21B, 61B, 97B, 127B, 161B, 187B, 219B, 247B, 281B, 325B, 359B, 389B, 427B, 459B, 489B
skip counting, 259B, 261B
sort and classify, 123B
subtraction, 89B, 101B, 103B, 107B
subtraction of two-digit numbers, 499B, 501B
subtraction related to addition, 197B, 331B
subtraction sentences, 91B
subtraction stories, 87B
subtract zero, 95B
tally charts, 129B
temperature, 295B
tens, 419B, 423B
tens, addition and subtraction of, 485B
tens, counting by, 245B
three-dimensional figures, 385B, 391B
time, 215B, 217B, 223B, 227B
two-dimensional figures, 385B, 391B
vertical addition, 75B
vertical subtraction, 111B
ways to make numbers, 65B, 67B, 69B
weight, 285B

Digital clocks, 209B, 223

Dimes, 353–354, 355–356

Directions, giving and following, 407–408

Doubles, 169–170, 195–196, 317–318, 329–330
plus 1, 171–172, 319–320

E

Early Finishers, 17B, 19B, 21B, 23B, 27B, 29B, 33B, 35B, 39B, 51B, 53B, 55B, 59B, 61B, 65B, 67B, 69B, 73B, 75B, 87B, 89B, 91B, 95B, 97B, 101B, 103B, 105B, 107B, 111B, 123B, 125B, 127B, 129B, 133B, 137B, 141B, 143B, 155B, 157B, 161B, 163B, 165B, 169B, 171B, 173B, 185B, 187B, 189B, 193B, 195B, 197B, 199B, 213B, 215B, 217B, 219B, 223B, 227B, 231B, 243B, 245B, 247B, 249B, 255B, 257B, 259B, 261B, 263B, 277B, 279B, 281B, 285B, 291B, 295B, 299B, 301B, 305B, 317B, 319B, 323B, 325B, 329B, 331B, 333B, 335B, 339B, 351B, 353B, 355B, 357B, 359B, 363B, 365B, 369B, 371B, 385B, 387B, 389B, 391B, 395B, 399B, 401B, 405B, 407B, 419B, 423B, 427B, 429B, 433B, 439B, 441B, 443B, 445B, 457B, 459B, 461B, 463B, 469B, 471B, 473B, 485B, 487B, 489B, 491B, 495B, 499B, 501B, 503B, 505B

English Language Learners Concepts are presented visually to aid in reading comprehension. Opportunities are provided throughout the program to build math concepts as well as language skills. The ELL teaching suggestions assist in teaching not only the vocabulary but the concepts needed to *understand* the mathematics.

English Language Learners (ELL). *See also* English Learner Guide under separate cover. 17B, 19B, 21B, 23B, 27B, 29B, 33B, 35B, 39B, 51B, 53B, 55B, 59B, 61B, 65B, 67B, 69B, 73B, 75B, 87B, 89B, 91B, 95B, 97B, 101B, 103B, 105B, 107B, 111B, 123B, 125B, 127B, 129B, 133B, 137B, 141B, 143B, 155B, 157B, 161B, 163B, 165B, 169B, 171B, 173B, 185B, 187B, 189B, 193B, 195B, 197B, 199B, 213B, 215B, 217B, 219B, 223B, 227B, 231B, 243B, 245B, 247B, 249B, 255B, 257B, 259B, 261B, 263B, 277B, 279B, 281B, 285B, 291B, 295B, 299B, 301B, 305B, 317B, 319B, 323B, 325B, 329B, 331B, 333B, 335B, 339B, 351B, 353B, 355B, 357B, 359B, 363B, 365B, 369B, 371B, 385B, 387B, 389B, 391B, 395B, 399B, 401B, 405B, 407B, 419B, 423B, 427B, 429B, 433B, 439B, 441B, 443B, 445B, 457B, 459B, 461B, 463B, 469B, 471B, 473B, 485B, 487B, 489B, 491B, 495B, 499B, 501B, 503B, 505B

Equal amounts, 363–364, 363A, 365, 365A, 371, 457

Equal parts, 457–458

Equal to (=), 13B, 35, 47B, 55, 415B, 443

Estimating
differences, 505–506
groups of ten, 255–256
numbers, 439–440
sums, 495–496
Evaluation.–*See* Assessment

Evening, 209B, 213

Even numbers, 263–264

F

Faces, of shapes, 387–388

Fact Strategies A strong foundation in basic skills is required for all students. Basic facts are presented in a sequential manner. Students receive extra practice throughout the program to increase mastery, improve retention, and build confidence.

Fact Strategies, *See* addition, fact families, subtraction

Fact families, 199–200, 335–338

Figures
faces and corners, 387–388
making new, 405–406
position, 401–404
three-dimensional, 385–386
two- and three- dimensional, 391–392
two-dimensional, 395–396

Focal Points, iii, iv–v, T1, T14–T15

Focus on Math Background
addition, 53A, 75A
addition and subtraction connected, 197A, 331A
addition of zero, 59A
addition sentences, 55A, 165A
addition stories, 51A
analog clock, 215A, 217A, 223A
bar graphs, 133A, 137A
capacity, 291A
commutative property of addition, 155A
comparing coins, 371A
comparing numbers, 35A, 443A
comparing time, 227A
counting, 23A
counting back, 185A
counting by tens, 245A
counting coins, 355A, 357A
counting on, 157A, 163A
counting to 20, 243A
directions, 407A
doubles, 169A, 195A, 317A, 329A
doubles plus 1, 171A, 319A
equal amounts, 363A, 365A
estimating, 255A, 439A
estimating differences, 505A
estimating sums, 495A
faces and corners, 387A
fact families, 199A, 335A
fractions, 457A, 463A
geometric vocabulary, 385A
geometry, 385A, 391A, 395A
hundred chart, 249A
length, 277A, 279A
making ten, 323A
number line, 189A
number sense, 27A
one half, 461A
ordering events, 213A
ordering numbers, 39A
patterns, 17A, 19A, 29A, 261A
picture graphs, 125A
place value, 419A, 429A, 433A, 445A
place value notation, 487A, 501A
position, 401A
regrouping, 491A, 499A
skip counting, 243A, 259A, 353A, 357A
sorting and classifying, 123A
subtraction, 89A, 101A, 103A, 107A, 111A
subtraction of zero, 95A
subtraction sentences, 91A
subtraction stories, 87A

Index

tally charts, 129A
tens and ones, 423A
two-digit addition and subtraction, 485A
ways to make numbers, 65A, 67A, 69A
ways to name numbers, 339A
weight, 285A

Foldables study organizer
for addition, 47, 63, 79, 151, 167, 177, 313, 327, 343, 481, 497, 509
for data, 119, 131, 147
for fractions, 453, 467, 477
for geometry, 381, 397, 411
for measurements, 273, 289, 309
for money, 347, 361, 377
for number patterns, 239, 253, 269
for number sense, 13, 31, 43
for place value, 415, 437, 449
for subtraction, 83, 99, 115, 181, 191, 205, 313, 327, 343, 481, 497, 509
for time, 209, 221, 235

Formative Assessment, 13F, 18, 20, 22, 26, 28, 30, 31, 32, 33, 36, 40, 45, 47F, 52, 54, 56, 60, 62, 63, 64, 66, 68, 72, 74, 76, 81, 83F, 88, 90, 92, 96, 98, 99, 100, 102, 104, 106, 110, 112, 117, 119F, 124, 126, 128, 130, 131, 132, 134, 138, 142, 144, 148, 151F, 156, 158, 162, 164, 166, 167, 168, 170, 172, 174, 179, 181E, 186, 188, 190, 191, 192, 194, 196, 198, 200, 207, 209E, 214, 216, 218, 220, 221, 222, 226, 228, 232, 237, 239F, 244, 246, 248, 252, 253, 254, 256, 260, 262, 264, 271, 273F, 278, 280, 282, 288, 289, 290, 294, 298, 300, 306, 311, 313F, 318, 320, 324, 326, 327, 328, 330, 332, 334, 336, 340, 345, 347F, 352, 354, 356, 358, 360, 361, 362, 364, 366, 370, 372, 379, 378, 381F, 386, 388, 390, 392, 396, 397, 398, 400, 404, 406, 408, 413, 415F, 422, 424, 428, 432, 434, 437, 438, 440, 442, 444, 446, 451, 453E, 458, 460, 462, 464, 467, 468, 470, 472, 474, 479, 481F, 486, 488, 490, 492, 496, 497, 498, 500, 502, 504, 506, 511

Fractions, 453A–480
equal parts, 457–458
non-unit, 469–470
one half, 461–462
one third and one fourth, 463–464
of a set, 471–472

G

Game Time
Adding Colors-two digit addition, 494
All Mixed Up-addition math facts, 160
Animal Race-using data, 136
Bigger the Better, The-number sense, 38
Buy Beavers-length, 284
Circle Up-adding doubles, 322
Corners- three-dimensional figures, 394
The Equalizer-fractions, 466
Lizzie the Lizard-making ten, 426
Related or Not?-fact families, 202
Slide Through the Digits-comparing numbers, 266
Snack Time-addition, 58
Subtracting to Swim-subtraction, 94
Switch It!-time, 230
Who Has More?-money, 374

Geometry, 381, 385, 385A, 387, 391, 391A, 395, 395A, 397, 405, 411

Gifted and Talented
diagnostic assessment options, 14, 48, 84, 120, 152, 182, 210, 240, 274, 314, 348, 382, 416, 454, 482
Game Time, 38, 58, 94, 136, 160, 202, 230, 266, 284, 322, 374, 394, 426, 466, 494
Small Group Options, 19B, 21B, 23B, 35B, 51B, 53B, 55B, 61B, 67B, 87B, 91B, 101B, 103B, 105B, 111B, 123B, 125B, 127B, 141B, 143B, 155B, 157B, 161B, 165B, 185B, 195B, 197B, 199B, 213B, 217B, 219B, 243B, 245B, 247B, 255B, 259B, 281B, 285B, 291B, 295B, 299B, 323B, 325B, 329B, 351B, 353B, 357B, 359B, 369B, 371B, 395B, 423B, 427B, 433B, 457B, 459B, 461B, 471B, 485B, 487B, 489B, 491B, 501B

Graphs. *See also* Data.
bar graphs, 133–134, 137–140
picture graphs, 125–126

Greater than (>), 13B, 35, 415B, 443

H

Half hour, 217–218, 223–226

Half past, 217

Hands-On Lab
addition, 53, 55, 75, 335, 487
addition and subtraction connected, 197, 199, 331
addition sentences, 59, 65, 155, 323, 329, 485
addition stories, 73
analog clock, 215, 217, 223
area, 301, 305
bar graphs, 133, 137
capacity, 291
certain or impossible, 143
coins, 351, 501
comparing numbers, 35B
comparing time, 227
counting, 27, 51
counting back, 185
counting by tens, 245
counting coins, 355, 357
counting on, 157, 163, 165
directions, 407
doubles, 195, 317
doubles plus 1, 319
equal amounts, 363, 365, 371, 457
equal parts, 463
estimating, 255, 439
estimating differences, 505
estimating sums, 495
fact families, 339
fractions, 469, 471
geometry, 385, 387, 391, 395, 405
hundred chart, 249
measurement, 277, 279
number lines, 39
number sentences, 111, 169, 171
numbers to 20, 29
number stories, 33
one half, 461
ordering events, 213
ordering numbers, 23, 443, 445
patterns, 17, 19, 21, 61, 263
picture graphs, 125
place value, 433
position, 401
regrouping, 491
skip counting, 259, 261, 353
subtraction, 87, 89, 335, 499
subtraction of zero, 95
subtraction sentences, 91, 101, 103, 107, 189, 329
tally charts, 129
temperature, 295
tens, 419, 423, 429
tens and ones, 243
Venn diagrams, 123
ways to make numbers, 67, 69
weight, 285
Health. *See* Learning Stations; Problem-Solving

Heavy/heavier/heaviest, 273B, 285

Holds less/least, 273B, 291

Holds more/most, 273B, 291

H.O.T. Problems Higher Order Thinking skills are developed and utilized in these problems found throughout the Student Edition.

H.O.T. Problems
algebra, 54, 170, 320
critical thinking, 92, 104
explaining math, 396
make it right, 60, 66, 76, 102, 260, 324, 406, 422, 464, 488
thinking math, 36, 140, 144, 156, 200, 226, 244, 304, 354

Hour hand, 215

Hour hand, on clocks, 209B

Hours, 215–216, 223–226

Hundred chart, 249–252
skip counting, 261–262

I

Impossible, 119B, 143

Independent Work Options, 17B, 19B, 21B, 23B, 27B, 29B, 33B, 35B, 39B, 51B, 53B, 55B, 59B, 61B, 65B, 67B, 69B, 73B, 75B, 87B, 89B, 91B, 95B, 97B, 101B, 103B, 105B, 107B, 111B, 123B, 125B, 127B, 129B, 133B, 137B, 141B, 143B, 155B, 157B, 161B, 163B, 165B, 169B, 171B, 173B, 185B, 187B, 189B, 193B, 195B, 197B, 199B, 213B, 215B, 217B, 219B, 223B, 227B, 231B, 243B, 245B, 247B, 249B, 255B, 257B, 259B, 261B, 263B, 277B, 279B, 281B, 285B, 291B, 295B, 299B, 301B, 305B, 317B, 319B, 323B, 325B, 329B, 331B, 333B, 335B, 339B, 351B, 353B, 355B, 357B, 359B, 363B, 365B, 369B, 371B, 385B, 387B, 389B,

391B, 395B, 399B, 401B, 405B, 407B, 419B, 423B, 427B, 429B, 433B, 439B, 441B, 443B, 445B, 457B, 459B, 461B, 463B, 469B, 471B, 473B, 485B, 487B, 489B, 491B, 495B, 499B, 501B, 503B, 505B

Individual needs. *See* Differentiated Instruction

Instructional Planning and Support. *See also* Pacing; Technology.

Intensive Intervention. *See* Intervention Options

Interpersonal Learners. *See* Learning Styles

Intervention Options
- Intensive Intervention, 14, 48, 84, 120, 152, 182, 210, 240, 274, 314, 348, 382, 416, 454, 482
- Strategic Intervention, 14, 48, 84, 120, 152, 182, 210, 240, 274, 314, 348, 382, 416, 454, 482

Intrapersonal Learners. *See* Learning Styles

K

Kinesthetic Learners. *See* Learning Styles

L

Language Arts. *See* Learning Stations

Learning Stations
- Art, 13H, 47G, 83G, 151G, 181G, 209G, 239G, 273G, 313G, 347G, 381G, 415G, 453G, 481G
- Health, 83G, 119G, 151H, 181H, 209G, 239H, 453H, 481H
- Language Arts, 13H, 47G, 83H, 119G, 151G, 181G, 209H, 239G, 273G, 313H, 347H, 381G, 415G, 453G, 481G
- Music, 13G, 83G
- Reading, 13G, 47G, 119G, 151G, 181G, 209G, 273G, 313G, 347G, 381G, 415G, 453G, 481G
- Science, 13G, 47H, 83H, 119H, 151H, 181H, 209H, 239H, 273H, 313H, 347H, 381H, 415H, 453H, 481H
- Social Studies, 47H, 119H, 239G, 273H, 313G, 347G, 381H, 415H

Learning Styles
- Auditory, 13G, 17B, 19B, 23B, 65B, 69B, 73B, 83G, 95B, 97B, 103B, 125B, 129B, 133B, 163B, 165B, 185B, 189B, 193B, 197B, 213B, 217B, 219B, 223B, 227B, 245B, 249B, 259B, 371B, 385B, 387B, 423B, 453H, 481H
- Interpersonal, 33B, 83H, 105B, 133B, 137B, 187B, 209G, 257B, 419B, 457B, 485B
- Intrapersonal, 173B, 273H, 291B, 299B, 313G, 325B, 369B, 381H, 389A, 395B, 399B, 427B, 429B, 433B
- Kinesthetic, 17B, 19B, 21B, 23B, 27B, 29B, 35B, 39B, 47H, 51B, 53B, 55B, 59B, 61B, 65B, 67B, 69B, 73B, 75B, 89B, 91B, 95B, 101B, 103B, 107B, 119G, 119H, 123B, 129B, 133B, 137B, 141B, 143B, 151H, 155B, 157B, 165B, 169B, 171B, 181G, 189B, 193B, 197B, 217B, 223B, 227B, 239G, 239H, 243B, 247B, 255B, 259B, 261B, 263B, 273G, 279B, 285B, 291B, 295B, 299B, 301B, 305B, 313G, 317B, 319B, 331B, 347H, 351B, 353B, 355B, 357B, 359B, 363B, 365B, 369B, 371B, 385B, 389A, 391B, 395B, 399B, 401B, 405B, 415G, 419B, 423B, 429B, 433B, 439B, 441B, 443B, 445B, 457B, 461B, 463B, 469B, 471B, 489B, 491B
- Linguistic, 39B, 51B, 61B, 73B, 83H, 95B, 101B, 103B, 111B, 119G, 133B, 137B, 143B, 151G, 163B, 165B, 171B, 173B, 181H, 185B, 197B, 223B, 243B, 245B, 249B, 255B, 273G, 281B, 285B, 295B, 299B, 313H, 317B, 333B, 347G, 347H, 353B, 357B, 359B, 381G, 389A, 391B, 395B, 399B, 401B, 407B, 415G, 415H, 419B, 423B, 429B, 433B, 441B, 443B, 445B, 453G, 457B, 469B, 471B, 473B, 481G, 485B, 489B, 503B
- Logical, 13G, 13H, 21B, 23B, 27B, 29B, 33B, 35B, 39B, 47G, 47H, 51B, 53B, 55B, 59B, 61B, 65B, 67B, 69B, 73B, 83G, 87B, 89B, 91B, 97B, 101B, 103B, 105B, 111B, 119G, 119H, 123B, 125B, 127B, 129B, 137B, 141B, 143B, 157B, 161B, 169B, 171B, 173B, 181G, 181H, 185B, 187B, 189B, 193B, 195B, 197B, 199B, 209G, 209H, 219B, 223B, 231B, 239G, 243B, 245B, 247B, 249B, 255B, 261B, 263B, 273G, 273H, 277B, 279B, 281B, 285B, 291B, 295B, 299B, 301B, 305B, 313G, 319B, 323B, 325B, 329B, 331B, 335B, 339B, 347G, 351B, 355B, 357B, 359B, 363B, 365B, 369B, 371B, 385B, 387B, 389A, 399B, 401B, 407B, 415H, 423B, 427B, 429B, 433B, 439B, 441B, 443B, 453H, 457B, 459B, 461B, 463B, 469B, 471B, 473B, 481H, 487B, 489B, 495B, 499B, 501B, 503B, 505B
- Social, 23B, 33B, 51B, 55B, 59B, 61B, 65B, 67B, 69B, 75B, 83H, 91B, 97B, 111B, 143B, 155B, 157B, 163B, 165B, 171B, 181H, 185B, 187B, 189B, 195B, 199B, 209H, 213B, 217B, 223B, 227B, 243B, 255B, 261B, 263B, 273G, 277B, 285B, 313H, 317B, 325B, 335B, 347G, 351B, 353B, 355B, 357B, 359B, 363B, 365B, 371B, 381G, 457B, 461B, 463B, 471B, 473B, 487B, 489B, 499B, 501B, 503B, 505B
- Verbal, 51B, 53B
- Visual/Spatial, 13G, 13H, 17B, 19B, 27B, 29B, 35B, 39B, 47G, 51B, 53B, 55B, 59B, 61B, 65B, 67B, 73B, 75B, 83G, 87B, 89B, 91B, 95B, 97B, 101B, 105B, 107B, 111B, 119G, 119H, 123B, 125B, 127B, 129B, 133B, 137B, 143B, 151G, 151H, 155B, 157B, 163B, 165B, 169B, 171B, 173B, 181G, 185B, 193B, 195B, 197B, 199B, 209G, 213B, 215B, 217B, 219B, 223B, 227B, 231B, 239G, 239H, 243B, 245B, 247B, 249B, 255B, 259B, 261B, 263B, 273G, 277B, 279B, 285B, 295B, 301B, 305B, 313G, 317B, 319B, 323B, 325B, 329B, 331B, 333B, 335B, 339B, 347G, 347H, 351B, 353B, 355B, 357B, 359B, 363B, 365B, 369B, 371B, 381G, 381H, 387B, 389A, 391B, 395B, 401B, 405B, 407B, 415G, 419B, 423B, 429B, 433B, 439B, 443B, 445B, 453G, 457B, 459B, 461B, 463B, 469B, 471B, 481G, 485B, 487B, 489B, 491B, 495B, 499B, 501B, 505B

Length
- comparing, 277–278
- nonstandard units of, 279–280

Less than (<), 13B, 35, 415B, 443

Leveled assignments. *See* Differentiated Instruction

Light/lighter/lightest, 273B, 285

Linguistic Learners. *See* Learning Styles

Literature Support, *See also* Teacher Reference Handbook *under separate cover*
- Chapter Literature List, 16, 50, 86, 122, 154, 184, 212, 242, 276, 316, 350, 384, 418, 456, 484
- Read-Aloud Anthology, 15, 49, 85, 121, 153, 183, 211, 241, 275, 315, 349, 383, 417, 455, 483

Logical Learners. *See* Learning Styles

Logical Reasoning. *See* Problem-Solving

Long/longer/longest, 273B, 277

Looking Ahead,
- Count On Tens and Ones, LA5
- Hundreds, Tens, Ones, LA7
- Place Value to 1,000, LA9
- Measure to the Nearest Centimeter, LA13
- Measure to the Nearest Inch, LA11
- Missing Addends, LA3

M

Manipulatives
- attribute blocks, 19A, 395A
- base-ten blocks, 245A, 427A, 429A, 433A, 443A, 485A, 487A, 489A, 491A, 499A, 501A
- coins, 351A, 353A, 355A, 357A, 359A, 363A, 365A, 369A, 371A, 501A
- color tiles, 143A
- connecting cubes, 33A, 39A, 55A, 69A, 87A, 89A, 101A, 103A, 105A, 107A, 111A, 137A, 143A, 155A, 157A, 161A, 163A, 169A, 171A, 173A, 185A, 197A, 199A, 219A, 243A, 245A, 255A, 257A, 259A, 279A, 281A, 301A, 319A, 323A, 331A, 389A, 419A, 423A, 427A, 429A, 433A, 441A, 443A, 459A, 471A, 489A
- demonstration clocks, 215A, 217A, 223A, 227A
- fraction circles, 457A

geometric solids, 385A, 387A, 399A
number cubes, 91A, 137A, 163A, 189A, 197A, 217A
number sense, 199A
pan balance, 285A
pattern blocks, 17A, 19A, 21A, 143A, 279A, 301A, 305A, 391A, 399A, 457A, 461A, 463A
spinners, 423A
student clocks, 215A, 217A, 219A, 223A, 227A, 231A
two-colored counters, 21A, 29A, 51A, 53A, 65A, 67A, 69A, 75A, 87A, 89A, 95A, 101A, 103A, 105A, 107A, 111A, 155A, 163A, 165A, 171A, 187A, 195A, 243A, 255A, 257A, 259A, 263A, 317A, 323A, 329A, 339A, 363A, 423A, 427A, 441A, 445A, 489A, 495A

Math at Home, 15–16, 18, 20, 22, 26, 28, 30, 34, 36, 49–50, 52, 54, 56, 60, 62, 66, 68, 72, 74, 76, 85–86, 88, 90, 92, 96, 98, 102, 104, 106, 110, 112, 121–122, 124, 126, 128, 130, 134, 138, 140, 142, 144, 153–154, 156, 158, 162, 164, 166, 170, 172, 183–184, 186, 188, 190, 194, 196, 198, 200, 211–212, 214, 216, 218, 226, 228, 241–242, 244, 246, 248, 252, 256, 258, 260, 262, 264, 275–276, 278, 280, 282, 288, 294, 298, 300, 304, 306, 315–316, 318, 320, 324, 326, 330, 332, 334, 336, 338, 340, 349–350, 352, 354, 356, 358, 360, 364, 368, 370, 372, 383–384, 386, 388, 390, 392, 396, 400, 404, 406, 408, 417–418, 422, 424, 428, 432, 436, 440, 442, 444, 446, 455–456, 460, 472, 474, 483–484, 486, 488, 490, 492, 496, 500, 502, 504, 506

Math Background. *See* Focus on Math Background

Math Online, 14, 31, 48, 63, 79, 84, 99, 115, 116, 120, 131, 135, 148, 152, 167, 178, 182, 191, 206, 210, 221, 229, 235, 236, 237, 240, 253, 265, 269, 270, 271, 274, 289, 310, 311, 314, 321, 327, 343, 344, 345, 348, 361, 377, 378, 382, 397, 411, 412, 413, 416, 437, 449, 450, 451, 454, 465, 467, 477, 478, 479, 482, 497, 509, 510, 511

Measurement
area, 301–304, 305–306
capacity, 291–294
comparing, 273A–312
lengths, 277–278
nonstandard units, 279–280
temperature, 295–298
time, 209A–238
weight, 285–288

Mid-Chapter Check, 31, 63, 99, 131, 167, 191, 221, 253, 289, 327, 361, 397, 437, 467, 497

Minus (–), 83B, 91

Minute hand, on clocks, 209B, 215

Modeling
addition, 53–54
numbers, 339–340
subtraction, 89–90

Money. *See also* entries for various money denominations.
counting, 357–358, 371–372

Morning, 209B, 213

Music. *See* Learning Stations; Problem-Solving

N

Nickels, 351–352, 355–356

Nonstandard units
of length, 279–280

Number lines, 13B, 39
for addition, 165–166
for subtraction, 189–190

Numbers, 13B, 23. *See also* Addition; Subtraction; Ways to make various numbers.
to 10, 23–26
to 100, 433–436
to 100, comparing, 443–444
to 100, ordering, 445–446
11 to 15, 27–28
16 to 20, 29–30
to 50, 429–432
comparing, 35–36
estimating, 439–440
even, 263–264
modeling, 339–340
odd, 263–264
ordering, 39–40
recognizing patterns, 239A–272

Number sentences, 61–62, 83A, 187–188. *See also* Problem-Solving Strategies.

O

O'clock, 209B, 215

Odd numbers, 263–264

One-fourth, 463–464

One-half, 461–462

Ones, 239B, 243
tens and, 423–424

One-third, 463–464

On-Level Suggestions. *See also* Early Finishers.
diagnostic assessment options, 14, 48, 84, 120, 152, 182, 210, 240, 274, 314, 348, 382, 416, 454, 482
Game Time, 38, 58, 94, 136, 160, 202, 230, 266, 284, 322, 374, 394, 426, 466, 494
leveled assignments, 18, 20, 25, 28, 30, 36, 38, 40, 52, 54, 56, 58, 60, 66, 68, 71, 76, 88, 90, 92, 94, 96, 102, 104, 109, 112, 124, 126, 130, 134, 136, 138, 144, 156, 158, 160, 164, 166, 170, 172, 186, 190, 196, 198, 200, 202, 214, 216, 218, 225, 228, 230, 244, 246, 251, 256, 260, 262, 264, 266, 278, 280, 282, 284, 287, 293, 297, 302, 306, 318, 320, 322, 324, 330, 332, 336, 340, 352, 354, 356, 358, 364, 366, 372, 374, 386, 388, 392, 394, 396, 403, 406, 408, 421, 424, 426, 431, 434, 440, 444, 446, 458, 462, 464, 466, 470, 472, 486, 488, 492, 494, 496, 500, 502, 506
leveled tests, 44, 80, 116, 148, 178, 206, 236, 270, 310, 344, 378, 412, 450, 478, 510

Ordering, 13B, 39
area, 305–306
capacity, 291–294
events, 213–214
lengths, 277–278
numbers to 100, 445–446
temperature, 295–298
weight, 285–288

P

Pacing, 13C–13E, 47C–47F, 83C–83F, 119C–119E, 151C–151E, 181C–181E, 209C–209E, 239C–239E, 273C–273E, 313C–313E, 347C–347E, 381C–381E, 415C–415E, 453C–453E, 481C–481E

Patterns Patterns are sometimes called the foundation of mathematics and are certainly required for future success in algebra.

Patterns, 13B, 17
creating, 19–20
extending, 17–18
in fact families, 335–338
problem-solving strategy with, 21–22, 247–248, 389–390
recognize number, 239A–272

Pattern unit, 13B, 17

Pennies, 351–352, 353–354, 355–356

Picture graphs, 125–126

Place value, 415A–452

Planning Guide. *See* Pacing

Plus (+), 47B, 55

Position, 401–404

Preparing for Standardized Tests,
Multiple-Choice Questions, TP2–TP4
Short-Response Questions, TP5–TP6

Problem of the Day, 17A, 19A, 21A, 23A, 27A, 29A, 33A, 35A, 39A, 51A, 53A, 55A, 59A, 61A, 65A, 67A, 69A, 73A, 75A, 87A, 89A, 91A, 95A, 97A, 101A, 103A, 105A, 107A, 111A, 123A, 125A, 127A, 129A, 133A, 137A, 141A, 143A, 155A, 157A, 161A, 163A, 165A, 169A, 171A, 173A, 185A, 187A, 189A, 193A, 195A, 197A, 199A, 213A, 215A, 217A, 219A, 223A, 227A, 231A, 243A, 245A, 247A, 249A, 255A, 257A, 259A, 261A, 263A, 277A, 279A, 281A, 285A, 291A, 295A, 299A, 301A, 305A, 317A, 319A, 323A, 325A, 329A, 331A, 333A, 335A, 339A, 351A, 353A, 355A, 357A, 359A, 363A, 365A, 369A, 371A, 385A, 387A, 389A, 391A, 395A, 399A, 401A, 405A, 407A, 419A, 423A, 427A, 429A, 433A, 439A, 441A, 443A, 445A, 457A, 459A, 461A, 463A, 469A,

471A, 473A, 485A, 487A, 489A, 491A, 495A, 499A, 501A, 503A, 505A
Problem Solving A three-pronged approach helps students apply skills to problem situations. Problem-Solving Strategy lessons teach strategies; Problem-Solving Investigations afford students diverse opportunities to select these strategies; Real-World Problem Solving exercises strengthen students' abilities to apply and solve problems outside the
Problem-Solving. *See also* Problem-Solving Investigations; Problem-Solving Strategies; Real-World Problem Solving.
  application, 124
  in art, 409–410
  critical thinking, 112, 318, 352, 392, 444, 462
  estimating, 496
  in health, 77–78
  logical reasoning, 18, 126, 246, 256, 356, 358, 372
  in music, 233–234
  number sense, 28, 30, 68, 96, 166, 172, 186, 198, 330, 332, 436, 440, 446, 500, 502
  reasoning, 214, 298, 492
  in science, 41–42, 145–146, 203–204, 307–308, 447–448, 475–476, 482
  in social studies, 113–114, 175–176, 203–204, 267–268, 341–342, 375–376, 507–508
  visual thinking, 52, 216, 264, 280, 294, 306, 388, 404, 458
Problem-Solving Investigations, 33–34, 73–74, 105–106, 141–142, 173–174, 193–194, 231–232, 257–258, 299–300, 333–334, 369–370, 399–400, 441–442, 473–474, 503–504. *See also* Problem-Solving; Problem-Solving Strategies; Real-World Problem Solving.
Problem-Solving Projects,
  Fruit Kabob Factory, P7
  I Spy Patterns. P3
  Let's Go to the Zoo!, P11
  Toys from the Past and Present, P15
Problem-Solving Strategies. *See also* Problem-Solving; Problem-Solving Investigations; Real-World Problem Solving.
  act it out, 161–162, 359–360
  draw a picture, 97–98, 325–326, 459–460
  find a pattern, 21–22, 247–248, 389–390
  guess and check, 281–282, 427–428, 489–490
  make a table, 127–128, 219–220
  write a number sentence, 61–62, 187–188
  Professional Development, 13F, 47F, 83F, 119F, 151F, 181E, 209E, 239F, 273F, 313F, 347F, 381F, 415F, 453E, 481F. *See also* Focus on Math Background.
Pyramids, 381B, 385

Q

Quarters, 365–368

R

Reaching All Learners. *See* Differentiated Instruction; Learning Styles; Small Group Options; Universal Access
Read-Aloud Anthology. *See* Literature Support
Reading and Writing Mathematics. *See* Learning Stations; Literature Support; Real-World Problem Solving; Writing in Math
Real-World Math, 40, 77, 113, 145, 175, 203, 233, 267, 307, 341, 375, 409, 447, 475, 507
Real-World Problem Solving. *See also* Problem-Solving; Problem-Solving Investigations; Problem-Solving Strategies.
  in math, 21A, 33A, 61A, 73A, 97A, 105A, 127A, 141A, 161A, 173A, 187A, 193A, 219A, 231A, 247A, 257A, 281A, 299A, 325A, 333A, 359A, 369A, 389A, 399A, 427A, 441A, 459A, 473A, 489A, 503A
  in science, 61A, 73A, 97A, 105A, 187A, 193A, 247A, 255A, 281A, 299A, 325A, 333A, 389A, 399A, 427A, 441A
  in social studies, 21A, 33A, 127A, 141A, 161A, 173A, 219A, 231A, 359A, 369A, 459A, 473A, 489A, 503A
Reasoning. *See* Problem-Solving
Rectangles, 381B, 395
Rectangular prisms, 381B, 385
Regrouping, 415B, 423–424
Research on Program, 119F, 309F, 313F, 347F
Rounding, 481B, 495

S

Science. *See* Learning Stations; Problem-Solving; Real-World Problem Solving
Shapes. *See* Geometry
Short/shorter/shortest, 277
Sides, of shapes, 381B, 395
Skills Trace. *See* Vertical Alignment
Skip counting
  by 2's, 5's and 10's, 259–260
  on a hundred chart, 261–262
  Small Group Options. *See* Below-Level Suggestions; English Language Learners (ELL); Gifted and Talented
Social Learners. *See* Learning Styles
Social Sciences. *See* Learning Stations; Problem-Solving; Real-World Problem Solving
Sorting and classifying, 119B, 123
Special Needs Students. *See* Differentiated Instruction; Learning Styles; Universal Access
Spheres, 381B, 385
Spiral Review These systematic and continuous reviews help maintain previously acquired skills and improve retention.
Spiral Review, 32, 64, 100, 132, 168, 192, 222, 254, 290, 328, 362, 398, 438, 468, 498
Squares, 381B, 395
Staff Development. *See* Professional Development
Standards Alignment. *See* Vertical Alignment
Strategic Intervention. *See* Intervention Options
Struggling Students. *See* Below-Level Suggestions
Subtraction, 83A–118, 181A–208, 313A–346, 481A–512
  from 10, 11, and 12, 107–110
  from 4, 5, and 6, 101–102
  from 7, 8, and 9, 103–104
  addition related to, 197–198, 331–332
  of all, 95–96
  counting back 1, 2, or 3, 185–186
  doubles, 195–196, 329–330
  estimating differences, 505–506
  fact families, 199–200
  modeling, 89–90
  number line for, 189–190
  of tens, 485–486
  two-digit, 499–500, 501–502
  vertical, 111–112
  of zero, 95–96
Subtraction sentences, 83B, 91–92
Subtraction stories, 87–88
Summative Assessment, 13F, 43, 45, 47F, 79, 81, 83F, 115, 117, 119F, 147, 149, 151F, 177, 179, 181E, 205, 207, 209E, 235, 237, 239F, 269, 271, 273F, 309, 311, 313F, 343, 345, 347F, 377, 379, 381F, 411, 413, 415F, 449, 451, 453E, 477, 479, 481F, 509, 511
Sums, 47B, 55, 481B, 485
  estimating, 495–496
Surveys, 119B, 129

T

Tables, 127–128, 219–220
Talk About It, 17, 19, 24, 27, 29, 35, 39, 51, 53, 55, 59, 65, 67, 70, 75, 87, 89, 91, 95, 101, 103, 108, 111, 123, 125, 129, 133, 137, 143, 155, 157, 163, 165, 169, 171, 185, 189, 195, 197, 199, 213, 215, 217, 224, 227, 243, 245, 250, 255, 259, 261, 263, 277, 279, 286, 292, 296, 302, 305, 317, 323, 329, 331, 335, 339, 351, 353, 355, 357, 363, 365, 371, 385, 387, 391, 395, 402, 405, 407, 420, 423, 430, 433, 439, 443, 445, 457, 461, 463, 469, 471, 485, 487, 491, 495, 499, 501, 505
Tally charts, 129–130

Technology
practice with, 37, 57, 93, 135, 139–140, 159, 201, 229, 265, 283, 321, 337–338, 367–368, 373, 393, 425, 435, 465, 493
student, 17B, 19B, 21B, 23B, 27B, 29B, 33B, 35B, 39B, 51B, 53B, 55B, 59B, 61B, 65B, 67B, 69B, 73B, 75B, 87B, 89B, 91B, 95B, 97B, 101B, 103B, 105B, 107B, 111B, 123B, 125B, 127B, 129B, 133B, 137B, 141B, 143B, 155B, 157B, 161B, 163B, 165B, 169B, 171B, 173B, 185B, 187B, 189B, 193B, 195B, 197B, 199B, 213B, 215B, 217B, 219B, 223B, 227B, 231B, 243B, 245B, 247B, 249B, 255B, 257B, 259B, 261B, 263B, 277B, 279B, 281B, 285B, 291B, 295B, 299B, 301B, 305B, 317B, 319B, 323B, 325B, 329B, 331B, 333B, 335B, 339B, 351B, 353B, 355B, 357B, 359B, 363B, 365B, 369B, 371B, 385B, 387B, 389B, 391B, 395B, 399B, 401B, 405B, 407B, 419B, 423B, 427B, 429B, 433B, 439B, 441B, 443B, 445B, 457B, 459B, 461B, 463B, 469B, 471B, 473B, 485B, 487B, 489B, 491B, 495B, 499B, 501B, 503B, 505B
TeacherWorks Plus, 17A, 19A, 21A, 23A, 27A, 29A, 33A, 35A, 39A, 51A, 53A, 55A, 59A, 61A, 65A, 67A, 69A, 73A, 75A, 87A, 89A, 91A, 95A, 97A, 101A, 103A, 105A, 107A, 111A, 123A, 125A, 127A, 129A, 133A, 137A, 141A, 143A, 155A, 157A, 161A, 163A, 165A, 169A, 171A, 173A, 185A, 187A, 189A, 193A, 195A, 197A, 199A, 213A, 215A, 217A, 219A, 223A, 227A, 231A, 243A, 245A, 247A, 249A, 255A, 257A, 259A, 261A, 263A, 277A, 279A, 281A, 285A, 291A, 295A, 299A, 301A, 305A, 317A, 319A, 323A, 325A, 329A, 331A, 333A, 335A, 339A, 351A, 353A, 355A, 357A, 359A, 363A, 365A, 369A, 371A, 385A, 387A, 389A, 391A, 395A, 399A, 401A, 405A, 407A, 419A, 423A, 427A, 429A, 433A, 439A, 441A, 443A, 445A, 457A, 459A, 461A, 463A, 469A, 471A, 473A, 485A, 487A, 489A, 491A, 495A, 499A, 501A, 503A, 505A
Tech Link, 139–140, 337–338, 367–368, 435–436

Temperature, 295–298

Tens, 419–422
addition and subtraction of, 485–486
counting by, 245–246
estimating with groups of, 255–256
making to add, 323–324
ones and, 423–424
skip counting by, 259–260

Test Practice, 45–46, 81–82, 117–118, 149–150, 180–181, 207–208, 237–238, 271–272, 311–312, 345–346, 379–380, 413–414, 451–452, 479–480, 511–512

Thermometer, 295–298

Time, 209A–238
events related to, 227–228
to the half hour, 217–218, 223–226
to the hour, 215–216, 223–226
ordering events, 213–214

Triangles, 381B, 395

Twenty, counting to, 243–244

U

Units, 273B, 279

Universal Access. *See also* Above-Level Suggestions; Below-Level Suggestions; Differentiated Instruction; Learning Styles; On-Level Suggestions.

V

Venn diagrams, 123

Verbal Learners. *See* Learning Styles

Vertical addition, 75–76

Vertical Alignment, 13B, 47B, 83B, 119B, 151B, 181B, 209B, 239B, 273B, 313B, 347B, 381B, 415B, 453B, 481B

Vertical subtraction, 111–112

Visual/Spatial Learners. *See* Learning Styles

Visual Thinking. *See* Problem-Solving

Visual Vocabulary Cards, 13B, 17A, 19A, 35A, 39A, 47B, 53A, 55A, 65A, 67A, 69A, 75A, 83B, 87A, 89A, 91A, 103A, 107A, 111A, 119B, 125A, 129A, 133A, 137A, 151B, 155A, 163A, 165A, 181B, 189A, 199A, 209B, 215A, 217A, 223A, 227A, 239B, 243A, 255A, 273B, 313B, 323A, 331A, 335A, 347B, 351A, 353A, 357A, 365A, 371A, 381B, 385A, 387A, 395A, 405A, 415B, 429A, 433A, 453B, 481B, 485A, 487A, 491A, 495A, 499A, 501A, 505A

Vocabulary
add, 47B, 53, 481B, 485
addend, 151B, 155
addition sentence, 47B, 55
after, 13B, 39, 209B, 213, 415B, 445
afternoon, 209B, 213
analog, 209B, 223
bar graph, 119B, 133
before, 13B, 39, 209B, 213, 415B, 445
between, 13B, 39, 415B, 445
cent, 347B, 351
certain, 119B, 143
circles, 381B, 395
compare, 415B, 443
cones, 381B, 385
count back, 181B, 185
count on, 151B, 157
cubes, 381B, 385
cylinders, 381B, 385
data, 119B, 125
difference, 83B, 91, 481B, 485
digital, 209B, 223
dime, 347B, 353
doubles, 151B, 169, 313B, 317
doubles plus 1, 151B, 171, 313B, 319
equal parts, 453B, 457
equal to (=), 13B, 35, 47B, 55, 415B, 443
estimate, 239B, 255, 415B, 439, 481B, 495
even, 239B, 263
evening, 209B, 213
fact family, 181B, 199, 313B, 315
fraction, 453B, 461
graph, 119B, 125
greater than (>), 13B, 35, 415B, 443
half hour, 209B, 217
half past, 209B, 217
heavy/heavier/heaviest, 273B, 285
holds less/least, 273B, 291
holds more/most, 273B, 291
hour, 209B, 215
hour hand, 209B, 215
hundred chart, 239B, 261
impossible, 119B, 143
length, 273B, 277
less than (<), 13B, 35, 415B, 443
light/lighter/lightest, 273B, 285
long/longer/longest, 273B, 277
measure, 273B, 279
minus (–), 83B, 91
minute hand, 209B, 215
morning, 209B, 213
nickel, 347B, 351
number, 13B, 23
number line, 13B, 39
o'clock, 209B, 215
odd, 239B, 263
one fourth, 453B, 463
one half, 453B, 461
ones, 239B, 243, 415B, 423
one third, 453B, 463
order, 13B, 39
pattern, 13B, 17
pattern unit, 13B, 17
penny, 347B, 351
picture graph, 119B, 125
plus (+), 47B, 55
pyramids, 381B, 385
quarter, 347B, 365
rectangles, 381B, 395
rectangular prisms, 381B, 385
regroup, 415B, 423
round, 481B, 495
short/shorter/shortest, 273B, 277
sides, 381B, 395
skip count, 239B, 259
sort, 119B, 123
spheres, 381B, 385
squares, 381B, 395
subtract, 83B, 89, 481B, 485
subtraction sentence, 83B, 91
sum, 47B, 55, 481B, 485
survey, 119B, 129
tally chart, 119B, 129
tens, 415B, 419
triangles, 381B, 395
unit, 273B, 279
weight, 273B, 285
zero, 47B, 59

Vocabulary Review and Test, 43, 79, 115, 147, 177, 205, 235, 269, 309, 343, 377, 411, 449, 477, 509

Index

W

Ways to make
10, 11, and 12, 69–72
4, 5, and 6, 65–66
7, 8, and 9, 67–68

Weight, 285–288

Writing in Math, 15, 18, 20, 26, 28, 30, 36, 40, 42, 49, 54, 56, 60, 66, 68, 72, 76, 78, 85, 88, 90, 92, 96, 102, 104, 110, 112, 114, 121, 124, 126, 130, 134, 138, 144, 146, 153, 156, 158, 164, 166, 170, 172, 176, 183, 186, 190, 196, 198, 200, 204, 211, 214, 216, 218, 226, 228, 234, 241, 244, 246, 252, 256, 260, 262, 264, 275, 278, 280, 282, 288, 294, 298, 300, 303, 306, 308, 315, 318, 320, 324, 326, 330, 332, 334, 336, 338, 340, 342, 349, 352, 354, 356, 358, 364, 366, 372, 376, 383, 386, 390, 392, 396, 400, 404, 408, 410, 417, 422, 424, 432, 440, 444, 446, 448, 455, 458, 460, 462, 464, 470, 472, 474, 476, 483, 486, 488, 490, 492, 496, 500, 502, 504, 506, 508

Z

Zero, 47B
addition of, 59–60
subtraction of, 95–96

Index